A2
mathematics

John Berry
Roger Fentem
Bob Francis
Ted Graham

series editor
John Berry

project contributors
Steve Dobbs, Howard Hampson, Penny Howe, Rob Lincoln, Sue de Pomerai, Claire Rowland, Stuart Rowlands, Stewart Townend, John White

Published by HarperCollins*Publishers* Limited
77–85 Fulham Palace Road
Hammersmith
London W6 8JB

www.**Collins**Education.com
On-line Support for Schools and Colleges

© HarperCollins*Publishers*
First published 2001
ISBN 000 322503 8

John Berry, Roger Fentem, Bob Francis and Ted Graham assert the moral right to be
identified as the authors of this work.

Production: Kathryn Botterill
Cover Design: Terry Bambrook
Internal Design and Illustration: Ken Vail Graphic Design, Cambridge
Project Editor: Joan Miller
Pure and Statistics questions updating: Roger Luther
Key Skills Consultants: Val Beamish and Andy Conway, Harrow College
Indexing Specialist: Richard Raper
Printed and Bound by Scotprint, Haddington

Acknowledgements
We are grateful to the following Awarding Bodies for permission to reproduce
questions from their past examination papers and specimen papers. The Awarding
Bodies accept no responsibility whatsoever for the accuracy or method of working in
the answers given, which are solely the responsibilty of the authors and publishers.
EDEXCEL
OCR
AQA (AEB)
AQA (NEAB)

Every effort has been made to contact all copyright holders. If any have been
inadvertantly overlooked, the publisher would be pleased to make full
acknowledgement at the first opportunity.

You might also like to visit:
www.**fire**and**water**.com
The book lover's website

A2
mathematics

Contents

Preface

discovering advanced mathematics: A2 mathematics

Mathematics is not just an important subject in its own right, but also a tool for solving problems. Mathematics at Advanced level is changing to reflect this: during the A-level course you must study at least one area of the application of mathematics. This is what we mean by 'mathematical modelling'. Of course, mathematicians have been applying mathematics to problems in mechanics and statistics for many years. But now, the process has been formally included throughout A-level mathematics.

Curriculum 2000 offers students the opportunity to study for an A-level qualification in mathematics by extending their study to the A2 material. This book follows on from the *discovering advanced mathematics* AS book and provides, in one volume, the A2 mathematics needed to complete an A-level.

A third innovation is the recognition that graphical and numerical methods play an important part in the teaching and learning of mathematics. This book shows how much easier it is to study this topic now that we have programmable calculators and computers. Curriculum 2000 expects you to know how to use appropriate technology in mathematics and be aware that this technology has limitations.

We have revised *discovering advanced mathematics* to meet the needs of the new A- and AS- specifications and the Common Core for mathematics. This book provides opportunities to study advanced mathematics while learning about modelling and problem solving. We show how to make best use of new technology, including graphic calculators.

In every chapter in this book, you will find:
- an introduction that explains a new idea or technique in a helpful context;
- plenty of worked examples to show you how the techniques are used;
- exercises in two sets, classwork problems for work in class and homework problems that 'mirror' the classwork problems so that you can practice the same work in a self-study sessions;
- consolidation exercises that test you in the same way as real examination questions;
- real questions from all the awarding bodies.

And then, once you have finished the chapter, modelling and problem solving exercises to help you pull together all of the ideas in the chapter.

I hope that you will enjoy studying advanced mathematics by working through this book. The authors thank the many people involved in developing the *discovering advanced mathematics* series.

John Berry, Series Editor, *April 2001*

PURE 1

Differentiation

In this chapter we introduce:

■ *the chain rule for differentiating composite functions (or a function of a function)*

■ *rules for differentiating products and quotients of functions*

■ *the differentiation of inverse functions.*

THE CHAIN RULE

Exploration 1.1

Differentiating $\mathbf{f}(x) = (x^2 + 1)^2$

Look at the following function $f(x) = (x^2 + 1)^2$.

■ Expand $f(x)$ to give a polynomial in x.
■ Find $f'(x)$.
■ Factorise $f'(x)$ showing that $(x^2 + 1)$ is a factor.

Repeat the exploration for $f(x) = (x^2 + 1)^3$ and $f(x) = (x^2 + 1)^4$.

■ Can you identify a rule for differentiating $f(x) = (x^2 + 1)^n$?

Composite functions

The functions $(x^2 + 1)^2$, $(x^2 + 1)^3$ and $(x^2 + 1)^4$ are examples of **composite functions** or **functions of a function**. This statement can be justified by letting $y = f(x)$ and noting that $y = u^n$ where $u = x^2 + 1$ so that y is a function of u and u is a function of x.

The answers to Exploration 1.1 are summarised in this table.

$f(x)$	$(x^2 + 1)^2$	$(x^2 + 1)^3$	$(x^2 + 1)^4$
$f'(x)$	$4x(x^2 + 1)$	$6x(x^2 + 1)^2$	$8x(x^2 + 1)^3$

We can generalise y to $f(x) = (x^2 + 1)^n \Rightarrow \dfrac{dy}{dx} = f'(x) = 2xn(x^2 + 1)^{n-1}$ suggesting the rule:

$$\frac{dy}{dx} = \frac{dy}{du} \times \frac{du}{dx}$$

This is called the **chain rule**.

To use the chain rule we introduce a new variable u.
For example, suppose:

$$y = (4x - 3)^3$$

Then let $u = 4x - 3$ so that $y = u^3$.

Now $\dfrac{dy}{du} = 3u^2$ and $\dfrac{du}{dx} = 4$, so using the chain rule:

$$\frac{dy}{dx} = \left(3u^2\right) \times 4 = 12u^2 = 12\left(4x - 3\right)^2$$

Exploration 1.2

Differentiating composite functions

Differentiate each of the following functions:

- by multiplying out the brackets and differentiating term by term,
- by using the chain rule.

a) $y = (3x + 1)^2$ **b)** $y = (1 - 2x)^3$ **c)** $y = (x^3 + 2)^2$

Does the chain rule work in each case?

Example 1.1

For the function $f(x) = e^{-x^2}$ find:

a) $f'(x)$ **b)** the stationary points of $f(x)$.

Hence sketch a graph of $f(x)$.

Solution

a) Let $u = x^2$ then $y = e^{-u}$.

Differentiating each function:

$$\frac{du}{dx} = 2x \text{ and } \frac{dy}{du} = -e^{-u}.$$

Applying the chain rule:

$$\frac{dy}{dx} = \frac{dy}{du} \times \frac{du}{dx} = \left(-e^{-u}\right) \times (2x)$$

Replacing u by x^2 gives:

$$f'(x) = \frac{dy}{dx} = -2xe^{-x^2}$$

b) For a stationary value:

$$f'(x) = -2xe^{-x^2} = 0 \implies x = 0$$

since $f(0) = e^{-0} = 1$ the only stationary point is $(0, 1)$.

Now examine the gradient either side of $x = 0$; for example:

$$f'(-0.5) = e^{-0.25} \text{ and } f'(0.5) = -e^{-0.25}.$$

We deduce that the stationary point is a local maximum, and since $f(x) \to 0$ as $x \to -\infty$ and as $x \to \infty$ the graph of $f(x)$ is bell-shaped as shown in the diagram.

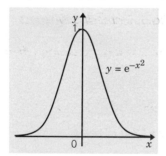

Note: This is an important function in statistics; it is used in defining the normal probability distribution function.

Example 1.2

Find $\dfrac{dy}{dx}$ for the function $y = \dfrac{1}{\left(x^3 - 1\right)^4}$.

Solution

Let $u(x) = x^3 - 1$ then $y = \dfrac{1}{u^4} = u^{-4}$

Differentiating each function:

$$\frac{du}{dx} = 3x^2 \text{ and } \frac{dy}{du} = -4u^{-5}$$

Applying the chain rule:

$$\frac{dy}{dx} = \frac{dy}{du} \times \frac{du}{dx} = \left(-4u^{-5}\right) \times \left(3x^2\right) = -\frac{12x^2}{u^5}$$

Replacing u by $x^3 - 1$ gives:

$$\frac{dy}{dx} = -\frac{12x^2}{\left(x^3 - 1\right)^5}$$

Rates of change

From your work on differentiation you know that the rate of change of a variable is given by $\frac{dy}{dt}$ where y is a function of time.

Sometimes y is a function of a variable other than t, for example, $y = f(s)$. Then we can use the chain rule to give:

$$\frac{dy}{dt} = \frac{dy}{ds} \times \frac{ds}{dt}$$

Example 1.3

The velocity of an object $v\ ms^{-1}$ is given by:
$$v = 1 + s^2$$
where s is its displacement from a fixed point, in metres. Find the acceleration of the object when $s = 3\,m$.

Solution

Acceleration a is the rate of change of velocity with time. Applying the chain rule:
$$a = \frac{dv}{dt} = \frac{dv}{ds} \times \frac{ds}{dt} = v\frac{dv}{ds}$$

since $\frac{ds}{dt} = v$, the velocity, and $v = 1 + s^2$,

$$\frac{dv}{ds} = 2s \implies a = (1 + s^2) \times (2s)$$

when $s = 3$, $a = (1 + 9) \times (6) = 60\,m\,s^{-2}$.

Example 1.4

The radius of a circular oil slick is increasing at the rate of $1.5\,ms^{-1}$.

a) Find the rate at which the area of the slick is increasing when its radius is $20\,m$.

b) Find the rate at which the perimeter of the slick is increasing when its radius is $20\,m$.

Solution

a) Area of circular oil slick of radius r is $A = \pi r^2$.

Differentiating, $\frac{dA}{dr} = 2\pi r = 40\pi$ (when $r = 20\,m$)

The rate at which the area is changing is:
$$\frac{dA}{dt} = \frac{dA}{dr} \times \frac{dr}{dt} \text{ (the chain rule)}$$

and $\frac{dr}{dt} = 1.5\,m\,s^{-1}$

So $\frac{dA}{dt} = (40\pi) \times (1.5) = 60\pi\ m^2\,s^{-1}$

b) Perimeter of circular oil slick of radius r is $C = 2\pi r$.
$$\frac{dC}{dt} = \frac{dC}{dr} \times \frac{dr}{dt} \text{ (the chain rule)}$$
$$\implies \frac{dC}{dr} = (2\pi) \times (1.5) = 3\pi\ m\,s^{-1}.$$

Example 1.5

A metal rod, of circular cross-section, is being heated and is expanding so that the volume of the rod increases at a rate of 200 cm³ s⁻¹.
After t seconds the length of the rod is ten times the radius of the rod. Find the rate of increase of the radius when the rod is 60 cm long.

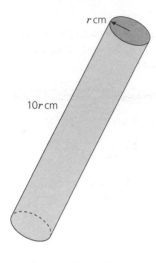

r cm

10r cm

Solution
Let the radius of the rod be r cm at time t, then the length of the rod is 10r cm. The volume of the rod $V = (\pi r^2) \times 10r = 10\pi r^3$ cm³.

$$\frac{dV}{dt} = 200 \text{ cm}^3 \text{ s}^{-1} \text{ (given in the question)}$$

with $V = 10\pi r^3$

$$\Rightarrow \quad \frac{dV}{dt} = \frac{dV}{dr} \times \frac{dr}{dt} \text{ (using the chain rule)}$$

$$\Rightarrow \quad \frac{dV}{dt} = 30\pi r^2 \times \frac{dr}{dt}$$

Hence the rate of increase of the radius is:

$$\frac{dr}{dt} = \frac{1}{30\pi r^2} \times \frac{dV}{dt}$$

When the length of the rod is 60 cm its radius is 6 cm.

So $\dfrac{dr}{dt} = \dfrac{1}{30\pi(6)^2} \times 200 = 0.059 \text{ cm s}^{-1}$ *(to 2 s.f.).*

EXERCISES

1.1 CLASSWORK

1 Differentiate these expressions.

a) $(2x-1)^5$ b) $(x^2+1)^4$ c) $\dfrac{1}{4x+1}$ d) $\dfrac{1}{x^3-x^2}$ e) $\sqrt{x-2}$

f) $\ln(x^2-1)$ g) e^{x^2+2x} h) $e^{\sqrt{x}}$ i) $(e^x+x)^4$ j) $\ln(4x-1)^3$

2 A curve has equation $y = e^{x^2}$. Find the coordinates of the point when the gradient is zero and sketch the curve.

3 A curve has equation $y = \left(x + \frac{1}{x}\right)^2$ for $x > 0$.
   a) Find the gradient of the curve at the points (0.5, 6.25) and (2, 6.25). Decide if the graph is increasing or decreasing at each point.
   b) Find and classify the stationary point and sketch the curve.

4 The velocity, $v \text{ m s}^{-1}$, of an object is given by:

$$v = \frac{4}{1+2s}$$

   where s is its displacement from a fixed point, in metres. Find the acceleration of the object when:
   a) $s = 0$ b) $s = 1 \text{ m}$ c) $s = 10 \text{ m}$.

5 A spherical balloon is being blown up so that its radius increases at a constant rate of 0.01 m s^{-1}.
   a) Find the rate of increase of its volume when the radius is 0.2 m.
   b) Find the rate of increase of the surface area of the balloon when the radius is 0.2 m.

6 The pressure P (N m^{-2}) and volume V (m^3) of a gas obey Boyle's law $P = \frac{c}{V}$ where c is a constant. In an experiment the volume of a quantity of gas is modelled by $V = 0.3e^{-4t} + 0.2$ at time t. Find the rate of change of the pressure when:

   a) $t = 0\,$s   **b)** $t = 2\,$s   **c)** $t = 100\,$s.

7 Wine is spilled onto a carpet forming a circular stain which increases in area at a rate of 150 mm^2 s^{-1}. Find the rate at which the radius is changing when the area of the stain is 1200 mm^2.

EXERCISES

1.1 HOMEWORK

1 Differentiate these expressions.

   a) $(3x + 2)^4$ **b)** $(t^3 - 1)^2$ **c)** $\frac{1}{s - 7}$ **d)** $\frac{1}{(2t + 1)^3}$

   e) $\frac{1}{4x^3 + x^2}$ **f)** $e^{x^3 - 2x^2}$ **g)** $e^{-2\sqrt{x}}$ **h)** $\frac{1}{\sqrt{e^x - x^2}}$

   i) $\ln(2s + 3)^4$ **j)** $\ln(4x^2 + 3x)$

2 A curve has equation $y = \sqrt{x^2 + 3x}$.

   a) Find the equation of the tangent to the curve at the point (1, 2). Is the graph increasing or decreasing at this point?
   b) Find the coordinates of any stationary points that exist for this curve.
   c) For what values of x does the curve exist?
   d) Find the slope of the tangent to the curve at the points (0, 0) and (–3, 0).
   e) Sketch the curve.

3 Find any stationary points on the following curves.

   a) $y = e^{x^2 - 1}$ **b)** $y = \ln(x^2 + 1)$ **c)** $y = \left(x - \frac{1}{x}\right)^4$ **d)** $y = \frac{1}{\sqrt{x^2 - 2x + 4}}$

4 The radius of a circular ink blot is increasing at a rate of 0.5 cm s^{-1}. Find the rate of increase of the area of the ink blot when its radius is 3 cm.

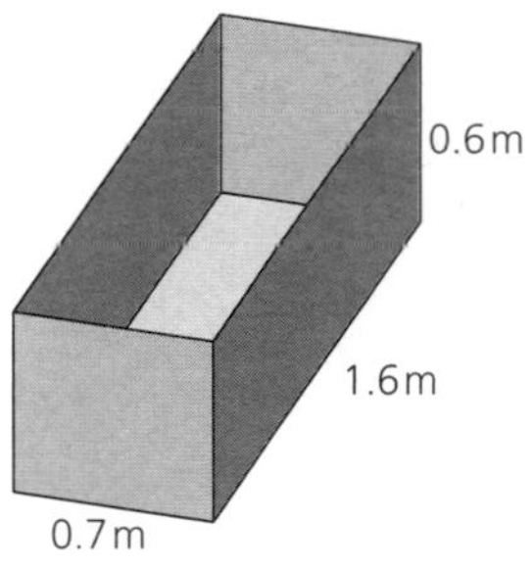

5 A domestic bath is modelled as a rectangular tank with dimensions as shown in the diagram. The bath is being filled by a mixer tap which delivers water at a rate of 0.07 m^3 min^{-1}. At time t the depth of water in the bath is h m. How fast is h changing?

0.6m / 1.6m / 0.7m

6 A current I amps flows through a resistance R ohms. The power developed is given by $P = I^2R$. Find the rate of change of power for a resistance of 20 ohms if:
   $$I = 5 + 2e^{-3t}$$
   where t is the time in seconds.

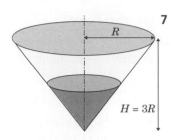

R

$H = 3R$

7 A cone has a vertical height, H, which is three times its base radius, R. The cone is supported with its axis of symmetry vertical as shown in the diagram. The cone is being filled with oil at the rate of 0.01 litres per second. At time t the depth of oil in the cone is h cm.

a) Show that the volume of oil in the cone at time t is:
$$V = \frac{\pi}{27} h^3$$

b) Find an expression for the rate of change of h in $\mathrm{cm\,s^{-1}}$.

THE PRODUCT RULE

Exploration 1.3

Differentiating products of functions

Look at the function $y = \mathrm{f}(x) = x^2(x + 1)^2$ which is a product of the two functions $u = x^2$ and $v = (x + 1)^2$.

■ Differentiate $\mathrm{f}(x)$ by multiplying out the brackets and differentiating term by term.

■ Is it true that $\dfrac{\mathrm{d}y}{\mathrm{d}x} = \dfrac{\mathrm{d}u}{\mathrm{d}x} \times \dfrac{\mathrm{d}v}{\mathrm{d}x}$?

■ Can you identify a rule for differentiating a product of two functions?

Repeat these steps for:

a) $\mathrm{f}(x) = x^3(2x - 1)^2$
b) $\mathrm{f}(x) = x^4(x^2 + x - 1)$.

The derivative of a product of two functions

From Exploration 1.3 we find that the derivative of a product of two functions does **not** equal the product of the derivative of the two functions.

To develop a rule, let $u = \mathrm{p}(x)$ and $v = \mathrm{q}(x)$. Consider the product $y = uv$ or $\mathrm{f}(x) = \mathrm{p}(x)\mathrm{q}(x)$ and the basic definition of differentiation given by:

$$\mathrm{f}'(x) \text{ is the limit of } \frac{\mathrm{f}(x+h) - \mathrm{f}(x)}{h} \text{ as } h \to 0.$$

For $\mathrm{f}(x) = \mathrm{p}(x)\mathrm{q}(x)$:

$$\mathrm{f}(x + h) - \mathrm{f}(x) = \mathrm{p}(x + h)\,\mathrm{q}(x + h) - \mathrm{p}(x)\mathrm{q}(x)$$

$$= [\mathrm{p}(x + h) \; - \; \mathrm{p}(x)]\mathrm{q}(x + h) \; + \; \mathrm{p}(x)[\mathrm{q}(x + h) \; - \; \mathrm{q}(x)]$$

these two extra terms cancel

Dividing both sides by h gives:

$$\frac{\mathrm{f}(x+h) - \mathrm{f}(x)}{h} = \left[\frac{\mathrm{p}(x+h) - \mathrm{p}(x)}{h}\right]\mathrm{q}(x+h) + \mathrm{p}(x)\left[\frac{\mathrm{q}(x+h) - \mathrm{q}(x)}{h}\right]$$

and taking the limit as $h \to 0$ gives the **product rule**:
$$\mathrm{f}'(x) = \mathrm{p}'(x)\,\mathrm{q}(x) + \mathrm{p}(x)\,\mathrm{q}'(x)$$

$$\text{or } \frac{\mathrm{d}y}{\mathrm{d}x} = \frac{\mathrm{d}u}{\mathrm{d}x}v + u\frac{\mathrm{d}v}{\mathrm{d}x}$$

Example 1.6

Find $\dfrac{dy}{dx}$ for the function $y = x^2(x+1)^2$.

Solution

Here $u = x^2$ and $v = (x+1)^2$ so:

$$\frac{du}{dx} = 2x \quad \text{and} \quad \frac{dv}{dx} = 2(x+1)$$

Apply the product rule:

$$\frac{dy}{dx} = \frac{du}{dx}v + u\frac{dv}{dx} = 2x \times (x+1)^2 + x^2 \times 2(x+1)$$
$$= 2x(x+1)[(x+1)+x] = 2x(x+1)(2x+1)$$

This should agree with the result from Exploration 1.3.

Example 1.7

For the function $f(x) = xe^{-2x}$:

a) *find $f'(x)$,*
b) *find and classify the stationary points of $f(x)$,*
c) *sketch a graph of $y = xe^{-2x}$.*

Solution

a) *$u = x$ and $v - e^{-2x}$*

$$\Rightarrow f'(x) = \frac{du}{dx}v + u\frac{dv}{dx} = 1 \times e^{-2x} + x \times -2e^{-2x} = (1-2x)e^{-2x}$$

b) *For a stationary point:*

$$f'(x) = (1-2x)e^{-2x} = 0$$
$$\Rightarrow 1 - 2x = 0$$
$$\Rightarrow x = \tfrac{1}{2}$$

There is one stationary point at $(\tfrac{1}{2}, \tfrac{1}{2}e^{-1})$.
Now investigate the gradient either side of the stationary point.

$$f'(0) = e^0 = 1 \text{ and } f'(1) = -e^{-2}$$

so the stationary point is a local maximum.

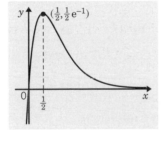

c) *The graph of $y = xe^{-2x}$ passes through the origin and*
$y \to 0$ as $x \to \infty$ and $y \to -\infty$ as $x \to -\infty$.
The graph of $f(x) = xe^{-2x}$ is shown in the diagram.

EXERCISES

1.2 CLASSWORK

1 Differentiate these expressions.

a) $(x-1)(x^2+1)$ **b)** $\sqrt{x}(1+x)$ **c)** $(x^2-1)(2x+1)^2$ **d)** $x(x-1)^{-1}$

e) $(x+1)(x-1)^3$ **f)** $(t^2+2)(t^3-1)$ **g)** $\sqrt{(s+1)}(s-1)^2$ **h)** u^2e^{-3u}

i) $(x-1)^2e^x$ **j)** $(2x+3)e^{-x^2}$ **k)** $(2x+1)\ln(2x+1)$ **l)** $e^{-x}\ln x$

2 A curve has equation $y = (x^2-2)e^{-2x}$.
  a) Find the equation of the tangent at the point (0, –2). Is the curve increasing or decreasing at this point?
  b) Find and classify the stationary points of the curve.

3 A curve has equation $y = x^3 e^{x^2}$. Find the equation of the tangent to the curve at the points (0, 0), (1, e^1) and (–1, –e^1).

Is the curve increasing or decreasing at each point? Classify the stationary point at the origin.

4 An object moves along the x-axis so that its position at time $t \geq 0$ is modelled by $x = (3 + 2t)e^{-0.25t}$.

a) Find a formula for the velocity of the object.
b) For what values of t is the velocity positive? Explain what a negative velocity means.
c) At what instant of time is the velocity greatest in magnitude? What is the velocity at this time?
d) What happens to the object as t increases?

5 A rectangular beam is to be cut from a log of cylindrical cross-section of radius 0.4 m.

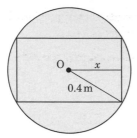

a) If x is half of the width of the beam (see diagram) show that the cross-sectional area of the beam is:

$$A = 4x\sqrt{0.16 - x^2}$$

b) What is the largest possible cross-sectional area of the beam?

1.2 HOMEWORK

1 Differentiate these expressions.

a) $(2x+1)(x-1)$ b) $(3t^2-5)(2t+3)$ c) $(s+3)(s^3-2s-4)$ d) $x^{-3}(2x + 1)$

e) $s\sqrt{s^2 + 1}$ f) $u e^{-u^2}$ g) $\left(1+3v^2\right)e^{-2v}$ h) $(1+x)^{-2}\left(3x^2 +x - 1\right)$

i) $(2 - 3x)\ln(0.5x - 2)$ j) $\left(t-\frac{1}{t}\right)e^{t^2}$ k) $e^{3x}\ln(2x-1)$ l) $(t^2+2t-1)^{\frac{1}{3}}(5t - 4)$

2 Find the product rule for the derivative of a function of three functions $f(x) = u(x)v(x)w(x)$.
Apply your rule to differentiate the following expressions.

a) $(x^2 - 1)(x + 1)(2x^3 - x^2)$ b) $(2x + 1)(3x^2 + 1)e^{-2x}$
c) $(x^2 + x)e^{-3x}\ln(x + 1)^2$

3 Find and classify the stationary points of the curve with equation $y = x^3(x^2 - 1)^2$.

4 A curve has equation $y = (x^2 - 1)\ln(2x + 3)$.

a) Find the equation of the tangent to the curve at the points (0, –ln 3) and (1.5, 1.25 ln 6). Is the curve increasing or decreasing at these points?
b) Find and classify the stationary points of the curve.
c) Sketch the curve for values of x between –2 and 2 for which the function exists.

5 The radius r m of an oil slick on a lake t hours after it was first noticed is given by:

$$r = 0.6 + (1.1 + 2t^2)e^{-0.5t}$$

a) Find the maximum radius of the slick and the time at which this occurs.
b) What are the initial and final radii of the oil slick?

THE QUOTIENT RULE

Quotients of functions

Look at the function $f(x) = \dfrac{x+2}{x-1}$ which is a quotient of two functions $u(x) = x + 2$ and $v(x) = x - 1$.

■ Writing the function as $y = (x + 2)(x - 1)^{-1}$ use the product rule to find $\dfrac{dy}{dx}$.

■ Is it true that $\dfrac{dy}{dx} = \dfrac{\frac{du}{dx}}{\frac{dv}{dx}}$?

Repeat these steps for: **a)** $y = \dfrac{x}{e^x}$ **b)** $y = \dfrac{e^x}{x}$.

The derivative of a quotient

From Exploration 1.4 we should see that the derivative of a quotient is somewhat different from the ratio of the derivatives of u and v.

To develop a rule consider the quotient $y = \dfrac{u}{v}$ written as a product:
$$y = uv^{-1}$$
Apply the product rule:
$$\frac{dy}{dx} = \frac{du}{dx}v^{-1} + u\frac{d}{dx}\left(v^{-1}\right)$$
To differentiate v^{-1} we apply the chain rule:
$$\frac{d}{dx}\left(v^{-1}\right) = \frac{d}{dv}\left(v^{-1}\right) \times \frac{dv}{dx} = -v^{-2}\frac{dv}{dx}$$
Thus $\dfrac{dy}{dx} = \dfrac{du}{dx}v^{-1} - uv^{-2}\dfrac{dv}{dx}$

$$\Rightarrow \quad \frac{dy}{dx} = \frac{v\dfrac{du}{dx} - u\dfrac{dv}{dx}}{v^2} \quad \text{This is the \textbf{quotient rule}.}$$

Example 1.8

Find $\dfrac{dy}{dx}$ for the function $y = \dfrac{x+2}{x-1}$.

Solution
Let $u = x + 2$ and $v = x - 1$ then:
$$\frac{du}{dx} = 1 \text{ and } \frac{dv}{dx} = 1$$
Apply the quotient rule:
$$\frac{dy}{dx} = \frac{v\dfrac{du}{dx} - u\dfrac{dv}{dx}}{v^2} = \frac{(x-1)(1) - (x+2)(1)}{(x-1)^2} = \frac{-3}{(x-1)^2}$$
This should agree with the result from Exploration 1.4.

Example 1.9

For the function $y = f(x) = \dfrac{x}{1 + x^2}$:

a) find $f'(x)$,

b) find and classify the stationary points of $f(x)$,

c) sketch a graph of $y = \dfrac{x}{1 + x^2}$.

Solution

a) $u = x$ and $v = 1 + x^2 \Rightarrow \dfrac{du}{dx} = 1$ and $\dfrac{dv}{dx} = 2x$

$$f'(x) = \frac{dy}{dx} = \frac{v\dfrac{du}{dx} - u\dfrac{dv}{dx}}{v^2} = \frac{(1+x^2)(1) - x(2x)}{(1+x^2)^2} = \frac{1-x^2}{(1+x^2)^2}$$

b) *For a stationary point:*

$$f'(x) = \frac{1-x^2}{(1+x^2)^2} = 0$$

$\Rightarrow 1 - x^2 = 0 \Rightarrow x = -1$ *or* $x = 1$

There are two stationary points at $(-1, -\frac{1}{2})$ *and* $(1, \frac{1}{2})$.

Now we investigate the gradient either side of each stationary point.

i) *Close to* $(-1, -\frac{1}{2})$: $f'(-2) = -\frac{3}{25}$ *and* $f'(0) = 1$

The point $(-1, -\frac{1}{2})$ *is a local minimum.*

ii) *Close to* $(1, \frac{1}{2})$: $f'(0) = 1$ *and* $f'(2) = -\frac{3}{25}$

The point $(1, \frac{1}{2})$ *is a local maximum.*

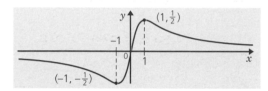

c) *The graph of* $y = \dfrac{x}{1+x^2}$ *passes through the origin,*

$y \to 0$ *as* $x \to \pm\infty$.

The graph of $f(x) = \dfrac{x}{1+x^2}$ *is shown in the diagram.*

EXERCISES

1.3 CLASSWORK

1 Differentiate these expressions.

a) $\dfrac{(x-4)^2}{x}$ b) $\dfrac{t^2}{t+3}$ c) $\dfrac{2-x}{x^2}$ d) $\dfrac{t^{\frac{5}{4}}}{4t-3}$

e) $\dfrac{x^2+5x+4}{2x^2-1}$ f) $\dfrac{t+t^{-1}}{t-t^{-1}}$ g) $\dfrac{e^{-2x}}{1+x}$ h) $\dfrac{1-t^2}{\ln(t+1)}$

i) $\dfrac{e^{x^2}}{1-x}$ j) $\dfrac{\ln(2t-3)}{2t-3}$ k) $\dfrac{x^3+x^2+x+1}{x+1}$ l) $\dfrac{\ln t}{t^3-2}$

2 A curve has equation $y = \dfrac{x^2-1}{2x+4}$.

a) Find and classify the stationary points of the curve.

b) Sketch the curve using a graphical calculator and confirm your answer to a).

3 Find and classify the stationary points of the curve with equation:

$$y = \frac{e^x}{1+x^2}.$$

4 A simple model for the flow rate, $f(v)$ (s^{-1}), of cars along a straight level road is: $\qquad f(v) = \dfrac{v}{4+0.7v^2}$

where v is the speed of the cars in m s^{-1}. Find the speed of the cars which gives a maximum flow rate. (Show that this speed does give a maximum value.)

5 A curve has equation $y = \dfrac{e^{2x}-e^{-2x}}{e^{2x}+e^{-2x}}$. Show that $\dfrac{dy}{dx} = 2(1-y^2)$.

Hence show that the curve has no stationary points.

1.3 HOMEWORK

1 Differentiate these expressions.

a) $\dfrac{(x+2)^2}{x^3}$ b) $\dfrac{5u}{(1-u)^3}$ c) $\dfrac{2x^2}{x-2}$ d) $\dfrac{s^{\frac{7}{3}}}{3s-1}$

e) $\dfrac{x^2-3x+2}{x^2+1}$ f) $\dfrac{s+2}{s^2-2s+1}$ g) $\dfrac{e^{4x}}{3-2x}$ h) $\dfrac{1+x+x^2}{\ln x}$

i) $\dfrac{e^{-2x^2}}{2+3x}$ j) $\dfrac{\ln(x-1)}{x-1}$ k) $\dfrac{e^{-x}}{1+e^{-2x}}$ l) $\dfrac{\sqrt{1-s}}{s+2}$

2 Find and classify the stationary points of the curve with equation

$$y=\frac{x^2}{x^2+4}$$

Sketch the curve, using a graphical calculator, and confirm your answer.

3 Find and classify the stationary points of each of the following curves.

a) $y=\dfrac{x+1}{x^3-2x^2+x}$ b) $y=\dfrac{1+x}{1-x}$

In each case, check your answers by sketching the curve using a graphical calculator.

4 An object moves along the x-axis so that its position at time $t\geq0$ is given by:

$$x=\frac{4t^2+t+4}{t^2+1}$$

a) Obtain an expression for the velocity of the object and find when the velocity is zero.
b) What is the greatest distance of the object from the origin?
c) What is the maximum speed of the object?

5 The power delivered into the load, x, of a class A amplifier of output resistance R ohms is given by: $P(x)=\dfrac{V^2x}{(x+R)^2}$

where V is the output voltage. Find the value of x such that P is a maximum.

DIFFERENTIATION OF INVERSE FUNCTIONS

Sometimes a function is given in the form $x=g(y)$ instead of $y=f(x)$. Then g is called the **inverse function** of f.
To differentiate an inverse function, we need another important result.

Exploration 1.5

Differentiating an inverse function

Take the function $x=\sqrt{y}$ for which $y=x^2$.

■ Find $\dfrac{dx}{dy}$ and $\dfrac{dy}{dx}$.

■ Try to formulate a simple relation between $\dfrac{dx}{dy}$ and $\dfrac{dy}{dx}$.

Verify your result for:

a) $y=x^3$, $x=y^{\frac{1}{3}}$ b) $y=\frac{1}{3}(2x-1)$, and $x=\frac{1}{2}(3y+1)$

The rule for differentiating inverse functions

The rule for differentiating inverse functions is: $\dfrac{dy}{dx} = \dfrac{1}{\left(\frac{dx}{dy}\right)}$

It is important to note that this rule only applies for **first-order** differentiation. This rule will be of particular use in Chapter 8, *Curves 2*, when we need to differentiate the inverse trigonometric functions.

Example 1.10

Find $\dfrac{dy}{dx}$ for the function $x = y\ln y$.

Solution

Since $x = y\ln y$ is a product of two functions:

$\dfrac{dx}{dy} = y\left(\dfrac{1}{y}\right) + (\ln y) = 1 + \ln y \Rightarrow \dfrac{dy}{dx} = \left(\dfrac{1}{\frac{dx}{dy}}\right) = \dfrac{1}{1 + \ln y}$

Example 1.11

Find $\dfrac{dy}{dx}$ for the function $y = a^x$ where a is constant.

Solution

The first step is to take logs of both sides.

$\ln y = x\ln a \Rightarrow x = \dfrac{\ln y}{\ln a} \Rightarrow \dfrac{dx}{dy} = \dfrac{1}{y\ln a}$ since $\ln a$ is constant.

Applying the rule for differentiating inverse functions:

$\dfrac{dy}{dx} = \dfrac{1}{\left(\frac{dx}{dy}\right)} = \dfrac{1}{\left(\frac{1}{y\ln a}\right)} = y\ln a$

In this case we substitute for y, so that: $\dfrac{dy}{dx} = a^x \ln a$

EXERCISES

1.4 CLASSWORK

In the following expressions find $\dfrac{dy}{dx}$.

1 $x = ye^{-y}$ **2** $x = \ln(y-1)$ **3** $y = 2^x$ **4** $x = e^y - e^{-y}$

The following problems contain a mixture of products and quotients of functions and composite functions. In each case identify the type of function and then use the appropriate rule to find its derivative.

5 $x\sqrt{x+2}$ **6** $(2x^3 - 3)^4$ **7** $\dfrac{x}{\sqrt{x+1}}$ **8** e^{4x^2+x-1}

9 $e^{x^2}(x^2 - 3x + 2)$ **10** $e^{-0.1t}(t+2)$ **11** $\dfrac{1}{(x^4+1)^2}$ **12** $(t-1)(t-2)^2$

13 $\sqrt{t^2 - t + 1}$ **14** $\dfrac{e^t}{t + t^{-1}}$

1.4 HOMEWORK

In each of the following expressions find $\dfrac{dy}{dx}$.

1 $x = \ln(2y+1)$ **2** $y = 4(3)^x$ **3** $x = e^{2y} + e^{-2y}$ **4** $x = y^2 - 2y + 1$

The following problems contain a mixture of products and quotients of functions and composite functions. In each case identify the type of function and then use the appropriate rule to find its derivative.

5 $\dfrac{x}{x^2 - 4}$ **6** $u\ln u$ **7** $(2t - \sqrt{t})(t + \sqrt{t})$ **8** $e^{t^2 - 3t + 4}$

9   $e^{2x-5}(x^2 - 4x - 1)$ 10 $\ln(t^2 + 3)$ 11 $\dfrac{x}{e^x - e^{-x}}$ 12 10^x

13   $\dfrac{3x + 1}{x - 2}$ 14 $\sqrt{s(2-s)^3}$

MATHEMATICAL MODELLING ACTIVITY

Problem statement

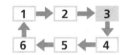
Specify the real problem

Mathematical models of traffic flow can help to show how to avoid traffic jams and to ensure optimum flow conditions in congested situations such as road tunnels, contraflow sections of motorways etc.

■   What is the speed of traffic required to obtain maximum traffic flow along a single carriageway road?

Set up a model

Set up a model

First you need to identify the important variables:
■   the speed of the traffic,
■   the length of the vehicles,
■   the distance between the vehicles,
■   the flow rate defined as the number of vehicles per hour passing a fixed point.

You will also need to make some assumptions before formulating the mathematical problem to solve. Here let's assume:
■   all vehicles are identical of length L m,
■   all vehicles travel at the same constant speed v m s^{-1},
■   the distance between the vehicles is the safe stopping distance given in the Highway Code (see Chapter 1, page 10).

Mathematical problem

Formulate the mathematical problem

Firstly, establish a relationship between the flow rate, f, and the speed of the vehicles, v. If the vehicles pass a given point t seconds apart then in one hour the flow rate (i.e. number of vehicles per hour) is:

$$f = \frac{3600}{t} \quad \text{(vehicles per hour)}$$

If the distance between the front of each pair of vehicles is d m then
$d = vt$ giving:

$$f = \frac{3600v}{d} \quad \text{(vehicles per hour)}$$

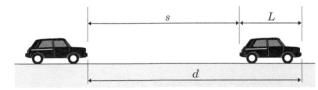

The distance d is made up of the length of a vehicle, L, and the 'safe stopping distance', s.
$$d = s + L$$
The formula for the flow rate then becomes:
$$f = \frac{3600v}{s + L}$$

Secondly, establish a model for the 'safe stopping distance'. Using the data from the *Highway Code* with distances in metres and speeds in m s^{-1}, confirm that the equation relating s and v is:
$$s = 0.682v + 0.076v^2$$

The mathematical problem is to find the value of v that will maximise the function:
$$f = \frac{3600v}{L + 0.682v + 0.076v^2}$$

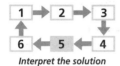

Solve the mathematical problem

Mathematical solution

$f(v)$ is a quotient of two functions. Applying the quotient rule:

$$f'(v) = \frac{3600\left[1\left(L + 0.682v + 0.076v^2\right)\right] - v(0.682 + 0.152v)}{\left(L + 0.682v + 0.076v^2\right)^2}$$

$$= \frac{3600\left[L - 0.076v^2\right]}{\left(L + 0.682v + 0.076v^2\right)^2}$$

For a maximum value:

$$f'(v) = 0 \implies L - 0.076v^2 = 0 \implies v = \sqrt{\frac{L}{0.076}} = 3.627\sqrt{L}$$

■ Confirm that this value of v gives a maximum value of $f(v)$.

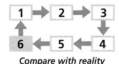

Interpret the solution

Interpretation

Results for small and medium sized cars and for a juggernaut are given in the following table (to the nearest integer).

Vehicle length L (m)	Speed v (m s^{-1})	Speed v (mph)	Separation s (m)	Flow rate f
4	7	16	9.5	2017
5	8	18	10.3	1880
15	14	31	24.4	1278

In simple terms, cars could be advised to travel at about 17 mph with a separation of about two car lengths in order to maximise the flow rate.

Compare with reality

Criticism

Speeds as low as 17 mph are unlikely to be popular with motorists. Observing vehicles you will notice that vehicles tend to travel closer than the safe stopping distances recommended by the *Highway Code*.

Refinement of the model

Investigate the effect of different models for the distance between the vehicles. For example:

■ s = thinking distance from *Highway Code*,
■ s = braking distance from *Highway Code*,
■ s = thinking distance + fraction of braking distance.

[Reference: Exploring Mechanics *by the MEW Group published by Hodder and Stoughton]*

CONSOLIDATION EXERCISES FOR CHAPTER 1

1   Find the coordinates of the points of the curve $y = \dfrac{x^2 - 1}{x}$ at which the gradient of the curve is 5.

2   Differentiate the following expressions.

   a) $(2x^2 - 1)(x^3 + 4)^3$ b) $\dfrac{x^2 + 1}{\sqrt{x}}$ c) $(x^2 + 2)^3$ d) $e^x \ln x$

   e) $\dfrac{x - 1}{2x - 3}$ f) $\left(x + \dfrac{1}{x}\right)^{-1}$

3 A curve has equation $y = \dfrac{x+3}{\sqrt{1+x^2}}$. Find and classify the stationary points of the curve.

4 A curve has equation $y = (x-1)(x-c)^2$ where c is a constant.
   a) Investigate the nature of the stationary points in the two cases:
      i) $c > 1$ **ii)** $0 < c < 1$.
   b) On separate diagrams sketch the curves for the two cases:
      i) $c > 1$ **ii)** $0 < c < 1$.

5 The radius of a circular disc is increasing at a rate of $0.01\,\mathrm{mm\,s^{-1}}$.
   Find the rate at which the area is increasing when its radius is $25\,\mathrm{mm}$.

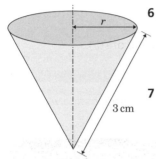

6 The figure shows a conical container with slant height 3 cm and radius of base r cm. It encloses a volume $V\,\mathrm{cm^3}$ where $V = \frac{1}{3}\pi r^2 \sqrt{9 - r^2}$.

   a) Determine the value of r for which $\frac{dV}{dr} = 0$.
   b) Show that this value of r gives a maximum value of V.

7 For a lens of constant focal length f cm, the object distance u cm and image distance v cm are connected by the relation $v = \dfrac{uf}{u - f}$.

   a) Find the derivative $\frac{dv}{du}$.
   b) If u is decreasing at a rate of $1.5\,\mathrm{cm\,s^{-1}}$ and $f = 8$ cm, calculate the rate at which v is changing when $u - 40$ cm. Is v increasing or decreasing?

8 A conveyor belt delivers coal onto a stockpile at the rate of $0.3\,\mathrm{m^3\,s^{-1}}$. The coal forms a conical heap with height equal to its radius. How fast is the height of the cone increasing when it consists of $20\,\mathrm{m^3}$ of coal?

9 The radius r cm of a circular ink spot, t seconds after it first appears, is given by:
$$r = \frac{1 + 4t}{2 + t}.$$
   Calculate:
   a) the time taken for the radius to double its initial value,
   b) the rate of increase of the radius in cm s^{-1} when $t - 3$,
   c) the value to which r tends as t tends to infinity.

   (AEB Question 10, Specimen Paper 1)

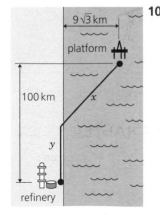

10 An oil production platform $9\sqrt{3}$ km offshore, is to be connected by a pipeline to a refinery on shore, 100 km down the coast from the platform as shown in the diagram.

   The length of underwater pipeline is x km and the length of pipeline on land is y km. It costs £2 million to lay each kilometre of pipeline underwater and £1 million to lay each kilometre of pipeline on land.
   a) Show that the total cost of this pipeline is £$C(x)$ million where:
   $$C(x) = 2x + 100 - \left(x^2 - 243\right)^{\frac{1}{2}}$$
   b) Show that $x = 18$ gives a minimum cost for this pipeline. Find this minimum cost and the corresponding total length of the pipeline.

   (Scottish Highers Question 11, Paper 2, 1993)

11 The volume of liquid, V cm^3, in a container when the depth is x cm $(x > 0)$ is given by:

$$V = \frac{30\sqrt{x}}{(x+9)} \; .$$

The container has height h cm.

a) Given that $x = h$ when $\dfrac{dV}{dx} = 0$, find the value of h, and hence determine the value of V when $x = h$.

b) Calculate the rate of change of the volume when the depth is 1 cm and increasing at a rate of $0.02 \, \text{cm s}^{-1}$, giving your answer in cm^3s^{-1}.

(AQA MBP4 Question 5 Specimen Paper 2000)

Summary

■ **The chain rule:**   If y is a **composite function** of x so that $y = f(u)$ where $u = u(x)$ then:
$$\frac{dy}{dx} = \frac{dy}{du} \times \frac{du}{dx}$$
This is often called the function of a function rule.

■ **The product rule:**   If y is a **product** of two functions so that $y = uv$ then:
$$\frac{dy}{dx} = v\frac{du}{dx} + u\frac{dv}{dx}$$

■ **The quotient rule:**   If y is a **quotient** of two functions so that $y = \dfrac{u}{v}$ then:

$$\frac{dy}{dx} = \frac{v\dfrac{du}{dx} - u\dfrac{dv}{dx}}{v^2}$$

■ **The inverse function rule:** If the relation between x and y is given in the form $x = f(y)$ then:
$$\frac{dy}{dx} = \left(\frac{dx}{dy}\right)^{-1}$$

PURE 2

The calculus of trigonometric functions

■ *We use the idea of finding the gradient function to discover the gradient functions for sin x, cos x and tan x.*

■ *To define the derivatives of trigonometric functions we must measure angles in radians. Make sure that you – and your calculator – are in radian mode throughout this chapter!*

DIFFERENTIATION

Exploration 2.1

Differentiating sin x, cos x and tan x

The diagram shows the graph of $f(x) = \sin x$ for $0 \le x \le 2\pi$.

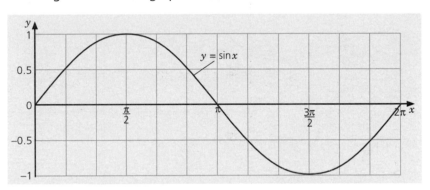

■ Use a numerical method to estimate the gradient, $f'(x)$, at intervals of $\frac{\pi}{6}$.

■ Copy this table and use your values to complete it.

x	0	$\frac{\pi}{6}$	$\frac{\pi}{3}$	$\frac{\pi}{2}$	$\frac{2\pi}{3}$	$\frac{5\pi}{6}$	π	$\frac{7}{6}\pi$	$\frac{4}{3}\pi$	$\frac{3}{2}\pi$	$\frac{5}{3}\pi$	$\frac{11}{6}\pi$	2π
$f(x)$	0	0.5	0.866	1	0.866	0.5	0	-0.5	-0.866	-1	-0.866	-0.5	0
$f'(x)$													

■ Sketch the graph of $y = f(x)$ and superimpose on it a graph of the gradient function.
■ Deduce the algebraic form for $f'(x)$.
■ Repeat the exploration for graphs of:
  $y = \cos x$, $y = \tan x$, $y = \sin ax$, $y = \cos ax$, $y = \sin^2 x$, etc.
■ What patterns do you get in finding the gradient functions?

Interpreting the results

The final row in the table should look like this.

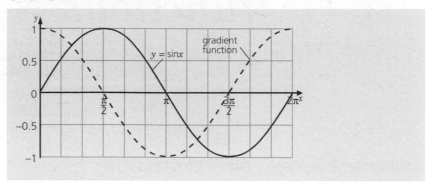

f'(x)	1	0.866	0.5	0	−0.5	−0.866	−1	−0.866	−0.5	0	0.5	0.866	1

Superimposing the graph of the gradient function on the original graph gives this result.

We can see that the gradient function is f'(x) = cos x i.e. the derivative of sin x is cos x. Graphical outputs from completing some of the other explorations give these curves.

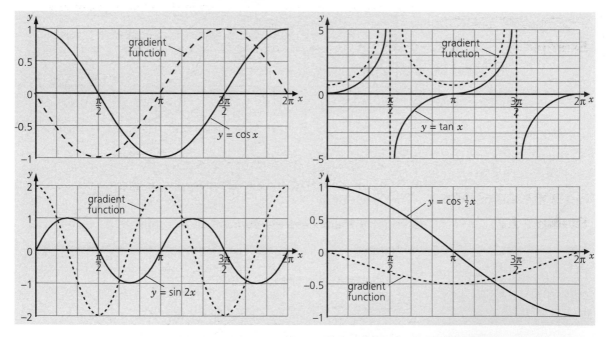

Examining the shape of the gradient function for each graph reveals the results in this table.

f(x)	f'(x)
$\sin x$	$\cos x$
$\cos x$	$-\sin x$
$\tan x$	$\sec^2 x$
$\sin ax$	$a \cos ax$
$\cos ax$	$-a \sin ax$

For $y = \sin^2 x$ and $y = \cos^2 x$, we can obtain the graphical output for the gradient functions as shown in this diagram.

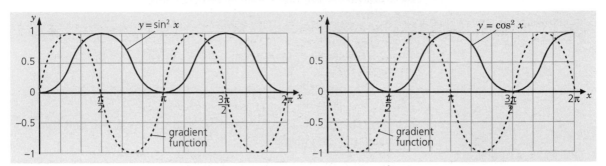

Examining the shape of the gradient function for each graph gives the additional results as in this table.

f(x)	f'(x)
$\sin^2 x$	$\sin 2x$
$\cos^2 x$	$-\sin 2x$

Starting with the two results:

$f(x) = \sin x \Rightarrow f'(x) = \cos x$ and

$f(x) = \cos x \Rightarrow f'(x) = -\sin x$

We can use techniques developed in Chapter 1, *Differentiation*, to prove the other results, as illustrated in the following examples.

Example 2.1

Show that the derivative of $\sin ax$ is $a \cos ax$.

Solution

Let $y = \sin ax$, then we require $\dfrac{dy}{dx}$.
Using the chain rule:

Let $u = ax \Rightarrow y = \sin u \Rightarrow \dfrac{dy}{du} = \cos u$ and $\dfrac{du}{dx} = a$

hence $\dfrac{dy}{dx} = \dfrac{dy}{du} \times \dfrac{du}{dx} = \cos u \times a = a \cos ax$

Example 2.2

Show that the derivative of $\tan x = \sec^2 x$.

Solution

Let $y = \tan x = \dfrac{\sin x}{\cos x}$, then we require $\dfrac{dy}{dx}$.

Using the quotient rule:
let $u = \sin x$ and $v = \cos x$ $\Rightarrow$ $\dfrac{du}{dx} = \cos x$ $\dfrac{dv}{dx} = -\sin x$

Hence $\dfrac{dy}{dx} = \dfrac{v\dfrac{du}{dx} - u\dfrac{dv}{dx}}{v^2} = \dfrac{\cos^2 x + \sin^2 x}{\cos^2 x} = \dfrac{1}{\cos^2 x} = \sec^2 x$

An alternative method

The derivative of $\sin^2 x$ can also be found by applying the chain rule, but a different result is obtained.
If $y = \sin^2 x$, let $u = \sin x \Rightarrow y = u^2$

and $\quad \dfrac{du}{dx} = \cos x \quad \dfrac{dy}{du} = 2u$

Hence $\quad \dfrac{dy}{dx} = \dfrac{dy}{du} \times \dfrac{du}{dx} = 2 \sin x \cos x$

Sketching the graphs of $y = 2 \sin x \cos x$ and $y = \sin 2x$, we find that the two forms are equivalent.

Now that we can differentiate trigonometric functions we can find rates of change for various wave models, as illustrated in the following example.

Example 2.3

The depth of water in a harbour, y metres, can be roughly modelled by the equation:

$$y = 4 \sin\left(\frac{\pi}{6} t\right) + 7$$

where t is the number of hours after midnight on a certain day. Find the rate of change of height at 10.00 and determine the times in the day when the water level is falling fastest.

Solution
A sketch graph of $y = 4 \sin\left(\dfrac{\pi}{6} t\right) + 7$ for $0 \le t \le 12$ is shown in the diagram.

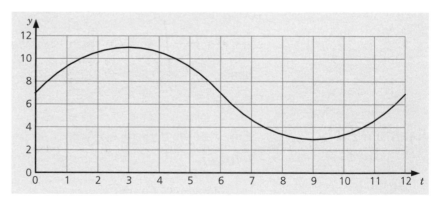

$$y = 4 \sin\left(\frac{\pi}{6} t\right) + 7 \Rightarrow \frac{dy}{dt} = 4 \times \frac{\pi}{6} \cos\left(\frac{\pi}{6} t\right) = \frac{2}{3} \pi \cos\left(\frac{\pi}{6} t\right)$$

when $\quad t = 10, \quad \dfrac{dy}{dt} = \dfrac{2}{3} \pi \cos\left(\dfrac{\pi}{6} \times 10\right) = \dfrac{1}{3} \pi \approx 1.05$

i.e. the depth is rising at a rate of just over 1 metre per hour.
To find the times at which the water level is falling fastest we need to minimise $\dfrac{dy}{dt}$ by differentiating again and equating to zero.

$\dfrac{d^2 y}{dt^2} = -\dfrac{\pi^2}{9} \sin\left(\dfrac{\pi}{6} t\right) = 0$ *for stationary values*
$\Rightarrow t = 0, \ 6, \ 12, \ 18 \text{ or } 24$

From the shape of the original graph we can see that minimum values for $\dfrac{dy}{dt}$ will occur at 06.00 and 18.00.

EXERCISES

1 Differentiate the following with respect to x.

a) $3\sin x$ b) $4\cos x$ c) $\frac{1}{2}\tan x$ d) $\frac{1}{4}\sin x$

e) $3\sin x + 4\cos x$ f) $5 - \tan x$ g) $x^2 + 8\sin x$ h) $e^{3x} + \tan x - 6$

2 Differentiate the following with respect to x.

a) $3\sin 7x$ b) $-4\cos 11x$ c) $\frac{5}{2}\tan 4x$

d) $3\sin(2x - 5)$ e) $4\tan\frac{1}{2}x - 6\sin\frac{1}{3}x$ f) $15\cos\frac{1}{5}x - 12\sin\frac{1}{4}x$

g) $\dfrac{5\ln 6x + 9\cos(5x + 7)}{10}$ h) $e^{4x} + 4^x - \sin(1 - 3x)$

3 Use the chain rule to differentiate these.

a) $\sin^2 x$ b) $\sin x^2$ c) $\cos\left(\dfrac{1}{x}\right)$

d) $\sqrt{1 + \cos x}$ e) $\tan^3 2x$ f) $\ln(1 + \sin 2x)$

g) $e^{\sin x}$ h) $\sin e^x$ i) $\ln\cos x$

j) $\cos\ln x$

4 Differentiate the following products.

a) $x\tan x$ b) $\sin x\cos 2x$ c) $x^3\cos 2x$

d) $e^x\cos x$ e) $e^{-\frac{1}{2}x}\sin 2x$ f) $\sqrt{x}\tan x$

g) $\sin x\ln x$ h) $xe^{\sin x}$

5 Use the quotient rule to differentiate these.

a) $\dfrac{\sin x}{x}$ b) $\dfrac{\sin^4 x}{\cos^3 x}$ c) $\dfrac{e^x}{\sin x}$

d) $\dfrac{\sin x}{\sqrt{x}}$ e) $\dfrac{x^2}{\sin x + \cos x}$ f) $\dfrac{x^2 + x + 1}{\tan x}$

6 By writing $\sec x$ as $\dfrac{1}{\cos x}$ and using the quotient rule, show that:

$$\frac{d}{dx}(\sec x) = \sec x\tan x.$$

Use a similar method to differentiate $\operatorname{cosec} x$ and $\cot x$.

Hence differentiate $\sec(3x - 1)$, $\operatorname{cosec}\frac{1}{2}x$ and $\frac{4}{5}\cot(\frac{3}{4}x - \frac{\pi}{4})$.

7 Show that the tangent to the curve $y = 3\cos x + \ln 4x$ at the point where $x = \pi$, has equation

$$y = \frac{1}{\pi}x + \ln 4\pi - 4$$

and find the equation of the normal at this point.

8 Find the equation of the tangent to the curve $y = 5\cos(4x - \frac{\pi}{6})$ at the point where $x = \frac{\pi}{4}$.

9 Find the equations of the tangent and normal to $y = \frac{3}{2}\sin x - 2\sin 2x$ when $x = \frac{\pi}{2}$.

10 Find the maximum and minimum values of the following in the domain $0 \le x \le \pi$.

    a) $\sin x \cos x$ **b)** $\cos x - \sin x$

    c) $\sin^3 x \cos x$ **d)** $2\sin x - \cos 2x$

11 Find the stationary points of the following functions in the domain $0 \le x \le \pi$ and distinguish between them. In each case, give a rough sketch of the graph of the function.

    a) $f(x) = \cos 3x$ **b)** $f(x) = x - \sin 2x$

    c) $f(x) = e^x \sin x$ **d)** $f(x) = \dfrac{4\sin x}{2 - \cos x}$

12 A mass, on the end of a spring, is oscillating in a vertical line between 30 cm and 70 cm above a bench, completing 30 oscillations per minute. The height of the mass, h cm, above the bench after t seconds from being let go from its lowest position can be modelled by a function of the form $h = c - a\cos(bt)$.

    a) Find values for a and c and explain why $b = \pi$.

    b) Sketch a graph of h against t for $0 \le t \le 2$.

    c) Find the velocity of the mass at **i)** $t = 1$, **ii)** $t = 1.5$.

    d) Find the acceleration of the mass at **i)** $t = 1$, **ii)** $t = 1.5$.

    e) Comment on your answers to **c)** and **d)**.

EXERCISES

2.1 HOMEWORK

The following results, which may be needed to answer some of the questions in this exercise, may be assumed.

$$\frac{d}{dx}(\sec x) = \sec x \tan x \qquad \frac{d}{dx}(\operatorname{cosec} x) = -\operatorname{cosec} x \cot x$$

$$\frac{d}{dx}(\cot x) = -\operatorname{cosec}^2 x$$

1 Differentiate the following with respect to x.

    a) $7\sin x$ **b)** $-\frac{3}{4}\cos x$ **c)** $-11\tan x$

    d) $\dfrac{\cos x}{5}$ **e)** $\dfrac{\sin x - \cos x}{10}$ **f)** $\dfrac{x^5 - 5\ln x + 3\cos x}{15}$

    g) $3\tan x + \ln 7x$ **h)** $\dfrac{25e^{\frac{x}{5}} - 2\cos x}{20}$

2 Differentiate the following with respect to x.

    a) $\dfrac{5\sin 5x}{4}$ **b)** $-\dfrac{\tan\frac{4}{3}x}{4}$ **c)** $\frac{3}{4}\cos 2x$

    d) $-\frac{6}{7}\cos 11x + \frac{1}{4}\tan 11x$ **e)** $\frac{5}{2}\sin(4x - 3) + \frac{2}{3}\cos(3x - 4)$

    f) $\sin(\frac{2\pi}{3} - 5x) + \cos(\frac{3\pi}{4} + 6x)$ **g)** $11\ln\dfrac{x}{5} - 5\tan\dfrac{x}{4} + \sqrt{x}$

    h) $\dfrac{\sqrt{x^7}}{21} + \cos(\frac{\pi}{9} - 6x) - \dfrac{5}{x}$

3   Use the chain rule to differentiate these.

a) $\cos^3 x$
b) $\sin^4 5x$
c) $\cos\sqrt{x}$

d) $\sqrt{x + \cos x}$
e) $\cos^6 \tfrac{1}{2}x$
f) $\ln(x + \sin x)$

g) $e^{\cos x}$
h) $\cos e^x$
i) $\ln(\sin 3x + \cos 3x)$

j) $\tan\left(\dfrac{1}{x^2}\right)$

4   Differentiate the following products.

a) $x^2 \sin^2 x$
b) $\cos^2 x \sin 4x$
c) $\tan 3x \sin 4x$

d) $x \sin 4x$
e) $\sin(4x + \tfrac{\pi}{3})\cos(2x - \tfrac{\pi}{4})$
f) $e^{-x}\sin x$

g) $(1 + x)^3 \cos 3x$
h) $\sec x \ln x$

5   Use the quotient rule to differentiate these.

a) $\dfrac{\cos x}{x}$
b) $\dfrac{1 + \sin x}{1 - \cos x}$
c) $\dfrac{\tan x}{e^x}$

d) $\dfrac{\ln x}{\tan x}$
e) $\dfrac{1 + \sin x}{1 - \sin x}$
f) $\dfrac{1 + \sec x}{1 - \sec x}$

6   By converting $x°$ to radians, find $\dfrac{d}{dx}(\sin x°)$, $\dfrac{d}{dx}(\cos x°)$ and $\dfrac{d}{dx}(\tan x°)$.

Hence differentiate $\sin 5x°$, $\cos\tfrac{1}{2}x°$ and $\tan(3x - 45)°$.

7   Show that the tangent to the curve $y = \dfrac{2}{\pi}\sin x - \dfrac{1}{x}$, at the point where $x = \dfrac{\pi}{2}$, has the equation $\pi^2 y = 4x - 2\pi$ and find the equation of the normal at this point.

8   Find the equations of the tangent and normal to $y = 5\tan(\tfrac{1}{2}x - \tfrac{\pi}{4})$ at the point where $x = \pi$.

9   Find the equations of the tangent and normal to $y = 16\sin x - 4e^{8x}$ when $x = 0$.

10   Find the maximum and minimum values of the following in the domain $0 \le x \le \pi$.

a) $2\sin x + \cos x$
b) $3\cos x - 4\sin x$

c) $3\cos x - \cos 3x$
d) $\sin x^2$

11   Find the stationary points of the following functions in the domain $0 \le x \le \pi$ and distinguish between them. In each case, give a rough sketch of the graph of the function.

a) $f(x) = \sin 5x$
b) $f(x) = 2x - \tan x$

c) $f(x) = \tan^2 x + 2\tan x$
d) $f(x) = 4\sin x + \dfrac{9}{1 + \sin x}$

12 The height of a car's suspension can be modelled by the equation

$h = 10e^{-0.1t}\cos\left(\frac{\pi}{6}t\right) + 15$, where h is height in cm and t is time in seconds.

a) Sketch a graph of h against t for $0 \le t \le 20$.
b) Find the value of:

$v = \dfrac{dh}{dt}$ and $a = \dfrac{dv}{dt}$ when

  i) $t = 8$,   ii) $t = 15$.

c) Relate your answers to part **b)** to the shape of the graph from part **a)**.
d) Find the time at which the suspension unit is closest to the ground. Find the clearance between the unit and the ground at this time.

INTEGRATION

In the first part of this chapter we discovered how to differentiate various trigonometric functions. Considering the process of integration as the reverse of differentiation gives the results in this table.

The following examples illustrate the way in which integrals involving trigonometrical functions can be used.

$f(x)$	$\int f(x)\,dx$
$\sin x$	$-\cos x$
$\cos x$	$\sin x$
$\sec^2 x$	$\tan x$
$\sin ax$	$-\dfrac{1}{a}\cos ax$
$\cos ax$	$\dfrac{1}{a}\sin ax$

Example 2.4

Find these integrals.

a) $\displaystyle\int \cos 3x\, dx$ **b)** $\displaystyle\int 5\sec^2\tfrac{1}{2}x\, dx$ **c)** $\displaystyle\int \tan^2 x\, dx$

Solution

a) $\displaystyle\int \cos 3x\, dx = \tfrac{1}{3}\sin 3x + c$

b) $\displaystyle\int 5\sec^2\tfrac{1}{2}x\, dx = 10\tan\tfrac{1}{2}x + c$

c) $\displaystyle\int \tan^2 x\, dx = \int\left(\sec^2 x - 1\right) dx = \tan x - x + c$

Example 2.5

Explain, in terms of area, why: $\displaystyle\int_0^\pi 2\cos x\, dx = 0$
and find the smallest positive value of θ such that $\displaystyle\int_0^\theta 2\cos x\, dx = 1$.

Solution
The integral represents the area between the graph $y = 2\cos x$ and the x-axis over the interval $0 \le x \le \pi$.
From the diagram we can see that half the area lies above the x-axis and half below. The definite integral is:

$$\int_0^\pi 2\cos x\, dx = \left[2\sin x\right]_0^\pi = 0 - 0 = 0$$

If $\displaystyle\int_0^\theta 2\cos x\, dx = 1$, then $\left[2\sin x\right]_0^\theta = 1$

$\Rightarrow$ $2\sin\theta - 2\sin 0 = 1$

$\Rightarrow$ $\sin\theta = \dfrac{1}{2}$

$\Rightarrow$ $\theta = \dfrac{\pi}{6}$ *(smallest positive value)*

Example 2.6

Show that: $\dfrac{d}{dx}\left(e^{-x}(\cos x + \sin x)\right) = -2e^{-x}\sin x$

and hence find the value of $\displaystyle\int_0^{\pi} e^{-x}\sin x.$

Illustrate your answer with a sketch.

Solution

Let $y = e^{-x}(\cos x + \sin x) = e^{-x}\cos x + e^{-x}\sin x.$
Using the product rule to differentiate each product separately:

$$\frac{dy}{dx} = e^{-x}(-\sin x) + \left(-e^{-x}\right)\cos x + e^{-x}(\cos x) + \left(-e^{-x}\right)\sin x$$

$$= -2e^{-x}\sin x$$

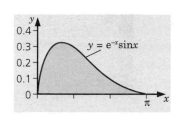

Hence $\displaystyle\int_0^{\pi} e^{-x}\sin x\ dx$

$$= -\tfrac{1}{2}\int_0^{\pi} -2e^{-x}\sin x\ dx$$

$$= -\tfrac{1}{2}\left[e^{-x}(\cos x + \sin x)\right]_0^{\pi}$$

$$= -\tfrac{1}{2}\left\{e^{-\pi}(-1+0) - e^{0}(1+0)\right\}$$

$$= \tfrac{1}{2}\left(e^{-\pi} + 1\right) \approx 0.522$$

EXERCISES

2.2 CLASSWORK

1 Find the following indefinite integrals.

a) $\displaystyle\int \sin 3x\,dx$

b) $\displaystyle\int \cos 6x\,dx$

c) $\displaystyle\int \cos\tfrac{1}{2}x\,dx$

d) $\displaystyle\int \tfrac{1}{2}\cos x\,dx$

e) $\displaystyle\int \cos\tfrac{3}{2}x\,dx$

f) $\displaystyle\int \sec^2 4x\,dx$

g) $\displaystyle\int 4\sec^2 x\,dx$

h) $\displaystyle\int (3\sin x - 2\cos x)\,dx$

i) $\displaystyle\int \tfrac{1}{2}(\sin x + \cos x)\,dx$

j) $\displaystyle\int \sin(2x+4)\,dx$

k) $\displaystyle\int 3\sec^2(\tfrac{\pi}{3} - x)\,dx$

l) $\displaystyle\int \cos(2x + \tfrac{\pi}{4})\,dx$

2 Evaluate the following definite integrals.

a) $\displaystyle\int_0^{\pi} \sin x\,dx$

b) $\displaystyle\int_{\frac{\pi}{6}}^{\frac{\pi}{2}} \cos x\,dx$

c) $\displaystyle\int_{-\frac{\pi}{4}}^{\frac{\pi}{4}} \sec^2 x\,dx$

d) $\displaystyle\int_0^{\frac{\pi}{4}} \cos 2x\,dx$

e) $\displaystyle\int_{-\frac{\pi}{2}}^{\frac{\pi}{2}} (1 + 2\sin 2x)\,dx$

f) $\displaystyle\int_{\frac{\pi}{2}}^{\pi} (2\cos x - \sin x)\,dx$

g) $\displaystyle\int_{-\frac{\pi}{2}}^{\frac{\pi}{2}} (\cos x + \sin 2x)\,dx$

h) $\displaystyle\int_0^{\frac{\pi}{9}} (\sin^2 x + \cos^2 x)\,dx$

i) $\displaystyle\int_0^{\pi} \sec^2 \tfrac{1}{4}x\,dx$

3 Show that $\dfrac{d}{dx}(\sin x + \tfrac{1}{2}\sin 2x + \tfrac{1}{3}\sin 3x) = (1 + 2\cos x)\cos 2x$ and hence

find the value of $\displaystyle\int_0^{\frac{\pi}{4}} (1 + 2\cos x)\cos 2x\,dx.$

4   The diagram shows the graphs of
$y = \sin x$ and $y = \cos x$ in the domain

$-\dfrac{\pi}{2} \le x \le \pi.$

a) Find area OAC.
a) Find area OBC.
b) Find area ACD.

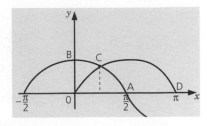

5   The diagram shows the graphs of $y = x$ and $y = \cos x$ in the domain

$0 \le x \le \dfrac{\pi}{2}.$

a) Verify that the graphs intersect
very close to $x = 0.7$.
b) Use an iterative method to find
the x-coordinate of the point of
intersection correct to **nine** d.p.
c) Hence find the area of the darker
shaded region correct to nine d.p.
d) Similarly, find the area of the
lighter shaded region correct to
nine d.p.

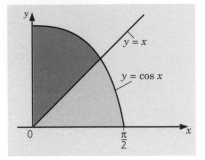

6   a)   Differentiate $y = \ln \sin x$ and hence write down $\int \cot x \, dx$.

b)   Find $\int \cot 5x \, dx$, $\int 3\cot \frac{1}{4} x \, dx$ and $\int \cot(4x + \pi) \, dx$.

EXERCISES

1   Find the following indefinite integrals.

a) $\displaystyle\int 3\cos 4x \, dx$

b) $\displaystyle\int 5\sin \tfrac{1}{3} x \, dx$

c) $\displaystyle\int \tfrac{1}{5}\sin \tfrac{1}{5} x \ dx$

d) $\displaystyle\int \frac{\sin x}{5} \, dx$

e) $\displaystyle\int \sin \tfrac{1}{5} x \, dx$

f) $\displaystyle\int \sec^2 \tfrac{3}{2} x \, dx$

g) $\displaystyle\int 7\sec^2 \frac{x}{7} \, dx$

h) $\displaystyle\int (4\sin 3x - 5\cos 7x) \, dx$

i) $\displaystyle\int \frac{\sin \tfrac{1}{2} x + \cos \tfrac{1}{2} x}{2} \, dx$

j) $\displaystyle\int \sin(\tfrac{x}{2} - 1) \, dx$

k) $\displaystyle\int 2\sec^2(x - \tfrac{\pi}{2}) \, dx$

l) $\displaystyle\int \cos(\tfrac{\pi}{4} - 3x) \, dx$

2   Evaluate the following definite integrals.

a) $\displaystyle\int_0^{\frac{\pi}{2}} \cos x \, dx$

b) $\displaystyle\int_{\frac{3\pi}{2}}^{2\pi} \sin x \, dx$

c) $\displaystyle\int_{-\frac{\pi}{8}}^{\frac{\pi}{8}} \frac{\sin 4x}{2} \, dx$

d) $\displaystyle\int_0^{\frac{\pi}{12}} 3\cos 2x \, dx$

e) $\displaystyle\int_{-\frac{\pi}{6}}^{\frac{\pi}{6}} (\cos x - \sin x) \ dx$

f) $\displaystyle\int_0^{\pi} 3\sin(\pi - x) \, dx$

g) $\displaystyle\int_{\frac{\pi}{4}}^{\frac{\pi}{2}} (\sin x + \sin 2x) \, dx$

h) $\displaystyle\int_0^{\pi} (1 - \cos 2x) \, dx$

i) $\displaystyle\int_0^{\frac{\pi}{8}} \sec^2 2x \, dx$

3   Differentiate $e^{-x}(\sin x - \cos x)$ and hence find the value of $\displaystyle\int_0^{\frac{\pi}{2}} e^{-x} \cos x \, dx$.
Illustrate the area represented by this integral.

4 The diagram shows the graphs of $y = \sin x$ and $3\pi y = 2\pi - 3x$ in the domain $0 \le x \le \pi$.

a) Verify that the graphs intersect at $\left(\frac{\pi}{6}, \frac{1}{2}\right)$ and find the x-coordinate of A.

b) Find the area of OAC.

c) Find the area of OBC.

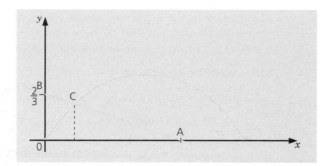

5 The diagram shows the graphs of $y = \sin x$ and $y = e^{-x}$ in the domain $0 \le x \le \pi$.

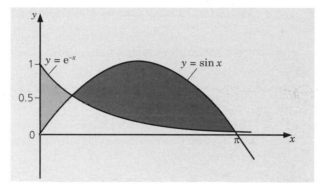

a) Verify that the graphs intersect very close to $x = 0.6$ and $x = 3$.

b) Use an iterative method to find the x-coordinates of the points of intersection correct to **nine** d.p.

c) Hence find the area of the **lighter** shaded region correct to nine d.p.

d) Similarly, find the area of the **darker** shaded region correct to nine d.p.

6 a) Differentiate $y = \ln \cos x$ and hence write down $\int \tan x \, dx$.

b) Find $\int \tan 3x \, dx$, $\int \tan \tfrac{1}{2}x \, dx$ and $\int \tan(\tfrac{\pi}{4} - 2x) \, dx$.

INTEGRATION OF POWERS OF TRIGONOMETRIC FUNCTIONS

Exploration 2.2

CALCULATOR ACTIVITY

You will need a graph plotter.

Make sure you are using radian mode and set the axes as follows.

$x_{\min} = 0;$ $x_{\max} = 2\pi;$ $x_{\mathrm{scl}} = \dfrac{\pi}{6}$

$y_{\min} = -1;$ $y_{\max} = 2;$ $y_{\mathrm{scl}} = 0.5$

- Plot the graphs of $y = \cos 2x$ and $y = \cos^2 x$.

- By a sequence of geometrical transformations show how you can transform the graph of $y = \cos^2 x$ onto the graph of $y = \cos 2x$.

- Establish the relationship between $\cos 2\theta$ and $\cos^2\theta$ for any angle θ.

- Repeat for $y = \cos 2x$ and $y = \sin^2 x$.

A stretch, factor 2, parallel to the y-axis followed by translation through -1 unit parallel to the y-axis will transform $y = \cos^2 x$ onto $y = \cos 2x$. From this we deduce the identity:

$$\cos 2\theta \equiv 2\cos^2\theta - 1$$

A similar result connecting $\cos 2\theta$ and $\sin^2\theta$ follows since:

$$\cos 2\theta \equiv 2(1 - \sin^2\theta) - 1$$
$$\Rightarrow \quad \cos 2\theta \equiv 1 - 2\sin^2\theta$$

This shows that to transform $y = \sin^2 x$ onto $y = \cos 2x$ the operations are stretch, factor 2, followed by reflection in the x-axis followed by a translation through $+1$ unit parallel to the y-axis.

The last calculator activity should also lead to the same conclusion.

The two trigonometrical identities which may be used to give both $\cos^2\theta$ and $\sin^2\theta$ in terms of $\cos 2\theta$ are:

$$\cos 2\theta \equiv 2\cos^2\theta - 1 \Rightarrow \cos^2\theta \equiv \tfrac{1}{2} + \tfrac{1}{2}\cos 2\theta$$
$$\cos 2\theta \equiv 1 - 2\sin^2\theta \Rightarrow \sin^2\theta \equiv \tfrac{1}{2} - \tfrac{1}{2}\cos 2\theta$$

These identities are very useful when we are integrating powers of trigonometrical functions. This is illustrated in the following examples.

Example 2.7

The curve $y = 2\sin x$, $0 \le x \le \pi$ is rotated through 2π about the x-axis. Find the volume of the solid of revolution generated.

Solution
The volume swept out is illustrated in the diagram.

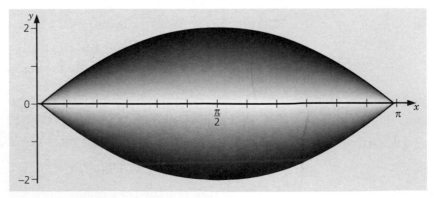

$$\text{Volume} = \int_0^\pi \pi y^2 \mathrm{d}x = \pi\int_0^\pi 4\sin^2 x\,\mathrm{d}x$$
$$= \pi\int_0^\pi (2 - 2\cos 2x)\mathrm{d}x = \pi\left[2x - \sin 2x\right]_0^\pi$$
$$= \pi\left\{(2\pi - 0) - (0 - 0)\right\} = 2\pi^2$$

Example 2.8

Sketch the graph of $y = \cos^3 x$, $-\pi \le x \le \pi$. Hence find the area enclosed by the curve and the x-axis over the interval $-\dfrac{\pi}{2} \le x \le \pi$.

Solution

The graph of $y = \cos^3 x$, $-\pi \le x \le \pi$, is shown in the diagram.

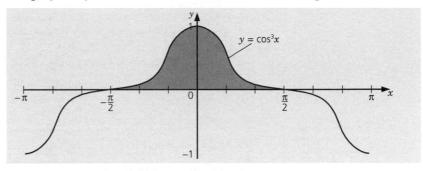

The area of the shaded region is given by:

$$\int_{-\frac{\pi}{2}}^{\frac{\pi}{2}} \cos^3 x \, dx$$

To integrate $\cos^3 x$ we make the following rearrangement.

$$\cos^3 x \equiv \cos^2 x \cos x \equiv \left(1 - \sin^2 x\right)\cos x$$

$$\equiv \cos x - \sin^2 x \cos x$$

$$\int_{-\frac{\pi}{2}}^{\frac{\pi}{2}} \cos^3 x \, dx = \int_{-\frac{\pi}{2}}^{\frac{\pi}{2}} \left(\cos x - \sin^2 x \cos x\right) dx$$

$$= \left[\sin x - \frac{1}{3}\sin^3 x\right]_{-\frac{\pi}{2}}^{\frac{\pi}{2}} = \left(1 - \frac{1}{3}\right) - \left(-1 + \frac{1}{3}\right) = \frac{4}{3}$$

EXERCISES

2.3 CLASSWORK

1 Find the following integrals.

a) $\displaystyle\int \sin^2 2x \, dx$ **b)** $\displaystyle\int \cos^2(3x - \tfrac{\pi}{3}) \, dx$

2 Evaluate these.

a) $\displaystyle\int_{-\pi}^{\pi} 3\cos^2 \tfrac{1}{2}x \, dx$ **b)** $\displaystyle\int_{0}^{1} \frac{\sin^2(3 - 2x)}{5} \, dx$

3 Sketch the following curves for the domain $0 \le x \le 2\pi$ and find the volume generated when each is rotated through 2π about the x-axis, between the x-values given.

a) $y = 1 + \sin x$ from $x = 0$ to $x = \dfrac{\pi}{2}$

b) $y = \sec x$ from $x = -\dfrac{\pi}{4}$ to $x = \dfrac{\pi}{4}$

c) $y = \tan x$ from $x = 0$ to $x = \dfrac{\pi}{4}$

4 **a)** Differentiate $\sin^3 x$ and hence show that

$$\int \sin^2 x \cos x\, dx = \tfrac{1}{3}\sin^3 x + c\,.$$

b) By writing $\cos^3 x$ as $\cos^2 x \cos x$, use an appropriate identity and the above result, to find $\int \cos^3 x\, dx$.

c) Find the volume generated when the curve $y = \cos^{\frac{3}{2}} x$ is rotated about the x-axis from $x = 0$ to $x = \dfrac{\pi}{2}$.

5 **a)** Show that $\int \cos^2 2x\, dx = \tfrac{1}{2}x + \tfrac{1}{8}\sin 4x + c$.

b) By writing $\cos^4 x$ as $(\cos^2 x)^2$, show that

$$\cos^4 x \equiv \tfrac{1}{4}(1 + 2\cos 2x + \cos^2 2x).$$

c) Use your result to find $\int \cos^4 x\, dx$.

d) Find the volume generated when the curve $y = 3\cos^2 x$ is rotated completely about the x-axis from $x = 0$ to $x = \dfrac{\pi}{2}$.

6 **a)** Show that $\dfrac{d}{dx}(\sec x) = \sec x \tan x$.

b) Differentiate $\tan^2 x$ and use the result from **a)** to differentiate $\sec^2 x$. Explain why your two answers are the same.

7 **a)** Use the result of question **6a)** to show that

$$\dfrac{d}{dx}(\ln(\sec x + \tan x)) = \sec x\,.$$

b) Deduce the expression for the indefinite integral $\int \sec x\, dx$.

c) Use the above result to evaluate $\int_{-\frac{\pi}{3}}^{\frac{\pi}{3}} \sec x\, dx$ and $\int_0^{\frac{\pi}{2}} \sec \tfrac{1}{2}x\, dx$.

8 Use an appropriate double angle formula and the result of **7b)** above, to find $\int_{-\frac{\pi}{6}}^{\frac{\pi}{6}} \dfrac{\cos 2x}{\cos x}\, dx$.

EXERCISES

2.3 HOMEWORK

1 Find the following integrals.

a) $\int \cos^2 5x\, dx$ **b)** $\int \tfrac{1}{2}\sin^2 \tfrac{1}{4}x\, dx$

2 Evaluate these.

a) $\int_0^{2\pi} \sin^2 2x\, dx$ **b)** $\int_{\frac{\pi}{3}}^{\frac{\pi}{2}} \cos^2(x - \tfrac{\pi}{6})\, dx$

3 **a)** Use the fact that $\sin 2x = 2\sin x \cos x$ to find $\int \sin x \cos x\, dx$.

b) Hence find the volume generated when $y = \sin x + \cos x$ is rotated through 360° about the x-axis between $x = 0$ and $x = \dfrac{3\pi}{4}$.

4 **a)** Differentiate $\cos^3 x$ and hence show that

$$\int \cos^2 x \sin x \, dx = -\tfrac{1}{3}\cos^3 x + c \,.$$

b) By writing $\sin^3 x$ as $\sin^2 x \sin x$, use an appropriate identity and the above result, to find $\int \sin^3 x \, dx$.

c) Find the area between the curve $y = 3\sin^3 x + \sin x$ and the x-axis from $x = 0$ to $x = \pi$.

5 **a)** Find $\dfrac{d}{dx}\left(e^x(\sin x - \cos x)\right)$ and $\dfrac{d}{dx}\left(e^x(\sin x + \cos x)\right)$.

b) Deduce the values of $\int e^x \sin x \, dx$ and $\int e^x \cos x \, dx$.

c) Find the area between the curve $y = e^x \sin x$ and the x-axis from $x = 0$ to $x = \pi$.

d) Find the volume generated when the area under $y = e^{0.5x}\sqrt{\cos x}$ is rotated completely about the x-axis from $-\dfrac{\pi}{2}$ to $\dfrac{\pi}{2}$.

6 **a)** Show that $\dfrac{d}{dx}(\operatorname{cosec} x) = -\operatorname{cosec} x \cot x$ and that $\dfrac{d}{dx}(\cot x) = -\operatorname{cosec}^2 x$.

b) Use the results from **a)** to differentiate $\operatorname{cosec}^2 x$ and $\cot^2 x$. Explain why your two answers are the same.

7 **a)** Use the results from question **6a)** to show that:

$$\dfrac{d}{dx}(\ln(\operatorname{cosec} x + \cot x)) = -\operatorname{cosec} x \,.$$

b) Deduce the indefinite integral $\int \operatorname{cosec} x \, dx$.

c) Use the above result to evaluate $\displaystyle\int_{\frac{\pi}{4}}^{\frac{3\pi}{4}} \operatorname{cosec} x \, dx$ and $\displaystyle\int_{\frac{\pi}{2}}^{\pi} \operatorname{cosec}\tfrac{1}{3}x \, dx$.

8 Use an appropriate double angle formula and the result of **7b)** above, to find $\displaystyle\int_{\frac{\pi}{4}}^{\frac{\pi}{2}} \dfrac{\cos 2x}{\sin x} \, dx$.

Exploration 2.3

SMALL ANGLES

sin x for small values of x

You will need a graph plotter.

■ Working in radians, plot the graphs of $y = \sin x$ and $y = x$ on the same axes for $-\pi \le x \le \pi$.

■ Tabulate values of $\sin x$ for *small* values of x, e.g. $-0.1 \le x \le 0.1$.

■ Describe the relationship between $\sin x$ and x when x is small and measured in radians.

■ Repeat for $y = \tan x$ and $y = x$.

■ Repeat for $y = \cos x$ and $y = \; y = 1 - \tfrac{1}{2}x^2$.

Interpreting the results

The three pairs of graphs, together with tabulated output are shown in the diagrams.

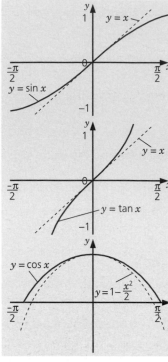

x	$\sin x$
−0.10	−0.099 83
−0.05	−0.049 98
0	0
0.05	0.049 98
0.10	0.099 83

x	$\tan x$
−0.10	−0.100 33
−0.05	−0.050 04
0	0
0.05	0.050 04
0.10	0.100 33

x	$\cos x$	$1-\frac{1}{2}x^2$
−0.10	0.995 00	0.995
−0.05	0.998 75	0.998 75
0	1.000 00	1
0.05	0.998 75	0.998 75
0.10	0.995 00	0.995

From the graphs and tables we see that, provided x is measured in radians and $|x|$ is small, the following **small angle approximations** are valid.

$$\sin x \approx x \qquad \tan x \approx x \qquad \cos x \approx 1 - \tfrac{1}{2}x^2$$

These approximate equivalences, for small values of x can be useful in finding approximate solutions to problems.

Example 2.9

Find small angle approximations to the following, where x is measured in radians.

a) $\dfrac{\sin 3x}{5x^2}$ *b)* $\dfrac{\sin x + \tan x}{1 - \cos 2x}$

Solution

a) $\dfrac{\sin 3x}{5x^2} \approx \dfrac{3x}{5x^2} = \dfrac{3}{5x}$

b) $\dfrac{\sin x + \tan x}{1 - \cos 2x} \approx \dfrac{x + x}{1 - \left(1 - \dfrac{(2x)^2}{2}\right)} = \dfrac{2x}{2x^2} = \dfrac{1}{x}$

Example 2.10

a) *Using a small angle approximation where terms in x^3 and higher may be neglected, show that:*

$$\frac{\cos^2 x}{x} \approx \frac{1}{x} - x$$

b) *Sketch graphs of:*

$$y = \frac{\cos^2 x}{x} \text{ and } y = \frac{1}{x} - x \text{ for } -\frac{\pi}{2} \le x \le \frac{\pi}{2}.$$

c) *Find a quadratic equation which approximates the solution of:*

$$\frac{\cos^2 x}{x} = 5$$

d) *Solve your equation in **c)**, explaining why only one of the roots is a very good approximation to the true solution.*

Solution

a) $\dfrac{\cos^2 x}{x} \approx \dfrac{\left(1 - \frac{1}{2}x^2\right)^2}{x} = \dfrac{1 - x^2 + \frac{1}{4}x^4}{x} \approx \dfrac{1}{x} - x$

b)

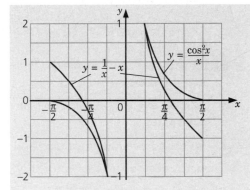

c) $\dfrac{\cos^2 x}{x} = 5 \Rightarrow \dfrac{1}{x} - x = 5$

will give a close approximation to the root of $\dfrac{\cos^2 x}{x} = 5$ *for small x.*

Also : $\quad \dfrac{1}{x} - x = 5 \Rightarrow 1 - x^2 = 5x$

$$\Rightarrow x^2 + 5x - 1 = 0$$

d) *Solutions to the quadratic equation are $x = 0.193$ and $x = -5.19$ (correct to three significant figures). The positive root, 0.193 agrees with the true solution correct to three significant figures, whereas the negative root is totally inadequate.*

EXERCISES

2.4 CLASSWORK

1 Find the approximate values of the following expressions when x is small and measured in radians.

a) $\dfrac{\sin 5x}{\sin 2x}$

b) $\dfrac{10x}{\sin 5x}$

c) $\dfrac{\cos 2x}{x \sin x}$

d) $\dfrac{3 \tan x - x}{\sin 3x}$

e) $\dfrac{1 - \cos 2x}{\sin x \tan x}$

f) $\dfrac{\cos x - 1}{\sin x}$

g) $\sqrt{2 + 2\cos x}$

h) $\dfrac{1 - \cos 3x}{1 - \cos 4x}$

i) $\dfrac{\sin x \cos x}{\sqrt{2} + \sin x}$

2 a) Use the small angle approximations to show that the function $f(x) = 1 + \sin^2 x \cos x$ can be approximated by the quadratic function $g(x) = 1 + x^2$ when x is small and measured in radians.

b) Sketch graphs of the two functions for the domain $-1 \le x \le 1$.

c) It can be shown that the integral $\displaystyle\int_0^{\frac{\pi}{6}} f(x)\,dx = 0.565\,265$ correct to six d.p.
Verify that even though $\dfrac{\pi}{6}$ is not a particularly small angle,

$$\int_0^{\frac{\pi}{6}} g(x)\,dx \quad \text{and} \quad \int_0^{\frac{\pi}{6}} f(x)\,dx \quad \text{are the same, correct to 2 d.p.}$$

d) Show that $f'(x) = 2\sin x - 3\sin^3 x$ and hence write down a cubic approximation to $f'(x)$.

e) Estimate the value of $f'(x)$ when $x = \dfrac{\pi}{6}$ and compare it with the true value.

3 a) Use the small angle formulae and the binomial theorem to find a quadratic approximation for the function $f(x) = \dfrac{3 \tan x}{1 + \sin x}$ and hence find the approximate value of the integral $\displaystyle\int_0^{0.1} \dfrac{3 \tan x}{1 + \sin x}\,dx$.

b) Revise your estimate for the integral by using a cubic approximation for $f(x)$.

EXERCISES

2.4 HOMEWORK

1 a) Use the small angle approximations to show that the function $f(x) = \cos x \cos 2x$ can be approximated by the quadratic function

$g(x) = 1 - 2.5x^2$ when x is small and measured in radians.

b) Sketch graphs of the two functions for the domain $-1 \le x \le 1$.

c) It can be shown that the integral $\displaystyle\int_{-0.2}^{0.2} f(x)\,dx = 0.386\,88$ correct to five d.p. Verify that $\displaystyle\int_{-0.2}^{0.2} g(x)\,dx = 0.386\,67$ correct to five d.p.

d) Find $f'(x)$ and hence find the gradient of $f(x)$ when $x = 0.2$.

e) Write down a cubic approximation to $f'(x)$ and find an approximation for the gradient of $f(x)$ when $x = 0.2$.

f) Comment on the relative accuracy of your integration and differentiation approximations.

2 **a)** By graph sketching, verify that $2\cos(x - \frac{\pi}{3}) \equiv \cos x + \sqrt{3}\sin x$.

b) Use the small angle formulae to show that
$2\cos(x - \frac{\pi}{3}) = 1 + \sqrt{3}x - \frac{1}{2}x^2$ when x is small and measured in radians.

c) Find the true value and an approximate value for $\int_{-0.05}^{0.05} \cos(x - \frac{\pi}{3})\,dx$ and compare them.

d) If x is so small that powers greater than 2 can safely be ignored, show further that $4\cos^2(x - \frac{\pi}{3}) \approx 1 + 2\sqrt{3}x + 2x^2$.

e) Use result **d)** to find the approximate value of $\int_{-0.05}^{0.05} \cos^2(x - \frac{\pi}{3})\,dx$.

3 **a)** Use the small angle approximations and the binomial theorem to find a cubic approximation to $f(x) = \dfrac{\sin 4x + \tan x}{5\cos 2x}$ when x is small and measured in radians.

b) Sketch graphs of $f(x)$ and your cubic function for the domain $-1 \le x \le 1$.

c) Find an approximate value for the integral $\int_0^{0.15} f(x)\,dx$ correct to six d.p.

d) The true value of the integral is 0.010 748 correct to six d.p. Can you explain why the result of your calculation in **c)** is not particularly accurate?

MATHEMATICAL MODELLING ACTIVITY

Problem statement

A manufacturer has designed a new concrete mixer in the shape of a cone of side length 1.4 metres. The cone is mounted with its axis vertical. Concrete is made by rotating a mixture of sand, cement and water inside the cone.

1.4 m

A builder wants to make the largest amount of concrete in any mix.

■ What angle, between the side and the vertical through the tip of the cone, would you recommend to give the cone the maximum volume?

(diagram: cycle 1→2→3→4→5→6 with label "Specify the real problem")

Set up a model

Firstly, identify the important variables. These are:
■ the volume of the cone
■ the angle between the side of the cone and the vertical axis.

You will also need to assume that the cone is full and does not spill when mixing.

(diagram: cycle 1→2→3→4→5→6 with label "Set up a model")

Mathematical problem

Firstly, establish the relationship between the volume within the cone (V) and the angle (θ).

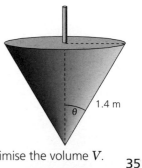

The volume of a cone is $\frac{1}{3} \times$ area of base $\times$ height. You should confirm that the equation connecting V and θ is:
$$V = \tfrac{1}{3}\pi(1.4)^3 \sin^2\theta\cos\theta = 2.87\sin^2\theta\cos\theta\,\text{m}^3$$

1.4 m

θ

The mathematical problem is to find the value of θ to maximise the volume V.

(diagram: cycle 1→2→3→4→5→6 with label "Formulate the mathematical problem")

35

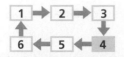

Solve the mathematical problem

Mathematical solution

To find where V reaches a maximum:

$$\frac{dV}{d\theta} = 2.87\left(2\sin\theta\cos^2\theta - \sin^3\theta\right) = 0 \qquad \text{for stationary values}$$

$$\Rightarrow \sin\theta = 0 \text{ or } \cos^2\theta = \tfrac{1}{3}$$

Solving for $\theta \Rightarrow \theta = 0°$ or $\theta = 54.7°$.

To investigate the stationary values consider $\dfrac{d^2V}{d\theta^2}$.

$$\frac{dV}{d\theta} = 2.87\sin\theta\left(3\cos^2\theta - 1\right)$$

$$\frac{d^2V}{d\theta^2} = 2.87\cos\theta\left(3\cos^2\theta - 1\right) + 2.87\sin\theta\left(-6\cos\theta\sin\theta\right)$$

For $\theta = 0$, $\dfrac{d^2V}{d\theta^2} = 5.74 > 0$ which (clearly) leads to a minimum value of V.

For $\theta = 54.7°$, $\dfrac{d^2V}{d\theta^2} = -6.63 < 0$ which leads to a maximum value for V.

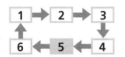

Interpret the solution

Interpreting the solution

To maximise the volume of concrete to be made in the concrete mixer the cone should be designed with an angle (θ) of 54.7°. This may seem to be a large angle! Discuss the effects of such a large angle and consider alternative angles.

CONSOLIDATION EXERCISES FOR CHAPTER 2

1 If $\dfrac{dy}{dx} = 6e^{3x} + 3\sin 2x$, find an expression for y.

(Oxford Question 3, Specimen Paper 2, 1994)

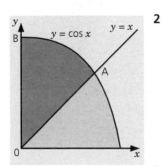

2 a) Part of the graphs for $y = x$ and $y = \cos x$ are shown. Taking $x = 0.8$ as the x-coordinate of the point A, calculate the area OAB shaded on the sketch.
   b) Given that $x = 0.8$ is an approximate solution to the equation $x = \cos x$, use a single application of the Newton-Raphson method to obtain a better solution.
   c) Draw a sketch which illustrates that the equation $x = \cos x$ has only one solution.

(SMP 16–19 Question 14, Specimen Paper, 1994)

3 a) Show that there is a root of the equation $8\sin x - x = 0$ lying between 2.7 and 2.8.
   b) Taking 2.8 as a first approximation to this root, apply the Newton-Raphson procedure once to $f(x) \equiv 8\sin x - x$ to obtain a second approximation, giving your answer to two decimal places.
   c) Explain, with justification, whether or not this second approximation is correct to two decimal places.
   d) Evaluate $f\left(\dfrac{5\pi}{2}\right)$, and hence, by sketching suitable graphs, determine the number of roots of the equation $8\sin x = x$ in the range $x > 0$.

(ULEAC Question 8, Specimen Paper 3, 1994)

4 Given that x is sufficiently small, use the approximations $\sin x \approx x$ and $\cos x \approx 1 - \frac{1}{2}x^2$ to show that:

$$\frac{\cos x}{1 + \sin x} \approx 1 - x + \frac{1}{2}x^2.$$

A student estimates the value of $\dfrac{\cos x}{1 + \sin x}$ when $x = 0.1$ by evaluating the approximation $1 - x + \frac{1}{2}x^2$ when $x = 0.1$. Find, to three decimal places, the percentage error made by the student.

(ULEAC Question 3, Paper 2, June 1993)

5 Differentiate $e^{2x}\cos x$ with respect to x.
The curve C has equation $y = e^{2x}\cos x$.
 a) Show that the turning points on C occur where $\tan x = 2$.
 b) Find an equation of the tangent to C at the point where $x = 0$.

(ULEAC Question 6, Paper 2, June 1992)

6 Consider the function $y = e^{-x}\sin x$, where $-\pi \le x \le \pi$.
 a) Find $\dfrac{dy}{dx}$.
 b Show that, at stationary points, $\tan x = 1$.
 c) Determine the coordinates of the stationary points, correct to two significant figures.
 d) Explain how you could determine whether your stationary points are maxima or minima. You are not required to do any calculations.

(MEI Question 3, Paper 2, January 1992)

7 **a)** **i)** Show that $(\cos x + \sin x)^2 = 1 + \sin 2x$, for all x.
 ii) Hence, or otherwise, find the derivative of $(\cos x + \sin x)^2$.
 b) **i)** By expanding $(\cos^2 x + \sin^2 x)^2$, find and simplify an expression for $\cos^4 x + \sin^4 x$ involving $\sin 2x$.
 ii) Hence, or otherwise, show that the derivative of $\cos^4 x + \sin^4 x$ is $-\sin 4x$.

(MEI Question 4, Paper 2, June 1992)

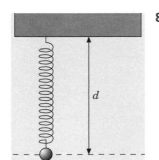

8 A mass is suspended from the end of a spring as shown. The spring is stretched and then released so that it oscillates. The distance, d cm, of the mass from the support t seconds after its release is given by $d = 10 + 3\cos 4t$.
 a) State the distance of the mass from the support when the spring is released. Find the period of oscillation of the mass.
 b) Calculate the time when d is first 9 cm.
 c) Calculate the speed of the mass 2 seconds after its release and state whether it is moving up or down.

(SMP 16–19 (Pure with Applications) Question 9, June 1994)

9 **a)** Use the identities for $\cos(A + B)$ and $\cos(A - B)$ to prove that
 i) $2\cos A \cos B \equiv \cos(A + B) + \cos(A - B)$
 ii) $\cos^2 A \equiv \frac{1}{2}(1 + \cos 2A)$

 b) Find $\int \cos 3x \cos x \, dx$
 c) Use the substitution $x = \cos t$ to evaluate

$$\int_0^{\frac{1}{2}} \frac{x^2}{\left(1 - x^2\right)^{\frac{1}{2}}} dx$$

(EDEXCEL P3 Question 6, Specimen Paper, 2000)

10 Sketch, for $0 \le x \le 2\pi$, the curve $y = \cos x$.
Hence sketch on different axes, for $0 \le x \le 2\pi$, the curves:
  i) $y = \sec x$
  ii) $y = \sec x - \cos x$.
Write down an integral equal to the area of the region R enclosed by the curve $y = \sec x - \cos x$, the x-axis and the line $x = \frac{\pi}{4}$. Hence find the area of R.
If R is rotated about the x-axis through four right angles, find the volume generated in terms of π.

(WJEC Question 12, Specimen Paper A1, 1994)

11 By using the substitution $u = \sin x$, or otherwise, find $\int \sin^3 x \sin 2x \, dx$ giving your answer in terms of x.

(OCR P3 Question 3, Specimen Paper, 2000)

12 The function f is defined by
  $$f : x \rightarrow \tan 3x - 4x$$
and has domain $0 \le x \le \frac{\pi}{6}$.
  a) Determine the value of x for which f is stationary.
  b) Explain why the range of f cannot be $f(x) \ge 0$.
  c) Find $\displaystyle\int_0^{\frac{\pi}{12}} f(x)\,dx$

(AQA MBP4 Question 7, Specimen Paper, 2000)

Summary

■ Differentiation of trigonometric functions:

$f(x)$	$f'(x)$
$\sin ax$	$a \cos ax$
$\cos ax$	$-a \sin ax$
$\tan ax$	$a \sec^2 ax$
$\sec (ax)$	$a \sec (ax) \tan (ax)$
$\csc (ax)$	$-a \csc (ax) \cot (ax)$
$\cot (ax)$	$-a \csc^2 (ax)$

where a is constant.

■ Small angle approximations:

when x is sufficiently small

$\sin x \approx x$
$\cos x \approx 1 - \frac{1}{2}x^2$.

Algebra

In this chapter we shall study:

- *the binomial series expansion for $(1 + x)^n$ for rational values of n,*
- *rational functions and their graphs,*
- *the idea of vertical, horizontal and slant asymptotes,*
- *partial fractions,*
- *a method for developing power series for rational functions,*
- *the remainder theorem for polynomials.*

BINOMIAL SERIES FOR RATIONAL INDICES

In your previous work on binomial series you found that, provided $|x|$ is small:

$$(1 + x)^n \approx 1 + nx \qquad n = 1, 2, 3, 4, 5, \ldots$$

We shall verify that both the binomial expansion and this approximation are valid for all rational numbers, including **fractions** and **negative numbers**.

Exploration 3.1

Fractional indices

- Choose several values of x close to 0 (positive and negative), e.g. 0.01, –0.02, etc. and find values for $\sqrt{1+x}$. Compare your results, when rounded to 2 d.p. and derive a suitable approximation without the use of a calculator.
- Repeat the process, this time for $\sqrt[3]{1+x}$. Again compare your results and find a suitable approximation.

Approximations

The approximation $(1 + x)^n \approx 1 + nx$, for small values of x, works for rational values of n.

$$\sqrt{1+0.02} = (1+0.02)^{\frac{1}{2}} = 1.009950494 \approx 1.01 = 1 + \tfrac{1}{2} \times 0.02$$

$$\sqrt[3]{1+0.03} = (1+0.03)^{\frac{1}{3}} = 1.009901634 \approx 1.01 = 1 + \tfrac{1}{3} \times 0.03$$

This is called a **first-order approximation**. A second-order approximation of the form:

$$(1+x)^n \approx 1 + nx + \frac{n(n-1)}{2}x^2$$

should give an even better approximation.

When $n = \tfrac{1}{2}$ and $x = 0.02$, $\sqrt{1.02} \approx 1 + \tfrac{1}{2} \times 0.02 - \tfrac{1}{8} \times 0.02^2 = 1.00995$

When $n = \tfrac{1}{3}$ and $x = 0.03$, $\sqrt[3]{1.03} \approx 1 + \tfrac{1}{3} \times 0.03 - \tfrac{1}{9} \times 0.03^2 = 1.0099$

Try first-order and second-order approximations to $\sqrt[3]{1.04}$.

Exploration 3.2

Negative indices

■ Choose several values of x close to 0 (positive and negative) and find values for $\dfrac{1}{1+x}$. Compare your results, rounded to 2 d.p. and derive a suitable approximation which does not require a calculator.

■ Repeat the process, this time for $\dfrac{1}{(1+x)^2}$. Again working to 2 d.p. find a suitable approximation.

Approximations

The first-order approximation $(1+x)^n \approx 1 + nx$, for small values of x, works for negative values of n:

$$\frac{1}{1+0.02} = (1+0.02)^{-1} = 0.980\,392\,1... \approx 0.98 = 1 - 0.02$$

$$\frac{1}{(1-0.01)^2} = (1-0.01)^{-2} = 1.020\,304\,0... \approx 1.02 = 1 + 0.02$$

Second-order approximations of the form:

$$(1+x)^n \approx 1 + nx + \frac{n(n-1)}{2}x^2$$

give even better approximations.

When $n = -1$, $x = 0.02$: $\quad \dfrac{1}{1+0.02} \approx 1 - 0.02 + 0.0004 = 0.9804$

When $n = -2$, $x = -0.01$: $\dfrac{1}{(1-0.01)^2} \approx 1 + 0.02 - 0.0003 = 1.0197$

For both rational and negative indices n, $\,{}^nC_r$ has no meaning since the definition:

$$^nC_r = \frac{n!}{r!(n-r)!}$$

only applies when n and r are **natural numbers** (non-negative integers). However, the alternative version:

$$^nC_r = \frac{n(n-1)(n-2)...(n-r+1)}{r(r-1)(r-2)...3 \times 2 \times 1}$$

can be evaluated for rational and negative n (r is always a natural number).

If n is **not** a natural number, then $(n-1)$, $(n-2)$, $(n-3)$, etc. always give a non-zero result. Therefore the binomial expansion of $(1+x)^n$ has no last term; it produces an **infinite series**.

$$(1+x)^n = 1 + nx + \frac{n(n-1)}{2!}x^2 + ... + \frac{n(n-1)(n-2)...(n-r+1)}{r!}x^r + ...$$

CALCULATOR ACTIVITY

Exploration 3.3

You will need a graphics calculator or graph-drawing package. Scale your axes:

$$x_{\min} = -3; \qquad x_{\max} = 5; \qquad x_{scl} = 1$$
$$y_{\min} = -1; \qquad y_{\max} = 5; \qquad y_{scl} = 1.$$

■ Plot the graph of $y = \sqrt{1+x}$.

■ Superimpose the first-order and second-order polynomial approximations given by the binomial series expansion.

■ How closely do the approximations fit the original curve?

■ What do all three curves have in common when $x = 0$?

- Repeat for different values of n, e.g. $y = \frac{1}{1+x} \Rightarrow n = -1$.
- Repeat for the expansion of $(1-x)^n$.
- What happens if n is a positive integer?
- Consider higher order approximations – do they always give a better fit to the original curve?

For the function $y = \sqrt{1+x} = (1+x)^{\frac{1}{2}}$, the first and second order approximations are given by:

$$y = 1 + \tfrac{1}{2}x \quad \text{and} \quad y = 1 + \tfrac{1}{2}x - \tfrac{1}{8}x^2.$$

The diagram shows the original curve and the two approximations.

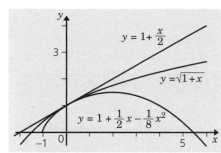

All three curves pass through $(0, 1)$.

The first-order and second-order approximations are a close fit to the original graph provided $|x|$ is small, with the quadratic approximation fitting better around $x = 0$. It is also important to note that all three curves have the same **gradient** when $x = 0$, i.e. the line $y = 1 + \tfrac{1}{2}x$ is a **tangent** to the original graph at the point $(0, 1)$ and to any higher order approximation.

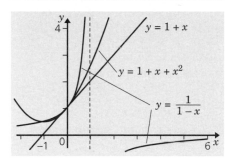

Similar patterns emerge for other values of n and for approximations to $y = (1-x)^n$, e.g. the graph of

$y = \dfrac{1}{1-x} \left(\equiv (1-x)^{-1} \right)$ has first-order and second-order approximations:

$$y = 1 + x \quad \text{and} \quad y = 1 + x + x^2$$

which are illustrated in the diagram.

CALCULATOR ACTIVITY

Exploration 3.4

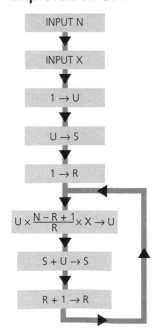

Try the program, outlined by this flowchart, which produces the sum of the first 1, 2, 3, 4, ... terms of a binomial series and will work for any value of n and x.

Run the program with different values of n and x and describe what happens 'in the long run'. Classify the sequence of partial sums as convergent or divergent, oscillating or non-oscillating.

Expected results

You probably chose various values of n and x in the last Calculator activity. Here are some examples showing what you might have found.

1 $n = 0.5$, $x = 0.1$ produces:

$\quad$ 1.05, $\quad$ 1.048 75, $\quad$ 1.048 812 5, $\quad$ 1.048 808 594, $\quad$ 1.048 808 867,
$\quad$ 1.048 808 847, $\quad$ 1.048 808 848, ...

This is an **oscillating convergent** sequence, the limit of which is $\sqrt{1+0.1} = 1.048\,808\,848...$

2 $n = -2$, $x = 3$ produces:

$\quad$ -5, $\quad$ 22, $\quad$ -86, $\quad$ 319, $\quad$ -1139, $\quad$ 3964, $\quad$ $-13\,532$, $\quad$ 45\,517,
$\quad$ $-151\,313$, $\quad$ 498\,226, ...

This is an **oscillating divergent** sequence, which has no limit.

3 $n = -3, x = -2$ produces:

      7,   31,   11,   351,   1023,   2815,   7423,   18 943,   47 103,

      114 687,   274 431, ...

This is a **non-oscillating divergent** sequence, which has no limit.

4 $n = -0.5, x = -0.2$ produces:

      1.1,   1.115,   1.1175,   1.1179375,   1.11801625,   1.118030688, ...

This is a **non-oscillating convergent** sequence, the limit of which is

$$\frac{1}{\sqrt{1-0.2}} = 1.118033989...$$

Your investigations should confirm the following summary of the behaviour of successive partial sums for the expansion of $(1 + x)^n$.

	$x < -1$	$-1 < x < 0$	$0 < x < 1$	$x > 1$
$n \in N$	oscillating	oscillating	non-oscillating	non-oscillating
$n \notin N$	non-oscillating divergent	non-oscillating convergent	oscillating convergent	oscillating divergent

When $x = 1$, the series for $(1 + x)^n$ converges to $2n$ provided $n > -1$.
When $x = -1$, the series for $(1 + x)^n$ has interesting patterns!

Results

The **binomial expansion** of $(1 + x)^n$ for any rational n, **converges** provided $-1 < x < 1$, i.e. $|x| < 1$.

Similarly, the **binomial expansion** of $(1 + ax)^n$ for any rational n, **converges** provided $-1 < ax < 1$, i.e. $|x| < \frac{1}{a}$.

Example 3.1

Find the first four terms in the expansion of $(1 + 2x)^{-3}$ and state the range of values of x for which the expansion converges. Use the expansion to estimate $\frac{1}{1.02^3}$ to 3 s.f.

Solution

$$(1 + 2x)^{-3} = 1 + (-3) \times 2x + \frac{(-3) \times (-4)}{2!} \times (2x)^2 + \frac{(-3) \times (-4) \times (-5)}{3!} \times (2x)^3 + \text{K}$$

$$= 1 - 6x + 24x^2 - 80x^3 + \text{K}$$

The series converges provided $-1 < 2x < 1 \Rightarrow -\frac{1}{2} < x < \frac{1}{2}$ *or* $|x| < \frac{1}{2}$.

Substituting $x = 0.01$:

$$\frac{1}{1.02^3} = (1 + 2 \times 0.01)^{-3} = 1 - 6 \times 0.01 + 24 \times 0.01^2 - 80 \times 0.01^3 + \text{K}$$

$$= 1 - 0.06 + 0.0024 - 0.000080 + \text{K}$$

$$= 0.942 \quad \text{(3 s.f.)}$$

Example 3.2

Find a quadratic function that approximates $(4 + x)^{\frac{1}{2}}$ for small values of x. Use it to approximate $\sqrt{3.97}$ to 6 s.f.

Solution

$$(4 + x)^{\frac{1}{2}} = \left(4(1 + \tfrac{1}{4}x)\right)^{\frac{1}{2}} = 4^{\frac{1}{2}}(1 + \tfrac{1}{4}x)^{\frac{1}{2}} = 2(1 + \tfrac{1}{4}x)^{\frac{1}{2}}$$

Now:

$$(1+\tfrac{1}{4}x)^{\frac{1}{2}} = 1+\tfrac{1}{2}\left(\tfrac{1}{4}x\right)+\frac{\left(\tfrac{1}{2}\right)\left(-\tfrac{1}{2}\right)}{2!}\left(\tfrac{1}{4}x\right)^2+\mathrm{L}$$

$$= 1+\tfrac{1}{8}x-\tfrac{1}{128}x^2+\mathrm{K}$$

$$\Rightarrow \qquad 2(1+\tfrac{1}{4}x)^{\frac{1}{2}} = 2+\tfrac{1}{4}x-\tfrac{1}{64}x^2+\mathrm{K}$$

which converges provided $-1<\tfrac{1}{4}x<1$

$\Rightarrow -4<x<4$ *or* $|x|<4$.

$\Rightarrow$ *the approximating quadratic function is* $2+\tfrac{1}{4}x-\tfrac{1}{64}x^2$.

To approximate $\sqrt{3.97}$ *let* $x=-0.03$

$$\Rightarrow \quad \sqrt{3.97} \approx 2+\tfrac{1}{4}\times(-0.03)-\tfrac{1}{64}\times(-0.03)^2$$

$$= 1.99249 \quad (6\ \text{s.f.})$$

Check the answer using a calculator.

Example 3.3

Expand $\dfrac{(3+x)}{(1-x)^2}$ *in ascending powers of* x *as far as the term in* x^4.

Solution

$$\frac{(3+x)}{(1-x)^2} \equiv (3+x)(1-x)^{-2}$$

Now

$$(1-x)^{-2} \equiv 1+(-2)(-x)+\frac{(-2)(-3)}{2!}(-x)^2+\frac{(-2)(-3)(-4)}{3!}(-x)^3$$

$$+\frac{(-2)(-3)(-4)(-5)}{4!}(-x)^4+\mathrm{K}$$

$$= 1+2x+3x^2+4x^3+5x^4+\mathrm{K}$$

$$\Rightarrow \quad (3+x)(1-x)^{-2} = (3+x)(1+2x+3x^2+4x^3+5x^4+\mathrm{K})$$

$$= 3+(6+1)x+(9+2)x^2+(12+3)x^3+(15+4)x^4+\mathrm{K}$$

$$= 3+7x+11x^2+15x^3+19x^4+\mathrm{K}$$

EXERCISES

3.1 CLASSWORK

1 For each of the following expressions, write down the first five terms of its binomial expansion. In each case state the range of values of x for which the series converges.

a) $(1+x)^{-1}$
b) $(1+3x)^{\frac{1}{2}}$
c) $(1-\tfrac{1}{3}x)^{-2}$
d) $\sqrt[3]{8+x}$

e) $(1+2x)^{-\frac{1}{2}}$
f) $(1+5x)^{\frac{3}{4}}$

2 Use appropriate binomial expansions to approximate each of the following to 3 s.f.

a) $\sqrt{1.04}$
b) $\sqrt{96}$
c) $\sqrt[3]{8.32}$

3 Expand $\dfrac{(1-x)}{(1+x)}$ in ascending powers of x, up to and including the term in x^3.

4 Show that $\sqrt{\dfrac{(1-x)}{(1+x)}} \equiv (1-x)^{\frac{1}{2}}(1+x)^{-\frac{1}{2}}$.

Using suitable binomial expansions show that:

$$\sqrt{\frac{(1-x)}{(1+x)}} \approx 1-x+\tfrac{1}{2}x^2-\tfrac{1}{2}x^3$$

Using a suitable value of x, estimate $\sqrt{\tfrac{2}{3}}$ to 3 s.f.

5 When $(1 + ax)^{-2}$ is expanded in ascending powers of x, the first four terms are $1 + Px + Qx^2 - \frac{1}{2}x^3$. Find a and then P and Q.

6 The first three terms of the expansion of $(1 + rx)^n$ are $1 - \frac{3}{2}x + \frac{27}{4}x^2$. Find the values of r and n, and the range of values of x for which the series converges.

EXERCISES

3.1 HOMEWORK

1 For each of the following expressions, write down the first four terms of its binomial expansion. In each case state the range of values of x for which the series converges.

   a) $(1 + x)^{-3}$ b) $(1 + 2x)^{-3}$ c) $\left(1 - \dfrac{x}{5}\right)^{-1}$ d) $\sqrt[3]{27 + x}$

   e) $(1 + 7x)^{\frac{1}{2}}$ f) $(1 - 3x)^{\frac{5}{4}}$

2 Use appropriate binomial expansions to approximate each of the following to 3 s.f.

   a) $\sqrt{0.95}$ b) $\sqrt{140}$ c) $(16.12)^{\frac{1}{4}}$

3 Expand $\dfrac{(1+x)}{\sqrt{1-x}}$ in ascending powers of x, up to and including the term in x^4.

4 The first three terms in the expansion of $(a - 3x)^{\frac{1}{2}}$, in ascending powers of x, are $2 - \frac{3}{4}x + bx^2$ where a and b are constants. Find the values of a and b.

5 Expand $(1 + x + x^2)^{\frac{1}{2}}$ as a series in ascending powers of x up to and including the term in x^4. Find the values of x for which the series is valid.

6 Expand $\left(1 - \dfrac{8}{x}\right)^{\frac{1}{3}}$ as a series in ascending powers of $\dfrac{1}{x}$ up to and including the term in $\dfrac{1}{x^3}$. State the set of values of x for which the expansion is valid.

THE GRAPHS OF RATIONAL FUNCTIONS

Exploration 3.5

Comparing curves

Draw graphs of the two functions $y = x^3 - x^2 - x$ and $y = \dfrac{1}{x - 1}$ for the domain $\{x : -1 \le x \le 2\}$.

Scale your calculator:
$x_{\min} = -1;$ $x_{\max} = 3;$ $x_{\text{scl}} = 1$
$y_{\min} = -4;$ $y_{\max} = 4;$ $y_{\text{scl}} = 1$

■ Describe the features of each curve such as stationary points, intersections with the axes.
■ What would you say is the essential difference for each curve?

Now add the graphs of the functions $y = 2(x^2 - 3x + 2)$ and
$y = \dfrac{1}{2(x^2 - 3x + 2)}$.

■ What can you say about these curves?

Interpreting the results

The four graphs are shown in the following diagrams.

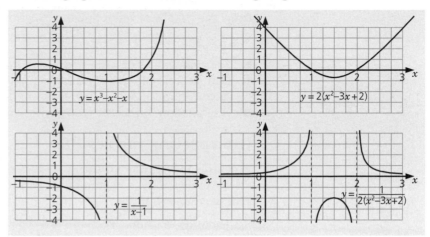

The graphs of the functions $y = x^3 - x^2 - x$ and $y = 2\left(x^2 - 3x + 2\right)$ remain finite over the domain $\{x : -1 \le x \le 3\}$.

These are examples of **continuous functions**. We can draw the curves 'without removing the pencil from the paper'.

The graphs of the functions $y = \dfrac{1}{x - 1}$ and $y = \dfrac{1}{2\left(x^2 - 3x + 2\right)}$ have breaks in them. They are examples of **discontinuous functions**. To draw these graphs with pencil and paper we would need to 'remove the pencil' as the curve 'jumps' at various values of x.

Take a closer look at $y = \dfrac{1}{x - 1}$. We can see that y increases without limit as x approaches 1 from above. The function does not exist when $x = 1$. A limit in which a function increases or decreases without bound as x approaches a value c is called an **infinite limit**. It is at this value of $x = 1$ that the function is discontinuous.

For the function $y = \dfrac{1}{2\left(x^2 - 3x + 2\right)}$, an infinite limit occurs at two values of x, which are $x = 1$ and $x = 2$.

The functions $y = \dfrac{1}{x - 1}$ and $y = \dfrac{1}{2\left(x^2 - 3x + 2\right)}$ are examples of **rational functions**. A rational function is a quotient of two functions in which both numerator and denominator are polynomials.

Further examples of rational functions are:
$$y = \frac{x - 1}{2x^2 + x - 1}, \quad y = \frac{4}{x}, \quad y = \frac{x}{x - 1}$$
The functions $y = \dfrac{\sin x}{x^2}$ and $y = \dfrac{x}{e^{x^2}}$ are not rational functions.

Exploration 3.6

Discontinuities

Draw the graphs of the following functions.

$$y = \frac{4}{x}, \quad y = \frac{1}{x-2}, \quad y = \frac{x}{x-1}, \quad y = \frac{x-1}{2x^2 + x - 1}$$

■ For what values of x does each function have an infinite limit?

■ Deduce a simple rule for deciding whether a function is discontinuous.

■ If a function is discontinuous, where do the discontinuities occur?

Interpreting the results

From this exploration we should deduce that a function is discontinuous if the denominator is zero. The roots of the denominator give the discontinuities.

For example, consider $y = \frac{x-1}{2x^2 + x - 1}$. The function is discontinuous where $2x^2 + x - 1 = 0$.

Solving for x we have $x = -1$ and $x = \frac{1}{2}$. At these values of x the function has an infinite limit.

For the other functions in Exploration 3.6:

$y = \frac{4}{x}$ is discontinuous at $x = 0$

$y = \frac{1}{x-2}$ is discontinuous at $x = 2$

$y = \frac{x}{x-1}$ is discontinuous at $x = 1$.

Vertical asymptotes

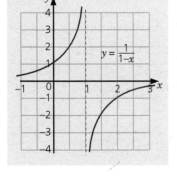

Look again at the graph of $y = \frac{1}{1-x}$.

If we could extend the graph towards infinity, it would get closer and closer to the vertical line $x = 1$. This line is called a **vertical asymptote** of the graph. For this function the graph approaches the asymptote at large positive values of y on one side, and at large negative values of y on the other side.

For some functions the graph approaches the asymptotes at large positive values of y on both sides or large negative values of y on both sides. These diagrams show examples.

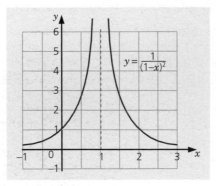

$$y = \frac{1}{(1-x)^2}$$

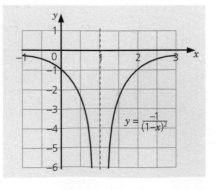

$$y = \frac{-1}{(1-x)^2}$$

We are already familiar with discontinuous functions and vertical asymptotes from work on trigonometric functions. The function $y = \sin x$ is continuous whereas the function $y = \tan x$ is discontinuous with asymptotes at $x = \pm\frac{\pi}{2}, \pm\frac{3\pi}{2}, \pm\frac{5\pi}{2}, \ldots$

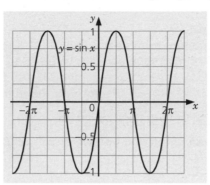
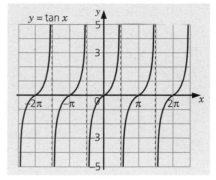

Finding vertical asymptotes

Example 3.4

Determine all the vertical asymptotes of the graphs of the following functions.

a) $y = \dfrac{1}{2(x+3)}$ **b)** $y = \dfrac{x^2+1}{x^2-1}$

Solution

Vertical asymptotes occur at the values of x where the denominator is zero and the numerator is not zero.

a) *For* $y = \dfrac{1}{2(x+3)}$ *the denominator is zero when $x = -3$.*

The numerator is always 1. Hence $x = -3$ is a vertical asymptote, as shown in the diagram.

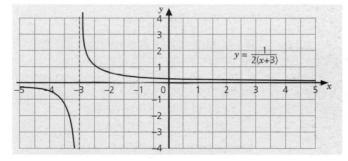

b) *For* $y = \dfrac{x^2+1}{x^2-1}$ *the denominator is zero when $x^2 - 1 = 0$.*
Solving for x we have $x = -1$ or $x = 1$.

At these two values of x the numerator is not zero. Hence $x = -1$ and $x = 1$ are two vertical asymptotes, as shown in the diagram.

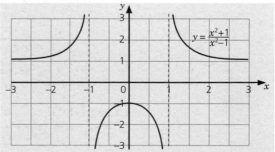

Common factors

Example 3.5

Determine the vertical asymptotes of the graph of the function

$$y = \frac{x^2 + 3x - 4}{x^2 - 1}.$$

Solution

The denominator is zero when $x = -1$ and $x = 1$.
For $x = -1$ the numerator has value -6 so that $x = -1$ is a vertical asymptote. For $x = 1$ the numerator also has a value of 0. So $(x - 1)$ is a factor of $x^2 + 3x - 4$. Factorising the numerator and denominator:

$$y = \frac{x^2 + 3x - 4}{x^2 - 1} = \frac{(x + 4)(x - 1)}{(x + 1)(x - 1)}$$

and dividing top and bottom by $(x - 1)$ (provided $x \neq 1$):

$$y = \frac{x + 4}{x + 1} \qquad x \neq -1$$

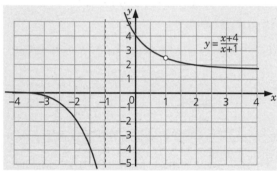

*The graph of this function shows that $x = -1$ is a vertical asymptote but $x = 1$ is not a vertical asymptote. In fact the graph is undefined at $x = 1$. This point is called a **removable discontinuity**.*

Exploration 3.7

Horizontal asymptotes

Draw the graph of the function $y = \frac{4x^2}{x^2 + 1}$.

■ Are there any vertical asymptotes?
■ What happens to the graph as x increases to large positive numbers and as x decreases to large negative numbers?

Repeat the exploration for the functions

$$y = \frac{x}{x + 1} \quad \text{and} \quad y = \frac{x^2 - 3x + 2}{2x^2 + x + 1}.$$

Interpreting the results

This exploration is an investigation of the behaviour of a function on an infinite interval.

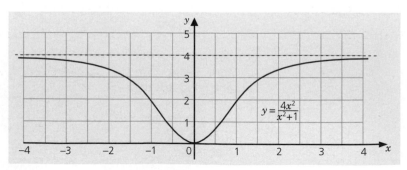

The graph of $y = \dfrac{4x^2}{x^2+1}$ approaches the horizontal line $y = 4$.

The following table of values shows the process.

$\leftarrow x$ decreases x increases $\rightarrow$

x	-1000	-100	-10	-1	0	1	10	100	1000
y	$3.999\,996$	3.9996	3.96	2	0	2	3.96	3.9996	$3.999\,996$

$\leftarrow y$ approaches 4 y approaches $4 \rightarrow$

The line $y = 4$ is an example of a **horizontal asymptote**.

Exploration 3.8

Investigating the limit of a function

For the functions $y = \dfrac{x}{x+1}$ and $y = \dfrac{x^2 - 3x + 2}{2x^2 + x + 1}$ calculate tables of values, similar to the table above, to confirm the horizontal asymptotes found in Exploration 3.7.

Example 3.6

Find the horizontal asymptote for the function $y = \dfrac{3x^2 - x + 1}{2x^2 + x - 1}$.

$y = \dfrac{3x^2 - x + 1}{2x^2 + x - 1}$

Solution

One method is to draw a graph of the function. Then from the graph we see that the curve tends towards the horizontal line $y = 1.5$.

An algebraic approach is to divide the dominant term in the numerator by the dominant term in the denominator.

As x increases: $3x^2 - x + 1$ *behaves like* $3x^2$

As x increases: $2x^2 + x - 1$ *behaves like* $2x^2$

$$\Rightarrow \quad y = \frac{3x^2 - x + 1}{2x^2 + x - 1} \to \frac{3x^2}{2x^2} \to 1.5$$

The horizontal asymptote is $y = 1.5$.

Example 3.7

Find the horizontal asymptote for the function $y = \dfrac{4}{x^2 + 2}$.

Solution

As x increases in value the numerator $= 4$ (for all values of x) and the denominator behaves like x^2.

$$\Rightarrow y = \frac{4}{x^2 + 2} \to \frac{4}{x^2} \to 0$$

The *x*-axis, $y = 0$ is a horizontal asymptote.
The graph shows the functions

$$y = \frac{4}{x^2 + 2} \quad \text{and} \quad y = \frac{4}{x^2}.$$

For values of *x* less than –4 or greater than 4 the curves are approximately identical. This

confirms that $y = \dfrac{4}{x^2 + 2}$

approaches $y = \dfrac{4}{x^2}$ as *x*

continuously increases and decreases in value.

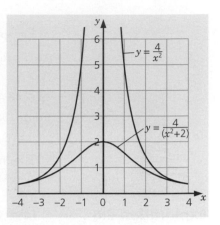

CALCULATOR ACTIVITY

Exploration 3.9

Slant asymptotes

Scale your calculator to:

$$x_{\min} = -5; \qquad x_{\max} = 5; \qquad x_{scl} = 1$$
$$y_{\min} = -25; \qquad y_{\max} = 25; \qquad y_{scl} = 5$$

Draw the graph of the function $y = \dfrac{3x^3}{x^2 - 4}$.

a) Describe the properties of the graph.

b) What happens as *x* increases to ∞ and decreases to –∞? Add the line $y = 3x$ to your graph.

Rescale your calculator and repeat the activity for the functions

$$y = \frac{x^2 - x + 4}{x - 1} \quad \text{and} \quad y = \frac{x^2 - 2x + 4}{x - 1} \quad \text{using the line } y = x \text{ for part } \textbf{b)}.$$

Interpreting the results

For $y = \dfrac{3x^3}{x^2 - 4}$ the denominator is zero when

$$x^2 - 4 = 0 \Rightarrow x = -2 \text{ or } x = 2.$$

At $x = -2$ the numerator $3(-2)^3 = -24$.

The line $x = -2$ is a vertical asymptote.

Similarly the line $x = 2$ is a vertical asymptote.

The graph has no horizontal asymptote. What happens as the value of *x* increases? Using the same approach as in Example 3.7:

$$y = \frac{3x^3}{x^2 - 4} \rightarrow \frac{3x^3}{x^2} \rightarrow 3x$$

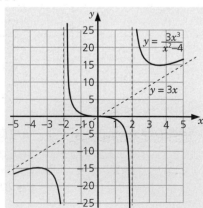

The line $y = 3x$ is called a **slant asymptote**. The graph of the function approaches the slant asymptote $y = 3x$ as x approaches $\pm \infty$.

For $y = \dfrac{x^2 - x + 4}{x - 1}$ the denominator is zero when $x - 1 = 0 \Rightarrow x = 1$.

At $x = 1$ the numerator = $1^2 - 1 + 4 = 4$.

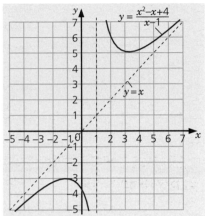

The line $x = 1$ is a vertical asymptote.

The graph has no horizontal asymptote. What happens as x approaches $\pm \infty$? Using the same approach as in Example 3.7, when x takes large positive (or large negative) values:

$$y = \frac{x^2 - x + 4}{x - 1} \to \frac{x^2 - x}{x - 1} \to x$$

The graph of the function approaches the slant asymptote $y = x$ as x approaches $\pm \infty$.

For $y = \dfrac{x^2 - 2x + 4}{x - 1}$, $x = 1$ is a vertical asymptote.

The slant asymptote looks as if it might be $y = x$ again. However the algebra shows that this is not correct. When x takes large positive (or large negative) values:

$$y = \frac{x^2 - 2x + 4}{x - 1} \to \frac{x^2 - 2x}{x - 1} \to x - 1$$

The graph of the function approaches the slant asymptote $y = x - 1$ as x approaches $\pm \infty$.

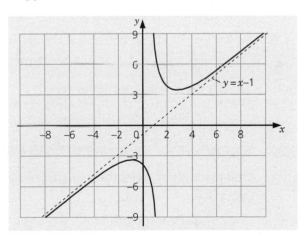

EXERCISES

3.2 CLASSWORK

1 Find the vertical asymptotes (if any) of the following functions.

a) $y = \dfrac{1}{x^2}$

b) $y = \dfrac{1}{x - 3}$

c) $y = \dfrac{1}{x^2 + x - 2}$

d) $y = \dfrac{x - 1}{x - 3}$

e) $y = \dfrac{1}{x^2 + x + 1}$

f) $y = \dfrac{x^2 - 1}{2x^3 - 11x^2 + 17x - 6}$

Use a graphics calculator or a computer graphing program to confirm your results.

2   Find the horizontal asymptotes of the following functions.

   a) $y = \dfrac{x-1}{x-3}$ **b)** $y = \dfrac{1}{x^2+x-2}$ **c)** $y = \dfrac{x^2-3x+2}{x^2-1}$

   d) $y = \dfrac{2+x}{1-x}$ **e)** $y = \dfrac{x^3-x^2+1}{4x^3+x-1}$ **f)** $y = \dfrac{x^2-1}{2x^3-11x^2+17x-6}$

   Use a graphics calculator or a computer graphing program to confirm your results.

3   For the following functions determine whether there is a removable discontinuity at $x = 1$.

   a) $y = \dfrac{x^2-3x+2}{x^2-1}$ **b)** $y = \dfrac{x^2+3x+2}{x^2-1}$

   c) $y = \dfrac{x^2+6x-7}{x-1}$ **d)** $y = \dfrac{x^2+1}{x-1}$

4   Sketch a graph of each of the following functions. In each case label the stationary points, intercepts, removable discontinuities and asymptotes. (Use differentiation to find the coordinates of the stationary points.)

   a) $y = \dfrac{2x}{x^2-1}$ **b)** $y = \dfrac{x+3}{x}$ **c)** $y = \dfrac{x^3}{x^2-1}$

   d) $y = \dfrac{x^2-4x+3}{x^2+2x-3}$ **e)** $y = \dfrac{2x^2-5x+5}{x-2}$ **f)** $y = \dfrac{4(x-1)^2}{x^2-4x+5}$

5   Construct a function for which the graph has the following features. (The answer is not unique. Compare the graph of your function with those found by other students.)

   a) vertical asymptote at $x = 2$ **b)** vertical asymptote at $x = -1$
        horizontal asymptote at $y = 1$ slant asymptote at $y = x + 1$

6   Find the vertical and horizontal asymptotes of the function:
   $$y = \frac{4x}{\sqrt{x^2-4}}.$$
   What is the domain of the function?
   Sketch the graph of the function to confirm your answers.

EXERCISES

3.2 HOMEWORK

1   Find the vertical asymptotes (if any) of the following functions.

   a) $y = \dfrac{3}{x}$ **b)** $y = \dfrac{4}{4+x}$ **c)** $y = \dfrac{4-x}{5-x}$

   d) $y = \dfrac{x}{4x^2-1}$ **e)** $y = \dfrac{3x-1}{2x^2+x-1}$ **f)** $y = \dfrac{x^2+2}{x^3-6x^2+11x-6}$

   Use a graphics calculator or a computer graphing program to confirm your results.

2   Find the horizontal asymptotes of the following functions.

   a) $y = \dfrac{4-x}{5-x}$ **b)** $y = \dfrac{x}{4x^2-1}$

   c) $y = \dfrac{x^2+x+2}{3x^2-x+2}$ **d)** $y = \dfrac{5x^2+2x-1}{7x^2-x+1}$

Use a graphics calculator or a computer graphing program to confirm your results.

3 For the following functions determine whether there is a removable discontinuity at $x = 2$.

a) $y = \dfrac{x^2 - 3x + 2}{x^2 - 2}$ **b)** $y = \dfrac{x^2 + x - 1}{x - 2}$

c) $y = \dfrac{3x - 6}{x - 2}$ **d)** $y = \dfrac{x^2 + 3x + 2}{x^2 - 3x + 2}$

4 Sketch a graph of each of the following functions. In each case label the stationary points, intercepts, removable discontinuities and asymptotes. (Use differentiation to find the coordinates of the stationary points.)

a) $y = \dfrac{x^2 + 1}{x - 2}$ **b)** $y = \dfrac{2x + 5}{x}$ **c)** $y = \dfrac{x^2 - 6x + 12}{x - 4}$

d) $y = \dfrac{2(x + 1)^2}{x^2 - 2x + 3}$ **e)** $y = \dfrac{4(x - 1)^2}{3(x + 2)^2}$ **f)** $y = \dfrac{3x - 2}{\sqrt{4x^2 + 1}}$

5 Construct a function for which the graph has the following features. (The answer is not unique. Compare the graph of your function with those found by other students.)

a) vertical asymptote at $x = -3$ **b)** vertical asymptote at $x = 0$
    horizontal asymptote at $y = 0$ slant asymptote at $y = 2x - 1$

6 Consider the function $y = \dfrac{ax}{x - b}$ where a and b are constants.

a) Investigate the graph of the function if $b \neq 0$ and a is varied. Choose positive and negative values of a.

b) Investigate the graph of the function if $a \neq 0$ and b is varied.

THE REMAINDER THEOREM

In this section we explore the division of a polynomial by a linear expression $x - a$.

Exploration 3.10

■ Divide the polynomial $f(x) = x^3 - 4x^2 + 7x - 4$ by $x - 1$.

■ Divide the polynomial $g(x) = x^3 - 4x^2 + 7x - 12$ by $x - 1$.

■ What can you say about these results?

Interpreting the results

For the first activity you should have found that $x - 1$ is a factor of $x^3 - 4x^2 + 7x - 4$ so that $\dfrac{x^3 - 4x^2 + 7x - 4}{x - 1} = x^2 - 3x + 4$.

For the second activity there is a remainder of -8 so that

$$\frac{x^3 - 4x^2 + 7x - 12}{x - 1} = x^2 - 3x + 4 - \frac{8}{x - 1}$$

and $x - 1$ is not a factor of $g(x)$.

The two polynomials can now be written as:

$f(x) \equiv x^3 - 4x^2 + 7x - 4 \equiv (x^2 - 3x + 4)(x - 1)$

$g(x) \equiv x^3 - 4x^2 + 7x - 12 \equiv (x^2 - 3x + 4)(x - 1) - 8$

Consider what happens when we substitute for $x - 1$ in each expression:
$f(1) = 0$
$g(1) = -8$

These are examples of the important theorems in the algebra of polynomials.

The factor theorem

If, for any polynomial p(x), p(a) = 0
then $(x - a)$ is a factor of p(x).

So if we wish to know if $(x - 2)$ is a factor of p(x) = $x^4 - 5x^2 + 6x - 8$ we need only to evaluate p(2).

$p(2) = 2^4 - 5 \times 2^2 + 6 \times 2 - 8 = 0 \Rightarrow x - 2$ is a factor of p(x)

The factor theorem is in fact a special case of the *remainder theorem*:
If a polynomial p(x) is divided by $(x - a)$ then the remainder is p(a).

Evaluating p(3) with p(x) = $x^4 - 5x^2 + 6x - 8$ we obtain p(3) = 46 so the remainder when p(x) is divided by $(x - 3)$ is 46.

The proof of the remainder theorem is straightforward.

When dividing a polynomial p(x) by $(x - a)$ the result is the quotient c(x) and remainder r where $\dfrac{p(x)}{x-a} = c(x) + \dfrac{r}{x-a}$

$$\Rightarrow p(x) = (x-a)c(x) + r$$

Putting $x = a$ gives p(a) = $0 \times c(a) + r \Rightarrow r = p(a)$

Example 3.8

What is the remainder when p(x) = $2x^4 - 3x^3 - 24x^2 + 13x + 12$ *is divided by:*

a) $x - 3$ *b)* $x + 2$ *c)* $x - 1$

Solution
a) *For* $x - 3$ *the value of a is equal to 3 so*
   $p(3) = 2 \times 3^4 - 3 \times 3^3 - 24 \times 3^2 + 13 \times 3x + 12 = -84$
   The remainder when p(x) *is divided by* $x - 3$ *is* -84.
b) *For* $x + 2$, p(-2) = -54 *so the remainder is* -54.
c) *For* $x - 1$, p(1) = 0 *so the remainder is* 0 *and we deduce that* $(x - 1)$ *is a factor of* p(x).

Example 3.9

The polynomial p(x) = $2x^3 - 3ax^2 + ax + b$ *has a factor of* $(x - 1)$ *and when divided by* $(x + 2)$ *has a remainder of* -54. *Find the values of* a *and* b *and factorise the polynomial.*

Solution
If $(x - 1)$ *is a factor of* p(x) *then* p(1) = 0
   $\Rightarrow p(1) = 2 - 3a + a + b = 2 - 2a + b = 0$
   $\Rightarrow b - 2a = -2$ (1)

Also $p(-2) = -54$ *by the remainder theorem*
$$\Rightarrow p(-2) = -16 - 12a - 2a + b = -16 - 14a + b = -54$$
$$\Rightarrow b - 14a = -38 \qquad\qquad (2)$$

Solving the simultaneous equations (1) *and* (2) *gives* $a = 3$ *and* $b = 4$.
Then $p(x) = 2x^3 - 9x^2 + 3x + 4$
Divide this by the factor $(x - 1)$:

$$
\begin{array}{r}
2x^2 - 7x - 4 \\
x - 1\overline{)2x^3 - 9x^2 + 3x + 4} \\
\underline{2x^3 - 2x^2} \\
-7x^2 + 3x + 4 \\
\underline{-7x^2 + 7x} \\
-4x + 4 \\
-4x + 4
\end{array}
$$

$p(x) = (x - 1)(2x^2 - 7x - 4)$
Factorising $2x^2 - 7x - 4$ *in the usual way we get:*
$2x^2 - 7x - 4 = (2x + 1)(x - 4)$ *so*
$p(x) = (x - 1)(2x + 1)(x - 4)$.

EXERCISES

3.3 CLASSWORK

1 For which of the following polynomials is $(x + 1)$ a factor?

    a) $x^2 + 3x + 2$ **b)** $x^4 + x^3 + 2x^2 - 2x + 1$

    c) $x^4 + 2x^3 + 2x^2 - x - 3$ **d)** $2x^4 + 2x^3 - 3x^2 - 6x - 3$

2 What is the remainder when $x^5 - x^3 + 2x^2 - 3$ is divided by $x - 2$?

3 When the polynomial $x^3 + ax^2 + bx - 10$ is divided by $(x + 1)$ and $(x - 1)$ the remainders are -6 and -10 respectively. Find the values of a and b.

4 Show that when polynomial $p(x)$ is divided by $ax + b$ the remainder is $p\left(\dfrac{-b}{a}\right)$.

5 Show that $3x - 2$ is a factor of $p(x) = 6x^6 - 4x^5 - 6x^4 - 5x^3 + 6x^2 + 9x - 6$.

6 **a)** Show that $x + a$ is a factor of $x^3 + a^3$ and $x^5 + a^5$.

    b) Prove that provided n is an odd integer $x + a$ is a factor of $x^n + a^n$ and hence factorise $x^n + a^n$.

EXERCISES

3.3 HOMEWORK

1 Find the remainders when the following polynomials are divided by $x - 2$.

    a) $x^3 - 2x + 5$ **b)** $x^4 - 3x^3 + x^2 - 2x + 4$

    c) $x^4 + x^3 + x^2 - 3x + 1$ **d)** $x^5 - x^3 + x - 7$

2 The polynomial $p(x) \equiv x^3 + ax^2 + bx + c$ has a factor $x + 3$. When $p(x)$ is divided by $x - 1$ and $x + 2$ the remainders are 56 and 32 respectively. Find the values of a, b and c.

3 If $f(x) \equiv x^4 + hx^3 + gx^2 - 16x - 12$ has factors $x + 1$ and $x - 2$ find the constants h and g and the remaining factors.

4 Use the factor theorem to show that $x^2 + 3x + 2$ is a factor of the polynomial $x^6 + 4x^5 + 4x^4 - 2x^3 - 4x^2 + x + 2$.

5 Find the remainder when $f(x) \equiv x^4 - ax^2 + (2a - 4)x + (3 - a)$ is divided by $x - 1$ where a is a constant. Deduce that $x - 1$ is a factor of $f(x)$ for all values of a.

6 When $p(x)$ is divided by $x - a$ the remainder is r. When $q(x)$ is divided by $x - a$ the remainder is s.

a) Prove that when $p(x) + q(x)$ is divided by $x - a$ the remainder is $r + s$.
b) Find the remainder when $p(x)q(x)$ is divided by $x - a$.

PARTIAL FRACTIONS

Exploration 3.11

Combining fractions

For each of these expressions, combine the two functions to give a single fraction.

■ $\dfrac{1}{2x + 1} + \dfrac{1}{x - 2}$

■ $\dfrac{2x}{x^2 + 1} + \dfrac{1}{x + 1}$

■ $\dfrac{2}{(x - 1)^2} + \dfrac{3}{(x - 1)}$

Interpreting the results

In this exploration, two separate rational fractions have been combined to produce a single fraction with a common denominator. For the first problem:

$$\frac{1}{2x + 1} + \frac{1}{x - 2} \equiv \frac{(x - 2) + (2x + 1)}{(2x + 1)(x - 2)} \equiv \frac{3x - 1}{(2x + 1)(x - 2)}$$

For the second and third problems:

$$\frac{2x}{x^2 + 1} + \frac{1}{x + 1} \equiv \frac{3x^2 + 2x + 1}{\left(x^2 + 1\right)(x + 1)}$$

$$\frac{2}{(x - 1)^2} + \frac{3}{(x - 1)} \equiv \frac{3x - 1}{(x - 1)^2}$$

There are many problems where we *start* with a single fraction and need to *split* it into the sum of two separate fractions. The process of decomposing a fraction is called splitting up a function into **partial fractions**. For example,

$\dfrac{1}{2x + 1}$ and $\dfrac{1}{x - 2}$ are partial fractions for $\dfrac{3x - 1}{(2x + 1)(x - 2)}$.

Of course in this case we know what the partial fractions are. The following examples show the method of approach when we do not already know what the partial fractions are.

Linear factors in the denominator

Example 3.10

Express $\dfrac{3x + 4}{(x - 1)(x + 6)}$ in partial fractions.

Solution

Rewrite the original expression as:

$$\frac{3x+4}{(x-1)(x+6)} \equiv \frac{A}{x-1} + \frac{B}{x+6}$$

where A and B are constants. Combining the fractions on the right-hand side:

$$\frac{3x+4}{(x-1)(x+6)} \equiv \frac{A(x+6)+B(x-1)}{(x-1)(x+6)}$$

$$\Rightarrow \quad 3x+4 \equiv A(x+6)+B(x-1)$$

This identity must hold true for all values of x, so we choose any value of x to find A and B.

When $x = 1$: $\quad 7 = 7A + 0B \quad \Rightarrow A = 1$

When $x = -6$: $\quad -14 = 0A + (-7)B \Rightarrow B = 2$

Note that the choice of x-values gives one constant immediately because one of the brackets is zero.

Hence $\dfrac{3x+4}{(x-1)(x+6)} \equiv \dfrac{1}{x-1} + \dfrac{2}{x+6}$

Example 3.11

Express $\dfrac{2}{\left(2x^2+9x+4\right)}$ *in partial fractions.*

Solution

The first step is to write the denominator $2x^2+9x+4$ *as a product of linear factors.*

We have $2x^2+9x+4 = (2x+1)(x+4)$

$$\frac{2}{2x^2+9x+4} \equiv \frac{A}{2x+1} + \frac{B}{x+4} \equiv \frac{A(x+4)+B(2x+1)}{(x+4)(2x+1)}$$

$$\Rightarrow \quad 2 \equiv A(x+4)+B(2x+1)$$

When $x = -4$: $\quad 2 = 0A + (-7)B \Rightarrow B = -\frac{2}{7}$

When $x = -\frac{1}{2}$: $\quad 2 = \frac{7}{2}A + 0B \Rightarrow A = \frac{4}{7}$

Hence $\dfrac{2}{2x^2+9x+4} = \dfrac{4}{7(2x+1)} - \dfrac{2}{7(x+4)}$

Quadratic factors in the denominator

Example 3.12

Express $\dfrac{1-7x}{\left(x^2+1\right)(x-3)}$ *as a sum of partial fractions.*

Solution

The partial fractions are of the form $\dfrac{Ax+B}{x^2+1}$ *and* $\dfrac{C}{x-3}$. *Note that if there is a quadratic factor in the denominator it is necessary to start with a linear factor in the numerator.*

$$\frac{1-7x}{\left(x^2+1\right)(x-3)} \equiv \frac{Ax+B}{x^2+1} + \frac{C}{x-3}$$

$$\equiv \frac{(Ax+B)(x-3)+C\left(x^2+1\right)}{\left(x^2+1\right)(x-3)}$$

$$\Rightarrow \quad 1-7x \equiv (Ax+B)(x-3)+C\left(x^2+1\right)$$

When $x = 3$: $\quad -20 = 0(3A + B) + 10C \Rightarrow C = -2$

The values of A and B can be found by substituting any values for x (except $x = 3$ because this has already been used).

When $x = 0$: $\quad 1 = B(-3) + C \quad\quad \Rightarrow B = -1$

When $x = 1$: $\quad -6 = (A + B)(-2) + 2C \Rightarrow A = 2$

Hence $\dfrac{1 - 7x}{(x^2 + 1)(x - 3)} \equiv \dfrac{2x - 1}{x^2 + 1} - \dfrac{2}{x - 3}$

Repeated factors in the denominator

Example 3.13

Express $\dfrac{2x + 1}{x(x + 3)^2}$ as partial fractions.

Solution

When the denominator includes a repeated factor we must include one fraction for each power of the factors.

$$\frac{2x + 1}{x(x + 3)^2} \equiv \frac{A}{x} + \frac{B}{x + 3} + \frac{C}{(x + 3)^2}$$

$$\equiv \frac{A(x + 3)^2 + Bx(x + 3) + Cx}{x(x + 3)^2}$$

$$\Rightarrow \quad 2x + 1 \quad \equiv A(x + 3)^2 + Bx(x + 3) + Cx$$

When $x = 0$: $\quad\quad 1 = 9A + 0B + 0C \Rightarrow A = \frac{1}{9}$

When $x = -3$: $\quad -5 = 0A + 0B - 3C \Rightarrow C = \frac{5}{3}$

To find B we choose any value of x (except $x = 0$ and $x = -3$).

Choose $x = 1$: $\quad 3 = 16A + 4B + C \quad \Rightarrow B = -\frac{1}{9}$

Hence $\dfrac{2x + 1}{x(x + 3)^2} \equiv \dfrac{1}{9x} - \dfrac{1}{9(x + 3)} + \dfrac{5}{3(x + 3)^2}$

Improper fractions

In all of the fractions that we have dealt with so far, the highest power in the numerator has been less than the highest power in the denominator. Such a fraction is called a **proper fraction**.

When the highest power in the numerator is greater than or equal to the highest power in the denominator, the fraction is called an **improper fraction**. For example:

$\dfrac{x}{x^2 - 1}$ is a proper fraction,

$\dfrac{x^2}{x^2 - 1}$ and $\dfrac{x^3}{x^2 - 1}$ are improper fractions.

Improper fractions can be rewritten in a form which only includes proper fractions by dividing the denominator into the numerator.

Example 3.14

Express $\dfrac{x^3 - x + 1}{x^2 - 3x + 2}$ as a sum of partial fractions.

Solution

This is an improper fraction. The first step is to write the fraction in the form $Ax + B + \dfrac{R}{x^2 - 3x + 2}$ where R is the remainder.

The fraction $\dfrac{R}{x^2 - 3x + 2}$ is now a proper
fraction which can be expressed as partial fractions.

$$\frac{x^3 - x + 1}{x^2 - 3x + 2} \equiv Ax + B + \frac{C}{x - 2} + \frac{D}{x - 1}$$

$$\equiv \frac{(Ax + B)(x - 2)(x - 1) + C(x - 1) + D(x - 2)}{(x - 2)(x - 1)}$$

$$\Rightarrow x^3 - x + 1 \equiv (Ax + B)(x - 2)(x - 1) + C(x - 1) + D(x - 2)$$

When $x = 1$: $1 = 0(A + B) + 0C + (-1)D$ $\Rightarrow D = -1$

When $x = 2$: $7 = 0(A + B) + C + 0D$ $\Rightarrow C = 7$

When $x = 0$: $1 = 2B - C - 2D$ $\Rightarrow B = 3$

When $x = -1$: $1 = 6(B - A) - 2C - 3D$ $\Rightarrow A = 1$

Hence $\dfrac{x^3 - x + 1}{x^2 - 3x + 2} = x + 3 + \dfrac{7}{x - 2} - \dfrac{1}{x - 1}$

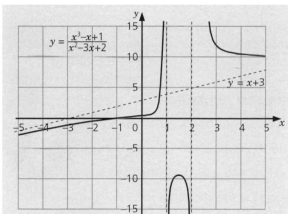

$y = \dfrac{x^3 - x + 1}{x^2 - 3x + 2}$

$y = x + 3$

*The diagram shows a graph of the function.
There are vertical asymptotes $x = 2$ and $x = 1$.
The line $y = x + 3$ is a slant asymptote.*

EXERCISES

3.4 CLASSWORK

1 Write the following in partial fractions.

a) $\dfrac{2}{(x - 1)(x + 1)}$ b) $\dfrac{1}{(x - 2)(x - 1)}$ c) $\dfrac{4}{x(x - 1)}$

d) $\dfrac{(x + 1)}{(x - 1)(x + 3)}$ e) $\dfrac{2x - 1}{x^2 - 3x + 2}$ f) $\dfrac{1}{x^2 + x - 2}$

g) $\dfrac{x^3}{x^2 + x - 2}$ h) $\dfrac{5(x + 1)}{25 - x^2}$ i) $\dfrac{1}{x(x^2 + 1)}$

j) $\dfrac{2}{(x - 4)(x^2 + 3)}$ k) $\dfrac{2 + x}{(1 + x)^2(3x + 2)}$ l) $\dfrac{x}{(x - 1)(x - 2)^2}$

2 Express $\dfrac{13x + 16}{(x - 3)(3x + 2)}$ in partial fractions.

Hence find the value of $\dfrac{d}{dx}\left[\dfrac{13x + 16}{(x - 3)(3x + 2)}\right]$ when $x = 2$.

3 Given that $y = \dfrac{2}{(x - 3)(x - 1)}$ express y as a sum of partial fractions.

Hence find $\dfrac{dy}{dx}$ and $\dfrac{d^2y}{dx^2}$.
Find and classify the stationary points of y.

3 Algebra

EXERCISES

3.4 HOMEWORK

1 Write the following in partial fractions.

a) $\dfrac{1}{x(x-3)}$ b) $\dfrac{1}{(x+1)(x+2)}$ c) $\dfrac{2x-3}{x^2-10x}$

d) $\dfrac{3-x}{(x+1)(2x-1)}$ e) $\dfrac{1}{4x^2-9}$ f) $\dfrac{x+1}{x^2+4x+3}$

g) $\dfrac{2x-3}{(x-1)^2}$ h) $\dfrac{3}{x(3x-1)^2}$ i) $\dfrac{2x-3}{x^3+10x}$

j) $\dfrac{x^2}{(x+1)(x-1)}$ k) $\dfrac{x^3-x+3}{x^2+x-2}$ l) $\dfrac{x+3}{(x^2+2)(x^2+1)}$

2 Express each of the following functions as a sum of partial fractions and hence find the first and second derivatives. Find and classify the stationary points of each function.

a) $y=\dfrac{3x-14}{(x-2)(x+6)}$ b) $y=\dfrac{(x^2-9)}{(x^2-4)}$

POWER SERIES FOR AN ALGEBRAIC FRACTION

The binomial expansion of the partial fractions of an algebraic fraction gives a simple method of giving a power series representation of the function.

Exploration 3.12

The binomial expansion revisited

■ Use the binomial expansion to find a series of ascending powers of x up to and including the term in x^2 for the function $\dfrac{1}{1+2x}$. State the range of values of x for which the expansion is valid.

■ Repeat the exploration for the function $\dfrac{1}{x-2}$.

■ Deduce the series expansion for the function $\dfrac{3x-1}{(2x+1)(x-2)}$ which has partial fractions $\dfrac{1}{2x+1}+\dfrac{1}{x-2}$.

Interpreting the results

The binomial expansion of $\dfrac{1}{1+ax}=(1+ax)^{-1}$ is $1-ax+a^2x^2-a^3x^3+\mathrm{K}$ and converges when $|ax|<1$. For the functions in Exploration 3.12:

$\dfrac{1}{1+2x}=1-2x+4x^2-8x^3$ for $|x|<\tfrac12$

$\dfrac{1}{x-2}=-\dfrac{1}{2(1-\tfrac12 x)}=-\dfrac12\left(1+\dfrac{x}{2}+\dfrac{x^2}{4}+\dfrac{x^3}{8}\right)=-\dfrac12-\dfrac{x}{4}-\dfrac{x^2}{8}-\dfrac{x^3}{16}-\mathrm{K}$

for $|x|<2$

Adding the two series:

$\dfrac{1}{1+2x}+\dfrac{1}{x-2}=\left(1-2x+4x^2-8x^3+\mathrm{K}\right)+\left(-\dfrac12-\dfrac{x}{4}-\dfrac{x^2}{8}-\dfrac{x^3}{16}-\mathrm{K}\right)$

$=\dfrac12-\dfrac94 x+\dfrac{31}{8}x^2-\dfrac{129}{16}x^3+\mathrm{K}$

Looking at the two ranges of values of x for convergence we see that $|x|<\tfrac12$ is contained within $|x|<2$. The interval of convergence is therefore $|x|<\tfrac12$ or $-\tfrac12<x<\tfrac12$.

60

Example 3.15

Given that x is small, find a cubic polynomial approximation for

$$f(x) = \frac{3x}{(x+2)(x-1)}.$$

Hence find the slope of the tangent to the graph of the function at x = 0, i.e. f'(0).

Solution

Let $\dfrac{3x}{(x+2)(x-1)} = \dfrac{A}{x+2} + \dfrac{B}{x-1} = \dfrac{A(x-1)+B(x+2)}{(x+2)(x-1)}$

$\Rightarrow \qquad 3x = A(x-1) + B(x+2)$

When $x = 1$: $\qquad 3 = 0A + 3B \quad \Rightarrow B = 1$

when $x = -2$: $\qquad -6 = -3A + 0B \quad \Rightarrow A = 2$.

Hence $\dfrac{3x}{(x+2)(x-1)} = \dfrac{2}{x+2} + \dfrac{1}{x-1}$

Applying the binomial expansion to the partial fractions:

$$\frac{2}{x+2} = \frac{1}{1+\frac{1}{2}x} = 1 - \frac{x}{2} + \frac{x^2}{4} - \frac{x^3}{8} + \dots \quad |x| < 2$$

$$\frac{1}{x-1} = \frac{-1}{1-x} = -1(1 + x + x^2 + x^3) + \dots \quad |x| < 1$$

Adding the two power series:

$$f(x) = \frac{3x}{(x+2)(x-1)} = -\frac{3x}{2} - \frac{3x^2}{4} - \frac{9x^3}{8} + \dots \quad \text{for } |x| < 1$$

$$\Rightarrow f'(x) = -\frac{3}{2} - \frac{3x}{2} - \frac{27x^2}{8} + \dots$$

In particular, $f'(x) = -\frac{3}{2}$. *The slope of the tangent to the graph of* $y = f(x)$ *at x = 0 is* $-\frac{3}{2}$.

The figure shows graphs of the function $y = \dfrac{3x}{(x+2)(x-1)}$ *and the*

polynomials $p_1 = -\dfrac{3}{2}x$, $p_2 = -\dfrac{3}{2}x - \dfrac{3x^2}{4}$ *and* $p_3 = -\dfrac{3}{2}x - \dfrac{3x^2}{4} - \dfrac{9x^3}{8}$

drawn on the same axes.

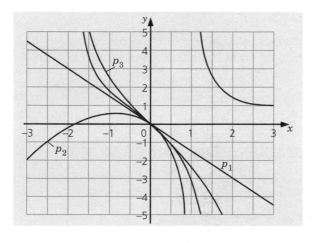

Notice how the fit of the polynomials improves for a larger range of values of x as the degree of the polynomials increases.

EXERCISES

3.5 CLASSWORK

1 Expand the following functions as series of ascending powers of x up to and including the term in x^3. State the range of values of x for which the expansion is valid.

a) $\dfrac{x+2}{1-x}$　　　　b) $\dfrac{x+1}{x+2}$　　　　c) $\dfrac{x^2-1}{x+3}$

d) $\dfrac{\sqrt{1-x}}{1+x}$　　　　e) $\dfrac{1}{(2-x)(1+2x)}$　　　　f) $\dfrac{1}{(1-x)(2-x)}$

g) $\dfrac{5}{(1+2x)(1-3x)}$　　　　h) $\dfrac{x+1}{(1-x)(3+x)}$

2 Use partial fractions and the binomial expansion to find a linear approximation for $\dfrac{1}{(1-2x)(2+x)}$.

3 If x is very small, find a quadratic approximation for $\dfrac{12}{(3+x)(1-x)^2}$.

EXERCISES

3.5 HOMEWORK

1 Expand the following functions as series of ascending powers of x up to and including the term in x^3. State the range of values of x for which the expansion is valid.

a) $\dfrac{x-3}{x+1}$　　　　b) $\dfrac{x}{1-2x}$　　　　c) $\dfrac{2x^2+1}{1-x}$

d) $\dfrac{1}{(2-x)(1+x)}$　　　　e) $\dfrac{\sqrt{4-x}}{1-3x}$　　　　f) $\dfrac{x-1}{(2-3x)(1+x)}$

g) $\dfrac{x}{(1+x)^2(2+x)}$　　　　h) $\dfrac{x^2+1}{x^2+3x-4}$

2 If x is very small find a cubic polynomial approximation for

$$\dfrac{x^2+1}{x^3-2x^2-x+2} .$$

3 Use partial fractions and the binomial expansion to find a series in ascending powers of x up to and including the terms in x^4 of the

function $y = \dfrac{x+2}{1-x}$.

Write down the polynomials P_0 (the constant approximation), P_1 (the linear approximation), P_2 (the quadratic approximation) and so on.

Use a graphics calculator or computer software to compare the graphs of the original function and the series expansions P_0, P_1, P_2, P_3 and P_4.

CONSOLIDATION EXERCISES FOR CHAPTER 3

1　a) Obtain the first four non-zero terms of the binomial expansion in ascending powers of x of $(1-x^2)^{-\frac{1}{2}}$, given that $|x| < 1$.

　　b) Show that, when $x = \frac{1}{3}(1-x^2)^{-\frac{1}{2}} = \frac{3}{4}\sqrt{2}$.

　　c) Substitute $x = \frac{1}{3}$ into your expansion and hence obtain an approximation to $\sqrt{2}$, giving your answer to five decimal places.

(ULEAC Question 4, Paper 2, January 1995)

2   In triangle ABC, AB = 3 cm, AC = 4 cm, BC = d cm and $\cos A = x$.

   a) Show that $d = 5\sqrt{1 - 0.96x}$.

   b) Given that x^3 and higher powers of x may be neglected, use a binomial expansion to express d in the form $p + qx + rx^2$, where p, q and r are constants whose values are to be found.

   c) Show that, when $x = 0.005$, the approximation found in part **b)** is correct to 3 decimal places.

   (ULEAC Question 7, Paper 2, June 1992)

3   **a)** Write down the expansion of $(2 - x)^4$.

   b) Find the first four terms in the expansion of $(1 + 2x)^{-3}$ in ascending powers of x. For what range of values of x is this expansion valid?

   c) When the expansion is valid:
   $$\frac{(2 - x)^4}{(1 + 2x)^3} = 16 + ax + bx^2 + \ldots .$$
   Find the values of a and b.

   (MEI Question 1, Paper 2, January 1995)

4   **a)** Write down the expansion of $(1 + x)^3$.

   b) Find the first four terms in the expansion of $(1 - x)^{-4}$ in ascending powers of x. For what values of x is this expansion valid?

   c) When the expansion is valid:
   $$\frac{(1 + x)^3}{(1 - x)^4} = 1 + 7x + ax^2 + bx^3 + \ldots .$$
   Find the values of a and b.

   (MEI Question 1, Paper 2, January 1994)

5   **a)** Use the formula for solving a quadratic equation to write down the two roots of the equation $x^2 + x + p = 0$, where p is a constant.

   b) Find the values of A, B and C for which:
   $$1 + Ap + Bp^2 + Cp^3$$
   is equal to the first four terms in the binomial expansion of $\sqrt{1 - 4p}$. State the condition for which the expansion is valid.

   c) Use your expansion to find approximations to the two roots of the equation, assuming that terms in p^4 and higher powers of p are so small that they may be neglected.

   d) Use your answer to part **c)** to find the approximate values of the two roots of the equation $10x^2 + 10x + 1 = 0$.

   (MEI Question 1, Paper 2, June 1993)

6   The polynomial p(x) is given by p$(x) = (2 + 3x)^5 + ax + 11$ where a is a constant.

   a) Given that p(x) leaves a remainder of 4 when divided by $(x + 1)$, find the value of a.

   Hence find the value of the remainder when p(x) is divided by $(3x + 1)$.

   b) Use the binomial theorem to determine the coefficient of x^4 when p(x) is expanded.

   (AQA B, Specimen Paper 4, 2000)

7 When the polynomial $p(x) = 2x^6 + ax^5 + 32x^2 - 26$ is divided by $(x + 1)$ the remainder is 15.
   a) Calculate the value of a.
   $p(x)$ is now divided by $(x - 2)$ giving the quotient $c(x)$ and remainder R so that $p(x) = (x - 2)c(x) + R$
   b) Calculate the value of R
   c) Calculate $c(-1)$.

(AQA A, Specimen Paper 3, 2000)

8   **a)** Express $\dfrac{1 - x - x^2}{(1 - 2x)(1 - x)^2}$ as the sum of three partial fractions.

   b) Hence, or otherwise, expand this expression in ascending powers of x up to and including the term in x^3.
   c) State the range of values of x for which the full expansion is valid.

(AQA A, Specimen Paper 3, 2000)

9 A curve has equation $y = \dfrac{1}{(x + 1)(x - 5)}$.

   a) Find the asymptotes of the function.
   b) Express y as a sum of partial fractions.
   c) Find and classify the stationary points of y.
   d) Sketch the curve using the information from parts **a)**–**c)**.

10 A curve has equation $y = \dfrac{2x^3 + x^2 - 7x + 7}{x^2 + x - 2}$.

   a) Find the vertical asymptotes of the function.
   b) Express y as a sum of partial fractions.
   c) Deduce the equation of the slant asymptote.
   d) Use a graphics calculator or computer software to sketch the curve and hence validate your answers.

11 Express $y = \dfrac{4x}{(1 + x)^2(2 - x)}$ as a sum of partial fractions.

   A curve has equation $y = \dfrac{4x}{(1 + x)^2(2 - x)}$.
   Determine the equation of the normal to the curve at the point (1, 1).

12 Express $\dfrac{1 + 2x}{(1 + x)(1 - 2x)}$ in partial fractions and hence obtain its series

   expansion in ascending powers of x up to and including the term in x^3.

   State the range of values of x for which the expansion is valid.

13 Express $f(x) \equiv \dfrac{4 - x}{(1 - x)(2 - x)}$ in partial fractions. Hence, or otherwise, for $|x| < 1$, obtain the expansion of $f(x)$ in ascending powers of x up to and including the term in x^3, simplifying each coefficient.

(ULEAC Question 4, Paper 2, January 1992)

14 $f(x) \equiv \dfrac{9 - 3x - 12x^2}{(1 - x)(1 + 2x)}$.

   a) Given that $f(x) \equiv A + \dfrac{B}{1 - x} + \dfrac{C}{1 + 2x}$, find the values of the constants A, B and C.
   b) Given that $|x| < \frac{1}{2}$, expand $f(x)$ in ascending powers of x up to and including the term x^3, simplifying each coefficient.
   c) Hence, or otherwise, find the value of $f'(0)$.

(ULEAC Question 8, Paper 2, January 1993)

15 $f(x) \equiv \dfrac{4+x}{(1+2x)(1-x)^2}$.

a) Express $f(x)$ in partial fractions.

b) Given that $|x| < \frac{1}{2}$, expand $f(x)$ in ascending powers of x, up to and including the term in x^3.

(ULEAC Question 5, Paper 2, May 1994)

16 **a)** $\dfrac{14x^2 + 13x + 2}{(x+1)(2x+1)^2} \equiv \dfrac{A}{x+1} + \dfrac{B}{2x+1} + \dfrac{C}{(2x+1)^2}$

Find the values of the constants A, B and C.

b) Given that $y = \dfrac{14x^2 + 13x + 2}{(x+1)(2x+1)^2}$, hence or otherwise find the value

of $\dfrac{\mathrm{d}y}{\mathrm{d}x}$ at $x = 0$.

(ULEAC Question 6, Paper 2, January 1995)

17 The function $f(x)$ is defined by:

$f(x) = \dfrac{2x+7}{x+3}$ $x \, \varepsilon \, \mathfrak{R}, \; x \neq -3$.

Find $f'(x)$ and hence show that the gradient of the curve $y = f(x)$ is negative for all values of x in the domain of f.

Sketch the graph of the curve $y = f(x)$. Label its asymptotes and its points of intersection with the x- and y-axes.

Write down the range of f.

Show that:

$f(x) = a + \dfrac{b}{x+3}$

where a and b are constants which are to be determined. Hence describe the geometrical transformation which transforms the graph of $y = f(x)$ into the graph of $y = \dfrac{1}{x}, x \neq 0$

(NEAB Question 14, Specimen Paper 1, 1994)

18 Express $\dfrac{1-x-x^2}{(1-2x)(1-x)^2}$ as the sum of three partial fractions. Hence, or

otherwise, expand this expression in ascending powers of x up to and including the term in x^3. State the range of values of x for which the full expansion is valid.

(NEAB Question 12, Specimen Paper 1, 1994)

19 Find the equations of the asymptotes of the curve $y = \dfrac{x^2+1}{x+1}$.

(UCLES Modular Question 1, Specimen Paper P4, 1994)

Summary

■ The binomial series is a special case of the binomial theorem when $a = 1$ and $b = x$ and is usually written:

$$(1+x)^n = 1 + nx + \frac{n(n-1)}{2!}x^2 + \dots$$
$$+ \frac{n(n-1)\dots(n-r+1)}{r!}x^r + \dots + nx^{n-1} + x^n$$

■ For negative and fractional values of n the binomial series gives an infinite number of terms. It converges provided $|x| < 1$.

■ Rational functions

A rational function is a quotient of two polynomial functions $y = \dfrac{f(x)}{g(x)}$. If there exists a value of $x = \alpha$, say, such that $g(\alpha) = 0$ but $f(\alpha) \neq 0$ then y has a **vertical asymptote** $x = \alpha$ and is said to be discontinuous at $x = \alpha$. If $y \to c$ as $x \to \pm \infty$ then $y = c$ is a **horizontal asymtote**. For some functions $y \to ax + b$ as $x \to \pm \infty$ then the line $y = ax + b$ is called a **slant asymptote**. If $f(\alpha) = 0$ and $g(\alpha) = 0$ at a point $x = \alpha$, then $x = \alpha$ is called a **removable discontinuity**.

■ Partial fractions

The process of decomposing a fraction is called 'splitting the function into partial fractions'.

■ Remainder theorem

If polynomial $p(x)$ is divided by $x - a$ the remainder is $p(a)$.

Integration

In this chapter we introduce methods or techniques of integration; in particular:

- *the use of substitutions,*
- *the method of integration by parts,*
- *the use of partial fractions to transform integrals.*

Some expressions have an integral that is a recognisable function, such as sin x. There are many others for which an exact integral cannot be found. In the latter cases it is necessary to adopt an approximate or numerical approach such as the trapezium rule. In your earlier work on integration, you integrated standard functions such as powers of x, polynomial, exponential and logarithmic functions. In this chapter we introduce methods of integration which attempt to transform non-standard functions which are difficult to integrate into standard functions that can be integrated.

USING SUBSTITUTIONS, PART 1

Exploration 4.1

Expanding and integrating

Look at the function $y = \mathrm{f}(x) = (x + 1)^3$.

- Expand $\mathrm{f}(x)$ to give a polynomial in x.
- Evaluate $\int \mathrm{f}(x)\,\mathrm{d}x$.
- Factorise your answer into the form $a(x + 1)^4 + b$.

Repeat the exploration for $\mathrm{f}(x) = (x + 1)^4$ and $\mathrm{f}(x) = (5x + 3)^2$. Can you identify a rule for integrating $\mathrm{f}(x) = (ax + b)^n$?

Interpreting the results

The functions $(x + 1)^3$, $(x + 1)^4$ and $(5x + 3)^2$ are examples of **composite functions** or **functions of a function**. For example if we let $u = 5x + 3$ then for $(5x + 3)^2$:
$\mathrm{f}(u) = u^2$ and $u = 5x + 3$
so f is a function of u and u is a function of x.

Summarising the results of Exploration 4.1 gives the following results.

From this exploration we can deduce that:

$\mathrm{f}(x)$	$\int \mathrm{f}(x)\,\mathrm{d}x$	
$(x + 1)^3$	$\frac{1}{4}x^4 + x^3 + \frac{3}{2}x^2 + x + c$	$\frac{1}{4}(x+1)^4 + \left(c - \frac{1}{4}\right)$
$(x + 1)^4$	$\frac{1}{5}x^5 + x^4 + 2x^3 + 2x^2 + x + c$	$\frac{1}{5}(x+1)^5 + \left(c - \frac{1}{5}\right)$
$(5x + 3)^2$	$\frac{25}{3}x^3 + 15x^2 + 9x + c$	$\frac{1}{15}(5x+3)^3 + \left(c - \frac{27}{15}\right)$

- expanding the functions and integrating term by term is inefficient and tedious,
- there must be a simple rule to integrate such functions.

The **chain rule for differentiation** (Chapter 1, *Differentiation*) provides a useful technique of integration.

The chain rule is:

$$\frac{df}{dx} = \frac{df}{du} \times \frac{du}{dx}$$

To find $\frac{df}{dx}$ if $f = (5x + 3)^3$, let $u = (5x + 3)$ and $f = u^3$

$$\Rightarrow \quad \frac{df}{dx} = \frac{df}{du} \times \frac{du}{dx} = 3u^2 \times 5 = 15u^2 = 15(x + 3)^2$$

When using the chain rule, we choose a new variable u, differentiate the function of u and then substitute back for x.

The same idea can be used as a technique of integration. We can change the variable and use the chain rule.

If $y = \int f(x)\, dx$ then $\frac{dy}{dx} = f(x)$.

Let $x = g(u)$ for some function g and a new variable u, so that y is now a function of u, i.e. $y = f(g(u))$. This is a composite function of u. Using the chain rule:

$$\frac{dy}{du} = \frac{dy}{dx} \times \frac{dx}{du} = f(x) \times \frac{dx}{du} = f(g(u))\frac{dx}{du}$$

and integrating with respect to u:

$$y = \int f(g(u))\, \frac{dx}{du}\, du$$

Compare this with $y = \int f(x)\, dx$ to give a rule for integration.

Integration by substitution

- Choose a new variable u to replace x.

- Replace dx by $\frac{dx}{du}\, du$.

- Integrate the new function of u.

Now let's try this method on the functions in Exploration 4.1.

For $\int (x + 1)^3 dx$ let $u = x + 1$; then $\frac{du}{dx} = 1$ so $dx = du$.

Substitute throughout for all the xs to give:

$$\int (x + 1)^3 dx = \int u^3 du = \tfrac{1}{4}u^4 + c$$

$\uparrow$

standard function

For $\int (5x + 3)^2 dx$ let $u = 5x + 3$; then $\frac{du}{dx} = 5$ so that $dx = \tfrac{1}{5} du$.

Substitute through for all the xs to give:

$$\int (5x + 3)^2\, dx = \int u^2 \times \tfrac{1}{5}\, du = \tfrac{1}{5}\int u^2\, du = \tfrac{1}{5}\left(\tfrac{1}{3}u^3\right) + c = \tfrac{1}{15}(5x + 3)^3 + c$$

Note that in finding dx in terms of du we use the rule:

$$\frac{dx}{du} = \frac{1}{\dfrac{du}{dx}}$$

Exploration 4.2

Integrating functions

Integrate each of the following functions:

■ by multiplying out the brackets and integrating term by term,
■ by using the given substitution.

a) $f(x) = (3x + 7)^2$ let $u = 3x + 7$

b) $f(x) = x^2(x^3 - 3)$ let $u = x^3 - 3$

c) $f(x) = x^2(x^3 - 3)^2$ let $u = x^3 - 3$

Interpreting the results

The functions $x^2(x^3 - 3)$ and $x^2(x^3 - 3)^2$ are the first examples of products of functions that can be integrated. For $x^2(x^3 - 3)^2$ letting

$u = x^3 - 3$ gives $\dfrac{du}{dx} = 3x^2$ and $dx = \dfrac{1}{3x^2}du$. Then:

$$\int x^2(x^3 - 3)^2\, dx = \int x^2(u^2)\frac{1}{3x^2}\, du = \tfrac{1}{3}\int u^2\, du = \tfrac{1}{9}u^3 + c = \tfrac{1}{9}(x^3 - 3)^3 + c$$

$\uparrow$

no *x*s allowed in here

The substitution $u = x^3 - 3$ works because the derivative of u is also part of the integral. All terms in x must disappear, leaving the new integral in terms only of u. This is how we know that the substitution is a good choice.

Example 4.1

Evaluate $y = \int(3x^2 + x - 4)^3(6x + 1)\, dx$.

Solution
Let $u = 3x^2 + x - 4 \Rightarrow \dfrac{du}{dx} = 6x + 1$.

Then:

$dx = \dfrac{dx}{du}\, du = \dfrac{1}{(6x + 1)}\, du$

Replacing $(3x^2 + x - 4)^3$ *by* u^3 *and* dx *by* $\dfrac{1}{(6x + 1)}\, du$:

$y = \int(3x^2 + x - 4)^3(6x + 1)\, dx = \int u^3(6x + 1)\dfrac{1}{(6x + 1)}\, du = \int u^3\, du$

$\Rightarrow y = \tfrac{1}{4}u^4 + c = \tfrac{1}{4}(3x^2 + x - 4)^4 + c$

Example 4.2

Evaluate $y = \int_0^1 x(5 + 2x^2)^4\, dx$.

Solution
In this example we need to change all the xs in the function, and also the limits.

Let $u = 5 + 2x^2 \Rightarrow \dfrac{du}{dx} = 4x$

Then:

$dx = \dfrac{dx}{du}\, du = \dfrac{1}{4x}\, du$

The x integral will be turned into a u integral. The limits on u are found from $u = 5 + 2x^2$ and the x limits 0 and 1.
$x = 0 \Rightarrow u = 5$ and $x = 1 \Rightarrow u = 7$
Replacing $(5 + 2x^2)^4$ by u^4, dx by $\dfrac{1}{4x}$ du and changing the limits gives:

$$y = \int_5^7 x\left(u^4\right)\frac{1}{4x}\,du = \tfrac{1}{4}\int_5^7 u^4 du = \tfrac{1}{4}\left[\frac{u^5}{5}\right]_5^7 = \frac{7^5}{20} - \frac{5^5}{20} = 684.1$$

Example 4.3

Find the total area enclosed by the curve $y = xe^{1-2x^2}$, the x-axis and the lines $x = 1$ and $x = -0.5$.

Solution

For problems of this type it is very important to sketch the function. A graphics calculator or computer software is valuable to provide a quick sketch. The graph of the curve $y = xe^{1-2x^2}$ and the total area required is as shown.

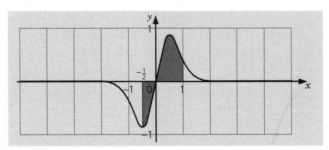

The area between $x = -\tfrac{1}{2}$ and $x = 0$ is
$$A_1 = -\int_{-\frac{1}{2}}^{0} xe^{1-2x^2}\,dx$$
and the area between $x = 0$ and $x = 1$ is
$$A_2 = \int_0^1 xe^{1-2x^2}\,dx.$$
The total area is $A_1 + A_2$.

Let $u = 1 - 2x^2 \Rightarrow \dfrac{du}{dx} = -4x$

Then:
$$dx = \frac{dx}{du}\,du = -\frac{1}{4x}\,du$$

For the limits $x = -\tfrac{1}{2}$ and $x = 0$ we have $u = \tfrac{1}{2}$ and $u = 1$.

For the limits $x = 0$ and $x = 1$ we have $u = 1$ and $u = -1$.
Substituting for all the xs and the limits:

$$A_1 = -\int_{\frac{1}{2}}^{1} -\tfrac{1}{4}e^u du = \left[\tfrac{1}{4}e^u\right]_{\frac{1}{2}}^{1} = \tfrac{1}{4}\left(e^1 - e^{\frac{1}{2}}\right) = 0.2674 \text{ (to 4 d.p.)}$$

$$A_2 = \int_1^{-1} -\tfrac{1}{4}e^u du = \left[-\tfrac{1}{4}e^u\right]_1^{-1} = -\tfrac{1}{4}\left(e^{-1} - e^1\right) = 0.5876$$

The total area is $A_1 + A_2 = 0.8550$ (correct to four d.p.).

We must be careful when interpreting integrals by areas. It would be easy to write the area – wrongly – as:

$$\int_{-\frac{1}{2}}^{1} xe^{1-2x^2}\,dx = \int_{\frac{1}{2}}^{-1} -\frac{1}{4}e^u\,du = -\frac{1}{4}\big[e^u\big]_{\frac{1}{2}}^{-1} = -\frac{1}{4}\left(e^{-1}-e^{\frac{1}{2}}\right) = 0.3202$$

This is **not** the total area required. To avoid making the mistake, always sketch the graph of the function.

EXERCISES

4.1 CLASSWORK

1 By using the given substitution evaluate the integrals.

a) $\int (x+5)^4\,dx \quad u = x + 5$

b) $\int (2x-3)^5\,dx \qquad u = 2x - 3$

c) $\int_0^3 \sqrt{x+1}\,dx \quad u = x + 1$

d) $\int x(3x^2+2)^{\frac{5}{4}}\,dx \quad u = 3x^2 + 2$

e) $\int_1^2 e^{4x-1}\,dx \quad u = 4x - 1$

f) $\int_0^1 8xe^{4x^2}\,dx \qquad u = 4x^2$

g) $\int (2x+3)(x^2+3x+7)\,dx \quad u = x^2 + 3x + 7$

h) $\int_1^2 (3x^2-1)(x^3-x+1)^2\,dx \quad u = x^3 - x + 1$

2 Evaluate the following integrals, choosing an appropriate substitution.

a) $\int (x-5)^6\,dx$

b) $\int_0^1 (2x+1)^3\,dx$

c) $\int \sqrt{3x-1}\,dx$

d) $\int x(x^2-1)^2\,dx$

e) $\int (2x-1)(x^2-x+3)^{-\frac{1}{2}}\,dx$

f) $\int_{-1}^1 (4x+1)(2x^2+x+3)^5\,dx$

g) $\int e^{2x+5}\,dx$

h) $\int (2x-3)e^{x^2-3x+1}\,dx$

3 Find the total area enclosed by the curve $y = 16 - (x-2)^4$ and the x-axis.

4 Find the total area enclosed by the curve $y = xe^{2-3x^2}$, the x-axis and the lines $x = 1$ and $x = -1$.

5 Find the volume generated when the area between the lines $y = 4 - x$, the y-axis and the x-axis is rotated completely about the x-axis.

6 Find the volume generated when the area between the curve $y = \sqrt{x}(2-x^2)$ and the x-axis is rotated about the x-axis.

7 In mechanics we define the work done by a force F(x) on an object that moves along the x-axis from $x = a$ to $x = b$ to be $W = \int F(x)\,dx$. Calculate the work done by an object that stretches a non-linear spring from $x = 0.2$ m to $x = 0.4$ m. The force exerted on the object by the spring is $20(x-0.1)^{\frac{3}{2}}$, for $x > 0.1$.

8 The length of the curve $y =$ f(x) between the points on the curve $(a,$ f$(a))$ and $(b,$ f$(b))$ is given by $s = \int_a^b \sqrt{1+f'(x)^2}\,dx$.

Find the length of the curve $y = x^{\frac{3}{2}}$ between the points on the curve $(1, 1)$ and $(4, 8)$.

EXERCISES

4.1 HOMEWORK

1 By using the given substitution evaluate the integrals.

a) $\int (3x+4)^3 \, dx \quad u = 3x+4$ **b)** $\int 2(x-3)^{-4} \, dx \qquad u = x-3$

c) $\int \sqrt{2x-1} \, dx \quad u = 2x-1$ **d)** $\int_0^2 (2x+1)^{\frac{5}{2}} \, dx \qquad u = 2x+1$

e) $\int_2^3 \dfrac{2}{(3x-4)^2} \, dx \quad u = 3x-4$ **f)** $\int e^{x-1} \, dx \qquad u = x-1$

g) $\int 3x^2(x^3-3) \, dx \quad u = x^3-3$ **h)** $\int (4x+1)e^{2x^2+x-2} \, dx \quad u = 2x^2+x-2$

2 Evaluate the following integrals choosing an appropriate substitution.

a) $\int (x+3)^4 \, dx$ **b)** $\int_1^2 (4x+3)^2 \, dx$

c) $\int \sqrt{2x+3} \, dx$ **d)** $\int_{-1}^1 (x-1)\sqrt{x^2-2x+3} \, dx$

e) $\int \dfrac{1}{(4x+2)^3} \, dx$ **f)** $\int e^{3x-1} \, dx$

g) $\int (2x+1)e^{x^2+x+4} \, dx$ **h)** $\int_0^2 xe^{-x^2} \, dx$

3 Find the total area enclosed by the curve $y = x(2-x^2)^2$ and the x-axis.

4 Find the total area enclosed by the curve $y = (2x-1)e^{x^2-x}$, the y-axis and the line $x = 1$.

5 Find the volume generated when the area between the lines $y = 2-x$, the x-axis and the y-axis is rotated completely about the x-axis.

6 Find the volume generated when the area between the curve $y = (1-0.5x)^2$ and the x-axis is rotated completely about the x-axis.

7 For a straight thin rod lying along the axis between $x = a$ and $x = b$, the position of the centre of mass (or centroid) is given by:

$$\bar{x} = \frac{\int_a^b x\rho(x) \, dx}{\int_a^b \rho(x) \, dx}$$

where $\rho(x)$ is the density of the rod.

Find the position of the centre of mass of a rod of length 1 metre having density $\rho(s) = (3+s^2)^2$ where s is the distance along the rod from one end.

8 If a square plate of side length a stands vertically in a liquid then the force exerted on one side of the plate by the pressure in the liquid is given by $\int_{h_1}^{h_2} ah\rho \, dh$ where ρ is the density of the liquid, h_1 and h_2 are the depths of the top and bottom of the plate respectively.

Find the force on a square plate of side length 0.5 metres in a liquid of density $\rho = 2\varepsilon^{-h^2}$ when one edge of the plate lies in the surface of the liquid.

USING SUBSTITUTIONS PART 2

Any function of the form $\dfrac{f'(x)}{f(x)}$ can be integrated using the substitution $u = f(x)$.

Exploration 4.3

Use substitution

Make the substitution $u = ax + b$ to find $\displaystyle\int \dfrac{1}{ax+b}\,dx$.

Use your answer to evaluate:

a) $\displaystyle\int \dfrac{1}{x+1}\,dx$

b) $\displaystyle\int \dfrac{1}{3x+2}\,dx$

c) $\displaystyle\int \dfrac{1}{1-4x}\,dx$.

Interpreting the results

The integral $\displaystyle\int \dfrac{1}{ax+b}\,dx = \dfrac{1}{a}\ln|ax+b|$ is an important result for the evaluation of $\displaystyle\int \dfrac{f'(x)}{f(x)}\,dx$.

Example 4.4

Evaluate $y = \displaystyle\int \dfrac{x+1}{x^2 + 2x - 1}\,dx$.

Solution

Let $u = x^2 + 2x - 1 \;\Rightarrow\; \dfrac{du}{dx} = 2x + 2 = 2(x+1)$

Then:
$$dx = \dfrac{dx}{du}\,du = \dfrac{1}{2(x+1)}\,du$$

Replacing $x^2 + 2x - 1$ *by u and dx by* $\dfrac{1}{2(x+1)}\,du$:

$$y = \int \dfrac{(x+1)}{u} \cdot \dfrac{1}{2(x+1)}\,du = \dfrac{1}{2}\int du = \dfrac{1}{2}\ln|u| + c = \dfrac{1}{2}\ln\left|x^2 + 2x - 1\right| + c$$

Example 4.5

Evaluate $y = \displaystyle\int_1^2 \dfrac{x^2 + 1}{x^3 + 3x}\,dx$.

Solution

Let $u = x^3 + 3x \Rightarrow \dfrac{du}{dx} = 3x^2 + 3 = 3(x^2 + 1)$

Then:
$$dx = \dfrac{dx}{du}\,du = \dfrac{1}{3(x^2 + 1)}\,du$$

For the limits $x = 1 \Rightarrow u = 4$ *and* $x = 2 \Rightarrow u = 14$.

Replacing $(x^3 + 3x)$ *by u, dx by* $\dfrac{1}{3(x^2 + 1)}\,du$ *and changing the limits gives:*

$$y = \int_1^2 \dfrac{x^2 + 1}{x^3 + 3x}\,dx = \int_4^{14} \dfrac{(x^2 + 1)}{u} \cdot \dfrac{1}{3(x^2 + 1)}\,du = \dfrac{1}{3}\int_4^{14} \dfrac{1}{u}\,du = \dfrac{1}{3}\ln[u]_4^{14}$$

$$= \dfrac{1}{3}\ln 14 - \dfrac{1}{3}\ln 4 = 0.4176 \ (\text{to 4 d.p.})$$

Example 4.6

Evaluate $y = \displaystyle\int_0^1 \dfrac{8x+3}{\sqrt{1+3x+4x^2}}\,\mathrm{d}x$.

Solution

Not all quotients will lead to natural logarithms.

Let $u = 1 + 3x + 4x^2 \Rightarrow \dfrac{\mathrm{d}u}{\mathrm{d}x} = 3 + 8x$

Then:

$\mathrm{d}x = \dfrac{\mathrm{d}x}{\mathrm{d}u}\,\mathrm{d}u = \dfrac{1}{(3+8x)}\,\mathrm{d}u$

For the limits $x = 0 \Rightarrow u = 1$ *and* $x = 1 \Rightarrow u = 8$.

Making the substitutions:

$y = \displaystyle\int_1^8 \dfrac{(8x+3)}{\sqrt{u}} \cdot \dfrac{1}{(8x+3)}\,\mathrm{d}u = \int_1^8 u^{-\frac{1}{2}}\,\mathrm{d}u = \left[2u^{\frac{1}{2}}\right]_1^8 = 2\sqrt{8} - 2\sqrt{1} = 3.657$

Example 4.7

Find the volume generated when the area between the curve

$y = \sqrt{\dfrac{x-1}{x^2 - 2x - 1}}$, *the x-axis and y-axis is rotated completely about the*

x-axis.

Solution

The figure shows a graph of $y = \sqrt{\dfrac{x-1}{x^2 - 2x - 1}}$, *the area to be rotated*

and the volume of the region.

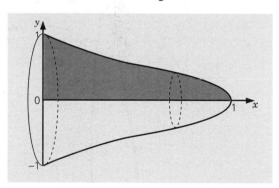

The volume of the region is $V = \displaystyle\int_0^1 \pi y^2 \,\mathrm{d}x$ *(from earlier work on integration).*

Substituting for $y \Rightarrow V = \displaystyle\int_0^1 \dfrac{\pi(x-1)}{(x^2 - 2x - 1)}\,\mathrm{d}x$

Let $u = x^2 - 2x - 1$ *then* $\mathrm{d}x = \dfrac{1}{2(x-1)}\,\mathrm{d}u$ *and the new limits are*

$u = -1$ *and* $u = -2$. *Making the subtitutions:*

$V = \displaystyle\int_{-1}^{-2} \pi \dfrac{(x-1)}{u} \cdot \dfrac{1}{2(x-1)}\,\mathrm{d}u = \dfrac{\pi}{2}\int_{-1}^{-2}\dfrac{1}{u}\,\mathrm{d}u = \dfrac{\pi}{2}\left|\ln|-2| - \ln|-1|\right| = \dfrac{\pi}{2}\ln 2 = 1.089$

EXERCISES

4.2 CLASSWORK

1 By using the given substitution evaluate the integrals.

a) $\int \dfrac{3}{1+2x}\,dx \quad u=1+2x$
b) $\int \dfrac{6}{2+3x}\,dx \quad u=2+3x$

c) $\int_1^3 \dfrac{3x}{2+x^2}\,dx \quad u=2+x^2$
d) $\int \dfrac{3x^2-2}{1-2x+x^3}\,dx \quad u=1-2x+x^3$

e) $\int_0^1 \dfrac{x^2}{\sqrt{x^3+5}}\,dx \quad u=x^3+5$
f) $\int \dfrac{e^{-2x}}{1-e^{-2x}}\,dx \quad u=1-e^{-2x}$

2 Evaluate the following integrals choosing an appropriate substitution.

a) $\int \dfrac{1}{2-3x}\,dx$
b) $\int_0^2 \dfrac{2}{2t+1}\,dt$
c) $\int \dfrac{x+1}{\sqrt{x^2+2x+2}}\,dx$

d) $\int \dfrac{1}{x\ln x}\,dx$
e) $\int \dfrac{e^x-e^{-x}}{e^x+e^{-x}}\,dx$
f) $\int \dfrac{x^2+2x}{x^3+3x^2+1}\,dx$

g) $\int_1^2 \dfrac{2t^3-t}{t^4-t^2+1}$
h) $\int \dfrac{e^x(1+x)}{xe^x-1}\,dx$

3 Find the total area enclosed by the curve $y=\dfrac{10}{2x+5}$, the y-axis and the line $x=2$.

4 Find the total area enclosed by the curve $y=\dfrac{2x^2}{x^3+1}-1$ and the x-axis.

(The curve cuts the x-axis at $x=\dfrac{(1-\sqrt5)}{2}$, $x=1$ and $x=\dfrac{(1+\sqrt5)}{2}$)

5 The distance, s, in metres, moved by a stone of mass 1 kg dropped, from rest, down a well satisfies the equation:

$$s=\int_0^u \dfrac{v\,dv}{10-0.4v^2}$$

where u is the speed when the stone has dropped through s metres.

a) By evaluating the integral find a formula for s as a function of u.
b) Find the distance travelled by the stone when its speed is 4 m s^{-1}.
c) Find a formula for u in terms of s.
d) Find the value of u when s becomes very large.

6 The temperature, T, of an object changes so that $\dfrac{dT}{dt}=-0.5(T-40)$. Initially the temperature of the object is 80°C.
From this information we can deduce that the time (in minutes) for the body to cool from 80°C to X°C is $t=\int_{80}^{X} \dfrac{-2}{T-40}\,dT$.

a) Evaluate the integral to find t as a function of X.
b) How long does it take for the temperature to fall below 60°C?
c) Find a formula for X in terms of t.
d) Find the value of X when t becomes very large. What does this mean physically?

EXERCISES

4.2 HOMEWORK

1 By using the given substitution evaluate these integrals.

a) $\displaystyle\int \frac{5}{1+4x}\,dx \qquad u = 1+4x$ **b)** $\displaystyle\int \frac{3}{0.5-2x}\,dx \qquad u = 0.5-2x$

c) $\displaystyle\int_0^1 \frac{x}{3+2x^2}\,dx \qquad u = 3+2x^2$ **d)** $\displaystyle\int_{-1}^2 \frac{2x-3}{x^2-3x+5}\,dx \quad u = x^2-3x+5$

e) $\displaystyle\int \frac{4t^3-3}{\sqrt{t^4-3t}}\,dt \quad u = t^4-3t$ **f)** $\displaystyle\int \frac{5e^{3x}}{2+e^{3x}}\,dx \qquad u = 2+e^{3x}$

2 Evaluate the following integrals choosing an appropriate substitution.

a) $\displaystyle\int \frac{1}{2+7x}\,dx$ **b)** $\displaystyle\int_0^1 \frac{t}{4-t^2}\,dt$ **c)** $\displaystyle\int \frac{v+0.5}{\sqrt{v^2+v-1}}\,dv$

d) $\displaystyle\int_0^2 \frac{t+1}{\sqrt{t^2+2t+1}}\,dt$ **e)** $\displaystyle\int \frac{x^2-x+1}{2x^3-3x^2+6x+1}\,dx$ **f)** $\displaystyle\int_2^5 \frac{t}{(t^2-3)^{\frac{3}{2}}}\,dt$

g) $\displaystyle\int \frac{2e^{2x}-1}{e^{2x}-x}\,dx$ **h)** $\displaystyle\int_1^5 \frac{e^x}{(1-e^x)^2}\,dx$

3 Find the volume generated when the area between the curve
$y = \dfrac{\sqrt{x}}{(1+3x^2)}$, the x-axis and the line $x = 1$ is rotated completely about
the x-axis.

4 Find the total area enclosed by the curve $y = \dfrac{5}{1+2x}$, the y-axis and
the line $x = 1$.

5 The distance, s, in metres, moved by a body of mass 1 kg thrown
straight upwards when its speed is U m s^{-1} satisfies the equation:

$$s = \int_{10}^U -\frac{v}{10+0.2v^2}\,dv$$

where the speed of the body is 10 m s^{-1} when released at $s = 0$. (The
term $0.2v^2$ is the air resistance on the body.)
a) By evaluating the integral find a formula for s as a function of U.
b) Find the maximum height reached by the body.

6 A sky diver falls so that her speed, U m s^{-1}, and time of drop, t s, are
related by:

$$t = \int_0^U \frac{1}{10-0.3v}\,dv$$

where the sky diver jumps from a balloon which is at rest.
a) By evaluating the integral find a formula for t as a function of U.
b) Find a formula for U as a function of t.
c) Find the value of U when t becomes very large. What does this
mean for the sky diver?

INTEGRATION BY PARTS

This method of integration works for some products of functions.

Exploration 4.4

Integrate by parts

Look at the function $f(x) = (x+1)e^x$.

- Differentiate f(x) using the product rule.
- Hence deduce the value of $\int xe^x dx$.
- Is it true that $\int uv\,dx = \int u\,dx \int v\,dx$?

Interpreting the results

From this exploration, we see that the integral of a product of two functions does not equal the product of the integrals of the two functions.

To develop a rule, we start with the product rule for differentiation:

$$\frac{d(uv)}{dx} = \frac{du}{dx}v + u\frac{dv}{dx}$$

Integrating both sides with respect to x:

$$uv = \int v\frac{du}{dx}dx + \int u\frac{dv}{dx}dx$$

$$\Rightarrow \int u\frac{dv}{dx}dx = uv - \int v\frac{du}{dx}dx$$

This is the formula for **integration by parts**. It is the integral of a product of functions written as u and $\frac{dv}{dx}$. The formula tells us that one function $\frac{dv}{dx}$ is being integrated and the other function, u, is being differentiated. The following example shows how the method works.

Example 4.8

Evaluate $y = \int_0^1 xe^{4x}\,dx$.

Solution
Let $u = x \Rightarrow \frac{du}{dx} = 1$

Let $\frac{dv}{dx} = e^{4x} \Rightarrow v = \frac{1}{4}e^{4x}$

$$\int_0^1 xe^{4x}\,dx = \left[x\left(\tfrac{1}{4}e^{4x}\right)\right]_0^1 - \int_0^1 \left(\tfrac{1}{4}e^{4x}\right)\cdot 1\,dx$$

$$= \left(\tfrac{1}{4}e^4 - 0\right) - \left[\tfrac{1}{16}e^{4x}\right]_0^1 = \tfrac{1}{4}e^4 - \left(\tfrac{1}{16}e^4 - \tfrac{1}{16}\right) = \tfrac{3}{16}e^4 + \tfrac{1}{16}$$

Example 4.9

Evaluate $y = \int_0^{\frac{\pi}{4}} x\cos 2x\,dx$.

Solution
Let $u = x \Rightarrow \frac{du}{dx} = 1$

Let $\frac{dv}{dx} = \cos 2x \Rightarrow v = \frac{1}{2}\sin 2x$

$$\int_0^{\frac{\pi}{4}} x \cos 2x \, \mathrm{d}x = x\left(\tfrac{1}{2}\sin 2x\right)_0^{\frac{\pi}{4}} - \int_0^{\frac{\pi}{4}} \left(\tfrac{1}{2}\sin 2x\right) \cdot 1 \, \mathrm{d}x$$

$$= \tfrac{\pi}{4}\left(\tfrac{1}{2}\sin\tfrac{\pi}{2}\right) - 0 - \left[-\tfrac{1}{4}\cos 2x\right]_0^{\frac{\pi}{4}}$$

$$= \tfrac{\pi}{8} + \left(\tfrac{1}{4}\cos\tfrac{\pi}{2} - \tfrac{1}{4}\cos 0\right) = \tfrac{\pi}{8} - \tfrac{1}{4}$$

Exploration 4.5

Choosing u wisely

■ What happens if, in Example 4.8, you let $u = e^{4x}$ and $\dfrac{\mathrm{d}v}{\mathrm{d}x} = x$?

■ Suggest a rule for choosing u in an integral of the form $\displaystyle\int x^n \mathrm{f}(x)\,\mathrm{d}x$ where n is a positive integer.

Interpreting the results

You will have found that using $u = e^{4x}$ with the method of integration by parts does not make the problem easier. We get:

$$\int x e^{4x}\,\mathrm{d}x = \frac{x^2}{2}e^{4x} - 2\int x^2 e^{4x}\,\mathrm{d}x$$

and this is more difficult than the original integral.

A general rule which works in cases where we can integrate $\mathrm{f}(x)$ is to let $u = x^n$. The second integral then contains nx^{n-1} i.e. the power of x reduces.

Example 4.10

Evaluate $y = \displaystyle\int e^{2x}\sin x\,\mathrm{d}x$.

Solution

Let $u = e^{2x} \;\Rightarrow\; \dfrac{\mathrm{d}u}{\mathrm{d}x} = 2e^{2x}$

Let $\dfrac{\mathrm{d}v}{\mathrm{d}x} = \sin x \;\Rightarrow\; v = -\cos x$

$$\int e^{2x}\sin x\,\mathrm{d}x = e^{2x}(-\cos x) - \int (2e^{2x})(-\cos x)\,\mathrm{d}x + c$$

$$= -e^{2x}\cos x + 2\int e^{2x}\cos x\,\mathrm{d}x + c \qquad (1)$$

where c is a constant of integration.
Now we have a second integral to evaluate using integration by parts.

It is important to continue to let $u = e^{2x}$ and $\dfrac{\mathrm{d}u}{\mathrm{d}x} = 2e^{2x}$.

Let $\dfrac{\mathrm{d}v}{\mathrm{d}x} = \cos x$ so $v = \sin x$

$$\int e^{2x}\cos x\,\mathrm{d}x = e^{2x}\sin x - \int (2e^{2x})(\sin x)\,\mathrm{d}x$$

Substituting into equation (1) gives:

$$\int e^{2x}\sin x\,\mathrm{d}x = -e^{2x}\cos x + 2\left(e^{2x}\sin x - 2\int e^{2x}\sin x\,\mathrm{d}x\right)$$

$$= -e^{2x}\cos x + 2e^{2x}\sin x - 4\int e^{2x}\sin x\,\mathrm{d}x + c$$

It appears that we are back where we started! However we can proceed by adding $4\displaystyle\int e^{2x}\sin x\,\mathrm{d}x$ *to each side. Then:*

$$5\int e^{2x}\sin x\,\mathrm{d}x = -e^{2x}\cos x + 2e^{2x}\sin x + c$$

$$\Rightarrow \int e^{2x}\sin x\,\mathrm{d}x = -\tfrac{1}{5}e^{2x}\cos x + \tfrac{2}{5}e^{2x}\sin x + A$$

where $A = \tfrac{1}{5}c$ is a constant of integration.

Example 4.11

Evaluate $y = \int x^2 e^x \, dx$.

Solution

Let $u = x^2 \Rightarrow \dfrac{du}{dx} = 2x$

Let $\dfrac{dv}{dx} = e^x \Rightarrow v = e^x$

$$\int x^2 e^x \, dx = x^2 e^x - \int 2x e^x \, dx = x^2 e^x - 2 \int x e^x \, dx + c$$

Now we have a second integral to evaluate using integration by parts.

Let $u = x \Rightarrow \dfrac{du}{dx} = 1$

Let $\dfrac{dv}{dx} = e^x \Rightarrow v = e^x$

$$\int x e^x \, dx = x e^x - \int 1 e^x \, dx = x e^x - \int e^x \, dx = x e^x - e^x$$

$$\Rightarrow \int x^2 e^x \, dx = x^2 e^x - 2\left(x e^x - e^x\right) + c = \left(x^2 - 2x + 1\right) e^x + c$$

The message in the example is to keep going and not give up.

Example 4.12

Evaluate $\int x^2 \ln x \, dx$.

Solution

Suppose that we follow our rule and let $u = x^2$ *and* $\dfrac{dv}{dx} = \ln x$.

Then $v = \int \ln x \, dx$ *is not a simple integral. The method of integration by parts will not make the integration easier.*

Instead of following the rule, in this case let $u = \ln x \Rightarrow \dfrac{du}{dx} = \dfrac{1}{x}$ *and*

let $\dfrac{dv}{dx} = x^2 \Rightarrow v = \tfrac{1}{3} x^3$.

$$\int x^2 \ln x \, dx = \tfrac{1}{3} x^3 \cdot \ln x - \int \tfrac{1}{3} x^3 \cdot \frac{1}{x} \, dx = \tfrac{1}{3} x^3 \ln x - \tfrac{1}{3} \int x^2 \, dx$$

Now the second integral is straightforward.

$$\int x^2 \, dx = \tfrac{1}{3} x^3 \Rightarrow \int x^2 \ln x \, dx = \tfrac{1}{3} x^3 \ln x - \tfrac{1}{9} x^3$$

For the integration of products of functions $\int fg \, dx$ try $u = f$ and

$\dfrac{dv}{dx} = g$ and see if the integration by parts helps. If not then try $u = g$

and $\dfrac{dv}{dx} = f$.

This method may not always be successful for integrating products of functions. With experience, it is possible to sense when this method will work. For some problems, as in the next example, the method of integration by parts may give a sequence from which we can make some progress.

Example 4.13

The integral I_n *is defined by* $I_n = \int x^n e^x \, dx$ *for positive integers.*

a) *Show that after one integration,* I_n *satisfies the sequence:*
   $$I_n = x^n e^x - n I_{n-1}$$

b) Evaluate I_0 directly.

c) Use I_0 and the sequence to evaluate $\int x^2 e^x \, dx$ and $\int x^4 e^x \, dx$.

Solution

a) Let $u = x^n \Rightarrow \dfrac{du}{dx} = nx^{n-1}$ and let $\dfrac{dv}{dx} = e^x \Rightarrow v = e^x$.

$$I_n = \int x^n e^x \, dx = x^n e^x - \int nx^{n-1} \cdot e^x \, dx = x^n e^x - n \int x^{n-1} e^x \, dx$$

$$\Rightarrow I_n = x^n e^x - nI_{n-1}$$

b) For $n = 0$, $I_0 = \int x^0 e^x \, dx = \int e^x \, dx = e^x$

c) Using the sequence in part **a)**:

$$I_1 = xe^x - I_0 = xe^x - e^x$$

$$I_2 = x^2 e^x - 2I_1 = x^2 e^x - 2\left(xe^x - e^x\right) = \left(x^2 - 2x + 2\right)e^x$$

$$I_3 = x^3 e^x - 3I_2 = x^3 e^x - 3(x^2 - 2x + 2)e^x = \left(x^3 - 3x^2 + 6x - 6\right)e^x$$

$$I_4 = x^4 e^x - 4I_3$$
$$= x^4 e^x - 4\left(x^3 - 3x^2 + 6x - 6\right)e^x = \left(x^4 - 4x^3 + 12x^2 - 24x + 24\right)e^x$$

$$\Rightarrow \int x^2 e^x \, dx = I_2 + c = \left(x^2 - 2x + 2\right)e^x + c$$

$$\Rightarrow \int x^4 e^x \, dx = I_4 + c = \left(x^4 - 4x^3 + 12x^2 - 24x + 24\right)e^x + c$$

EXERCISES

4.3 CLASSWORK

1 Use the method of integration by parts to evaluate the following integrals.

a) $\int xe^{-3x} \, dx$

b) $\int_0^1 xe^{2x} \, dx$

c) $\int x^4 \ln x \, dx$

d) $\int_1^2 x^2 e^{-3x} \, dx$

e) $\int e^x(x+3) \, dx$

f) $\int x \sin 3x \, dx$

g) $\int_0^{\frac{\pi}{2}} x^2 \cos x \, dx$

h) $\int_1^4 \ln x \, dx$

i) $\int \ln(2x+3) \, dx$

j) $\int \left(x^2 + x + 2\right)e^x \, dx$

k) $\int_1^2 x^n \ln x \, dx \quad n \neq -1$

l) $\int x(x-1)^4 \, dx$

m) $\int_0^1 3x^2(2x+1)^5 \, dx$

n) $\int e^{2x} \sin 3x \, dx$

2 Let n be any positive integer and define I_n to be the integral
$I_n = \int_1^2 (\ln x)^n \, dx$.

a) Show that $\int_1^2 \ln x \, dx = 2 \ln 2 - 1$.

b) Show that after integration, I_n satisfies the sequence
$I_n = 2(\ln 2)^n - nI_{n-1}$.

c) Use the sequence to find the value of $\int_1^2 (\ln x)^4 \, dx$.

3 The integral I_n is defined by $I_n = \int x^n e^{-x^2} \, dx$ where n is a positive even integer.

a) Show that after one integration, I_n satisfies the sequence
$$I_n = -\frac{1}{2} x^{n-1} e^{-x^2} + \frac{(n-1)}{2} I_{n-2}.$$

b) Use the sequence to express $\int x^2 e^{-x^2}\, dx$, $\int x^4 e^{-x^2}\, dx$ and $\int x^6 e^{-x^2}\, dx$ in terms of I_0.

4 The integral I_n is defined by $I_n = \int x^n \cos x\, dx$ where n is a positive integer.

a) Show that after one integration I_n satisfies the sequence
$$I_n = x^n \sin x - n\int x^{n-1} \sin x\, dx \cdot$$

b) Establish the sequence for I_n.
$$I_n = x^n \sin x + nx^{n-1} \cos x - n(n-1)I_{n-2}.$$

c) Evaluate I_0 and use the sequence to evaluate $\int x^4 \cos x\, dx$ and $\int x^6 \cos x\, dx$.

EXERCISES

4.3 HOMEWORK

1 Use the method of integration by parts to evaluate the following integrals.

a) $\displaystyle\int xe^{5x}\, dx$

b) $\displaystyle\int_0^1 xe^{-0.5x}\, dx$

c) $\displaystyle\int x^2 e^{2x}\, dx$

d) $\displaystyle\int_1^2 x^5 \ln x\, dx$

e) $\displaystyle\int_0^1 x^2(1-x)^9\, dx$

f) $\displaystyle\int (x+1)\ln(x+1)\, dx$

g) $\displaystyle\int (2x^2 - 3x + 1)e^{-x}\, dx$

h) $\displaystyle\int x \sin 4x\, dx$

i) $\displaystyle\int_0^{\frac{\pi}{4}} x^3 \cos 2x\, dx$

j) $\displaystyle\int x^3 e^{x^2}\, dx$

k) $\displaystyle\int_{-1}^2 (x+1)^2 e^{-3x}\, dx$

l) $\displaystyle\int_1^3 (x^2 - x)(3-x)^7\, dx$

m) $\displaystyle\int \frac{x}{\sqrt{1+x}}\, dx$

n) $\displaystyle\int e^{-x} \sin 2x\, dx$

2 The integral I_n is defined by $I_n = \displaystyle\int x^n \ln x\, dx$.

a) Evaluate the integral for I_n when $n \neq -1$.

b) Show that when $n = -1$, $I_{-1} = \frac{1}{2}(\ln x)^2$.

3 The integral I_n is defined by $I_n = \displaystyle\int_0^1 (1-x^2)^{n+\frac{1}{2}}\, dx$ where n is a non-negative integer.

a) Show that after one integration I_n satisfies the sequence
$$I_n = \frac{(2n+1)}{2(n+1)} I_{n-1}.$$

b) Given that $I_0 = \frac{\pi}{4}$ use the sequence to find $\displaystyle\int_0^1 (1-x^2)^{\frac{5}{2}}\, dx$.

4 Establish a sequence for the integral:
$$I_n = \int x^n \sin x\, dx$$
where n is a positive integer.

Evaluate I_1 and use your sequence to evaluate $\displaystyle\int x^5 \sin x\, dx$.

INTEGRATION BY PARTIAL FRACTIONS

Exploration 4.6

Integrate using partial fractions

Use the function:

$$f(x) = \frac{2}{(x-1)(x-3)}.$$

■ Write $f(x)$ as partial fractions.

■ By integrating each term evaluate:

$$\int \frac{2}{(x-1)(x-3)} \, dx \; .$$

Interpreting the results

Using partial fractions gives a useful technique for evaluating some integrals involving fractions of polynomials. In the exploration the partial fractions for $f(x)$ are:

$$f(x) = \frac{1}{x-3} - \frac{1}{x-1}$$

Now each term can be integrated to give:

$$\int \frac{2}{(x-1)(x-3)} \, dx = \int \left(\frac{1}{x-3} - \frac{1}{x-1} \right) dx = \ln|x-3| - \ln|x-1| + c = \ln\left|\frac{x-3}{x-1}\right| + c$$

It is convenient in these problems to write the constant of integration as $\ln A$. The solution can then be written as $\ln A\left|\dfrac{x-3}{x-1}\right|$.

Before using partial fractions, look very carefully at the fraction to be integrated. Substitution might be a quicker method of approach.

Example 4.14

Evaluate the integral $\displaystyle\int \frac{x-2}{x^2 - 4x + 3} \, dx$

a) *using a substitution,*
b) *using partial fractions.*

Solution

a) With a fraction of polynomials it is always worth investigating if it is in the form $\dfrac{f'(x)}{f(x)}$.

Let $u = x^2 - 4x + 3$ so $\dfrac{du}{dx} = 2x - 4 = 2(x - 2)$

and $dx = \dfrac{dx}{du} \, du = \dfrac{1}{2(x-2)} \, du$

Substituting for $x^2 - 4x + 3 = u$ and for dx:

$$\int \frac{x-2}{x^2 - 4x + 3} \, dx = \int \frac{(x-2)}{u} \cdot \frac{1}{2(x-2)} \, du = \frac{1}{2} \int \frac{1}{u} \, du = \frac{1}{2}\ln|u| + c$$

Replacing u by $x^2 - 4x + 3$:

$$\int \frac{x-2}{x^2 - 4x + 3} \, dx = \frac{1}{2}\ln\left|x^2 - 4x + 3\right| + c$$

b) Using partial fractions, factorise $x^2 - 4x + 3$ to give $(x-3)(x-1)$.
   Now write the function as partial fractions.

$$\frac{x-2}{x^2 - 4x + 3} = \frac{x-2}{(x-3)(x-1)} = \frac{\frac{1}{2}}{x-3} + \frac{\frac{1}{2}}{x-1}$$

Integrating each side:

$$\int \frac{x-2}{x^2-4x+3}\,dx = \int \frac{\frac{1}{2}}{x-3}+\frac{\frac{1}{2}}{x-1}\,dx = \tfrac{1}{2}\ln|x-3|+\tfrac{1}{2}\ln|x-1|+c$$

$$= \tfrac{1}{2}\ln|x-3||x-1|+c = \tfrac{1}{2}\ln\left|x^2-4x+3\right|+c$$

The answers are exactly of the same form, however the substitution method is often more straightforward.

Example 4.15

Evaluate $\displaystyle\int_2^5 \frac{x^2-2}{x^2-1}\,dx$.

Solution

This improper fraction must be divided out into the form $A+\dfrac{B}{x^2-1}$.

$$\frac{x^2-2}{x^2-1}=\frac{(x^2-1)-1}{(x^2-1)}=1-\frac{1}{x^2-1}=1-\left(\frac{\frac{1}{2}}{(x-1)}-\frac{\frac{1}{2}}{x+1}\right)$$

Then:

$$\int_2^5 \frac{x^2-2}{x^2-1}\,dx = \int_2^5\left(1-\frac{\frac{1}{2}}{(x-1)}+\frac{\frac{1}{2}}{(x+1)}\right)dx = \left[x-\tfrac{1}{2}\ln|x-1|+\tfrac{1}{2}\ln|x+1|\right]_2^5$$

$$=\left(5-\tfrac{1}{2}\ln4+\tfrac{1}{2}\ln6\right)-\left(2-\tfrac{1}{2}\ln1+\tfrac{1}{2}\ln3\right)\quad -3-\tfrac{1}{2}\ln2=2.6534$$

Example 4.16

When modelling the growth of a bacterial colony in a laboratory experiment using the logistic equation, it is found that the area of a shallow dish occupied by the bacteria and the time are related by:

$$t = \int_1^A \frac{16}{x(12-x)}\,dx$$

where the area of the dish occupied by the bacteria is A cm² and the time is t days.

At the start of the experiment the area of culture is 1 cm².

a) Evaluate the integral to form t as a function of A.
b) After how many days will the area of culture be 8 cm²?
c) Rearrange the formula in part a) to give a formula for A in terms of t. Sketch a graph of A against t.
d) According to the model, what is the maximum area of shallow dish occupied by the bacteria?

Solution

a) Using partial fractions $\dfrac{16}{x(12-x)}=\dfrac{4}{3}\left(\dfrac{1}{x}+\dfrac{1}{12-x}\right)$

$$\text{Then }t = \int_1^A \frac{16}{x(12-x)}\,dx = \int_1^A \frac{4}{3}\left(\frac{1}{x}+\frac{1}{12-x}\right)dx$$

$$=\left[\frac{4}{3}\left(\ln|x|-\ln|12-x|\right)\right]_1^A$$

$$=\frac{4}{3}\left(\ln\frac{11A}{12-A}\right)$$

b) For A = 8, $t=\dfrac{4}{3}\ln\dfrac{88}{4}=\dfrac{4}{3}\ln22=4.12$.

The area of culture is 8 cm² after 4.12 days.

c) $t = \dfrac{4}{3}\ln\dfrac{11A}{12-A} \Rightarrow \ln\dfrac{11A}{12-A} = 0.75t$

Taking exponentials of each side: $\dfrac{11A}{12-A} = e^{0.75t}$

Rearranging for A gives:

$A = \dfrac{12e^{0.75t}}{11+e^{0.75t}}$

A graph of A against t shows the logistic model that is common in population modelling.

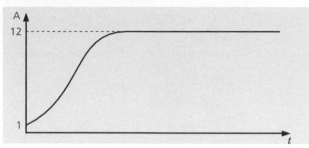

d)   *As t increases the graph shows that the area occupied by the bacteria tends to a maximum value 12 cm². This can be confirmed algebraically in the following way.*

$$t \to \infty \Rightarrow A \to \dfrac{12e^{0.75t}}{e^{0.75t}} = 12$$

EXERCISES

4.4 CLASSWORK

1   In each problem express the given function in partial fractions and hence evaluate the integral.

a) $\displaystyle\int \dfrac{1}{x(2+x)}\,dx$ b) $\displaystyle\int_0^1 \dfrac{1}{(x+1)(x+2)}\,dx$ c) $\displaystyle\int \dfrac{2}{(2-x)(2+x)}\,dx$

d) $\displaystyle\int \dfrac{x}{(x-1)(x+1)}\,dx$ e) $\displaystyle\int_1^2 \dfrac{x}{(x+1)(x+2)}\,dx$ f) $\displaystyle\int_1^2 \dfrac{1}{t^2(1+t)}\,dt$

g) $\displaystyle\int \dfrac{5}{x^2+x-6}\,dx$ h) $\displaystyle\int \dfrac{3}{x^2-1}\,dx$ i) $\displaystyle\int \dfrac{x+2}{(x-2)(x+3)}\,dx$

j) $\displaystyle\int_2^4 \dfrac{1}{x(x-1)(x+1)}\,dx$ k) $\displaystyle\int \dfrac{x^2-4}{x(x-1)}\,dx$ l) $\displaystyle\int \dfrac{x^3+2}{x(x+1)}\,dx$

2   Find the total area enclosed by the curve $y = \dfrac{x^2+7x+8}{x^2+3x+2}\,dx$, the y-axis, the x-axis and the line $x = 4$.

3   Find the total area enclosed by the curve $y = \dfrac{x}{4-x^2}$, the x-axis and the lines $x = -1$ and $x = 1$.

4   Find the volume generated when the area between the curve

$y = \dfrac{1}{\sqrt{x(5-x)}}$, the x-axis and the lines $x = 1$ and $x = 4$ is rotated

completely about the x-axis.

5   In modelling the growth of a sunflower plant it is found that the height of a sunflower plant, H m, is related to the time, t days, by

$t = \displaystyle\int_{0.2}^H \dfrac{25}{h(2.5-h)}\,dh$.

At the start of the experiment the height of the plant is 0.2 m.
a) Evaluate the integral to find t as a function of H.
b) After how many days is the sunflower plant i) 1 metre high,
ii) 2 metres high?
c) Rearrange the formula in part a) to give a formula for H in terms of
t. Sketch a graph of H against t.
d) According to the model, what is the maximum height of the
sunflower plant?

6   In a reaction between ethylene bromide and potassium iodide in 99%
methanol, $C_2H_4Br_2 + 2KI \rightarrow C_2H_4 + 2KBr + I_2$ it is found that the
concentration of iodine I_2, x mol dm^{-3} is related to the time, t minutes,
after the reaction began by:

$$kt = \int_0^x \frac{dc}{(a-c)(a-3c)}$$

where $k = 0.3$ dm^3 mol^{-1} min^{-1} is the reaction rate constant and a is the
initial concentration of the chemicals.
a) Evaluate the integral to form t as a function of x.
b) Rearrange the formula in a) to give a formula for x in terms of t.
c) Find the value of x when t becomes very large.

7   The slope of the tangent to a curve at any point is given by:
$$\frac{dy}{dx} = \frac{1}{x^2 + 4x + 3}$$
The curve passes through the point (0, 0). Find the equation of the
curve.

EXERCISES

4.4 HOMEWORK

1   In each problem express the given function in partial fractions and
hence evaluate the integral.

a) $\int \frac{1}{x(x+1)}\, dx$ b) $\int_3^5 \frac{1}{(x-1)(x-2)}\, dx$ c) $\int \frac{3}{(x+2)(x-3)}\, dx$

d) $\int \frac{x}{(x-1)(x-2)}\, dx$ e) $\int \frac{x+1}{(x-1)(x+2)}\, dx$ f) $\int \frac{2x+3}{(x-1)(x+1)}\, dx$

g) $\int \frac{1}{t^2-25}\, dt$ h) $\int_0^4 \frac{v}{25-v^2}\, dv$ i) $\int \frac{1}{(x-1)(x+1)(x+2)}\, dx$

j) $\int \frac{8-x}{x^3-4x}\, dx$ k) $\int_2^3 \frac{t^2-t+1}{t(t^2-1)}\, dt$ l) $\int_0^1 \frac{x}{(1+x)^2}\, dx$

2   Find the total area enclosed by the curve $y = \frac{5x}{x+4}$, the x-axis and the
line $x = 4$.

3   Find the total area enclosed by the curve $y = \frac{7(2-x)}{(x+2)^2}$, the y-axis, the
x-axis and the line $x = 4$.

4   Find the volume generated when the area between the curve
$y = \frac{1}{\sqrt{(x+1)(x+4)}}$, the y-axis and the line $x = 2$ is rotated completely
about the x-axis.

5   In a certain autocatalytic reaction, the reaction time t is related to the amount of product x, by the formula:

$$kt = \int_{\frac{1}{2}M}^{x} \frac{dc}{c(M-c)}$$

where k and M are constants, and initially $x = \frac{1}{2}M$ when $t = 0$.
a) Evaluate the integral.
b) Rearrange the equation connecting t and x from part a) giving x in terms of t.
c) Find the value of x when t becomes very large.

6   The speed, U m s^{-1}, of a body moving in a fluid at time t seconds satisfies the equation:

$$t = \int_{10}^{U} \frac{-2dv}{v(1+0.2v)}$$

where initially the speed of the body is 10 m s^{-1}.
a) Evaluate the integral.
b) Find the time taken for the body to reach a speed of 5 m s^{-1}.
c) Rearrange the formula in part a) to obtain a formula for U in terms of t.
d) Find the value of U when t becomes very large.

7   The speed of a parachutist U m s^{-1} at time t seconds satisfies the equation:

$$t = \int_{0}^{U} \frac{dv}{10 - 0.2v^2}.$$

a) Evaluate the integral giving t as a function of U.
b) Rearrange the formula in part a) to obtain a formula for U in terms of t.
    Sketch the graph of U against t.
c) Find the values of U when t becomes very large. Explain what this means for the parachutist.

SUMMARY OF INTEGRATION TECHNIQUES

We now have several methods of integration. When we have to evaluate an integral it is important to run through the various methods to see if one will work. The flowchart on page 91 gives a systematic way to approach the evaluation of an integral. There are other methods but we do not need to cover them at this level.

CONSOLIDATION EXERCISES FOR CHAPTER 4

1   Use the flowchart on page 91 to classify each of the following integrals. Hence evaluate the integral using the appropriate method.

a) $\displaystyle\int_{2}^{3} \frac{x+2}{(x+5)(x-1)} \, dx$ b) $\displaystyle\int xe^{-2x} \, dx$ c) $\displaystyle\int xe^{-3x^2} \, dx$

d) $\displaystyle\int_{0}^{1} \frac{3x^2+1}{x^3+x+4} \, dx$ e) $\displaystyle\int_{0}^{3} \frac{1}{\sqrt{1+t}} \, dt$ f) $\displaystyle\int t\sqrt{7+t^2} \, dt$

g) $\displaystyle\int x^2 \ln x \, dx$ h) $\displaystyle\int_{2}^{5} t\sqrt{2t^2-5} \, dt$ i) $\displaystyle\int \frac{1}{3x+5} \, dx$

j) $\displaystyle\int \frac{t^2}{(t^3+9)^5} \, dt$ k) $\displaystyle\int x^2 \sin 4x \, dx$ l) $\displaystyle\int e^{-2x} \cos 3x \, dx$

2   In a physics experiment it is found that the temperature, $T°$C, at time t seconds is given by:

$$T = 90 - \int \frac{80}{(2t+1)^2}\ \mathrm{d}t.$$

a) Find a formula for the temperature as a function of time.
b) Find the value of T when t becomes very large.

3   The length of a curve $y = \mathrm{f}(x)$ between the points on the curve

$(a,\ \mathrm{f}(a))$ and $(b,\ \mathrm{f}(b))$ is given by:

$$s = \int_a^b \sqrt{1 + \mathrm{f}'(x)^2}\ \mathrm{d}x$$

Find the length of the curve $y = 3x^{\frac{3}{2}}$ between the points on the curve $(0, 0)$ and $(1, 3)$.

4   Find the volume generated when the area between the curve

$y = \dfrac{5}{\sqrt{(x+1)(x+2)}}$, the y-axis and the line $x = 2$ is rotated

completely about the x-axis.

5   The concentration, x, of one of the products in an nth order chemical reaction is related to the reaction time t by the formula:

$$kt = \int_0^x \frac{\mathrm{d}c}{(a-c)^n}$$

where a and k are constants. Evaluate this integral in the two cases:
a) $n = 1$ and   b) $n \neq 1$.
If T denotes the value of t when $x = \frac{1}{2}a$ find the value of T in each case.

6   In a particular third-order chemical reaction the reaction time t is related to the amount of product, x, by the formula:

$$kt = \int_0^x \frac{\mathrm{d}c}{(2-c)(3-c)(1-c)}$$

where k is called the velocity constant.

a) Evaluate the integral.
b) Rearrange the equation connecting x and t from part a) to form a quadratic equation in x. Hence write x as a function of t.

7   The speed, U m s^{-1}, of a body moving in a fluid at time t seconds satisfies the equation:

$$t = \int_{100}^U \frac{-\mathrm{d}v}{v(1+0.1v)} \quad \text{where the speed of the body at time } t = 0 \text{ is } 100 \text{ m s}^{-1}.$$

a) By evaluating the integral find a formula that gives t as a function of U.
b) Find the time taken for the body to reach 50 m s^{-1}.
c) Find a formula for U in terms of t.
d) Find the value of U when t becomes very large.

8 $\mathrm{f}(x) \equiv \dfrac{x^2 + 6x + 7}{(x+2)(x+3)},\ x \in \Re.$

Given that $\mathrm{f}(x) \equiv A + \dfrac{B}{x+2} + \dfrac{C}{x+3}$

a) find the values of the constants A, B and C,

b) show that $\int_0^2 \mathrm{f}(x)\ \mathrm{d}x = 2 + \ln\dfrac{25}{18}.$

(ULEAC Question 7, Specimen Paper 2, 1994)

9 A sketch of the curve with equation $y = \dfrac{1+2x}{(1-x)^2}$ is shown below.

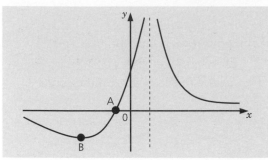

a) Write down the coordinates of A, and state the equation of the asymptote, shown as a broken line.

b) Find the equation of the tangent to the curve with equation:

$$y = \frac{1+2x}{(1-x)^2} \text{ at point } (0, 1).$$

Hence determine the coordinates of the other point at which this tangent intersects the curve.

(Oxford Question 6, Specimen Paper 2, 1994)

10 a) Express $f(x) = \dfrac{x^2+7x+2}{(1+x^2)(2-x)}$ in terms of partial fractions.

b) Hence prove that $\displaystyle\int_0^1 f(x)\,dx = \frac{11}{2}\ln 2 - \frac{\pi}{4}$.

(Oxford Question 6, Specimen Paper 5, 1994)

11 a) Differentiate $(1 + x^3)^{\frac{1}{2}}$ with respect to x.

b) Use the result from a), or an appropriate substitution, to find the value of:

$$\int_0^2 \frac{x^2}{\sqrt{(1+x^3)}}\,dx.$$

(AEB Question 8, Specimen Paper 1, 1994)

12 The diagram shows a sketch of the curve defined for $x > 0$ by the equation $y = x^2 \ln x$.

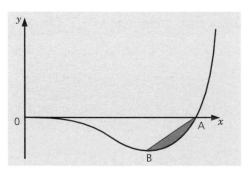

The curve crosses the x-axis at A and has a local minimum at B.

a) State the coordinates of A and calculate the gradient of the curve at A.

b) Calculate the coordinates of B in terms of e and determine the value of $\dfrac{d^2y}{dx^2}$ at B.

c) The region bounded by the line segment at AB and an arc of the curve is R, as shaded in the diagram.

Show that the area of R is $\left(\dfrac{4 - e^{-\frac{3}{2}} - 9e^{-1}}{36} \right)$.

(AEB Question 13, Specimen Paper 1, 1994)

13 A particle P moves along a straight line which passes through a point O. At time t seconds the velocity of P is v m s^{-1}, its displacement from O is s metres and its acceleration is:

$$-\frac{1}{(1+t)^2} \text{ m s}^{-2}.$$

Initially P is at rest and its displacement from O is 1 metre. Find v in terms of t. Hence show that:

$s = \ln(1+t) - t + 1$

Show that when P reaches O, t lies between 2 and 2.2.

Obtain this value of t to four significant figures by using the iteration $t_{n+1} = \ln(t_n + 1) + 1$ six times, starting with $t_0 = 2.1$ and listing the result of each iteration obtained on your calculator.

(NEAB Question 8, Specimen Paper 1, 1994)

14 Using the substitution $2x = \sin\theta$, or otherwise, find the exact value of

$$\int_0^{\frac{1}{4}} \frac{1}{\sqrt{\left(1-4x^2\right)}}\, dx.$$

(NEAB Question 2, Specimen Paper 2, 1994)

15 Express $\dfrac{18}{x^2(x+3)}$ in the form $\dfrac{A}{x} + \dfrac{B}{x^2} + \dfrac{C}{(x+3)}$, and state the values of the constants A, B and C.

Hence show that $\displaystyle\int_1^3 \frac{18}{x^2(x+3)}\, dx = 4 - 2\ln 2$

(AQA MBP4 Question 6, Specimen Paper 2000)

16 $f(x) = \dfrac{x+4}{(x+1)^2(x+2)}$

a) Express $f(x)$ in the form $\dfrac{A}{(x+1)^2} + \dfrac{B}{(x+1)} + \dfrac{C}{(x+2)}$ where the constants A, B and C are to be found.

b) Evaluate $f'(1)$ giving your answer as an exact rational number.

The finite region R is bounded by the curve with equation $y = f(x)$, the coordinate axes and the line $x = 3$.

c) Find the area of R, giving your answer in the form $p + \ln q$ where p and q are rational numbers to be found.

(EDEXCEL Question 5, Specimen Paper 3, 2000)

17 Express $\dfrac{15 - 13x + 4x^2}{(1-x)^2(4-x)}$ in partial fractions.

Hence show that $\displaystyle\int \frac{15 - 13x + 4x^2}{(1-x)^2(4-x)}\, dx = 1 + \ln 4$

(OCR Question 7, Specimen Paper 3, 2000)

18 By using the substitution $u = \sin x$, or otherwise, find $\int \sin^3 x \sin 2x\, dx$ giving your answer in terms of x.

(OCR Question 3, Specimen Paper 3, 2000)

19 a) Using the substitution $u = x^2 + 4$, or otherwise, find the indefinite integral $\displaystyle\int \frac{x}{x^2+4}\, dx.$

b) You are given that $f(x) = \dfrac{2}{(2x+1)} - \dfrac{x}{(x^2+4)}.$

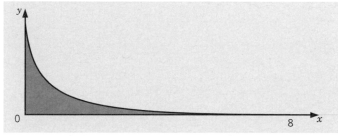

The figure shows the graph of $y = f(x)$ between $x = 0$ and $x = 8$. Show that the area of the shaded region between this graph and the axes is equal to **exactly** $\frac{1}{2}\ln 17$.

c) Find an expression for $f'(x)$. Use this to calculate the gradient of the graph at $x = 0$ and $x = 8$.

d) Write $f(x)$ as a single fraction in its simplest form.

(Oxford & Cambridge Question 6, Specimen Paper 2, 1994)

20 Use integration by parts to show that $\displaystyle\int_2^4 x \ln x \, dx = 7 \ln 4 - 3$.

(ULEAC Question 2, Paper 2, January 1995)

21 a) By using integration by parts, show that $\displaystyle\int x \ln x \, dx = \frac{x^2}{2} \ln x - \frac{x^2}{4} + C$, where C is a constant.

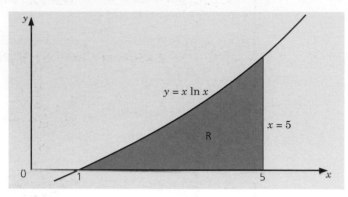

The above diagram shows the shaded region R which is bounded by the curve with equation $y = x \ln x$, the x-axis, and the line with equation $x = 5$.

b) Find the area of R.

Estimate the area of R by tabulating values of $x \ln x$ at $x = 1, 2, 3, 4$ and 5 and applying the trapezium rule, giving the result to two decimal places.

c) Find the percentage error in using the trapezium rule to estimate R.

(ULEAC Question 9, Paper 2, January 1993)

22 a) You are given that $f(x) = 2x^3 - x^2 - 7x + 6$.

   i) Show that $f(1) = 0$.

    Hence find the three factors of $f(x)$.

   ii) Solve the inequality $f(x) > 0$.

b) **i)** Given that $\dfrac{x^2 + 2x + 7}{(2x+3)(x^2+4)} \equiv \dfrac{A}{(2x+3)} + \dfrac{Bx+C}{(x^2+4)}$ find the values of the constants A, B and C.

   ii) Use your answer to **b) i)** to find $\displaystyle\int \frac{x^2 + 2x + 7}{(2x+3)(x^2+4)} \, dx$.

(MEI Question 1, Paper 3, January 1994)

Summary

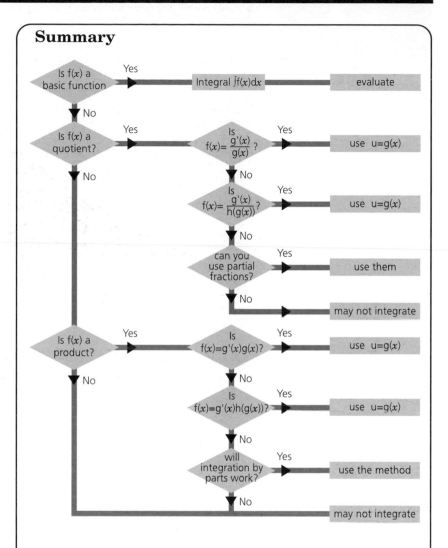

- ## Integration by substitution

    To evaluate $\int f(x)\,dx$ when f(x) is not a basic function:

    if $f(x) = g'(x)g(x)$ let $u = g(x)$

    if $f(x) = \dfrac{g'(x)}{g(x)}$ let $u = g(x)$

    if $f(x) = h\big(g(x)\big)g'(x)$ let $u = g(x)$.

- ## Integration by parts

    To integrate a product of functions try the formula for integration by parts:

    $$\int u\, \tfrac{dv}{dx}\, dx = uv - \int v\, \tfrac{du}{dx}\, dx \; \tfrac{g'(x)}{g(x)}$$

Vectors

In this chapter we:

- *introduce the idea of a vector and the algebra of vectors,*
- *explore the use of vectors in two dimensional and three-dimensional geometry.*

WHAT IS A VECTOR?

Exploration 5.1

Displacements

The map shows some English cities.

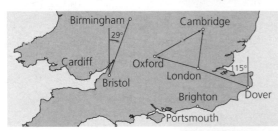

- How would you describe a straight line journey ('a crow's flight') between London and Cambridge or between Oxford and Cambridge?

To be able to describe the journeys you need to specify two quantities: a distance and a direction. The table shows these quantities for the two journeys.

	Distance (km)	Direction
London to Cambridge	82	11°
Oxford to Cambridge	107	61°

These journeys are called **displacements** and are examples of vectors. A quantity that has both *size* (or magnitude) and *direction* is called a **vector**. There are other quantities that are completely specified by their size and no direction is associated with them. These are called **scalars**. For example, temperature and mass are scalar quantities.

If you have studied mechanics then you may be familiar with the use of vectors in modelling force, velocity, acceleration and the use of scalars in modelling area, volume, mass, energy. Each vector quantity requires size and direction for a complete description. In this introduction to vectors we concentrate on geometrical applications of vectors.

Notation

In two dimensions a vector is represented on a diagram by a straight line with an arrow-head. The length of the line represents the size of the vector and the arrow specifies the direction. To describe the direction clearly we usually state the angle made by the vector with a fixed or given base line.

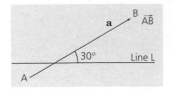

The diagram shows a displacement vector from A to B. On the diagram it is labelled as $\overrightarrow{AB}$ or **a**. In a book, a vector is usually printed in bold, for example **a** or **AB**, or with an arrow above the letters $\overrightarrow{AB}$. When you write vectors by hand it is usual to underline the symbol representing the vector, for example $\underline{a}$ or $\underline{AB}$. The magnitude or size of the vector **a** is handwritten as a (not underlined), or sometimes $|\underline{a}|$. In a book, it is written as **a**, or $|\mathbf{a}|$. Often the fixed line from which directions are specified is the *x*-axis with the anticlockwise direction taken to be positive.

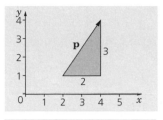

Components of a vector

An alternative way of describing a vector is in terms of **components** in specified directions, in two dimensions these are the *x*- and *y*-axes.

For example, the vector **p** in the diagram is denoted by $\begin{pmatrix} 2 \\ 3 \end{pmatrix}$; it is described as 2 units in the *x*-direction and 3 units in the *y*-direction.

Example 5.1

Show the vector $\mathbf{a} = \begin{pmatrix} 3 \\ 4 \end{pmatrix}$ *on a diagram and find the magnitude and direction of* **a**.

Solution
The vector **a** *is 3 units in the x-direction and 4 units in the y-direction.*
The magnitude of **a** *is given by the length of AB in the triangle.*

$$AB = \mathbf{a} = \sqrt{3^2 + 4^2} = 5$$
The direction is given by the angle θ.

$$\tan\theta = \frac{4}{3}$$
$$\theta = 53.13° \text{ (to 2 decimal places)}$$

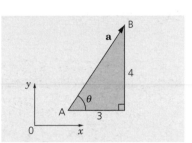

Example 5.2

The vector **b** *has magnitude 8 units and direction 75°. Write* **b** *in component form.*

Solution
The vector **b** *is shown as* $\overrightarrow{OP}$ *in the triangle OPQ.*
The components of **b** *are* OQ *and* QP.
$$OQ = 8\cos75° = 2.07$$
$$QP = 8\sin75° = 7.73$$
$$\mathbf{b} = \begin{pmatrix} 2.07 \\ 7.73 \end{pmatrix} \text{ to 2 decimal places}$$

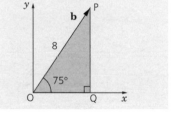

The relationship between magnitude and direction (r, θ) and component form can be written as a general rule.

$$\mathbf{a} = \begin{pmatrix} a_1 \\ a_2 \end{pmatrix} = \begin{pmatrix} r\cos\theta \\ r\sin\theta \end{pmatrix}$$

This general rule can be used for all angles θ in the range $0 \le \theta < 360°$.

Example 5.3

The vector **c** *has magnitude 10 units and direction 250°. Write* **c** *in component form.*

Solution
For vector **c**, *r = 10 and* θ = 250°.
$$\mathbf{c} = \begin{pmatrix} 10\cos250° \\ 10\sin250° \end{pmatrix} = \begin{pmatrix} -3.42 \\ -9.40 \end{pmatrix}$$
to 2 decimal places

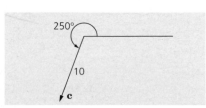

Example 5.4

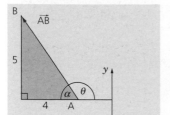

Show the vector $\overrightarrow{AB} = \begin{pmatrix} -4 \\ 5 \end{pmatrix}$ *on a diagram and find the magnitude and direction of* $\overrightarrow{AB}$.

Solution
The vector $\overrightarrow{AB}$ *has components –4 in the x-direction (or +4 in the negative x-direction) and 5 in the y-direction.*

The magnitude of $\overrightarrow{AB} = \sqrt{4^2 + 5^2} = 6.40$
The direction is the angle θ. From the triangle it is easier to find the angle 180° – θ labelled as α.

$$\tan \alpha = \frac{5}{4}$$
$$\alpha = 51.34°$$

The direction of $\overrightarrow{AB}$ *is* $\theta = 180° - 51.34° = 128.66°$

It is usually a good idea to draw a diagram showing the direction of a vector. This will help to avoid errors when interpreting the calculator answer.

EXERCISES

5.1 CLASSWORK

1 Draw a vector that represents the displacement of the triangle ABC to DEF. Describe the properties of the vector.

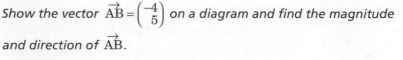

2 Use the map on page 92 to describe the displacement vectors of Birmingham from Bristol and of Dover from London.

3 The diagram shows five vectors in the x–y plane. Write each vector in component form. Find the magnitude and direction of each vector.

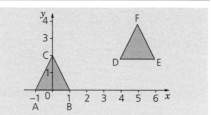

4 Show the following displacement vectors on a diagram on the x–y plane.

a) $\mathbf{r} = \begin{pmatrix} 5 \\ 0 \end{pmatrix}$ starting at the origin

b) $\mathbf{s} = \begin{pmatrix} 3 \\ -1 \end{pmatrix}$ starting at the point (1, 4)

c) $\mathbf{t} = (4, 135°)$ starting at the point (–1, 2)

d) $\mathbf{u} = (2, 180°)$ starting at the point (–1, –2)

5 Write the following vectors in component form.

a) 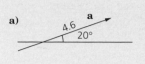   b) 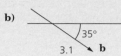   c)   d)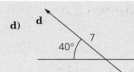

6 Write in component form the displacement vectors joining the given points.

a) (1, 0) to (3, 1) **b)** (0, 0) to (–4, 6) **c)** (–2, 1) to (–3, 2)
d) (–4, –3) to (–2, –1) **e)** (–1, –2) to (0, 0) **f)** (4, 2) to (–3, –2)
g) (7, 3) to (–1, 2) **h)** (–3, –4) to (4, 3)

EXERCISES

5.1 HOMEWORK

1 Draw a vector that represents the displacement of the rectangle ABCD to EFGH. Describe the properties of the vector.

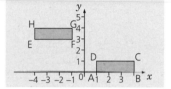

2 A, B, C and D are four points in the *x–y* plane.

a) On the diagram draw the vectors $\overrightarrow{AB}$, $\overrightarrow{BD}$, $\overrightarrow{CA}$ and $\overrightarrow{AD}$.
b) Write each vector in component form.
c) Find the magnitude and direction of each vector.

3 Show the following vectors on a diagram in the *x–y* plane.

a) $\mathbf{a} = \begin{pmatrix} 2 \\ 1 \end{pmatrix}$ starting at the point (2, 2)

b) $\mathbf{b} = \begin{pmatrix} -2 \\ -3 \end{pmatrix}$ starting at point (0, –1)

c) $\mathbf{c} = (3, 40°)$ starting at the origin

d) $\mathbf{d} = (4, 225°)$ starting at the point (3, –1)

4 Find the magnitude and direction of the following vectors.

a) $\begin{pmatrix} 2 \\ 1 \end{pmatrix}$ **b)** $\begin{pmatrix} 3 \\ -4 \end{pmatrix}$ **c)** $\begin{pmatrix} -1 \\ 1 \end{pmatrix}$

d) $\begin{pmatrix} 3 \\ -2 \end{pmatrix}$ **e)** $\begin{pmatrix} -2 \\ -4 \end{pmatrix}$ **f)** $\begin{pmatrix} 1.6 \\ 3.1 \end{pmatrix}$

5 Write the following vectors in component form.

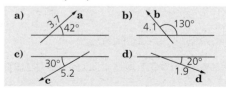

6 Find the magnitude and direction of the displacement vectors joining the given points.

a) (0, 0) to (4, 0) **b)** (1, 1) to (3, 3) **c)** (0, 1) to (–3, –1)
d) (0, –1) to (–1, 4) **e)** (4, –2) to (–4, –2) **f)** (1, –1) to (–4, –5)
g) (4, 5) to (0, 0) **h)** (2, –1) to (–3, –6)

ALGEBRA OF VECTORS

How can we add vectors? Can we multiply two vectors? These questions lead us into exploring the algebra of vectors.

Exploration 5.2

Equality of vectors

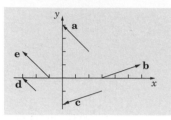

The diagram shows five vectors in the x-y plane.

■ Write each vector in component and magnitude-direction form.
■ What can you say about vectors **a** and **e**?
■ What can you say about vectors **b** and **c**?
■ What can you say about vectors **d** and **a**?

Manipulating vectors

This exploration introduces the important ideas of equal vectors, the negative of a vector and scaling vectors. The vectors **a** and **e** have the same magnitude and direction (2.83, 135°) and hence have the same components $\begin{pmatrix} -2 \\ 2 \end{pmatrix}$.

They are examples of **equal** vectors.

Two vectors are equal if:
■ **they have the same magnitude**
■ **they point in the same direction.**

Notice that this does not say anything about where the vector is situated. In this diagram, for example, all the vectors are equal.

Now consider the vectors $\mathbf{b} = \begin{pmatrix} 3 \\ 1 \end{pmatrix}$ and $\mathbf{c} = \begin{pmatrix} -3 \\ -1 \end{pmatrix}$.

There is a simple relationship between **b** and **c**: **c = –b**

We say that **–b** is the negative of the vector **b**.

The negative of a vector
■ **has the same magnitude**
■ **has the opposite direction.**

Finally consider vectors $\mathbf{a} = \begin{pmatrix} -2 \\ 2 \end{pmatrix}$ and $\mathbf{e} = \begin{pmatrix} -1 \\ 1 \end{pmatrix}$. We can see that

a = 2**e** or $\mathbf{e} = \frac{1}{2}\mathbf{a}$. The numbers 2 and $\frac{1}{2}$ are scalars. Here in each case we are multiplying a vector by scalar.

When a vector **a** is multiplied by a scalar s then the result is a vector which:

■ is s times as long as **a**
■ has the same direction as **a**.

Exploration 5.3

Unit vectors

Draw any vector and label it **a**.
What can you say about the vector $\dfrac{\mathbf{a}}{|\mathbf{a}|}$?

(Remember that $|\mathbf{a}|$ is the magnitude of **a** and is a scalar quantity.)

Interpreting the results

You should have found that the vector $\dfrac{\mathbf{a}}{|\mathbf{a}|}$ is in the same direction as **a** but has magnitude 1. Such a vector is called a **unit vector**.

Example 5.5

*The vector **a** has magnitude 4 units and direction 60°.*

*a) Describe the unit vector **e** in the direction of **a**.*
*b) Vectors **b**, **c** and **d** have magnitudes 2, 3.5 and 7 units respectively, and **b** and **c** point in the same direction as **a** whereas **d** is opposite to **a**. Write down **b**, **c** and **d** in terms of **e**.*

Solution
*a) The unit vector **e** has magnitude 1 unit and direction 60°.*
*b) Since **b** and **c** are in the same direction as **a** they are also in the same direction as **e**. So:* **b** = 2**e**   **c** = 3.5**e**
*Now **d** is in the opposite direction to **a**, and hence **e**, so we have:* **d** = −7**e**.

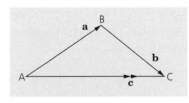

Unit vectors are used to denote directions in space. In two dimensions, there are two very important unit vectors that point along the *x*- and *y*-axes. They are labelled **i** and **j** as shown in the diagram. The unit vectors **i** and **j** are called **Cartesian unit vectors**.

As we shall see all vectors in two dimensions can be written in terms of **i** and **j**. For example, take the two vectors **a** and **b** shown in the diagram. The vector **a** has magnitude 3 units and points in the same direction as **i** so that **a** = 3**i**. The vector **b** has magnitude 1.5 units and points in the opposite direction to **j** so that **b** = −1.5**j**.

A natural question is what about vectors that are not parallel to **i** and **j**?

Adding vectors geometrically

The addition of two vectors can best be illustrated by exploring the operation of one displacement followed by another. This is shown in the diagram. The displacement $\overrightarrow{AB}$ moves from A to B and then the displacement $\overrightarrow{BC}$ moves from B to C. So the net result of $\overrightarrow{AB}$ followed by $\overrightarrow{BC}$ is the displacement $\overrightarrow{AC}$. The two displacements and their net result form a triangle.

The rule for adding two vectors in this way is called the **triangle law of addition** and we write:

$$\overrightarrow{AB} + \overrightarrow{BC} = \overrightarrow{AC} \text{ or } \mathbf{a} + \mathbf{b} = \mathbf{c}$$

The sum of two vectors (or more than two vectors) is called the **resultant** vector. Often the resultant is denoted by a double arrow.

Exploration 5.4

Adding vectors algebraically

Two vectors **a** and **b** are written in component form as

$$\mathbf{a} = \begin{pmatrix} 3 \\ 1 \end{pmatrix} \text{ and } \mathbf{b} = \begin{pmatrix} -1 \\ 2 \end{pmatrix}.$$

■ Draw a diagram to show the addition **a** + **b**.
■ What is the component form of **a** + **b**?
  Deduce a rule for adding vectors algebraically.
■ Use the addition rule for vectors to write **a** and **b** in terms of the unit vectors **i** and **j**.

Interpreting the results

From this exploration you can deduce that to add vectors $\begin{pmatrix} a_1 \\ a_2 \end{pmatrix}$ and $\begin{pmatrix} b_1 \\ b_2 \end{pmatrix}$ you add the components. $\begin{pmatrix} a_1 \\ a_2 \end{pmatrix} + \begin{pmatrix} b_1 \\ b_2 \end{pmatrix} = \begin{pmatrix} a_1 + b_1 \\ a_2 + b_2 \end{pmatrix}$

In terms of the Cartesian unit vectors **i** and **j** we can write:

$$\mathbf{a} = \begin{pmatrix} a_1 \\ a_2 \end{pmatrix} = a_1 \mathbf{i} + a_2 \mathbf{j}$$

The magnitude of **a** is $a = \sqrt{a_1^2 + a_2^2}$.

Subtracting vectors

Subtracting one vector from another vector is the same as adding the negative of the subtracted vector. For example, take the vectors $\mathbf{a} = \begin{pmatrix} 3 \\ 1 \end{pmatrix} = 3\mathbf{i} + \mathbf{j}$ and $\mathbf{b} = \begin{pmatrix} -1 \\ 2 \end{pmatrix} = -\mathbf{i} + 2\mathbf{j}$. To show the vector $\mathbf{a} - \mathbf{b}$ on a diagram we draw the vectors **a** and $-\mathbf{b}$ and then add them, using the triangle rule.

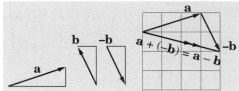

The figure shows **a**, **b**, $-\mathbf{b}$ and the subtraction $\mathbf{a} - \mathbf{b}$.

The resultant of $\mathbf{a} + (-\mathbf{b}) = \mathbf{a} - \mathbf{b} = \begin{pmatrix} 4 \\ -1 \end{pmatrix}$.

Algebraically subtracting vectors, like adding vectors, is straightforward in that we just subtract components.

$$\mathbf{a} - \mathbf{b} = \begin{pmatrix} 3 \\ 1 \end{pmatrix} - \begin{pmatrix} -1 \\ 2 \end{pmatrix} = \begin{pmatrix} 3 - (-1) \\ 1 - 2 \end{pmatrix} = \begin{pmatrix} 4 \\ -1 \end{pmatrix} \quad \text{or}$$

$$\mathbf{a} - \mathbf{b} = (3\mathbf{i} + \mathbf{j}) - (-\mathbf{i} + 2\mathbf{j}) = 4\mathbf{i} - \mathbf{j}$$

Position vectors

If we are given a vector such as $\mathbf{a} = 3\mathbf{i} - \mathbf{j}$, all this tells us is the magnitude and direction of **a**. It could be drawn anywhere. Such vectors are sometimes called **free vectors**. There is one special vector which is not free and always starts at the origin. It is called a **position vector**. Thus if $3\mathbf{i} - \mathbf{j}$ is a position vector, then it joins the origin to the point with coordinates $(3, -1)$.

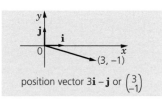

position vector $3\mathbf{i} - \mathbf{j}$ or $\begin{pmatrix} 3 \\ -1 \end{pmatrix}$

For two points A and B with position vectors **a** and **b** the vector $\mathbf{b} - \mathbf{a}$ is the displacement vector $\overrightarrow{AB}$.

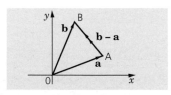

Example 5.6

Two vectors **a** *and* **b** *are expressed in Cartesian unit vector form as* $\mathbf{a} = \mathbf{i} + 3\mathbf{j}$ *and* $\mathbf{b} = -3\mathbf{i} + 2\mathbf{j}$.

a) *Show each of these vectors on a diagram starting at the origin.*
b) *Find the magnitude and direction of each vector.*
c) *On a diagram show the vectors* $\mathbf{a} + \mathbf{b}$ *and* $\mathbf{a} - \mathbf{b}$.
d) *Find* $\mathbf{a} + \mathbf{b}$, $\mathbf{a} - \mathbf{b}$, $3\mathbf{a} + 2\mathbf{b}$ *and* $-4\mathbf{a} - 3\mathbf{b}$ *in terms of* **i** *and* **j**.
e) *Write down a unit vector in the direction of* $3\mathbf{a} + 2\mathbf{b}$.

Solution

a)

b) $|\mathbf{a}| = a = \sqrt{1^2 + 3^2} = 3.16$ *and the direction is* $\tan^{-1}\left(\frac{3}{1}\right) = 71.57°$

$|\mathbf{b}| = b = \sqrt{(-3)^2 + 2^2} = 3.61$ *and the direction is*

$180° - \tan^{-1}\left(\frac{2}{3}\right) = 146.31°$

c) *The figure shows that to add* **a** *and* **b** *we move the tail of* **b** *to the head of* **a**.

d) $\mathbf{a} + \mathbf{b} = (\mathbf{i} + 3\mathbf{j}) + (-3\mathbf{i} + 2\mathbf{j}) = -2\mathbf{i} + 5\mathbf{j}$
$\mathbf{a} - \mathbf{b} = (\mathbf{i} + 3\mathbf{j}) - (-3\mathbf{i} + 2\mathbf{j}) = 4\mathbf{i} + \mathbf{j}$
$3\mathbf{a} + 2\mathbf{b} = 3(\mathbf{i} + 3\mathbf{j}) + 2(-3\mathbf{i} + 2\mathbf{j}) = -3\mathbf{i} + 13\mathbf{j}$
$-4\mathbf{a} - 3\mathbf{b} = -4(\mathbf{i} + 3\mathbf{j}) - 3(-3\mathbf{i} + 2\mathbf{j}) = 5\mathbf{i} - 18\mathbf{j}$

e) *From the result of Exploration 5.3 a unit vector in the direction of* $3\mathbf{a} + 2\mathbf{b}$ *is given by:*

$$\mathbf{e} = \frac{3\mathbf{a} + 2\mathbf{b}}{|3\mathbf{a} + 2\mathbf{b}|} = \frac{-3\mathbf{i} + 13\mathbf{j}}{\sqrt{(-3)^2 + 13^2}} = \frac{-3}{\sqrt{178}}\mathbf{i} + \frac{13}{\sqrt{178}}\mathbf{j}$$

Example 5.7

The diagram shows an irregular pentagon ABCDE in which AE and BC are parallel and AB and DC are parallel.

Let $\overrightarrow{AB} = \mathbf{p}$ *and* $\overrightarrow{BC} = \mathbf{q}$.
Write the following vectors in terms of **p** *and* **q**.

a) $\overrightarrow{DC}$　**b)** $\overrightarrow{AE}$　**c)** $\overrightarrow{EA}$

d) $\overrightarrow{EB}$　**e)** $\overrightarrow{EC}$　**f)** $\overrightarrow{BC}$

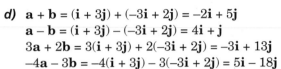

Solution

a) $\overrightarrow{DC}$ *is parallel to* $\overrightarrow{AB}$ *and half its length, and so* $\overrightarrow{DC} = \frac{1}{2}\mathbf{p} = 0.5\mathbf{p}$

b) $\overrightarrow{AE}$ *is parallel to* $\overrightarrow{BC}$ *and 0.6 of its length, hence* $\overrightarrow{AE} = 0.6\mathbf{q}$

c) $\overrightarrow{EA} = -\overrightarrow{AE} = -0.6\mathbf{q}$

d) $\overrightarrow{EB} = \overrightarrow{EA} + \overrightarrow{AB} = -0.6\mathbf{q} + \mathbf{p}$

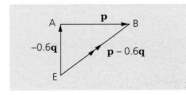

e) $\overrightarrow{EC} = \overrightarrow{EB} + \overrightarrow{BC} = (-0.6\mathbf{q} + \mathbf{p}) + \mathbf{q} = 0.4\mathbf{q} + \mathbf{p}$

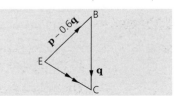

f) $\overrightarrow{ED} = \overrightarrow{EC} + \overrightarrow{CD} = (0.4\mathbf{q} + \mathbf{p}) + (-0.5\mathbf{p}) = 0.4\mathbf{q} + 0.5\mathbf{p}$

EXERCISES

5.2 CLASSWORK

1 The diagram shows eight vectors in the x–y plane. Find:

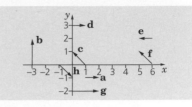

a) the vector equal to **a**
b) the vector equal to **c**
c) the relation between **e** and **a**
d) the relation between **g** and **a**.

2 ABCD is a parallelogram and $\overrightarrow{AB} = \mathbf{a}$, $\overrightarrow{BC} = \mathbf{b}$.

a) Write the following vectors in terms of **a** and **b**.

i) $\overrightarrow{CD}$ ii) $\overrightarrow{AD}$ iii) $\overrightarrow{AC}$

b) The midpoint of BC is M, find the following vectors.

i) $\overrightarrow{AM}$ ii) $\overrightarrow{MD}$

3 The vectors **a** and **b** are given by: $\mathbf{a} = \begin{pmatrix} -1 \\ 3 \end{pmatrix}$ $\mathbf{b} = \begin{pmatrix} 2 \\ -1 \end{pmatrix}$.

a) On a diagram show the vectors **a**, **b**, **a** + **b** and **a** − **b**.
b) Find a unit vector in the direction of **a** + **b** and show this vector on your diagram.

4 The diagram shows four vectors **a**, **b**, **c** and **d**. Write each vector in terms of the unit vectors **i** and **j**.

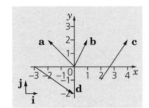

5 The vectors **a**, **b**, **c** and **d** are given by:

$$\mathbf{a} = \begin{pmatrix} 2 \\ 3 \end{pmatrix} \quad \mathbf{b} = \begin{pmatrix} -1 \\ -2 \end{pmatrix} \quad \mathbf{c} = \begin{pmatrix} 2 \\ 1 \end{pmatrix} \quad \mathbf{d} = \begin{pmatrix} 1 \\ -3 \end{pmatrix}$$

Find the following vectors in component form.
a) **a** + **b**   b) **a** + **c**   c) **b** + **d**   d) **a** + **b** + **c**
e) $2\mathbf{a} + 3\mathbf{d}$ f) **b** − **c**   g) $3\mathbf{c} - \mathbf{d}$

6 The vectors **r**, **s** and **t** are given by: $\mathbf{r} = \mathbf{i} + \mathbf{j}$, $\mathbf{s} = -\mathbf{i} + \mathbf{j}$, $\mathbf{t} = 2\mathbf{i} - 3\mathbf{j}$.
Find the following vectors in terms of **i** and **j**.
a) **r** + **s**   b) **s** + **t**   c) **r** + **s** + **t**   d) **r** − **t**
e) $2\mathbf{r} - 3\mathbf{s}$ f) $3(\mathbf{r} - \mathbf{s}) + 2(\mathbf{s} + \mathbf{t})$

7 P and Q are points in the x–y plane with coordinates (4, 1) and (−3, −2).

a) Write down the position vectors of P and Q.
b) Find the displacement of Q from P.

8 Find unit vectors in the same direction as each of the following vectors.

a) $\begin{pmatrix} 3 \\ 4 \end{pmatrix}$ b) $5\mathbf{i} + 12\mathbf{j}$ c) $4\mathbf{i} - 3\mathbf{j}$ d) $\begin{pmatrix} -3 \\ -3 \end{pmatrix}$

e) $-4\mathbf{i}$ f) $\begin{pmatrix} 0 \\ 2 \end{pmatrix}$ g) $\begin{pmatrix} r\cos\theta \\ r\sin\theta \end{pmatrix}$ h) $a\mathbf{i} + b\mathbf{j}$

9 ABC is a triangle and $\overrightarrow{AB} = \mathbf{a}$, $\overrightarrow{AC} = \mathbf{b}$. The points P and Q are the midpoints of sides AB and AC.

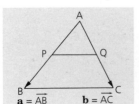

a = $\overrightarrow{AB}$ b = $\overrightarrow{AC}$

a) Find the vectors $\overrightarrow{AP}, \overrightarrow{AQ}, \overrightarrow{PQ}$ and $\overrightarrow{BC}$ in terms of **a** and **b**.
b) What can you deduce about PQ and BC?

10 The points A, B and C have position vectors **a**, **b** and $k(2\mathbf{a} + \mathbf{b})$ respectively. Find the numerical value of k if:

a) $\overrightarrow{BC}$ is parallel to **a**   b) $\overrightarrow{AC}$ is parallel to **b**
c) A, B and C lie on the same straight line (they are called collinear).

EXERCISES

5.2 HOMEWORK

1 The diagram shows six vectors in the x–y plane.

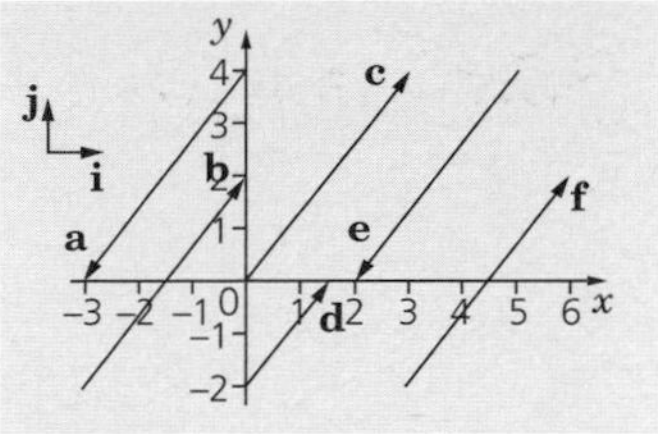

a) Which vectors are equal to the vector $3\mathbf{i} + 4\mathbf{j}$?
b) Which vector is the position vector of the point $(3, 4)$?
c) Which vectors are equal to the vector $-3\mathbf{i} - 4\mathbf{j}$?

2 ABCDEF is a regular hexagon and the sides $\overrightarrow{AB}$ and $\overrightarrow{BC}$ are represented by the vectors $\mathbf{a}$ and $\mathbf{b}$. The length of AD is twice the length BC.

a) Show that $\overrightarrow{CD} = \mathbf{b} - \mathbf{a}$.

b) Write down the vectors $\overrightarrow{DE}$, $\overrightarrow{BD}$ and $\overrightarrow{BF}$ in terms of $\mathbf{a}$ and $\mathbf{b}$.

3 A vector $\mathbf{a}$ has length 20 mm and direction 30°, and vector $\mathbf{b}$ has length 30 mm and direction 45°.
a) Draw a diagram to scale to find the magnitude and direction of the vectors $\mathbf{c} = \mathbf{a} + \mathbf{b}$ and $\mathbf{d} = \mathbf{a} - \mathbf{b}$.
b) Draw the vector $\mathbf{e} = 3\mathbf{a} + 3\mathbf{b}$ and give the magnitude and direction of $\mathbf{e}$. What is the relation between $\mathbf{e}$ and $\mathbf{c}$?

4 The vectors $\mathbf{r}$, $\mathbf{s}$, $\mathbf{t}$ and $\mathbf{u}$ are given by: $\mathbf{r} = \begin{pmatrix} 0 \\ 1 \end{pmatrix}$ $\mathbf{s} = \begin{pmatrix} -2 \\ 0 \end{pmatrix}$ $\mathbf{t} = \begin{pmatrix} -2 \\ -1 \end{pmatrix}$ $\mathbf{u} = \begin{pmatrix} 4 \\ 3 \end{pmatrix}$
Find the following vectors in component form.
a) $\mathbf{r} + \mathbf{s}$ b) $\mathbf{r} + \mathbf{t}$ c) $\mathbf{s} - \mathbf{u}$ d) $2\mathbf{r} + 3\mathbf{u}$
e) $2(\mathbf{s} - \mathbf{t}) + 3(\mathbf{u} - \mathbf{r})$ f) $2\mathbf{r} + 3\mathbf{s} - 4\mathbf{t} + \mathbf{u}$

5 The vectors $\mathbf{a}$, $\mathbf{b}$ and $\mathbf{c}$ are given by: $\mathbf{a} = -2\mathbf{i} + \mathbf{j}$ $\mathbf{b} = \mathbf{i} + 2\mathbf{j}$ $\mathbf{c} = 3\mathbf{i} - \mathbf{j}$
Find the following vectors in terms of $\mathbf{i}$ and $\mathbf{j}$.
a) $\mathbf{a} + \mathbf{b}$ b) $\mathbf{a} + \mathbf{c}$ c) $\mathbf{b} - \mathbf{c}$
d) $2\mathbf{b} - 3\mathbf{a}$ e) $\mathbf{a} + \mathbf{b} - \mathbf{c}$ f) $2\mathbf{a} - \mathbf{b} + 4\mathbf{c}$

6 Find unit vectors in the same direction as each of the following vectors.
a) $\begin{pmatrix} 4 \\ 3 \end{pmatrix}$ b) $\begin{pmatrix} -7 \\ 0 \end{pmatrix}$ c) $\mathbf{i} + \mathbf{j}$ d) $12\mathbf{i} - 5\mathbf{j}$
e) $\begin{pmatrix} -2 \\ 2 \end{pmatrix}$ f) $\begin{pmatrix} 0 \\ 3 \end{pmatrix}$ g) $-2\mathbf{i} - 3\mathbf{j}$ h) $\begin{pmatrix} r \\ s \end{pmatrix}$

7 A, B, C and D are points in the x–y plane with coordinates $(-2, -3)$, $(-1, 4)$, $(4, 3)$, $(3, -4)$.

a) Write down the position vectors of A, B, C and D.

b) Find the displacements $\overrightarrow{AB}$, $\overrightarrow{BC}$, $\overrightarrow{DC}$ and $\overrightarrow{AD}$.
c) What can you deduce about the quadrilateral ABCD?

8 The vectors $\mathbf{a}$, $\mathbf{b}$ and $\mathbf{c}$ are given by: $\mathbf{a} = \begin{pmatrix} 2 \\ 1 \end{pmatrix}$ $\mathbf{b} = \begin{pmatrix} 4 \\ -2 \end{pmatrix}$ $\mathbf{c} = \begin{pmatrix} 1 \\ -1 \end{pmatrix}$

The point P is the end of the displacement vector $-2\mathbf{a} + \mathbf{b} - 3\mathbf{c}$ and $(-1, 0)$ is its starting point. What is the position vector of P?

9 OABC is a quadrilateral and $\overrightarrow{OA} = \mathbf{a}$, $\overrightarrow{OB} = \mathbf{b}$ and $\overrightarrow{OC} = \mathbf{c}$. D is the midpoint of BC, and G is the point on AD such that AG : GD = 2 : 1.

Write the vectors $\overrightarrow{OD}$ and $\overrightarrow{OG}$ in terms of $\mathbf{a}$, $\mathbf{b}$ and $\mathbf{c}$.

10 ABCDE is a pentagon. Use the triangle law of vector addition to show that: $\overrightarrow{AB} + \overrightarrow{BC} + \overrightarrow{CD} + \overrightarrow{DA} + \overrightarrow{AE} = 0$

PRODUCTS OF VECTORS

Having defined the addition (and subtraction) of two vectors and scaling of a vector it is natural to ask if we can multiply two vectors. Certainly we cannot ever divide one vector by another.

There are two ways of multiplying two vectors. One leads to a scalar quantity and the other leads to a vector quantity. Just as the laws of addition and scaling of vectors are defined because of their application to physical quantities such as displacement, the products are defined in such a way as to have geometrical and physical relevance. In this chapter we investigate scalar products.

The scalar product

Given two vectors **a** and **b** and an angle θ between their directions, then the **scalar product** of **a** and **b** is defined as:

$$\mathbf{a} \cdot \mathbf{b} = |\mathbf{a}||\mathbf{b}|\cos\theta = ab\cos\theta$$

The notation used in this definition is very important; the dot between **a** and **b** must be clearly shown. (A cross, $\times$, is used for another type of product of vectors.)

The product is pronounced 'a dot b' and is often called the **dot product** to remind us of the symbol used in its notation.

The outcome of the scalar product is a **scalar quantity**.

Perpendicular vectors

If the angle between two vectors is 90° they are **perpendicular vectors**. Now since $\cos 90° = 0$ it follows that $\mathbf{a} \cdot \mathbf{b} = |\mathbf{a}||\mathbf{b}|\cos 90° = 0$. So we have a simple test for perpendicular vectors.

If **a** and **b** are perpendicular vectors $\mathbf{a} \cdot \mathbf{b} = 0$ and conversely, if the scalar product of two non-zero vectors is zero, then the vectors are perpendicular.

Example 5.8

*Three vectors **a**, **b** and **c** are shown in the diagram.*

Find the values of $\mathbf{a} \cdot \mathbf{b}$, $\mathbf{b} \cdot \mathbf{c}$, $\mathbf{a} \cdot \mathbf{c}$ and $\mathbf{a} \cdot \mathbf{a}$.

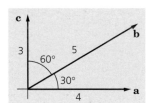

Solution
From the figure $|\mathbf{a}| = 4$, $|\mathbf{b}| = 5$, $|\mathbf{c}| = 3$.
Using the definition:

$$\mathbf{a} \cdot \mathbf{b} = |\mathbf{a}||\mathbf{b}|\cos 30° = 20\cos 30° = 10\sqrt{3} = 17.32$$

$$\mathbf{b} \cdot \mathbf{c} = |\mathbf{b}||\mathbf{c}|\cos 60° = 15\cos 60° = 7.5$$

$$\mathbf{a} \cdot \mathbf{c} = |\mathbf{a}||\mathbf{c}|\cos 90° = 0$$

$$\mathbf{a} \cdot \mathbf{a} = |\mathbf{a}||\mathbf{a}|\cos 0° = 16$$

(Remember $\cos 0° = 1$)
This last result shows that the scalar product of a vector with itself, i.e. $\mathbf{a} \cdot \mathbf{a}$, gives the square of the magnitude of the vector.

Exploration 5.5

Scalar products and components

Consider the Cartesian unit vectors **i** and **j**.

■ Find the scalar products $\mathbf{i} \bullet \mathbf{i}$, $\mathbf{i} \bullet \mathbf{j}$, $\mathbf{j} \bullet \mathbf{i}$ and $\mathbf{j} \bullet \mathbf{j}$.
■ For two vectors $\mathbf{a} = a_1\mathbf{i} + a_2\mathbf{j}$ and $\mathbf{b} = b_1\mathbf{i} + b_2\mathbf{j}$ find an expression for the scalar products $\mathbf{a} \bullet \mathbf{b}$ and $\mathbf{b} \bullet \mathbf{a}$.

Interpreting the results

From this exploration you should have obtained the results:
$$\mathbf{a} \bullet \mathbf{b} = \mathbf{b} \bullet \mathbf{a}$$
which shows that the scalar product is commutative.

$$\left(a_1\mathbf{i} + a_2\mathbf{j}\right) \bullet \left(b_1\mathbf{i} + b_2\mathbf{j}\right) = \begin{pmatrix} a_1 \\ a_2 \end{pmatrix} \bullet \begin{pmatrix} b_1 \\ b_2 \end{pmatrix} = a_1 b_1 + a_2 b_2$$

Example 5.9

The vectors **a**, **b** *and* **c** *are given by:*
$$\mathbf{a} = \begin{pmatrix} 2 \\ 4 \end{pmatrix} \quad \mathbf{b} = \begin{pmatrix} 1 \\ -1 \end{pmatrix} \quad \mathbf{c} = \begin{pmatrix} 2 \\ -1 \end{pmatrix}$$

a) *Find the scalar products* $\mathbf{a} \bullet \mathbf{b}$ *and* $\mathbf{a} \bullet \mathbf{c}$.
b) *Use the answers to part a) to find the angles between* **a** *and* **b** *and between* **a** *and* **c**.

Solution

a) $$\mathbf{a} \bullet \mathbf{b} = \begin{pmatrix} 2 \\ 4 \end{pmatrix} \bullet \begin{pmatrix} 1 \\ -1 \end{pmatrix} = 2 \times 1 + 4 \times -1 = -2$$

$$\mathbf{a} \bullet \mathbf{c} = \begin{pmatrix} 2 \\ 4 \end{pmatrix} \bullet \begin{pmatrix} 2 \\ -1 \end{pmatrix} = 2 \times 2 + 4 \times -1 = 0$$

b) *The scalar product definition gives:* $\cos\theta = \dfrac{\mathbf{a} \bullet \mathbf{b}}{|\mathbf{a}||\mathbf{b}|}$

Now $|\mathbf{a}| = \sqrt{20}$ *and* $|\mathbf{b}| = \sqrt{2}$ *so for vectors* **a** *and* **b**:

$$\cos\theta = \frac{-2}{\sqrt{20}\sqrt{2}} = -0.3162$$
$$\theta = 108.43°$$

For vectors **a** *and* **c** *the scalar product is zero. Therefore the vectors are perpendicular.*

EXERCISES

5.3 CLASSWORK

1 Find the scalar products of the following pairs of vectors.

a) $2\mathbf{i} + \mathbf{j}$ and $\mathbf{i} - 4\mathbf{j}$ b) $\mathbf{i} + \mathbf{j}$ and $-4\mathbf{i} + 3\mathbf{j}$

c) $\begin{pmatrix} 7 \\ 2 \end{pmatrix}$ and $\begin{pmatrix} 1 \\ -5 \end{pmatrix}$ d) $\begin{pmatrix} 2 \\ 3 \end{pmatrix}$ and $\begin{pmatrix} -6 \\ 4 \end{pmatrix}$

e) $5\mathbf{i} + 6\mathbf{j}$ and $-\mathbf{i} + \mathbf{j}$ f) $-\mathbf{i} - \mathbf{j}$ and $-2\mathbf{i} + 3\mathbf{j}$

2 Find the angle between each of the following pairs of vectors.

a) $2\mathbf{i} + \mathbf{j}$ and $3\mathbf{i} + 4\mathbf{j}$ b) $-3\mathbf{i}$ and $-\mathbf{i} + 5\mathbf{j}$ c) $\begin{pmatrix} 4 \\ 1 \end{pmatrix}$ and $\begin{pmatrix} 1 \\ 1 \end{pmatrix}$

d) $\begin{pmatrix} 2 \\ -1 \end{pmatrix}$ and $\begin{pmatrix} 1 \\ 2 \end{pmatrix}$ e) $\begin{pmatrix} 7 \\ 2 \end{pmatrix}$ and $\begin{pmatrix} 1 \\ -5 \end{pmatrix}$ f) $-\mathbf{i} - \mathbf{j}$ and $-2\mathbf{i} + 3\mathbf{j}$

3 The two vectors **x** and **y** are given by **x** = **i** + 2**j** and **y** = **i** + m**j**. Determine the value of m if:

a) **x** and **y** are perpendicular vectors
b) **x** and **y** are parallel vectors
c) the angle between **x** and **y** is 30°.

4 ABCD is a square and $\mathbf{a} = \begin{pmatrix} 1 \\ 1 \end{pmatrix}$, $\mathbf{b} = \begin{pmatrix} 4 \\ 1 \end{pmatrix}$, $\mathbf{c} = \begin{pmatrix} 4 \\ 4 \end{pmatrix}$, $\mathbf{d} = \begin{pmatrix} 1 \\ 4 \end{pmatrix}$ are the position vectors of its vertices.

a) Find the displacements $\overrightarrow{AC}$ and $\overrightarrow{BD}$.
b) Show that the diagonals of the square are perpendicular.

5 **a** and **b** are perpendicular vectors with magnitudes 3 and 4 respectively.

a) If **x** = **a** − 2**b** and **y** = 2**a** + 3**b** find the scalar product **x** • **y**.
b) If **z** = 2**a** + m**b** find the value of m such that **y** and **z** are perpendicular vectors.

EXERCISES

5.3 HOMEWORK

1 Find the scalar products of the following pairs of vectors.

a) 4**i** + 3**j** and 5**i** − 12**j**
b) −3**i** − 4**j** and **i** + **j**
c) $\begin{pmatrix} 1 \\ -5 \end{pmatrix}$ and $\begin{pmatrix} 2 \\ 1 \end{pmatrix}$
d) $\begin{pmatrix} -2 \\ 1 \end{pmatrix}$ and $\begin{pmatrix} 3 \\ 6 \end{pmatrix}$
e) $\begin{pmatrix} -3 \\ 5 \end{pmatrix}$ and $\begin{pmatrix} -2 \\ -1 \end{pmatrix}$
f) $\begin{pmatrix} 0 \\ 3 \end{pmatrix}$ and $\begin{pmatrix} -1 \\ 0 \end{pmatrix}$

2 Find the angle between each of the following pairs of vectors.

a) −**i** + 5**j** and 2**i** + **j**
b) 3**i** and −**i** + 2**j**
c) $\begin{pmatrix} 2 \\ 3 \end{pmatrix}$ and $\begin{pmatrix} 4 \\ 1 \end{pmatrix}$
d) $\begin{pmatrix} -3 \\ -4 \end{pmatrix}$ and $\begin{pmatrix} 1 \\ 1 \end{pmatrix}$
e) −2**i** + **j** and 3**i** + 6**j**
f) −**i** − 2**j** and 3**i** − **j**

3 The two vectors **u** and **v** are given by **u** = 3**i** + 2**j** and **v** = 2**i** + k**j**. Determine the value of k if:

a) **u** and **v** are perpendicular vectors
b) **u** and **v** are parallel vectors
c) the angle between **u** and **v** is 45°.

4 The three vectors **a**, **b** and **a** − m**b** are all unit vectors and the angle between **a** and **b** is 60°.

a) Find the scalar product of **a** − m**b** with itself.
b) Hence find the value of the non-zero coefficient m.

5 **a** and **b** are perpendicular vectors with magnitudes 2 and 3 respectively.

a) If **x** = −2**a** + 3**b** and **y** = 3**a** − 4**b** find the scalar product **x** • **y**.
b) if **z** = m**a** − 4**b** find the value of m such that **x** and **z** are perpendicular vectors.

VECTORS AND GEOMETRY IN TWO DIMENSIONS

Vector algebra can provide a useful and time-saving approach to many geometrical problems. This idea has been illustrated in a few exercises in the previous sections; the rest of this chapter is about the use of vectors in geometrical applications.

Example 5.10

ABC is a triangle; the points D and E divide the sides AB and BC respectively so that the ratios DB : AB and BE : BC are both equal to m.

Show that DE is parallel to AC and the ratio DE : AC is also equal to m.

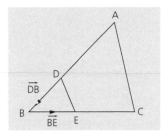

Solution

The diagram shows the triangle and the points D and E.
The problem is to show that DE is parallel to AC and DE = mAC, so our approach to solving the problem is to show that $\overrightarrow{DE} = m\,\overrightarrow{AC}$.

Consider the displacements $\overrightarrow{DB}$ and $\overrightarrow{AB}$.

These vectors are parallel and DB : AB = m : 1 so that $\overrightarrow{DB} = m\,\overrightarrow{AB}$.

Similarly $\overrightarrow{BE} = m\,\overrightarrow{BC}$. Using the triangle law of addition for vectors on triangles BDE and BAC we have:

$$\Delta BDE: \quad \overrightarrow{DE} = \overrightarrow{DB} + \overrightarrow{BE} = m\,\overrightarrow{AB} + m\,\overrightarrow{BC} = m\left(\overrightarrow{AB} + \overrightarrow{BC}\right)$$

$$\Delta BAC: \quad \overrightarrow{AC} = \overrightarrow{AB} + \overrightarrow{BC}$$

So that $\quad \overrightarrow{DE} = m\,\overrightarrow{AC}$
which is the required result.

Exploration 5.6

The vector equation of a line

The position vectors of a set of points are given by the vector equation:

$$\mathbf{r} = \begin{pmatrix} 3 \\ -1 \end{pmatrix} + t\begin{pmatrix} 1 \\ 2 \end{pmatrix}$$

where *t* is a **parameter** which may take any value.
- Find the position vectors of points with values of *t* equal to –2, –1, 0, 1, 2, 3.
- Plot these points on a Cartesian graph.
- What is the shape of the graph of the vector equation?

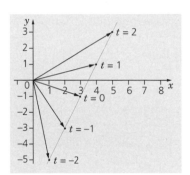

Interpreting the results

This exploration leads to the straight line shown in the diagram.

As *t* increases the point moves along the line. Suppose now we begin with two points on a line and find the vector equation of the line. The diagram on the next page shows two points with position vectors $\mathbf{a} = \begin{pmatrix} -1 \\ -2 \end{pmatrix}$ and $\mathbf{b} = \begin{pmatrix} 4 \\ 1 \end{pmatrix}$, respectively.

$\mathbf{a} = -\mathbf{i} - 2\mathbf{j}$ and $\mathbf{b} = 4\mathbf{i} + \mathbf{j}$.

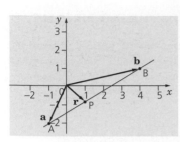

Point P is any point on the line AB with position vector **r**.

The displacement vector $\overrightarrow{AB} = \mathbf{b} - \mathbf{a} = \begin{pmatrix} 4 \\ 1 \end{pmatrix} - \begin{pmatrix} -1 \\ -2 \end{pmatrix} = \begin{pmatrix} 5 \\ 3 \end{pmatrix}$

The displacement vector $\overrightarrow{AP} = \mathbf{r} - \mathbf{a} = \mathbf{r} - \begin{pmatrix} -1 \\ -2 \end{pmatrix}$

Since AP and AB are parallel we have: $\overrightarrow{AP} = t\,\overrightarrow{AB}$

where t is a scalar quantity.

Substituting for $\overrightarrow{AP}$ and $\overrightarrow{AB}$:

$$\mathbf{r} - \begin{pmatrix} -1 \\ -2 \end{pmatrix} = t\begin{pmatrix} 5 \\ 3 \end{pmatrix} \;\Rightarrow\; \mathbf{r} = \begin{pmatrix} -1 \\ -2 \end{pmatrix} + t\begin{pmatrix} 5 \\ 3 \end{pmatrix}$$

This is the equation of the straight line through AB.

For $t = 0$: $\mathbf{r} = \begin{pmatrix} -1 \\ -2 \end{pmatrix}$ which is the point A.

For $t = 1$: $\mathbf{r} = \begin{pmatrix} 4 \\ 1 \end{pmatrix}$ which is the point B.

For $0 < t < 1$ points on the line are between A and B.

More generally, using the vectors **a** and **b** gives: $\mathbf{r} - \mathbf{a} = t(\mathbf{b} - \mathbf{a})$

Since $\overrightarrow{AP} = \mathbf{r} - \mathbf{a}$, $\overrightarrow{AB} = \mathbf{b} - \mathbf{a}$ and $\overrightarrow{AP} = t\,\overrightarrow{AB}$:

$\qquad \mathbf{r} = \mathbf{a} + t(\mathbf{b} - \mathbf{a}) \qquad \mathbf{r} = (1-t)\mathbf{a} + t\mathbf{b}$

This is the parametric equation of a straight line given the position vector (or coordinates) of two points lying on the line.

Example 5.11

Find the vector equation of the straight line through the point (1, 4), parallel to the vector $\mathbf{d} = \mathbf{i} - 2\mathbf{j}$.

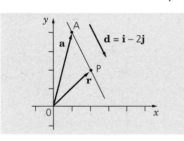

Solution

The diagram shows the given point (1, 4) labelled as A and the direction of the vector **d**. *P is any point on the line.*

The vector $\overrightarrow{AP} = \mathbf{r} - \mathbf{a}$ *is parallel to the vector* **d** *so we can write:*
$\qquad \mathbf{r} - \mathbf{a} = t\mathbf{d} \;\Rightarrow\; \mathbf{r} = \mathbf{a} + t\mathbf{d}$
Substituting for **a** *and* **d** *gives:* $\mathbf{r} = (\mathbf{i} + 4\mathbf{j}) + t(\mathbf{i} - 2\mathbf{j})$

Alternatively we can write $\mathbf{r} = \begin{pmatrix} 1 \\ 4 \end{pmatrix} + t\begin{pmatrix} 1 \\ -2 \end{pmatrix}$.

Exploration 5.7

Subdividing a straight line

Choose any two points on a line in the *x-y* plane and label them A and B.

- Write down the vector equation of the line.
- What is special about the point with $t = \frac{1}{2}$?
- What is special about the point with $t = \frac{1}{3}$?
- What is special about the point with $t = \frac{3}{4}$?
- A point P divides AB in the ratio 3 : 5. What value of t leads to the point P?

Interpreting the results

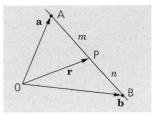

This exploration shows an interesting result. If a point P divides the line AB into the ratio $m : n$ then the position vector of P is:

$$\mathbf{r} = \frac{n}{m+n}\mathbf{a} + \frac{m}{m+n}\mathbf{b}$$

The intersection of two lines

Example 5.12

Two straight lines are given by the vector equations:

$$\mathbf{r}_1 = \begin{pmatrix} 2 \\ -1 \end{pmatrix} + t\begin{pmatrix} 1 \\ 3 \end{pmatrix} \quad and \quad \mathbf{r}_2 = \begin{pmatrix} 1 \\ -2 \end{pmatrix} + s\begin{pmatrix} -1 \\ -2 \end{pmatrix}$$

Find the position vector of the point of intersection of these two lines.

Solution

At the point of intersection of the two lines the position vectors from the two vector equations are equal.

$$\begin{pmatrix} 2 \\ -1 \end{pmatrix} + t\begin{pmatrix} 1 \\ 3 \end{pmatrix} = \begin{pmatrix} 1 \\ -2 \end{pmatrix} + s\begin{pmatrix} -1 \\ -2 \end{pmatrix}$$

This gives two simultaneous equations for t and s.

$$2 + t = 1 - s \Rightarrow t + s = -1$$
$$-1 + 3t = -2 - 2s \Rightarrow 3t + 2s = -1$$

Solving for t and s gives t = 1 and s = −2.
Thus the position vector of the point of intersection is: $\mathbf{r} = \begin{pmatrix} 3 \\ 2 \end{pmatrix}.$

EXERCISES

5.4 CLASSWORK

1 Consider the equation $\mathbf{r} = (1 - t)\mathbf{a} + t\mathbf{b}$ and the position vectors $\mathbf{a} = 2\mathbf{i} + \mathbf{j}$ and $\mathbf{b} = -3\mathbf{i} + 2\mathbf{j}$.

   a) Write down the position vectors of the points for which $t = -1, 0, 1$ and 2.
   b) Show these points on a diagram and verify that they are collinear.

2 Find the vector equations of the lines joining the following pairs of points.
   a) (0, 1) to (1, 2)   b) (2, 3) to (−1, −3)   c) (−2, 1) to (−3, 4)

3 Find the vector equation of the line through the given point $\mathbf{a}$ and parallel to the given vector $\mathbf{d}$.

   a) $\mathbf{a} = -\mathbf{i} + \mathbf{j}, \mathbf{d} = 2\mathbf{i} + \mathbf{j}$ b) $\mathbf{a} = \begin{pmatrix} 3 \\ -1 \end{pmatrix}, \mathbf{d} = \begin{pmatrix} 6 \\ 1 \end{pmatrix}$ c) $\mathbf{a} = 3\mathbf{i} + 4\mathbf{j}, \mathbf{d} = -2\mathbf{i} - 3\mathbf{j}$

4 The Cartesian form of the equation of a straight line is given in variables x and y as $y = 3x + 1$.
   a) Choose any two values of x to find the coordinates of two points on the line.
   b) Find the vector equation of the straight line.

5 Repeat question 4 for the following straight lines.
   a) $y = -2x + 5$ b) $y = 3x - 2$

6 The position vector of a general point on a line is given in Cartesian coordinates by $\mathbf{r} = x\mathbf{i} + y\mathbf{j}$. The vector equation of a straight line is given by: $\mathbf{r} = \begin{pmatrix} 3 \\ -1 \end{pmatrix} + t\begin{pmatrix} 6 \\ 1 \end{pmatrix}.$

   a) Show that x and y satisfy the equations: $x = 3 + 6t \quad y = -1 + t$.
   b) By eliminating t find the Cartesian equation of the straight line.

7   Repeat question 6 for the following straight lines.

a) $\mathbf{r} = (-\mathbf{i} + 2\mathbf{j}) + t(-3\mathbf{i} - \mathbf{j})$ b) $\mathbf{r} = \begin{pmatrix} 1 \\ 1 \end{pmatrix} + s\begin{pmatrix} 2 \\ 3 \end{pmatrix}$

8   Find the position vector of the point of intersection of each of the following pairs of lines.

a) $\mathbf{r}_1 = \begin{pmatrix} 2 \\ 1 \end{pmatrix} + t\begin{pmatrix} 0 \\ 1 \end{pmatrix}, \mathbf{r}_2 = \begin{pmatrix} -1 \\ 2 \end{pmatrix} + s\begin{pmatrix} 3 \\ 1 \end{pmatrix}$

b) $\mathbf{r}_1 = \begin{pmatrix} -1 \\ -1 \end{pmatrix} + t\begin{pmatrix} 4 \\ -4 \end{pmatrix}, \mathbf{r}_2 = \begin{pmatrix} -2 \\ 0 \end{pmatrix} + s\begin{pmatrix} -1 \\ 1 \end{pmatrix}$

c) $\mathbf{r}_1 = \begin{pmatrix} 0 \\ 2 \end{pmatrix} + t\begin{pmatrix} -2 \\ 3 \end{pmatrix}, \mathbf{r}_2 = \begin{pmatrix} 1 \\ 0 \end{pmatrix} + s\begin{pmatrix} 9 \\ -14 \end{pmatrix}$

d) $\mathbf{r}_1 = \begin{pmatrix} -2 \\ -1 \end{pmatrix} + t\begin{pmatrix} 2 \\ 4 \end{pmatrix}, \mathbf{r}_2 = \begin{pmatrix} 0 \\ -2 \end{pmatrix} + s\begin{pmatrix} 3 \\ -9 \end{pmatrix}$

9   Four points A, B, C and D have coordinates (–2, 3), (–3, –1), (4, –3) and (5, 3) respectively.

a) Find the vector equation of the line through the points A and C.
b) Find the vector equation of the line through the points B and D.
c) Find the position vectors of the midpoints of AC and BD.
d) Find the angle between the lines AC and BD.
e) Find the coordinates of the point of intersection of the lines AC and BD.

10   ABC is a triangle. The median of a triangle is the line joining a vertex to the midpoint of the opposite side. Use vector algebra methods to show that the three medians of a triangle trisect each other.

EXERCISES

5.4 HOMEWORK

1   Consider the equation $\mathbf{r} = (1 - t)\mathbf{a} + t\mathbf{b}$ and the position vectors $\mathbf{a} = \begin{pmatrix} -1 \\ 4 \end{pmatrix}$ and $\mathbf{b} = \begin{pmatrix} 2 \\ -1 \end{pmatrix}$.

a) Write down the position vectors of the points for which t = –2, –1, 0, 1 and 2.
b) Show these points on a diagram and verify that they are collinear.

2   Find the vector equations of the lines joining the following pairs of points.
a) (–1, 0) to (3, 4)   b) (5, 12) to (0, –1)
c) (2, 1) to (–1, 3)

3   Find the vector equation of the line through the given point $\mathbf{a}$ and parallel to the given vector $\mathbf{d}$.

a) $\mathbf{a} = \begin{pmatrix} 2 \\ 3 \end{pmatrix}, \mathbf{d} = \begin{pmatrix} -2 \\ 4 \end{pmatrix}$ b) $\mathbf{a} = 5\mathbf{i}, \mathbf{d} = -\mathbf{i} + \mathbf{j}$ c) $\mathbf{a} = 3\mathbf{j}, \mathbf{d} = 3\mathbf{i}$

4   Find the vector equation of each of the following lines given in Cartesian form.
a) $y = 4x - 1$ b) $y = -x + 4$ c) $3y = 2x - 1$

5   Find the Cartesian equation of each of the following lines given in vector form.

a) $\mathbf{r} = \begin{pmatrix} -2 \\ 1 \end{pmatrix} + t\begin{pmatrix} 1 \\ 1 \end{pmatrix}$ b) $\mathbf{r} = \begin{pmatrix} -3 \\ 4 \end{pmatrix} + t\begin{pmatrix} 2 \\ -1 \end{pmatrix}$ c) $\mathbf{r} = -4\mathbf{i} + \mathbf{j} + t(\mathbf{i} - \mathbf{j})$

6   Find the position vector of the point of intersection for each of the following pairs of lines.

a) $\mathbf{r}_1 = \begin{pmatrix} 2 \\ 0 \end{pmatrix} + t\begin{pmatrix} 3 \\ 4 \end{pmatrix}, \mathbf{r}_2 = \begin{pmatrix} 4 \\ 5 \end{pmatrix} + s\begin{pmatrix} -4 \\ -3 \end{pmatrix}$

b) $\mathbf{r}_1 = \begin{pmatrix} -1 \\ 1 \end{pmatrix} + t\begin{pmatrix} 1 \\ 3 \end{pmatrix}, \mathbf{r}_2 = \begin{pmatrix} -2 \\ -3 \end{pmatrix} + s\begin{pmatrix} 0 \\ 2 \end{pmatrix}$

c) $\mathbf{r}_1 = \begin{pmatrix} 5 \\ 12 \end{pmatrix} + t\begin{pmatrix} 1 \\ 4 \end{pmatrix}, \mathbf{r}_2 = \begin{pmatrix} 0 \\ 7 \end{pmatrix} + s\begin{pmatrix} 1 \\ -1 \end{pmatrix}$

7 The vector equations of two lines are:

$$\mathbf{r}_1 = \begin{pmatrix} -1 \\ 1 \end{pmatrix} + t\begin{pmatrix} 3 \\ 4 \end{pmatrix}, \mathbf{r}_2 = \begin{pmatrix} 2 \\ -1 \end{pmatrix} + s\begin{pmatrix} -4 \\ 3 \end{pmatrix}$$

Show that the two lines are perpendicular.

8 Four points A, B, C and D in the x–y plane have position vectors
$\mathbf{a} = 6\mathbf{i} + 8\mathbf{j}$, $\mathbf{b} = \frac{3}{2}\mathbf{a}$, $\mathbf{c} = 6\mathbf{i} + 3\mathbf{j}$ and $\mathbf{d} = \frac{5}{3}\mathbf{c}$.

a) Find the vector equation of each of the lines AD and BC.

b) Find the angle between the lines AD and BC.

c) Find the position vector of the point of intersection of the lines AD and BC.

9 Two points A and B have Cartesian coordinates (1, 3) and (–1, 7).

a) Find the equation of the straight line through the points A and B.

b) Find the coordinates where the straight line intersects the x- and y-axes.

10 Use vector algebra methods to show that the diagonals of a parallelogram bisect each other.

VECTORS AND GEOMETRY IN THREE DIMENSIONS

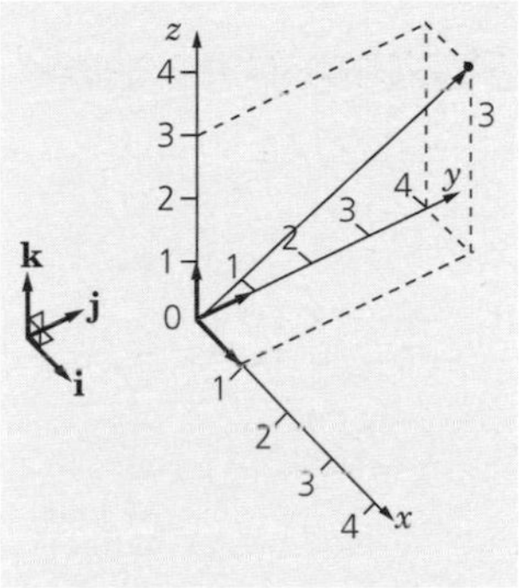

To specify the position of a point in three dimensions we introduce a third coordinate. Through the origin O of the two-dimensional Cartesian coordinate system, we draw a third axis called the **z-axis**, perpendicular to both the x- and y-axes of the two-dimensional system. Any point P can be represented uniquely by its perpendicular distances from the x–y, x–z and y–z planes.

The diagram shows the point (1, 4, 3). A third unit vector $\mathbf{k}$ is introduced pointing in the z-direction.

The position vector of P is written as: $\mathbf{i} + 4\mathbf{j} + 3\mathbf{k}$ or $\begin{pmatrix} 1 \\ 4 \\ 3 \end{pmatrix}$

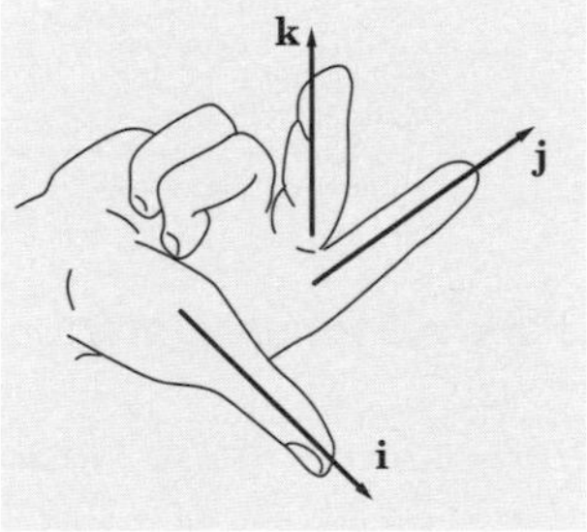

The coordinate system introduced in this way is called a **right-handed** system.

The ideas of vector algebra introduced for two dimensions can be extended to three dimensions.

For any vector $\mathbf{a}$ we may write: $\mathbf{a} = x\mathbf{i} + y\mathbf{j} + z\mathbf{k} = \begin{pmatrix} x \\ y \\ z \end{pmatrix}$

or using subscript notation: $\mathbf{a} = a_1\mathbf{i} + a_2\mathbf{j} + a_3\mathbf{k} = \begin{pmatrix} a_1 \\ a_2 \\ a_3 \end{pmatrix}$

Exploration 5.8

Vectors in three dimensions

Two vectors in three dimensions are written as:
$$\mathbf{a} = a_1\mathbf{i} + a_2\mathbf{j} + a_3\mathbf{k} \quad \text{and} \quad \mathbf{b} = b_1\mathbf{i} + b_2\mathbf{j} + b_3\mathbf{k}$$

■   Show that the magnitude of the vector is: $|\mathbf{a}| = \sqrt{a_1^2 + a_2^2 + a_3^2}$.

■   Show that the scalar product of the two vectors is:
$$\mathbf{a} \bullet \mathbf{b} = a_1 b_1 + a_2 b_2 + a_3 b_3 .$$

■   If **a** and **b** are the position vectors of two points A and B, show that the equation of a straight line through A and B is:
$$\mathbf{r} = \mathbf{a} + t(\mathbf{b} - \mathbf{a}) = (1-t)\mathbf{a} + t\mathbf{b} .$$

Example 5.13

The vectors **a** and **b** are given by $\mathbf{a} = \mathbf{i} + 2\mathbf{j} + 3\mathbf{k}$ and $\mathbf{b} = 2\mathbf{i} - 2\mathbf{j} - \mathbf{k}$.

a)   Find the vectors $\mathbf{a} + \mathbf{b}$ and $2\mathbf{a} - 3\mathbf{b}$.

b)   Find the magnitudes of the vectors **a** and **b**.

c)   Find the angle between the vectors **a** and **b**.

Solution

a) $\mathbf{a} + \mathbf{b} = (\mathbf{i} + 2\mathbf{j} + 3\mathbf{k}) + (2\mathbf{i} - 2\mathbf{j} - \mathbf{k}) = 3\mathbf{i} + 2\mathbf{k}$
   $2\mathbf{a} - 3\mathbf{b} = 2(\mathbf{i} + 2\mathbf{j} + 3\mathbf{k}) - 3(2\mathbf{i} - 2\mathbf{j} - \mathbf{k}) = -4\mathbf{i} + 10\mathbf{j} + 9\mathbf{k}$

b) $|\mathbf{a}| = \sqrt{1^2 + 2^2 + 3^2} = \sqrt{14}$

   $|\mathbf{b}| = \sqrt{2^2 + (-2)^2 + (-1)^2} = \sqrt{9} = 3$

c)   To find the angle between the two vectors we can use the scalar product.

$$\cos\theta = \frac{\mathbf{a} \bullet \mathbf{b}}{|\mathbf{a}||\mathbf{b}|}$$

$$= \frac{(1 \times 2) + (2 \times (-2)) + (3 \times (-1))}{\sqrt{14}\sqrt{3}}$$

$$= \frac{-5}{\sqrt{14}\sqrt{3}} = -0.7715$$

$$\theta = 140.5°$$

The acute angle between the two vectors is 39.5°.

Example 5.14

The lines L and M have the vector equations:

$$\mathrm{L} : \mathbf{r} = \begin{pmatrix} 1 \\ 1 \\ -2 \end{pmatrix} + t\begin{pmatrix} 1 \\ -1 \\ 0 \end{pmatrix} \mathrm{M} : \mathbf{r} = \begin{pmatrix} -1 \\ 2 \\ 1 \end{pmatrix} + s\begin{pmatrix} -3 \\ 2 \\ 3 \end{pmatrix} \text{ where } t \text{ and } s \text{ are parameters.}$$

a)   Find the position vector of the point of intersection of these lines.

b)   Find the angle between the two lines.

Solution

a)   The lines intersect if there is a point on each line with the same position vector.

$$\begin{pmatrix} 1 \\ 1 \\ -2 \end{pmatrix} + t\begin{pmatrix} 1 \\ -1 \\ 0 \end{pmatrix} = \begin{pmatrix} -1 \\ 2 \\ 1 \end{pmatrix} + s\begin{pmatrix} -3 \\ 2 \\ 3 \end{pmatrix}$$

This leads to three simultaneous equations.

$$1 + t = -1 - 3s$$
$$1 - t = 2 + 2s$$
$$-2 = 1 + 3s$$

Solving for s and t gives s = −1 and t = 1.
The position vector of the point of intersection is: $\mathbf{r} = \begin{pmatrix} 2 \\ 0 \\ -2 \end{pmatrix}$.

b) *The direction of line L is* $\begin{pmatrix} 1 \\ -1 \\ 0 \end{pmatrix}$ *and of line M is* $\begin{pmatrix} -3 \\ 2 \\ 3 \end{pmatrix}$ *and so the*

angle between the two lines is given by:

$$\cos\theta = \frac{\begin{pmatrix} 1 \\ -1 \\ 0 \end{pmatrix} \bullet \begin{pmatrix} -3 \\ 2 \\ 3 \end{pmatrix}}{\sqrt{2}\sqrt{22}} = \frac{-3 - 2 + 0}{\sqrt{44}} = -0.7538$$

$$\theta = 138.9°$$

The two lines L and M intersect at the point $\begin{pmatrix} 2 \\ 0 \\ -2 \end{pmatrix}$ and have an acute angle of 41.10° between them.

Skew lines

In the last example the two lines L and M had a point of intersection. For many pairs of lines, this is not the case. Since we have three simultaneous equations with two unknown parameters, it might be that we cannot solve the equations uniquely. Many pairs of straight lines have the following properties.

- ■ The two lines are in parallel planes.
- ■ The two lines do not touch each other.

Straight lines that do not touch are called skew lines. They are like the paths of two aircraft flying at different heights. From the vapour trails seen on the ground it looks as if the paths intersect but there is no danger of a collision if the aircraft are at different heights.

Exploration 5.9

Skew lines

The three lines L, M and N have the vector equations:
L: $\mathbf{r} = (1 + t)\mathbf{i} + (1 - t)\mathbf{j} - 2\mathbf{k}$
M: $\mathbf{r} = (3 - s)\mathbf{i} - (1 - s)\mathbf{j} + (s - 2)\mathbf{k}$
N: $\mathbf{r} = (1 + u)\mathbf{i} - (1 + 3u)\mathbf{j} - u\mathbf{k}$

where t, s and u are parameters.
- ■ Investigate which pairs of lines intersect.

EXERCISES

5.5 CLASSWORK

1 Find the vector equations of the lines:
a) through the points (1, −1, 2) and (2, −1, 1)
b) through the points (−1, −2, −1) and (3, 1, −2)
c) through the point (2, 1, 1) in the direction $\begin{pmatrix} -1 \\ 0 \\ 2 \end{pmatrix}$
d) through the point (1, 0, −1) in the direction $2\mathbf{i} + \mathbf{j} - 3\mathbf{k}$.

2 Find the acute angle between the following pairs of vectors.

a) $\mathbf{i} + \mathbf{j} + \mathbf{k}$ and $2\mathbf{i} - \mathbf{j} + \mathbf{k}$ **b)** $\begin{pmatrix} 1 \\ 0 \\ -1 \end{pmatrix}$ and $\begin{pmatrix} 2 \\ 1 \\ 0 \end{pmatrix}$

c) $\begin{pmatrix} -1 \\ 2 \\ 3 \end{pmatrix}$ and $\begin{pmatrix} 3 \\ 0 \\ 1 \end{pmatrix}$ **d)** $\mathbf{i} + 2\mathbf{j} - \mathbf{k}$ and $2\mathbf{i} + 3\mathbf{k}$

3 Find the angle between each of the following pairs of lines.

a) $\mathbf{r} = \begin{pmatrix} 2 \\ 1 \\ 1 \end{pmatrix} + t\begin{pmatrix} -1 \\ 0 \\ 2 \end{pmatrix}$ and $\mathbf{r} = \begin{pmatrix} -1 \\ 1 \\ 0 \end{pmatrix} + s\begin{pmatrix} -3 \\ 1 \\ 1 \end{pmatrix}$

b) $\mathbf{r} = \begin{pmatrix} 0 \\ -1 \\ 2 \end{pmatrix} + t\begin{pmatrix} 3 \\ 4 \\ 1 \end{pmatrix}$ and $\mathbf{r} = \begin{pmatrix} 1 \\ 3 \\ -2 \end{pmatrix} + s\begin{pmatrix} 1 \\ 1 \\ -2 \end{pmatrix}$

c) $\mathbf{r} = (1 + t)\mathbf{i} + (1 - t)\mathbf{j} - 2\mathbf{k}$ and $\mathbf{r} = (3 - s)\mathbf{i} - (1 - s)\mathbf{j} + (s - 2)\mathbf{k}$

4 Which of the following pairs of lines intersect? For those that do, find the point of intersection.

a) $\mathrm{L}: \mathbf{r} = \begin{pmatrix} 1 \\ 0 \\ -1 \end{pmatrix} + t\begin{pmatrix} 1 \\ 3 \\ 4 \end{pmatrix}$ $\mathrm{M}: \mathbf{r} = \begin{pmatrix} -5 \\ -7 \\ -7 \end{pmatrix} + s\begin{pmatrix} 4 \\ 1 \\ -2 \end{pmatrix}$

b) $\mathrm{L}: \mathbf{r} = \mathbf{i} + (1 + t)\mathbf{j} - (2 + t)\mathbf{k}$ $\mathrm{M}: \mathbf{r} = (3 - s)\mathbf{i} + (s - 1)\mathbf{j} + (s - 2)\mathbf{k}$

c) $\mathrm{L}: \mathbf{r} = \begin{pmatrix} -3 \\ 1 \\ 4 \end{pmatrix} + t\begin{pmatrix} -1 \\ 0 \\ 2 \end{pmatrix}$ $\mathrm{M}: \mathbf{r} = \begin{pmatrix} -2 \\ 2 \\ 1 \end{pmatrix} + s\begin{pmatrix} 2 \\ 1 \\ -1 \end{pmatrix}$

d) $\mathrm{L}: \mathbf{r} = -\mathbf{i} + 2t\mathbf{j} - (1 + t)\mathbf{k}$ $\mathrm{M}: \mathbf{r} = s\mathbf{i} + 2(2 - s)\mathbf{j} - (5 + s)\mathbf{k}$

5 The coordinates of two points A and B are (1, –1, 2) and (2, 1, 3) respectively. Find the position vector of the point P which subdivides the line AB in the ratio 5 : 3.

6 The straight line l_1 has vector equation:
$$\mathbf{r} = 2\mathbf{i} + 9\mathbf{j} + 10\mathbf{k} + p(\mathbf{i} + 6\mathbf{j} + 5\mathbf{k})$$
where p is a scalar variable and $\mathbf{i}$, $\mathbf{j}$ and $\mathbf{k}$ are mutually perpendicular unit vectors.

a) Show that the point A with position vector $\mathbf{i} + 3\mathbf{j} + 5\mathbf{k}$ lies on l_1. The points B and C have position vectors $2\mathbf{i} + \mathbf{j} + 6\mathbf{k}$ and $3\mathbf{i} + 3\mathbf{j} + 9\mathbf{k}$ respectively. The straight line l_2 passes through the points B and C.
b) Determine a vector equation for the line l_2.
c) Prove that the lines l_1 and l_2 intersect and find the position vector of the point of intersection, D.
d) Calculate, to the nearest degree, the acute angle between the lines l_1 and l_2.
e) Prove that the straight line through A and B is perpendicular to l_2. Hence, or otherwise, find the position vector of E such that l_2 is a line of symmetry of triangle ADE.

(OUDLE Question 12, 1991)

EXERCISES

5.5 HOMEWORK

1 Find the vector equation of the lines:
a) through the points (0, 1, 0) and (2, –1, 3)
b) through the points (2, 0, 1) and (–1, 2, 4)
c) through the point (3, 4, 1) in the direction $\mathbf{i} + \mathbf{j} + \mathbf{k}$
d) through the point (–1, –1, 2) in the direction $\begin{pmatrix} 5 \\ 0 \\ -1 \end{pmatrix}$.

2 Find the acute angle between each of the following pairs of vectors.

a) $-\mathbf{i} - \mathbf{j} + 2\mathbf{k}$ and $2\mathbf{i} - \mathbf{j} + 3\mathbf{k}$ **b)** $\begin{pmatrix} 2 \\ 1 \\ 3 \end{pmatrix}$ and $\begin{pmatrix} 2 \\ -1 \\ 4 \end{pmatrix}$ **c)** $\begin{pmatrix} 1 \\ -3 \\ 2 \end{pmatrix}$ and $\begin{pmatrix} 1 \\ -1 \\ -2 \end{pmatrix}$

d) $\mathbf{i} - \mathbf{j}$ and $3\mathbf{i} + \mathbf{j} + 5\mathbf{k}$

3 Which of the following pairs of lines intersect? For those that do intersect find the point of intersection and the acute angle between the lines.

a) $\mathbf{r} = \begin{pmatrix} 2 \\ 1 \\ 2 \end{pmatrix} t$ and $\mathbf{r} = \begin{pmatrix} 0 \\ 3 \\ 8 \end{pmatrix} + s \begin{pmatrix} -1 \\ 1 \\ 3 \end{pmatrix}$

b) $\mathbf{r} = \begin{pmatrix} 1 \\ 1 \\ -2 \end{pmatrix} + t \begin{pmatrix} 0 \\ 1 \\ -1 \end{pmatrix}$ and $\mathbf{r} = \begin{pmatrix} -1 \\ 1 \\ -3 \end{pmatrix} + s \begin{pmatrix} 6 \\ -3 \\ 6 \end{pmatrix}$

c) $\mathbf{r} = \begin{pmatrix} 3 \\ 4 \\ 1 \end{pmatrix} t$ and $\mathbf{r} = \begin{pmatrix} 2 \\ 2 \\ 3 \end{pmatrix} + s \begin{pmatrix} 1 \\ 2 \\ -1 \end{pmatrix}$

d) $\mathbf{r} = -2\mathbf{i} + 5\mathbf{j} - 11\mathbf{k} + u(3\mathbf{i} + \mathbf{j} + 3\mathbf{k})$ and $\mathbf{r} = 8\mathbf{i} + 9\mathbf{j} + t(4\mathbf{i} + 2\mathbf{j} + 5\mathbf{k})$

4 ABCD is a square with centre at the origin and $\mathbf{a} = 24\mathbf{i}$, $\mathbf{b} = 24\mathbf{j}$, $\mathbf{c} = -24\mathbf{j}$ and $\mathbf{d} = -24\mathbf{j}$. V is the vertex of the square pyramid where $\mathbf{v} = 24\mathbf{k}$.

The point P divides AV in the ratio 3 : 5 and the point Q divides DV in the ratio 2 : 1. Find the position vectors of P and Q in terms of $\mathbf{i}$, $\mathbf{j}$ and $\mathbf{k}$.

5 The point A has position vector $\mathbf{i} + 3\mathbf{j} - 4\mathbf{k}$ relative to a fixed origin O. The vector equation of the line l_1 passing through A is $\mathbf{r} = \mathbf{i} + 3\mathbf{j} - 4\mathbf{k} + s(2\mathbf{i} + \mathbf{j} + 3\mathbf{k})$, where s is a scalar parameter.

a) The point B(a, b, 5) lies on l_1. Determine the values of constants a and b.

b) Determine the acute angle between the vector $\overrightarrow{OA}$ and the line l_1, giving your answers to the nearest 0.1°.

c) Write down, in terms of a parameter, t, the vector equation of line l_2 which passes through C(1, 2, −1) and D(4, 2, 8).
Show that the lines l_1 and l_2 intersect and find the position vector of the point of intersection.

(OUDLE, Question 14, 1992)

6 The points A, B, C have position vectors $\mathbf{a} = 2\mathbf{i} + \mathbf{j} - \mathbf{k}$, $\mathbf{b} = 3\mathbf{i} + 4\mathbf{j} - 2\mathbf{k}$, $\mathbf{c} = 5\mathbf{i} - \mathbf{j} + 2\mathbf{k}$ respectively, relative to a fixed origin O.

a) Evaluate the scalar product $(\mathbf{a} - \mathbf{b}) \bullet (\mathbf{c} - \mathbf{b})$.
Hence calculate the size of angle ABC, giving your answer to the nearest 0.1°.

b) Given that ABCD is a parallelogram determine the position vector of D.

c) The point E lies on BA produced so that $\overrightarrow{BE} = 3\overrightarrow{BA}$. Write down the position vector of E.

(OUDLE, Question 10, 1993)

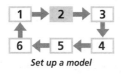

Specify the real problem

MATHEMATICAL MODELLING ACTIVITY

Problem statement

Near misses

Although the sky is large, there are occasionally collisions between aircraft and much more frequently there are 'near misses' when they pass very close to one another. This happens despite the care which air traffic controllers take to ensure that it does not. Similar problems arise with ships, particularly in crowded sea-lanes such as the English Channel.

Suppose there are two tankers, the *Arabian Queen* and the *Bountiful Princess* (which we shall refer to as A and B) both heading for the Straits of Hormuz at the entrance to the Persian Gulf. A is steering a course of 300° at 8 knots when she picks up B on her radar. B is 23 nautical miles away on a bearing of 175° steering on course 322° at 14 knots. Does either ship need to take avoiding action?

Note: 1 knot is a speed of 1 nautical mile per hour. 1 nautical mile is approximately 1.3 miles or 2 km.

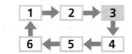

Set up a model

Set up a model

Firstly identify the important variables:
- velocity of each tanker
- position of each tanker relative to a fixed origin
- distance between tankers at any time.

You will also need to make certain assumptions to simplify the model:
- each tanker travels in a straight line
- each tanker travels with constant speed.

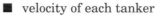

Formulate the mathematical problem

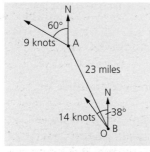

Mathematical problem

The diagram shows the initial positions and course of the two tankers.

In vector notation the velocities of A and B are:
$$\mathbf{v}_A = \begin{pmatrix} -9\cos 30° \\ 9\cos 60° \end{pmatrix} = \begin{pmatrix} -7.79 \\ 4.5 \end{pmatrix} \quad \mathbf{v}_B = \begin{pmatrix} -14\cos 52° \\ 14\cos 38° \end{pmatrix} = \begin{pmatrix} -8.62 \\ 11.03 \end{pmatrix}$$

The position of each tanker at a general time t can be found by integrating the constant vector $\mathbf{v}$.
$$\mathbf{r} = \int \mathbf{v}\, dt + \mathbf{r}_0 = \mathbf{v}t + \mathbf{r}_0$$

where $\mathbf{r}_0$ is the initial position of the tanker. Choose point B as the fixed origin. Then:
$$\mathbf{r}_B = \begin{pmatrix} -8.62 \\ 11.03 \end{pmatrix} t$$

and $\mathbf{r}_A = \begin{pmatrix} -7.79 \\ 4.5 \end{pmatrix} t + \begin{pmatrix} -23\cos 85° \\ 23\cos 5° \end{pmatrix} = \begin{pmatrix} -7.79t - 2.00 \\ 4.5t + 22.91 \end{pmatrix}$

The displacement vector $\mathbf{d} = \mathbf{r}_A - \mathbf{r}_B = \begin{pmatrix} -7.79t - 2.00 \\ 4.5t + 22.91 \end{pmatrix} - \begin{pmatrix} -8.62t \\ 11.03t \end{pmatrix}$

$$= \begin{pmatrix} 0.83t - 2.00 \\ -6.53t + 22.91 \end{pmatrix}$$

The distance between the tankers is $|\mathbf{d}|$. The mathematical problem is to find the value t that minimises $|\mathbf{d}|$.

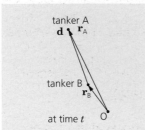

at time t

Solve the mathematical problem

Mathematical solution

$$|\mathbf{d}| = \sqrt{(0.83t - 2)^2 + (-6.53t + 22.91)^2}$$
$$= \sqrt{43.33t^2 - 302.52t + 528.87}$$

The minimum value of $|\mathbf{d}|$ occurs for the minimum value of the quadratic: $y = 43.33t^2 - 302.52t + 528.87$.

The value of t can be found by calculus methods or a graph or a table of values using a graphics calculator. Show that $t = 3.49$ hours to 2 d.p. and then $|\mathbf{d}| = 0.90$.

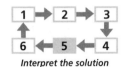
Interpret the solution

Interpretation

The minimum distance between the two tankers is 0.90 nautical miles and occurs after 3.49 hours. Avoiding action is probably not necessary and the tankers can travel on their chosen bearings.

CONSOLIDATION EXERCISES FOR VECTORS

1 A windsurfer heads across a lake so that her position vector t seconds after leaving the shoreline is given by: $\mathbf{r}_1 = \begin{pmatrix} 4.8t \\ 6.4t \end{pmatrix}$

A rowing boat is crossing the lake and its position vector is given by:

$$\mathbf{r}_2 = \begin{pmatrix} 28 - 1.2t \\ 22.4 + 1.6t \end{pmatrix} \text{(The units of position are metres.)}$$

a) How far apart are the rowing boat and windsurfer when the surfer leaves the shoreline?

b) Does the rowing boat need to change speed or direction to avoid colliding with the windsurfer?

2 The position vectors of the points A and B relative to a fixed origin O are $\mathbf{a} = 2\mathbf{i} - \mathbf{j} + 6\mathbf{k}$ and $\mathbf{b} = 3\mathbf{i} - 2\mathbf{j} + 7\mathbf{k}$ respectively.

a) Write down the vector $\overrightarrow{AB}$. By considering the scalar product $\overrightarrow{AB} \bullet \overrightarrow{OB}$, find, to the nearest 0.1°, the size of angle ABO.

b) Write down a vector equation of the straight line through A and B in terms of a parameter t.

c) The point P lies on the line AB and is such that OP is perpendicular to AB. Determine the position vector of P.
Hence show that the shortest distance from O to the line AB is $\sqrt{14}$.

(OUDLE Question 13, 1990)

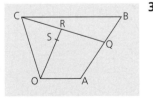

3 OABC is a trapezium. The position vectors A, B and C (relative to O as origin) are $\mathbf{a}$, $\mathbf{b}$ and $\mathbf{b} - 3\mathbf{a}$ respectively. Q is the point on AB such that AQ : QB = 2 : 1, R is the point on QC such that QR : RC = 2 : 3 and S is the point on RO such that RS : SO = 1 : 5. Show that the position vector of R is $-\mathbf{a} + \frac{4}{5}\mathbf{b}$, and find the position vector of S. Deduce that SQ is parallel to OA.

(OCSEB Question A12, SMP1R, 1993)

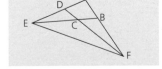

4 The points A, B, C, D and E have position vectors $\mathbf{i} + 11\mathbf{j}$, $2\mathbf{i} + 8\mathbf{j}$, $-\mathbf{i} + 7\mathbf{j}$, $-2\mathbf{i} + 8\mathbf{j}$ and $-4\mathbf{i} + 6\mathbf{j}$ respectively. The lines AB and DC intersect at F.

a) Find the vector equations of the lines AB and DC.

b) Find the position vector of the point F.

c) Show that FD is perpendicular to EA and hence find the position vector of the centre of the circle through E, D and F.

5   Three points P, Q and R have position vectors **p**, **q** and **r** respectively, where **p** = 7**i** + 10**j**, **q** = 3**i** + 12**j**, **r** = –**i** + 4**j**.

a) Write down the vectors $\overrightarrow{PQ}$ and $\overrightarrow{RQ}$, and show that they are perpendicular.

b) Using a scalar product, or otherwise, find the angle PRQ.

c) Find the position vector of S, the midpoint of PR.

d) Show that $|\overrightarrow{QS}| = |\overrightarrow{RS}|$. Using your previous results, or otherwise, find the angle PSQ.

(MEI, Pure 3, January 1995)

6   Referred to a fixed origin O, the points A and B have position vectors 3**i** – **j** + 2**k** and –**i** + **j** + 9**k** respectively.

a) Show that $\overrightarrow{OA}$ is perpendicular to $\overrightarrow{AB}$.

b) Find in vector form, an equation of the line L_1 which passes through A and B.

The line L_2 has equation **r** = (8**i** + **j** – 6**k**) + μ(**i** – 2**j** – 2**k**), where μ is a scalar parameter.

c) Show that the lines L_1 and L_2 intersect and find the position vector of their point of intersection.

d) Calculate, to the nearest tenth of a degree, the acute angle between L_1 and L_2.

(Edexcel Question 8, Specimen Paper 3, 2000)

7   The points A and B have position vectors **a** = 4**i** + 5**j** + 6**k** and **b** = 4**i** + 6**j** + 2**k** respectively, relative to a fixed origin O. The line L_1 has vector equation **r** = **i** + 5**j** – 3**k** + s(**i** + **j** – **k**) where s is a scalar parameter.

a) Write down a vector equation for the line L_2 which passes through the points A and B, giving the equation in terms of a scalar parameter t.

b) Show that the lines L_1 and L_2 intersect and state the position vector of the point of intersection.

c) Calculate the acute angle between the lines L_1 and L_2, giving your answer to the nearest tenth of a degree.

(AQA MB Question 7, Specimen Paper 5, 2000)

8   The points A and B have coordinates (3, 2, 4) and (4, 4, –3) respectively. The line L_1, which passes through A, has equation

$$\mathbf{r} = \begin{pmatrix} 3 \\ 2 \\ 4 \end{pmatrix} + t \begin{pmatrix} 5 \\ 1 \\ 1 \end{pmatrix}.$$

Show that $\overrightarrow{AB}$ is perpendicular to L_1.

The line L_2, which passes through B, has equation $\mathbf{r} = \begin{pmatrix} 4 \\ 4 \\ -3 \end{pmatrix} + s \begin{pmatrix} 2 \\ 1 \\ -2 \end{pmatrix}$.

Show that the lines L_1 and L_2 intersect, and find the coordinates of their point of intersection.

(OCR Question 5, Specimen Paper 3, 2000)

9   The lines L and M have vector equations

$$\text{L:}\quad \mathbf{r} = \begin{pmatrix} 3 \\ 2 \\ 4 \end{pmatrix} + s \begin{pmatrix} 1 \\ 3 \\ -5 \end{pmatrix} \quad \text{and M:}\quad \mathbf{r} = \begin{pmatrix} -3 \\ 4 \\ 6 \end{pmatrix} + t \begin{pmatrix} 1 \\ -2 \\ 2 \end{pmatrix}.$$

The plane Π has vector equation $\mathbf{r} \bullet \begin{pmatrix} 2 \\ 0 \\ -1 \end{pmatrix} = 16$

a) Show that the lines L and M meet and that A (1, –4, 14) is their point of intersection.

b) Find the position vector of the point of intersection, B, of L and Π

c) i) Show that the cosine of the angle between the vectors

$\begin{pmatrix} 1 \\ 3 \\ -5 \end{pmatrix}$ and $\begin{pmatrix} 2 \\ 0 \\ -1 \end{pmatrix}$ is $\dfrac{\sqrt{7}}{5}$

ii) Hence find, to the nearest degree, the angle between L and Π.

d) Write down the Cartesian equation of the plane Π.

(AQA Question 8, Specimen Paper 3, 2000)

Summary

- A vector quantity has magnitude and direction.

- A scalar quantity has magnitude only.

- In two dimensions we write a vector in component form as:
  $\mathbf{a} = \begin{pmatrix} a_1 \\ a_2 \end{pmatrix}$ or $\mathbf{a} = a_1\mathbf{i} + a_2\mathbf{j}$

- The magnitude of $\mathbf{a}$ is $|\mathbf{a}| = \sqrt{a_1^2 + a_2^2}$.

- The direction of $\mathbf{a}$ is the angle $\mathbf{a}$ makes with the x-axis measured in an anticlockwise direction.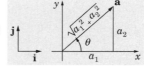

- In three dimensions we write a vector in component form as:
  $\mathbf{a} = \begin{pmatrix} a_1 \\ a_2 \\ a_3 \end{pmatrix}$ or $\mathbf{a} = a_1\mathbf{i} + a_2\mathbf{j} + a_3\mathbf{k}$

- The magnitude of $\mathbf{a}$ is $\sqrt{a_1^2 + a_2^2 + a_3^2}$.

- The position vector $\mathbf{f}$ of a point P is the vector $\overrightarrow{OP}$ from the origin to the point.

- Vectors are added according to the triangle rule of vector addition.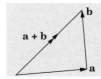

- The scalar product of two vectors is given by: $\mathbf{a} \bullet \mathbf{b} = |\mathbf{a}||\mathbf{b}|\cos\theta$
  $= a_1b_1 + a_2b_2$ in two dimensions
  $= a_1b_1 + a_2b_2 + a_3b_3$ in three dimensions

- The vector equation of a line through points A and B with position vectors $\mathbf{a}$ and $\mathbf{b}$ is: $\mathbf{r} = \mathbf{a} + t(\mathbf{b} - \mathbf{a}) = (1 - t)\mathbf{a} + t\mathbf{b}$.

- The vector equation of a line through a point A with position vector $\mathbf{a}$ in the direction of $\mathbf{a}$ vector $\mathbf{d}$ is: $\mathbf{r} = \mathbf{a} + t\mathbf{d}$.

PURE

6

Proof

In this chapter we:

■ *show how to use algebra to prove a conjecture,*

■ *introduce the proof of a conjecture using the method of contradiction,*

■ *show how to disprove a conjecture by finding a counter-example.*

THE NEED FOR PROOFS

Pure mathematics is concerned with establishing the truth of statements. In a mathematical argument we need to use careful reasoning to ensure that the conclusions are correct. But why should mathematicians feel the need for a rigorous proof of a statement? A simple answer is that mathematicians are reluctant to take anything on trust. This chapter is devoted to the topic of proof. We begin by exploring the need for proof and the language of proof.

Exploration 6.1

The bridges of Konigsberg

The old town of Konigsberg in East Prussia was built on the banks of the River Pregel, with islands that were linked to each other and the river banks by seven bridges.

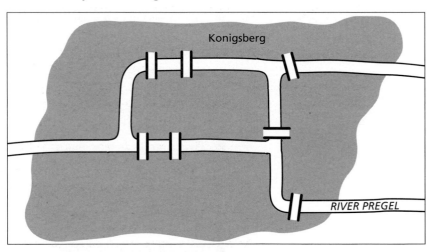

The citizens of the town tried for many years to find a route for a walk that would cross each bridge only once and allow them to end their walk where they had started.

Can you find a suitable route?

Exploration 6.2

Exploring conjectures

Discuss the following conjectures with a partner and decide if they are always true, sometimes true or never true. Amend each conjecture so that it is always true.

- Multiplying makes numbers bigger.
- The sum of two or more consecutive positive integers has an odd factor greater than 1.
- The sum of four even, positive integers is divisible by 4.
- 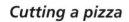 $\sqrt{a^2 - b^2} = a - b$
- If you are given that $ca > cb$ then you can deduce that $a > b$.

Note: A conjecture is a proposition or statement that we think may be true but that we have not proved!

Exploration 6.3

Cutting a pizza

A friend of mine cuts a circular pizza in a peculiar way. When there are two people she marks two points on the circumference and cuts along a straight line joining the points, thus dividing the pizza into two pieces. (The pieces are often different sizes.)

For three people she marks three points on the circumference and cuts along the straight lines joining the points. How many pieces of pizza does this produce?

By drawing appropriate diagrams, find how many pieces are produced with **a)** four, **b)** five points on the circumference. (No three of the cuts meet at a point.)

Find a formula relating the numbers of pieces of pizza and the number of points on the circumference.

Now try it with six points. Does your formula still hold true?

Conclusions

Did you find a route for the citizens of Konigsberg?

Can you prove it? Unless your studies include the Decision and Discrete Mathematics module, probably not. The proof involves an area of mathematics called **graph theory**.

Note: Konigsberg was renamed Kaliningrad. After bombing in World War II, only four of the bridges now remain. In 1736 Euler proved that it is impossible to find a route.

The pizza-cutting problem shows how careful you need to be when solving problems. It is easy to propose the formula: number of pieces $= 2^{n-1}$, where n is the number of points on the circumference. The formula works for $n \leq 5$ but fails for $n = 6$. This is an example of using a counter-example to disprove a conjecture.

In attempting these three investigations you may, unknowingly and informally, have used the methods of proof described in this chapter. Also, Exploration 6.2 shows the need for precision when writing mathematics.

Exploration 6.4

THE LANGUAGE AND NOTATION OF MATHEMATICS

Types of numbers

Carry out the following activities with a partner.

- Each of you write down 20 numbers so that together you have 40 numbers.
- Order the numbers, from smallest to largest.
- Classify your 40 numbers into the following types: counting numbers, natural numbers, integers, rational numbers, real numbers.
- Are all of your numbers classified?

Interpreting the results

You have been manipulating numbers since your early childhood, from the counting numbers 1, 2, 3, 4 ... to irrational numbers such as $\sqrt{2}$, $\sqrt{3}$, π. It is likely that in your classification in Exploration 6.4 you listed all the 40 numbers as real numbers, but only a few as counting numbers. Mathematicians are very precise about classifying numbers. The following table summarises the definition of and notation for the types of numbers of Exploration 6.4.

Name	Symbol	Description
Counting numbers	Z^+	1, 2, 3, 4 ...
Natural numbers	N	0, 1, 2, 3, 4 ...
Integers	Z	..., –3, –2, –1, 2, 3 ...
Rational numbers	Q	$\frac{m}{n}$ where m and n are integers with $n \neq 0$
Real numbers	$\Re$	Rational and irrational numbers

Note the hierarchy in the table. For example, the natural numbers are the counting numbers and 0; the rational numbers include the integers, and so on.

In mathematics, we often need to say that a variable **belongs to the set of** one of these types of numbers. For example, in saying that n **belongs to the set of integers** we are also saying that n is not a fraction or an irrational number. The mathematical notation for **belongs to the set of** is the symbol $\in$.

$n \in Z$ means 'n belongs to the set of integers', i.e. n is an integer.

$a \in Q$ means 'a is a rational number', it may be a counting number, a natural number, an integer or a fraction.

$x \in \Re$ means x is any of the numbers in the table.

Exploration 6.5

Implications

Consider the following pairs of statements P and Q.

In each case decide if P being true leads to Q being true.

a) P: Julie has been to Helsinki. Q: Julie has been to Finland.
b) P: $n = 5$ Q: $n^2 - 7n + 10 = 0$
c) P: $n = 1$ Q: $n^2 + 3n + 1 = 0$
d) P: $n^2 - 3n + 2 = 0$ Q: $n = 2$
e) P: The object has six faces. Q: The object is a cube.
f) P: m and n are odd positive integers. Q: $m + n$ is an even integer.
g) P: mn is a natural number where m and n are natural numbers. Q: m and n are odd natural numbers.
h) P: $x = 5$ Q: $4 < x < 6$

A proof is essentially a sequence of statements, starting from those we know are true or are given, and finishing with the statement to be proved. Each statement is true because the previous statements are true.

Note: The statement to be proved is often called a conjecture.

This leads to the idea of **implication**.

$$\text{implication}$$
One statement is true $\longrightarrow$ another statement is true.

This diagram suggests that there is a direction through a proof. The symbol used to denote an implication is $\Rightarrow$. The mathematical statement:

$$P \Rightarrow Q$$

asserts that if statement P is true then so is statement Q. If P does not lead to Q we write $P \nRightarrow Q$.

Note: $P \Rightarrow Q$ is read as 'P implies Q'.

Consider again the pairs of statements in Exploration 6.5.

a) $P \Rightarrow Q$ If Julie has been to Helsinki then she has been to Finland.
b) $P \Rightarrow Q$ If $n = 5$ then $n^2 - 7n + 10 = 5^2 - 7 \times 5 + 10 = 0$.
c) $P \nRightarrow Q$ If $n = 1$ then $n^2 + 3n + 1 = 5 \neq 0$.
d) $P \nRightarrow Q$ This might surprise you. If $n^2 - 3n + 2 = 0$ then $n = 2$ or $n = 1$ and so the statement Q is not complete.
e) $P \nRightarrow Q$ An object with six faces does not have to be a cube.
f) $P \Rightarrow Q$ If m and n are odd positive integers then $m + n$ is even.
g) $P \nRightarrow Q$ For example if $mn = 24$ then $m = 8$, $n = 3$ or $m = 6$, $n = 4$ i.e. m and n are not both odd natural numbers.
h) $P \Rightarrow Q$ If $x = 5$ then it certainly lies between 4 and 6.

Example 6.1

P is the statement $n > 5$, Q is the statement $n > 0$, where n is any integer.

Which of the following statements is true?
a) $P \Rightarrow Q$ **b)** $Q \Rightarrow P$

Solution

a) $P \Rightarrow Q$ is a true statement because any integer greater than 5 is positive.

b) $Q \Rightarrow P$ is not a true statement. For example if $n = 2$ then Q is true but P is false.

The statement $P \Rightarrow Q$ can also be written as $Q \Leftarrow P$ and is read 'as Q is implied by P'.

Exploration 6.6

Converse of a conjecture

Consider again the pairs of statements in Exploration 6.5. For which pairs can you write $Q \Rightarrow P$?

Interpreting the results

For the following pairs of statements d), e), g) we can write $Q \Rightarrow P$. This is called the **converse** of the statement $P \Rightarrow Q$.

When both implications $P \Rightarrow Q$ and $Q \Rightarrow P$ hold true we write $P \Leftrightarrow Q$.

This statement says, 'statement P is equivalent to statement Q'.

For example, if P is the statement '$n^2 - n - 2 = 0$' and Q is the statement '$n = 2$ or $n = -1$' then $P \Leftrightarrow Q$.

Sometimes the words 'necessary' and 'sufficient' are used in the context of implications and conjectures. For example, consider the two statements.

$P: n > 0$ $Q: n > 5$

It is necessary that $n > 0$ for it to be true that $n > 5$, i.e. P is a necessary condition for Q and as an implication we write $P \Leftarrow Q$ (P is implied by Q). However, it is not sufficient that $n > 0$ to imply that $n > 5$, because in the case of $n = 1$, P is true but Q is false. So $P \nRightarrow Q$.

If P is both a necessary and sufficient condition for Q, then $P \Leftrightarrow Q$.

EXERCISES

6.1 CLASSWORK

1 Insert the correct symbol ($\Rightarrow$, $\Leftarrow$ or $\Leftrightarrow$) between the following statements.

a) $n = 2$ ☐ $n^2 - n - 2 = 0$

b) $ab = 0$ ☐ $a = 0$ or $b = 0$

c) n is a multiple of 2 ☐ n is a multiple of 4

d) $n^2 - 5n + 4 = 0$ ☐ $n = 1$ or $n = 4$

e) $\sin \theta = \frac{1}{2}$ ☐ $\theta = \frac{\pi}{6}$

f) $y = x^3$ ☐ $\frac{dy}{dx} = 3x^2$

2 The following four statements P, Q, R and S are given for a positive integer n.

P: n is a multiple of 3.
Q: n is a multiple of 9.
R: The sum of the digits of n is a multiple of 3.
S: The sum of the digits of n is a multiple of 9.

Classify the following statements as true or false. If a statement is false give values of n which disprove it.

a) $P \Rightarrow Q$
b) P is true if Q is true.
c) $P \Leftrightarrow S$
d) S is a sufficient condition for R.
e) Q is a necessary and sufficient condition for R.
f) $R \Rightarrow P$

3 The following statements are always true, sometimes true or never true. Give examples for those which are never true. (Do not try to prove the statements you think are true.) Amend any statements so that they are all always true.

a) The square of an even integer is even.
b) If $x > 7$ then $-x > -7$.
c) The sum of the first n positive odd integers is a square.
d) The function $f : x \mapsto x^2 - 4x + 5$ for $x > 0$ has an inverse function.
e) To multiply by 10 you add a nought.

4 State the converse of each of the following statements, and say whether or not the converse is true.

a) If 4 divides n then 4 divides n^2, where n is a positive integer.
b) For a polynomial $P(x)$, if $P(a) = 0$ then $(x - a)$ is a factor of $P(x)$.
c) If $y = \sin x$ then $\frac{dy}{dx} = \cos x$.
d) Every prime number greater than 3 is of the form $6n \pm 1$ where n is a positive integer.

EXERCISES

6.1 HOMEWORK

1 Insert the correct symbol ($\Rightarrow$, $\Leftarrow$ or $\Leftrightarrow$) between the following statements.

a) $n^2 - 3n + 2 = 0$ ☐ $n = 2$ or $n = 1$
b) $n = 4$ ☐ $n^2 - 9n + 20 = 0$
c) n is a multiple of 9 ☐ n is a multiple of 3.
d) $\theta = \pi$ ☐ $\cos \theta = -1$
e) $P(a) = 0$ ☐ $(x - a)$ is a factor of $P(x)$, where $P(x)$ is a polynomial.
f) m is odd ☐ $m = 2n + 1$ for some integer n.

2 State the converse of each of the following statements and say whether or not the converse is true.

a) If triangle ABC has a right angle at A then $a^2 = b^2 + c^2$.
b) If $x = \sqrt{2}$ then $x^2 - 2 = 0$.
c) If n is an even integer then n^3 is an even integer.
d) If p is a prime number greater than 3 then $p^2 - 1$ is divisible by 24.

3 For each of the following, state whether the first statement P is necessary or sufficient for the second statement Q (or both, or neither).

a) P: $n > 4$ Q: $n > -1$

b) P: ABCD is a parallelogram. Q: the diagonals of ABCD are perpendicular.

c) P: ABC is a triangle in which A is an obtuse angle. Q: $a^2 > b^2 + c^2$

d) P: $n^2 + n$ is even for integer n. Q: n is an even integer.

e) P: John has been to New York. Q: John has been to the USA.

4 Given the two statements:

P: n is a positive integer investigate the truth of: Q: $f(n) = n^2 + n + 37$ is a prime number > 37

a) $P \Rightarrow Q$ b) $Q \Rightarrow P$.

PROOF BY DIRECT METHOD

A proof of a mathematical statement is a logical argument consisting of steps justified by implications. We begin with one of the simplest forms of proof in which we assume that P is true and deduce Q. This is the direct form of proof.

Example 6.2

Conjecture: The square of any odd integer is odd.
Proof: Let n be any odd integer.
What do I know?   All odd integers can be written in the form $2k + 1$.
What do I want?   To show that n^2 is odd.

$\Rightarrow n^2 = (2k + 1)^2$
$\Rightarrow n^2 = 4k^2 + 4k + 1$
$\Rightarrow n^2 = 2(2k^2 + 2k) + 1$
$\Rightarrow n^2 = 2m + 1$ where $m = 2k^2 + 2k$ is an integer.

So n^2 is odd since it is in the form $2m + 1$.

Example 6.3

Conjecture: For positive real numbers a and b, $a < b \Rightarrow a^2 < b^2$.
Proof:
What do I know? a, b are positive real numbers: $a < b$
What do I want? $a^2 < b^2$

Multiply the given inequality by a on both sides.
$a < b \Rightarrow a^2 < ab$ (The inequality is unchanged because $a > 0$.)
Multiply the given inequality by b on both sides.
$a < b \Rightarrow ab < b^2$ (The inequality is unchanged because $b > 0$.)
$a^2 < ab$ and $ab < b^2 \Rightarrow a^2 < b^2$
So we have proved that if $a < b$ then $a^2 < b^2$.

In each of these examples we were careful to identify what we knew, i.e. our starting points and our goal. In each case the first step in the proof requires a previously known result: in Example 6.2 we used the fact that every odd integer can be written as $2 \times$ integer $+ 1$ (i.e. $2k + 1$ for some integer k). In Example 6.3 we could proceed with multiplying each side of an inequality because $a > 0$ and $b > 0$.

The method of direct proof of $P \Rightarrow Q$ involves the following steps.

| Step 1 | Assume P to be true. |
| Step 2 | Demonstrate that Q is true as a consequence of the assumption in Step 1. |

EXERCISES

6.2 CLASSWORK

1   Prove that the square of any even integer is even.

2   Prove that the function $f : x \mapsto 2x - 1$ where x is real and one-to-one.

3   Prove that the sum of the first n positive odd integers is a square number.

4   Prove that if p is a prime number greater than 3 then $p^2 - 1$ is divisible by 24. (Hint: p can be written in the form $6n \pm 1$.)

5   Prove that for negative real numbers a and b, $a < b \Rightarrow a^2 > b^2$.

6   Prove that for all positive integers n the number $n^2 + n$ is even.

7   Prove that for real numbers a and b, $a < b \Rightarrow 4ab < (a + b)^2$.
    Is this condition also necessary? If so, prove it. If not, find a necessary and sufficient condition.

8   ABC is a triangle in which angle A is obtuse and sides a, b and c are opposite angles A, B and C respectively. Prove that $a^2 > b^2 + c^2$.

EXERCISES

6.2 HOMEWORK

1   Prove that for real non-zero numbers a and b, the quadratic equation $x^2 + 2ax + b = 0$ has two distinct real solutions if $a^2 - b > 0$.

2   Prove that if a, b and c are odd integers then $a + b + c$ is an odd integer.

3   Prove that if n is a factor of the integers a and b then n is also a factor of $ax + by$ for any integers x and y.

4   Prove that for every positive integer n, n^5 has the same units digit as n. Hence prove that $n^5 - n$ is divisible by 10 for every positive integer n.

5   Prove that for all integers a, b and c:
    (a divides b) and (b divides c) $\Rightarrow$ (a divides c)

6   Form a conjecture about the set of numbers formed if you add 4 to the product of two integers which differ by 4. Prove your conjecture.

7   Prove that the function $f : x \mapsto 4x - x^2$ where $x \geq 2$ is one-to-one.

8   Group the positive odd numbers into categories according to their remainder when divided by 8.
    Write down the squares of the first five odd integers. Write down a conjecture in words about the remainder when the square of an odd integer is divided by 8.
    Prove your conjecture.

PROOF BY CONTRADICTION

Exploration 6.7

Square numbers

Consider the conjecture: An even perfect square is the square of an even number.

- Try it out with some numbers, until you understand what this conjecture means.
- Suppose you start with an odd number, prove that the square is always odd.
- What can you deduce?

Interpreting the results

The method of proof in this activity is more elaborate than the direct method but is a very common and powerful method of proof.

The method is called **proof by contradiction**.

Note: The method is often described as *reductio ad absurdum* or reduction to the absurd.

It is important to understand what you are trying to prove. It is easy to prove that the square of an even number is even.

Note: An even number can be written as $2n$ and $(2n)^2 = 4n^2 = 2(2n^2)$ which is even.

We are trying to prove the converse, i.e. if we start with an even square number then this number can only have been obtained by squaring an even number.

We begin by assuming the conjecture to be false, i.e. we start with an odd number and try to show that its square is even. Any odd number can be written in the form $2k + 1$, where k is an integer.

$$(2k + 1)^2 = 4k^2 + 4k + 1 = 2(2k^2 + 2k) + 1 = 2m + 1$$

which is odd. The square of an odd number is always odd, i.e. it cannot be even. So if n^2 is even n cannot be odd, so n is even.

Example 6.4

Conjecture: There do not exist integers m and n such that: $18m + 20n = 1201$.

What do I know? m, n are integers.

What do I want? Show that $18m + 20n \neq 1201$.

Getting started: Assume that I can find integers m and n such that $18m + 20n = 1201$.
Since 18 is even and 20 is even, $18m + 20n = 2(9m + 10n)$ is even. But 1201 is odd.
So if we assume that integers m and n can be found then we have a contradiction: even = odd. Hence integers m and n cannot be found.

Example 6.5

Conjecture: $\sqrt{2}$ is irrational.

What does it mean? A rational number is one that can be written as a fraction $\frac{m}{n}$ where m and n are integers and have no common factors. The conjecture says that $\sqrt{2}$ cannot be written in this form.

Getting started: Assume that $\sqrt{2}$ is rational so that:
$\sqrt{2} = \frac{m}{n}$ and m, n are integers with no common factors. Square both sides.
$2 = \frac{m^2}{n^2}$
$2n^2 = m^2$

$\Rightarrow m^2$ is even
$\Rightarrow m$ is even

Note: Here we are using what we know from Exploration 6.7.

Assume that $m = 2k$ for integer k.
$m^2 = 4k^2$
$\Rightarrow 2n^2 = 4k^2$
$\Rightarrow n^2 = 2k^2$
$\Rightarrow n^2$ is even
$\Rightarrow n$ is even.
Thus we have shown that m and n are even, so they have a common factor 2. But this is a contradiction because we have previously said that m and n have no common factors.

Where did we go wrong? Since everything else has been systematically proved, it must be our initial assumption that $\sqrt{2}$ is rational.
Hence $\sqrt{2}$ is irrational.

Example 6.6

Conjecture: There are infinitely many prime numbers.

Note: This is a very famous proof first given about 2300 years ago by the Greek mathematician Euclid.

Getting started: Assume that there is only a finite set of primes that can be put in an ordered list:
$2, 3, 5, 7, \ldots, p$
Multiply these numbers together to form the number N:
$N = 2 \times 3 \times 5 \times 7 \times \ldots \times p$
N is not a prime number. Consider the number $N + 1$.
If you divide $N + 1$ by any of this list of primes 2, 3, 5, 7, $\ldots$, p you always get a remainder of 1.
So $N + 1$ is not divisible by any prime.
Either $N + 1$ is a prime larger than p or it can be factorised into prime factors. But these factors cannot be from the list 2, 3, 5, 7, $\ldots$, p.
So we have found another prime number that is not in the assumed list.

Where did we go wrong? It must be in our initial assumption that there is only a finite number of primes.
Hence there are infinitely many primes.

The method of proof by contradiction consists of eliminating the possibility that the statement to be proved is false, by proving that the opposite (negative) statement cannot be true. This method of proving statement P involves the following steps.

Step 1: Assume that statement P is false.
Step 2: Deduce from the assumption that there is a contradiction of some sort.
Step 3: Infer that the assumption in Step 1 was wrong, which is equivalent to saying that P is true.

EXERCISES

1 m and n are integers and the product mn is odd.
Prove that m is odd.

2 Prove that 101 is an odd integer.

3 Prove that there do not exist integers m and n such that
$34m + 50n = 1357$.

4 Prove that if n is an integer such that n^3 is even then n itself is even.

5 Prove that the cube root of 2 is not a rational number.

6 Prove by contradiction that there does not exist a largest integer.

7 A basic Pythagorean triple is a set of three positive integers a, b, c
such that $a^2 = b^2 + c^2$ and a, b, c have no common factors.

a) Prove that a, b and c cannot all be odd.
b) Prove that c cannot be even.

EXERCISES

1 Prove that there do not exist integers m and n such that $6m + 8n = 91$.

2 Prove that if n^2 is a perfect square which is a multiple of 3 (i.e. $n^2 = 3k$)
then n is a multiple of 3.

3 Prove that $\sqrt{3}$ is not a rational number.

4 Prove by contradiction that there does not exist a smallest positive
real number.

5 Suppose that x, y and z are non-zero real numbers, not all equal to
each other. Prove that $\frac{x}{y}$, $\frac{y}{z}$, $\frac{z}{x}$ are not all equal.

6 a) Prove that for any real number $a \neq 0$, $a^2 > 0$.
b) Prove by the method of contradiction that the non-zero integer 1
is a positive number.

7 Prove that if a, b and c are integers such that $a > b$, then $ac \leq bc \Rightarrow c \leq 0$.

FINDING COUNTER-EXAMPLES

For a statement to be true it must always be true, not true some of the
time. If you can find one particular case for which the statement is
false then the general statement is not true. Such a case is called a
counter-example.

Exploration 6.8

Fermat's conjecture for primes

The 17th-century French mathematician Pierre de Fermat discovered
in 1640 that the numbers $2^1 + 1$, $2^2 + 1$, $2^4 + 1$, $2^8 + 1$ and $2^{16} + 1$ are
prime numbers.

He conjectured that all the numbers of the form $2^m + 1$ ($m = 2^n$, n an
integer) were prime.

- Confirm that Fermat's conjecture is true for $n = 1, 2, 3$ and 4.
- Show that the conjecture fails for $n = 5$.

Note: Leonhard Euler found the counter-example in 1739.

Interpreting the results

It was probably much easier for you to find the counter example, using a calculator or computer software, than it was for Euler in the 18th century. In some situations you can prove a conjecture by testing all cases and showing that it is true for each one of them. This is called **proof by exhaustion**.

Example 6.7

Conjecture: There is no integer n for which $n^4 + 4$ is exactly divisible by 7.

Getting started: The integers can be written in many different ways. In this example we start with the statement that every integer is of the form $n = 7k + r$ where $r = 0, 1, 2, 3, 4, 5$ or 6.
So $n^2 + 4 = (7k + r)^2 + 4$
$\qquad = 49k^2 + 14kr + r^2 + 4$
Now $49k^2 + 14kr$ is divisible by 7 ($49k^2 + 14kr = 7m$ for an integer m).
Thus $n^2 + 4$ is divisible by 7 if $r^2 + 4$ is divisible by 7. The values of r are 0, 1, 2, 3, 4, 5 and 6, so we can test each one.

r	0	1	2	3	4	5	6
$r^2 + 4$	4	5	8	13	20	29	40

None of these is divisible by 7 so $r^2 + 4$ is not divisible by 7.

Hence $n^2 + 4$ is not divisible by 7.

Note: The method of proof by exhaustion involves trying each possible case. It is worth trying if there are not too many cases!

EXERCISES

6.4 CLASSWORK

Disprove the statements in questions 1–5 by finding a counter-example for each one.

1 If you have two simultaneous linear equations in two unknowns, you can always calculate the values of the two unknowns.

2 The function defined by f: $x \mapsto 2x - x^2$ for $x \in \Re$ is one-to-one.

3 a) Prove that if 4 divides m, then 4 divides m^2.
a) Is the converse true: if 4 divides m^2 does 4 divide m?

4 Multiplying by positive numbers makes numbers bigger.

5 $\sqrt{a^2 + b^2} = a + b$

6 Use the method of proof by exhaustion to show that the circle with the equation $x^2 + y^2 = 36$ passes through exactly four points for which both the x- and y-coordinates are integers.

7 Use the method of proof by exhaustion to show that the number 163 is prime.

8 Show that there is no integer n for which $n^2 - 2$ is exactly divisible by 5.

EXERCISES

6.4 HOMEWORK

1 Disprove the following statements by finding a counter-example for each one.
a) If the graph of $y = f(x)$ is below the x-axis for $x = 2$ and above the x-axis for $x = 4$ then it must be zero for some value of x between 3 and 4.
b) The sum of four even numbers is divisible by 4.
c) $a^2 + b^2 = (a + b)^2$
d) If x is any number less than 4 then x^2 must be less than 16.
e) $\dfrac{1}{a} + \dfrac{1}{b} = \dfrac{1}{a+b}$ for all numbers a and b.

2 Use the method of proof by exhaustion to show that the number 199 is prime.

3 Use the method of proof by exhaustion to prove that the equation $x^2 = 2$ does not have integer solutions.

4 The integers m and n are such that $0 \leq n < m \leq 5$. Use the method of proof by exhaustion to show that the equation $m^n = n^m$ has exactly one solution.

CONSOLIDATION EXERCISES FOR CHAPTER 6

1 In each of the following, decide whether each conjecture is true or false. If you think the conjecture is true then prove it using a suitable method. If it is false give a counter-example.
a) No square number ends in 2.
b) If n is prime then $n^2 + n + 1$ is prime.
c) If m and n are odd numbers then $m^2 + n^2$ cannot be divisible by 4.
d) The sum of any three consecutive integers is divisible by 6.
e) The value of $n^2 + n + 41$ is a prime number for all positive integer values of n.
f) 101 is a prime number.

2 Prove the proposition that every prime number greater than 3 can be written in the form $6n \pm 1$ where n is a positive integer.
Show, by means of a counter-example, that the converse is false.

3 Explain what is wrong with the following argument.
Conjecture: $1 = 2$
Proof: Assume that $x = y$:
$\Rightarrow xy = y^2$
$\Rightarrow xy - x^2 = y^2 - x^2$
$\Rightarrow x(y - x) = (y + x)(y - x)$
$\Rightarrow x = y + x$
$\Rightarrow x = 2x$ since $y = x$
$\Rightarrow 1 = 2$

4 a) Give either a direct proof or a counter-example for each of the following statements about positive numbers.

   i) even + odd = odd
   ii) odd + odd = even
   iii) even $\times$ odd = odd
   iv) odd $\times$ odd = even

b) Give either a proof or a counter-example for each of the following statements about positive numbers.

   i) rational + irrational = irrational
   ii) irrational + irrational = irrational
   iii) rational $\times$ irrational = irrational
   iv) irrational $\times$ irrational = irrational

5 a) Prove that every odd integer can be written in the form $4n + 1$ or $4n - 1$.
   b) Prove that the product of two integers of the form $4n + 1$ is itself of the form $4n + 1$.
   c) Find a counter-example that shows that the converse of the statement in **b)** is not true.

6 Prove the following result.
'A triangle with sides that can be written in the form $n^2 + 1$, $n^2 - 1$ and $2n$ (where $n > 1$) is right-angled.'

Show, by means of a counter-example, that the converse is false.
(MEI Question X, Specimen Paper 2000 P1)

7 Consider the statement: 'If n is any integer then $n^2 - n$ is even.'
Prove this statement using two of the methods in this chapter.

8 Prove that the smallest value of n $(n > 1)$ for which $1^2 + 2^2 + 3^2 + \ldots + n^2$ is a perfect square is 24.

9 a) Prove that every positive integer can be written in the form $3k + r$ where k is a positive integer and $r = 0$, 1 or 2.

Hence prove that for each positive integer n, $n^3 - n$ is a multiple of 3.
   b) Prove that for each positive integer n, $n^5 - n$ is a multiple of 5.
   c) Investigate whether it is true that for each positive integer n, $n^m - n$ is a multiple of m for every positive integer m.

10 If a, b and c denote positive real numbers prove that:
   a) $a^2 + b^2 + c^2 > bc + ca + ab$.
   b) $2(a^3 + b^3 + c^3) > bc(b + c) + ca(a + c) + ab(a + b)$

Summary

- $P \Rightarrow Q$ asserts that if statement P is true then so is statement Q;

- $P \Leftarrow Q$ asserts that if statement Q is true then so is statement P;
  P is a necessary condition for Q

- $P \Leftrightarrow Q$ statement P is equivalent to statement Q
  P is both a necessary and sufficient condition for Q

- The **converse** of $P \Rightarrow Q$ is $P \Leftarrow Q$ or $Q \Rightarrow P$

- **Proof by direct method**
  Step 1 Assume P to be true.
  Step 2 Demonstrate that Q is true as a consequence of the assumption in Step 1.

- **Proof by contradiction**
  Step 1: Assume that statement P is false.
  Step 2: Deduce from the assumption that there is a contradiction of some sort.
  Step 3: Infer that the assumption in Step 1 was wrong, which is equivalent to saying that P is true.

- **Proof by counter-example**
  A general statement can be disproved by finding a single counter-example.

7

Curves 1

In this chapter we introduce:

■ *the basic geometry of the circle,*

■ *three other special curves – the ellipse, hyperbola and parabola,*

■ *a calculus technique to find the equations of tangents and normals to these curves, called implicit differentiation.*

CARTESIAN EQUATION OF A CIRCLE

CALCULATOR ACTIVITY

Exploration 7.1

Investigating circles

Set the scales on your graphics calculator or computer program to:

$$y_{min} = -5; \qquad y_{max} = 5; \qquad y_{scl} = 1$$

and so that the line $y = x$ appears to make an angle $45°$ to the x-axis. (Zoom Square is a common command to achieve this feature.)

Use the basic equation $x^2 + y^2 = 1$.

■ Rearrange the equation into the forms $y = +\sqrt{f(x)}$ and $y = -\sqrt{f(x)}$.

■ Draw graphs of the functions $y = \pm\sqrt{f(x)}$.
■ Where does the graph cut the x- and y-axes?

■ Describe the graph of the equation $x^2 + y^2 = 1$.

Repeat the activity for the equations $x^2 + y^2 = 4$, $x^2 + y^2 = 9$

and $x^2 + y^2 = 25$.

Deduce the graph of the equation $x^2 + y^2 = r^2$.

Interpreting the results

The following table shows the conclusions that we should expect from this activity.

Equation	Curve
$x^2 + y^2 = 1$	circle of radius 1, centre $(0, 0)$
$x^2 + y^2 = 4$	circle of radius 2, centre $(0, 0)$
$x^2 + y^2 = 9$	circle of radius 3, centre $(0, 0)$
$x^2 + y^2 = 25$	circle of radius 5, centre $(0, 0)$

We conclude that the equation $x^2 + y^2 = r^2$ is the equation of a circle of radius r and centre $(0, 0)$.

But what about circles that are not centred at $(0, 0)$ but at some other point, say (a, b)?

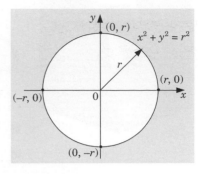

Exploration 7.2

Equations of circles

Take the equation of a circle of radius r and centre $(0, 0)$, $x^2 + y^2 = r^2$.
- Describe the effect on the circle of replacing x by $(x - a)$.
- Describe the effect on the circle of replacing y by $(y - b)$.
- Deduce the equation of a circle of radius r and centre (a, b).

Sketch the circle without using a calculator.

Interpreting the results

The equation $(x - a)^2 + y^2 = r^2$ is a translation by an amount a of the circle $x^2 + y^2 = r^2$ parallel to the x-axis and the equation $x^2 + (y - b)^2 = r^2$ is a translation of the circle by an amount b parallel to the y-axis.

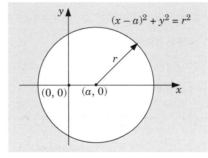

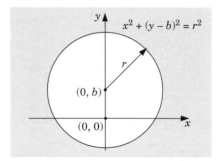

Putting these two translations together we deduce the general result that the equation of a circle of radius r and centre (a, b) is

$$(x - a)^2 + (y - b)^2 = r^2.$$

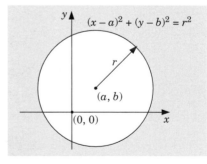

Example 7.1

Find the equation of the circle with centre (1, 3) and radius 2.

Solution

Substituting for $a = 1$, $b = 3$ and $r = 2$ in the general formula for a circle gives:

$$(x - 1)^2 + (y - 3)^2 = 2^2$$

Multiplying out the brackets:

$$x^2 - 2x + 1 + y^2 - 6y + 9 = 4$$

$$\Rightarrow x^2 + y^2 - 2x - 6y + 6 = 0$$

The diagram shows the circle.

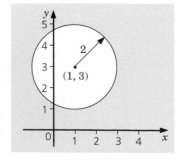

Example 7.2

A circle has the equation $x^2 - 6x + y^2 + 8y - 11 = 0$. *Find the centre and radius.*

Solution

The first step is to write the equation in standard form. To do this complete the square for each pair $(x^2 - 6x)$ *and* $(y^2 + 8y)$.

$x^2 - 6x = (x - 3)^2 - 9$

$y^2 + 8y = (y + 4)^2 - 16$

The equation of the circle becomes:

$(x - 3)^2 - 9 + (y + 4)^2 - 16 - 11 = 0$

$\Rightarrow (x - 3)^2 + (y + 4)^2 = 36 = 6^2$

The circle has centre (3, −4) and radius 6.

Example 7.3

Find the centre and radius of the circle with equation
$2x^2 + 2y^2 + 3x - 4y + 1 = 0$

Solution

The standard form of the equation of a circle always starts with $x^2 + y^2$. *So dividing the given equation by 2:*

$x^2 + y^2 + \frac{3}{2}x - 2y + \frac{1}{2} = 0$

Completing the squares:

$\left(x + \frac{3}{4}\right)^2 - \frac{9}{16} + (y - 1)^2 - 1 + \frac{1}{2} = 0 \Rightarrow \left(x + \frac{3}{4}\right)^2 + (y - 1)^2 = \frac{17}{16}$

The circle has centre $(-\frac{3}{4}, 1)$ and radius $\frac{\sqrt{17}}{4}$.

EXERCISES

7.1 CLASSWORK

1 Write down the equation of each circle.

a) centre (0 , 0), radius 7   b) centre (4 , 0), radius 4
c) centre (2 , 1), radius 5   d) centre (−3 , 2), radius 3
e) centre (0 , 5), radius 2.5   f) centre (−1, −1), radius 6

2 Find the centre and radius of the circles with the following equations.

a) $x^2 + y^2 = 121$ b) $x^2 + (y - 5)^2 = 81$

c) $(x - 3)^2 + (y - 4)^2 = 25$ d) $(x - 2)^2 + (y + 3)^2 = 16$

e) $(x + 4)^2 + y^2 - 49 = 0$ f) $x^2 + y^2 - 2y + 1 = 36$

g) $x^2 - 4x + y^2 = 60$ h) $x^2 + 3x + y^2 - 5y = 66$

i) $x^2 + y^2 - 2x - 4y - 131 = 0$ j) $4x^2 - 28x + 4y^2 - 16y = 35$

3 Determine which of the following equations represent circles.

a) $x^2 + y^2 = 16$ b) $x^2 - y^2 = 16$ c) $x^2 + y^2 + 8x - 9 = 0$

d) $x^2 + 2y^2 - 2x - 3 = 0$ e) $x^2 = y^2 - 4y + 1$ f) $x^2 + y^2 + 6x + 8y = 0$

4 Find the equation of the circle with PQ as diameter where:

a) P is the point (2, 0) and Q is the point (8, 8),
b) P is the point (−1, 1) and Q is the point (0, 2),
c) P is the point (−2, −3) and Q is the point (1, 2).

5 Find the coordinates of the points where a circle with equation $(x-15)^2 + (y+5)^2 = 169$ intersects the x-axis. Show that the circle does not intersect the y-axis.

6 Find the coordinates of the points of intersection of the circle $x^2 + y^2 - 2x - 3y - 131 = 0$ with the x- and y-axes.

EXERCISES

7.1 HOMEWORK

1 Write down the equation of each circle.

a) centre (0, 0), radius 6   **b)** centre (3, 0), radius 1

c) centre (0, –2), radius $\frac{1}{2}$ **d)** centre (3, –2), radius 4

e) centre (–4, –5), radius 1.5   **f)** centre $(\frac{1}{2}, \frac{1}{4})$, radius 2

2 Find the centre and radius of the circles with the following equations.

a) $x^2 + y^2 = 81$ **b)** $(x-1)^2 + y^2 = 49$

c) $x^2 + (y+2)^2 = 100$ **d)** $(x-1)^2 + (y+2)^2 = 4$

e) $(x+3)^2 + (y-1)^2 - 16 = 0$ **f)** $x^2 + y^2 - 6x + 2y + 1 = 0$

g) $x^2 + y^2 - 12x - 52 = 0$ **h)** $x^2 + y^2 - 5y + 0.25 = 0$

i) $2x^2 + 2y^2 - 3x - 5y = 0$ **j)** $3x^2 + 3y^2 - 6x + 12y = 17$

3 Determine which of the following equations represent circles.

a) $x^2 - y^2 = 25$ **b)** $x^2 + y^2 = 25$

c) $x^2 + 2y^2 - 2x + 3y - 5 = 0$ **d)** $x^2 + y^2 - 2x - 4y + 5 = 0$

e) $x^2 + y^2 + x + y - 1 = 0$ **f)** $y^2 = x^2 + 3x - 2$

4 Find the coordinates of the points of intersection P_1, P_2 and Q_1, Q_2 of the circle $x^2 + y^2 - 12x - 16y + 15 = 0$ with the x- and y-axes respectively. Is PQ a diameter of the circle for each pair P_1, Q_1 and P_2, Q_2?

5 Find the equation of the circle with AB as diameter where:
a) A is the point (0, 2) and B is the point (2, 0),
b) A is the point (2, 3) and B is the point (–1, –1),
c) A is the point (0, 0) and B is the point (5, 12).

6 The circle shown has equation $x^2 + y^2 - 4x + 6y - 3 = 0$ and the line AB is a diameter that is parallel to the x-axis. Find the coordinates of A and B.

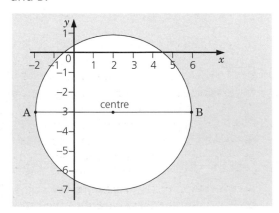

THE ELLIPSE, HYPERBOLA AND PARABOLA
CALCULATOR ACTIVITY

Exploration 7.3

Different curves

Set the scales on your graphics calculator or computer program to:

$$y_{min} = -2; \qquad y_{max} = 2; \qquad y_{scl} = 1$$

and so that $x^2 + y^2 = 1$ gives a circle (i.e. Zoom Square).

a) Take the equation $\dfrac{x^2}{4} + \dfrac{y^2}{4} = 1$.

Rearrange in the form $y = \pm f(x)$.
Draw the graph of the equation and describe the curve.

b) Take the equation $\dfrac{x^2}{4} + y^2 = 1$.

Rearrange in the form $y = \pm g(x)$.
Draw the graph of the equation and describe the curve.
Where does it cut the x-axis and y-axis?

c) Take the equation $\dfrac{x^2}{4} - \dfrac{y^2}{4} = 1$

Rearrange in the form $y = \pm h(x)$.
Draw the graph of the equation and describe the curve.
Where does it cut the x-axis? Does it cut the y-axis?

Interpreting the results

The following figures show the three curves that we should expect to obtain in the calculator activity.

a)

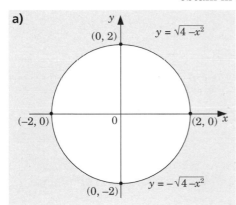

b)

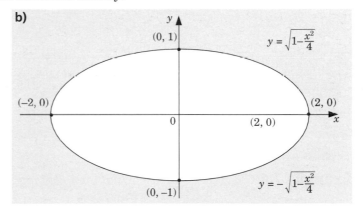

For each curve, we have seen that a change in the sign or value of the coefficient of y^2 in the equation of a circle leads to a different curve. These are other members of a special family of curves called **conic sections**. Curve b) is an example of an **ellipse**. Curve c) is an example of a **hyperbola**. There is a fourth conic section called a **parabola**. An example of a parabola with formula $y^2 = 4x$ is shown in **d)**.

c)

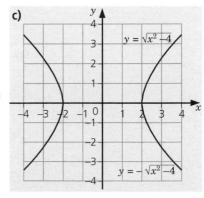

d)

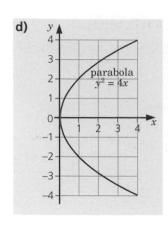

The curves are called conic sections because each one can be obtained by cutting a slice or section through a cone.

We have already seen that the general equation of a circle, with centre (0, 0) and radius r, is $x^2 + y^2 = r^2$ which can be written as:

$$\frac{x^2}{r^2} + \frac{y^2}{r^2} = 1$$

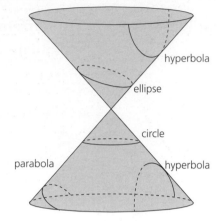

The following table shows the general equations for the other conic sections.

Ellipse	Hyperbola	Parabola
$\dfrac{x^2}{a^2} + \dfrac{y^2}{b^2} = 1$	$\dfrac{x^2}{a^2} - \dfrac{y^2}{b^2} = 1$	$y^2 = 4ax$

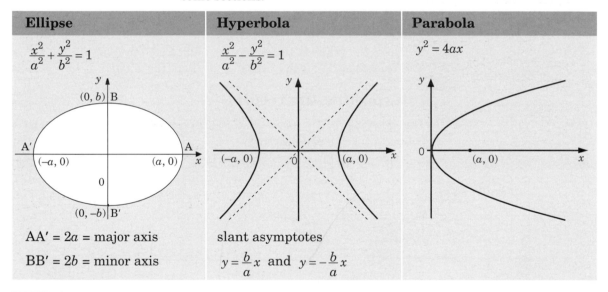

Ellipse	Hyperbola	Parabola
AA′ = 2a = major axis BB′ = 2b = minor axis	slant asymptotes $y = \dfrac{b}{a}x$ and $y = -\dfrac{b}{a}x$	

Example 7.4

Write each of the following equations in standard form and hence classify the curves.

a) $x^2 - y^2 - 2x - 4y - 12 = 0$ **b)** $2x - y^2 - 2y - 1 = 0$

c) $x^2 + y^2 - 2x + 4y - 4 = 0$ **d)** $x^2 + 4y^2 - 2x + 16y + 8 = 0$

Solution

For each equation we need to complete the square so that it can be written in the form $\dfrac{(x - ?)^2}{a^2} \pm \dfrac{(y - ?)^2}{b^2} = 1$. The values of a and b and the occurrence of the + or – sign will allow us to classify the curve as a circle, ellipse, hyperbola or parabola.

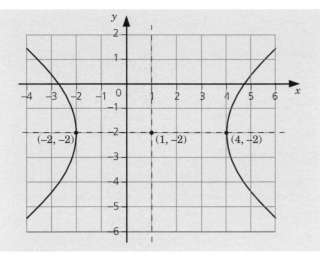

a)

$$x^2 - y^2 - 2x - 4y - 12 = 0$$

$$\Rightarrow \left((x-1)^2 - 1\right) - \left((y+2)^2 - 4\right) - 12 = 0$$

$$\Rightarrow (x-1)^2 - (y+2)^2 - 9 = 0$$

$$\Rightarrow \frac{(x-1)^2}{3^2} - \frac{(y+2)^2}{3^2} = 1$$

This is the equation of a hyperbola with centre (1, –2).

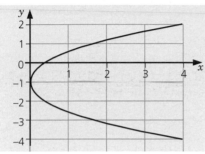

b)

$$2x - y^2 - 2y - 1 = 0$$

$$\Rightarrow 2x - (y+1)^2 = 0$$

$$\Rightarrow (y+1)^2 = 2x$$

This is a parabola with centre (0, –1).

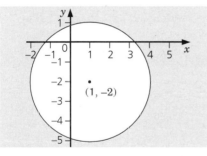

c)

$$x^2 + y^2 - 2x + 4y - 4 = 0$$

$$\Rightarrow \left((x-1)^2 - 1\right) + \left((y+2)^2 - 4\right) - 4 = 0$$

$$\Rightarrow (x-1)^2 + (y+2)^2 - 9 = 0$$

$$\Rightarrow \frac{(x-1)^2}{3^3} + \frac{(y+2)^2}{3^3} = 1$$

This is the equation of a circle with centre (1, –2) and radius 3.

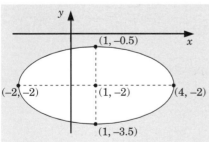

d)

$$x^2 + 4y^2 - 2x + 16y + 8 = 0$$

$$\Rightarrow \left((x-1)^2 - 1\right) + 4\left((y+2)^2 - 4\right) + 8 = 0$$

$$\Rightarrow (x-1)^2 + 4(y+2)^2 - 9 = 0$$

$$\Rightarrow \frac{(x-1)^2}{3^2} + \frac{(y+2)^2}{\left(\frac{3}{2}\right)^2} = 1$$

This is the equation of an ellipse with centre (1, –2), major axis 6 and minor axis 3.

CALCULATOR ACTIVITY

Exploration 7.4   *Asymptotes*

Set the scales on your graphics calculator or computer program to:

$$x_{min} = -10; \qquad x_{max} = 10; \qquad x_{scl} = 1$$
$$y_{min} = -10; \qquad y_{max} = 10; \qquad y_{scl} = 1$$

Use the equation $x^2 - y^2 = 25$.

- Draw the graph of the equation; which conic section have you drawn?
- Find the equations of the slant asymptotes.
- What is the angle between the asymptotes?
- On the same axes draw the graph of the equation $xy = 25$.
- Describe the transformation between the two curves.

Interpreting the results

The curves in this activity are special types of hyperbolae called **rectangular hyperbolae**. The asymptotes are perpendicular and have equations $y = x$ and $y = -x$.

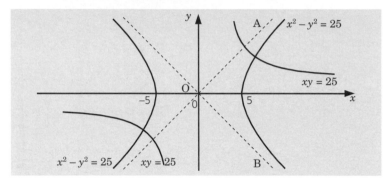

The two branches of the curves $xy = 25$ can be made to coincide with the two branches of $x^2 - y^2 = 25$ by a rotation through $45°$ clockwise. The x-axis will then lie along OB and the y-axis will lie along OA.

In the standard form of the equation of a rectangular hyperbola, $a = b$ so:

$$\frac{x^2}{a^2} - \frac{y^2}{a^2} = 1 \text{ or } x^2 - y^2 = a^2$$

A special type of rectangular hyperbola that has the x- and y-axes as asymptotes is $xy = a^2$.

EXERCISES

7.2 CLASSWORK

1 Sketch the graphs of the following equations and classify each curve as one of the conic sections.

   a) $\dfrac{x^2}{9} + \dfrac{y^2}{25} = 1$ **b)** $4x^2 + y^2 - 16x - 6y - 24 = 0$

   c) $\dfrac{x^2}{9} - \dfrac{y^2}{25} = 1$ **d)** $y^2 - 8x = 0$

   e) $xy - 4 = 0$ **f)** $\dfrac{y^2}{4} - \dfrac{x^2}{16} = 1$

2 Write down the equations of the following ellipses.
   a) centre (0, 0),   major axis 4, minor axis 6
   b) centre (1, 2),   major axis 2, minor axis 3
   c) centre (–2, –1), major axis 5, minor axis 4

3 Write down the equations of the rectangular hyperbolae which pass through these pairs of points.
   a) (3, 0) and (–3, 0)   **b)** (4, 0) and (–2, 0)
   c) (0, 2) and (0, –2)

4   Write each of the following equations in standard form and hence classify the curve as one of the conic sections.

   a) $x^2 + 2y^2 + 2x - 12y - 6 = 0$ **b)** $x^2 - 2y^2 + 2x - 8 = 0$

   c) $x^2 - y^2 - 3x + 5y - 20 = 0$

EXERCISES

7.2 HOMEWORK

1   Sketch the graphs of the following equations and classify each curve as one of the conic sections.

   a) $9x^2 + 4y^2 = 36$ **b)** $9x^2 - 4y^2 = 36$

   c) $x^2 - y^2 - 2x - 3y - 2.25 = 0$ **d)** $x^2 + y^2 - 2x - 3y + 2.25 = 0$

   e) $9x^2 + 4y^2 + 36x + 24y + 71 = 0$ **f)** $y^2 - 4x - 2y - 7 = 0$

2   Write each of the equations in question **1** in standard form and confirm your classification.

3   Write down the equations of the following ellipses.
   a) centre (0, 0),   major axis 8, minor axis 2
   b) centre (−1, 3),   major axis 1, minor axis 3
   c) centre (0.5, 2.5), major axis 3, minor axis 4

4   Write down the equation of the hyperbola:
   a) which passes through the point (4, 0) and has slant asymptotes
      $y = \pm 2x$,
   b) which passes through the point (−1, 0) and has slant asymptotes
      $y = \pm x$,
   c) which passes through the point (2, 0) and the point (4, $5\sqrt{3}$).

INTERSECTION OF CURVES AND LINES

Example 7.5

Find the points of intersection of the circle $x^2 + y^2 - 2x - 4y - 20 = 0$ and the line $y = 2x + 5$.

Solution
In general a line will:
- *intersect a circle at two distinct points,*
- *touch a circle as a tangent, or*
- *miss the circle completely.*

A graph of the line and circle shows that, in this case, there are two points of intersection.

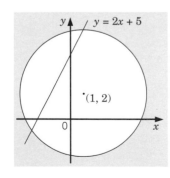

To find the coordinates of the points of intersection we solve the equations:

$x^2 + y^2 - 2x - 4y - 20 = 0$

$y = 2x + 5$

simultaneously. The x-values are given by:

$x^2 + (2x + 5)^2 - 2x - 4(2x + 5) - 20 = 0$

$\Rightarrow 5x^2 + 10x - 15 = 0$

$\Rightarrow 5(x - 1)(x + 3) = 0$

$\Rightarrow x = 1 \ or \ x = -3$

The points of intersection of the line and the circle are (1, 7) and (−3, −1).

Example 7.6

The line through the origin $y = mx$ is a tangent to the circle $x^2 + y^2 - 2x - 4y + 1 = 0$. Find the possible values of m and the corresponding coordinates of the points of contact.

Solution

Substituting $y = mx$ in $x^2 + y^2 - 2x - 4y + 1 = 0$:

$$x^2 + m^2x^2 - 2x - 4mx + 1 = 0$$
$$\Rightarrow \left(1 + m^2\right)x^2 - (2 + 4m)x + 1 = 0$$

The line is a tangent if there is only one root to this equation.

$$\Rightarrow (2 + 4m)^2 = 4\left(1 + m^2\right)$$
$$\Rightarrow 4 + 16m + 16m^2 = 4 + 4m^2$$
$$\Rightarrow 12m^2 + 16m = 0$$
$$\Rightarrow m = 0 \text{ or } m = -\tfrac{4}{3}$$

There are two tangents to the circle which pass through the origin and these have equations $y = 0$ and $y = -\tfrac{4}{3}x$.

The points of contact are (1, 0) and $\left(-\tfrac{3}{5}, \tfrac{4}{5}\right)$ = (–0.6, 0.8).

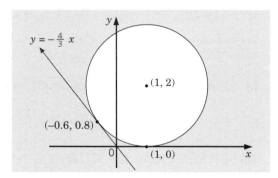

Example 7.7

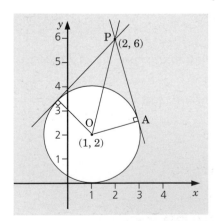

Find the length of the tangent from the point (2, 6) to the circle $x^2 + y^2 - 2x - 4y + 1 = 0$.

Solution

In standard form the circle has equation:
$$(x - 1)^2 + (y - 2)^2 = 4$$

The centre is (1, 2) and the radius is 2.

Since each tangent is perpendicular to a radius, Pythagoras' theorem can be used to give:

$$OP = \sqrt{(6 - 2)^2 + (2 - 1)^2} = \sqrt{17}$$

$$AP = \sqrt{OP^2 - OA^2} = \sqrt{17 - 4} = \sqrt{13}$$

Example 7.8

Show that the point P (2, –1) lies on the circle $x^2 + y^2 - 2x + 6y + 5 = 0$.
Find the equation of the tangent to the circle through P.

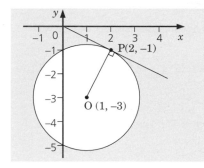

Solution

In standard form the equation of the circle is:
$$(x - 1)^2 + (y + 3)^2 = 5$$

The circle has centre (1, –3) and radius $\sqrt{5}$.

The point (2, –1) lies on the circle since $(2 - 1)^2 + (-1 + 3)^2 = 5$.
The radius OP is perpendicular to the tangent. The gradient of
OP is:
$$\frac{(-1) - (-3)}{2 - 1} = 2$$

Hence the gradient of the tangent is $-\frac{1}{2}$.

The equation of the tangent is $\dfrac{y - (-1)}{x - 2} = -\dfrac{1}{2} \Rightarrow y = -\dfrac{1}{2}x$.

EXERCISES

7.3 CLASSWORK

1   Find the points of intersection of the given curve and line.

  a) circle $x^2 + y^2 = 9$, line $y = x - 3$

  b) circle $x^2 + y^2 + 4y = 0$, line $y = 2x - 1$

  c) circle $x^2 + y^2 + 8x - 9 = 0$, line $y = 1 - 3x$

  d) circle $x^2 + y^2 - 4x + 6y - 12 = 0$, line $y = -x$

  e) ellipse $9x^2 + 4y^2 = 36$, line $y = x + 2$

2   The line $y = mx$ is a tangent to the circle $x^2 + y^2 + 2x + 14y + 40 = 0$. Find the possible values of m and the coordinates of the points of contact.

3   The line $y = mx + 1$ is a tangent to the circle $x^2 + y^2 - 10x - 12y + 51 = 0$. Find the possible values of m and the coordinates of the points of contact.

4   Find the length of the tangent from the given point to the given circle.

  a) point (0, 0), circle $x^2 + y^2 + 6x - 4y + 12 = 0$

  b) point (2, 0), circle $x^2 + y^2 + 2x + 4y + 4 = 0$

  c) point (4, 5), circle $x^2 + y^2 = 9$

5   Show that the given point P lies on the given circle. Find the equation of the tangent to the circle through P.
  a) P(3, 4), circle $x^2 + y^2 = 25$

  b) P(6, 3), circle $x^2 + y^2 - 10x - 12y + 51 = 0$

  c) P(7, –2), circle $x^2 + y^2 - 6x - 2y - 15 = 0$

6   The line $y = mx + c$ is a tangent to the circle $x^2 + y^2 = r^2$.
  Show that $c^2 = r^2(1 + m^2)$.

7   Find the values of c for which the line $y = 2x + c$:

a) touches,
b) cuts in two points,
c) does not meet the circle $x^2 + y^2 - 2x = 0$.

8   Find the points of intersection of the rectangular hyperbola $xy = 1$ and the circle $x^2 + y^2 + 2x + 2y - 6 = 0$.

9   Find the points of intersection of the circle $x^2 + y^2 = 9$ and the ellipse $\dfrac{x^2}{16} + \dfrac{y^2}{2} = 1$.

10   The circle shown in the diagram has equation $(x - 1)^2 + (y - 1)^2 = 5$.

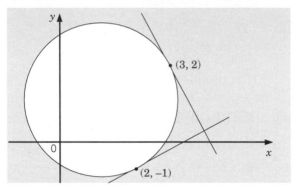

Tangents are drawn at the points (3, 2) and (2, −1).
Write down the coordinates of the centre of the circle and hence show that the tangents are perpendicular to each other.

(Question 5, SEB Paper 1, 1994)

11   An ear-ring is to be made from silver wire and is designed in the shape of two touching circles with two tangents to the outer circle as shown in the top diagram.
The bottom diagram shows a drawing of this ear-ring related to the coordinate axes.
The circles touch at (0, 0).
The equation of the inner circle is $x^2 + y^2 + 3y = 0$.
The outer circle intersects the y-axis at (0, −4).
The tangents meet the y-axis at (0, −6).
Find the total length of silver wire required to make this ear-ring.

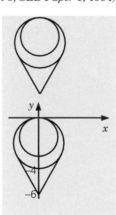

(Question 5, SEB Paper 2, 1989)

EXERCISES

7.3 HOMEWORK

1   Find the points of intersection of the given curve and line.

a) circle $x^2 + y^2 = 2$, line $y = 1 - 2x$

b) circle $x^2 + y^2 - 3x - 2 = 0$, line $y = x + 1$

c) circle $x^2 + y^2 - 3y + 3 = 0$, line $2y + x = 3$

d) hyperbola $xy = 5$, line $y = x - 4$

e) ellipse $4x^2 + y^2 = 4$, line $3y - x = 0$

2 The line $y = mx$ is a tangent to the circle $x^2 + y^2 - 2x + 6y + 2 = 0$. Find the possible values of m and the coordinates of the points of contact.

3 The line $y = mx + 3$ is a tangent to the circle $x^2 + y^2 - 4x - 5 = 0$. Find the possible values of m and the coordinates of the points of contact.

4 Find the values of m for which the line $y = mx + 4$:

  a) touches,

  b) cuts in two points,

  c) does not meet the circle $x^2 + y^2 + 4y - 5 = 0$.

5 The line $y = mx + c$ is a tangent to the ellipse $\dfrac{x^2}{a^2} + \dfrac{y^2}{b^2} = 1$.

Show that $c^2 = a^2m^2 + b^2$.

6 Find the length of the tangent from the given point to the given circle.

  a) point (0, 0), circle $x^2 + y^2 + 6x + 8y + 16 = 0$

  b) point (0, 5), circle $x^2 + y^2 + 4y - 5 = 0$

  c) point (–2, –3), circle $x^2 + y^2 - 3x - y + 1 = 0$

7 Show that the points (–2, –4), (3, 1) and (–2, 0) lie on the circle

$x^2 + y^2 - 2x + 4y - 8 = 0$. Find the equation of the tangent to the circle through each point.

8 Find the points of intersection of the rectangular hyperbola $xy = 4$ and the hyperbola $x^2 - 2y^2 - 4 = 0$.

9 Find the points of intersection of the parabola $y^2 = 4x$ and the circle $x^2 + y^2 + 2x - 7 = 0$.

10 AB is a tangent at B to the circle with centre C and equation $(x - 2)^2 + (y - 2)^2 = 25$. The point A has coordinates (10, 8). Find the area of triangle ABC.

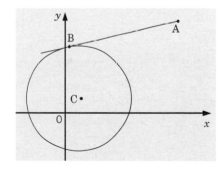

(SEB Question 16, Paper 1, 1992)

11 A bakery firm makes gingerbread men each 14 cm high with circular heads and bodies.

The equation of the 'body' is $x^2 + y^2 - 10x - 12y + 45 = 0$ and the line of centres is parallel to the y-axis. Find the equation of the 'head'.

(SEB Question 7, Paper 1, 1990)

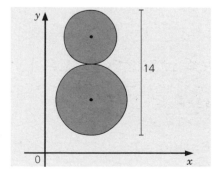

IMPLICIT DIFFERENTIATION

The functions we have met so far in this book have almost all been written in the form $y = f(x)$. This is called the **explicit form** of a function. The relation $y = x^2 - 2x + 1$ is an example of an explicit function. Some functions are written in an **implied form** from which it is difficult to extract the relation in the form $y = f(x)$. For example, $xe^y - y = 0$ is written in such a form. This is called the **implicit form** of a function or an **implicit function**.

To differentiate functions given in implicit form, we need to use a technique called **implicit differentiation**.

Exploration 7.5

Implicit differentiation

Take the equation of a circle $x^2 + y^2 = 1$.

- Rearrange the equation into the form $y = f(x)$.
- Find $\dfrac{dy}{dx}$.
- Rearrange your formula for $\dfrac{dy}{dx}$ to show that $x + y\dfrac{dy}{dx} = 0$.

Repeat the steps for the following equations.

a) For $2x^2 - 3y^2 - x = 0$ show that $4x - 6y\dfrac{dy}{dx} - 1 = 0$

b) For $e^y x - x^2 = 0$ show that $xe^y\dfrac{dy}{dx} + e^y - 2x = 0$

Deduce a technique for differentiating an implicit function.

Interpreting the results

The chain rule (as well as the other rules) of differentiation is particularly important in implicit differentiation. Consider the equation $x^2 + y^2 = 1$ and differentiate with respect to x term by term.

Use the chain rule.

$$\frac{d(x^2)}{dx} = 2x \text{ and } \frac{d(y^2)}{dx} = \frac{d(y^2)}{dy}\frac{dy}{dx} = 2y\frac{dy}{dx}$$

$$\frac{d(1)}{dx} = 0$$

Substituting these results gives:

$$2x + 2y\frac{dy}{dx} = 0 \implies x + y\frac{dy}{dx} = 0$$

This is a more straightforward method of approach than setting up an explicit function first as we did in Exploration 7.5.

Example 7.9

Differentiate the following to find $\dfrac{dy}{dx}$.

a) $2x^2 - 3y^2 - x = 0$

b) $e^y x - x^2 = 0$

Compare the method with your approach in Exploration 7.5.

Solution

a) $2x^2 - 3y^2 - x = 0$

Differentiating term by term:

$4x - 6y\dfrac{dy}{dx} - 1 = 0$, *since*

$\dfrac{d(3y^2)}{dx} = \dfrac{d(3y^2)}{dy}\dfrac{dy}{dx} = 6y\dfrac{dy}{dx}$ *by the chain rule.*

Rearranging to find $\dfrac{dy}{dx}$:

$\dfrac{dy}{dx} = \dfrac{4x - 1}{6y}$

b) $e^y x - x^2 = 0$

Differentiating term by term:

$\left(e^y\dfrac{dy}{dx}\right)x + e^y - 2x = 0$ *using the product rule and chain rule.*

Rearranging to find $\dfrac{dy}{dx}$ *we get* $\dfrac{dy}{dx} = \dfrac{2x - e^y}{xe^y}$

Example 7.10

Find the value of $\frac{dy}{dx}$ *for the equation* $2x^2 + 3y^2 - 3x + 2y = 0$ *at the point* $(1, \frac{1}{3})$. *Hence find the equations of the tangent and normal to the curve at* $(1, \frac{1}{3})$.

Solution

Differentiating term by term:

$4x + 6y\dfrac{dy}{dx} - 3 + 2\dfrac{dy}{dx} = 0$

$\Rightarrow \quad \dfrac{dy}{dx} = \dfrac{3 - 4x}{2 + 6y}$

At the point $\left(1, \frac{1}{3}\right)$:

$\dfrac{dy}{dx} = \dfrac{3 - 4(1)}{2 + 6\left(\frac{1}{3}\right)} = -\dfrac{1}{4}$

The gradient of the tangent at $(1, \frac{1}{3})$ *is* $-\frac{1}{4}$.

The equation of the tangent is:

$\dfrac{y - \frac{1}{3}}{x - 1} = -\dfrac{1}{4} \quad \Rightarrow \quad 12y + 3x = 7$

The gradient of the normal at $(1, \frac{1}{3})$ *is* $-\dfrac{1}{\left(-\frac{1}{4}\right)} = 4$.

The equation of the normal is $\dfrac{y - \frac{1}{3}}{x - 1} = 4 \quad \Rightarrow \quad 3y - 12x = -11$

EXERCISES

7.4 CLASSWORK

In questions **1–10**, find $\frac{dy}{dx}$ using implicit differentiation.

1 $x^2 + y^2 = 5$

2 $x^2 - y^2 = 5$

3 $x^2 + y^2 - 2x + 4y - 1 = 0$

4 $(x - 1)^2 - 2(y + 1)^2 = 4$

5 $x^3 - xy + y^2 = 6$ **6** $\sqrt{xy} = x - 2y$

7 $e^{-2y}\sin 5x = 1$ **8** $\sin x + \cos y = 0.5$

9 $y = \cos(xy)$ **10** $e^{3y} = x^2 - xy$

In questions **11–18**, find the value of $\frac{dy}{dx}$ at the given point.

11 $x^2 + y^2 = 25$, point (3, 4)

12 $x^2 - y^2 = 3$, point (2, –1)

13 $x^2 + y^2 - 4x + 6y - 13 = 0$, point (1, 2)

14 $x^2 - xy + y^2 = 13$, point (3, –1)

15 $(x + y)^3 = x^3 + y^3$, point (–1, 1)

16 $\sqrt{xy} = x + y - 3$, point (4, 1)

17 $\left(x^2 + y^2\right)^2 = 4x^2 y$, point (1, 1)

18 $x\sin y = 1$, point $\left(2, \frac{\pi}{6}\right)$

19   Show that for the circle with equation $(x - a)^2 + (y - b)^2 = r^2$, $\frac{dy}{dx} = -\frac{(x - a)}{(y - b)}$.

20   If $x^2 + y^2 = 9$ use implicit differentiation to show that $\frac{d^2 y}{dx^2} = -\frac{9}{y^3}$.

In questions **21–26** find the equations of the tangent and normal to the conic section at the given point.

21   circle $x^2 + y^2 = 16$, point $\left(2, \sqrt{12}\right)$

22   circle $x^2 + y^2 - 2x + 4y - 20 = 0$, point (5, 1)

23   circle $x^2 + y^2 + 6x - 2y - 3 = 0$, point (–1, –2)

24   ellipse $9x^2 + 4y^2 + 54x - 8y - 95 = 0$, point (1, 4)

25   parabola $y^2 - 2y + 1 - 2x = 0$, point (2, 3)

26   hyperbola $x^2 - y^2 + 2x - 6y - 20 = 0$, point (3, –1)

27   Show that the equation of the tangent to the circle $(x - a)^2 + (y - b)^2 = r^2$ at the point (x_1, y_1) has equation $(y - y_1)(y_1 - b) + (x - x_1)(x_1 - a) = 0$.

EXERCISES

7.4 HOMEWORK

In questions **1–10**, find $\frac{dy}{dx}$ using implicit differentiation.

1 $x^2 + y^2 = 8$ **2** $x^2 - y^2 = 8$

3 $2x^2 + 3y^2 = 6$ **4** $y^2 - 4y = 3x - 4$

5 $(x - 4)^2 + (y + 3)^2 = 9$ **6** $x^2 - 2y^2 + 3x + 5y - 11 = 0$

7 $x\sin y = y\cos x$ **8** $x^2 e^{-y} - xy = 0$

9 $\sin(x + y) = x$ **10** $y = \sin(xy)$

In questions **11–18**, find the value of $\frac{dy}{dx}$ at the given point.

11 $x^2 + y^2 = 5$, point (1, 2)

12 $x^2 + 2y^2 = 19$, point $(-1, 3)$

13 $x^2 + 3xy + y^3 = 11$, point $(2, 1)$

14 $x^2 + 9y^2 - 4x + 3y - 6 = 0$, point $(0, -1)$

15 $(1 - x^2)y = 2x$, point $(0, 0)$

16 $x^2 \cos y = 1$, point $\left(\sqrt{2}, \frac{\pi}{3}\right)$

17 $e^x y = 4 + xy$, point $(0, 4)$

18 $y\sqrt{x} - x\sqrt{y} = 6$, point $(4, 9)$

19 Show that for the rectangular hyperbola with equation
$(x - a)^2 - (y - b)^2 = r^2$, $\dfrac{dy}{dx} = \dfrac{(x - a)}{(y - b)}$.

20 If $y \sin x = e^x$ show that $\dfrac{d^2 y}{dx^2} + 2 \cot x \dfrac{dy}{dx} - 2y = 0$.

In questions **21–26** find the equations of the tangent and normal to the conic section at the given point.

21 circle $x^2 + y^2 = 36$, point $(-4, \sqrt{20})$

22 circle $x^2 + y^2 + 2y - 1 = 0$, point $(1, -2)$

23 circle $x^2 + y^2 - 3x + 8y - 20 = 0$, point $(3, 2)$

24 hyperbola $xy - y + 3x = 11$, point $(2, 5)$

25 ellipse $4x^2 + y^2 - 4x + 2y - 16 = 0$, point $(-1, 2)$

26 hyperbola $2x^2 - y^2 + 4x + 4y - 43 = 0$, point $(4, -1)$

27 Show that the equation of the tangent to the hyperbola
$\dfrac{(x - a)^2}{A^2} - \dfrac{(y - b)^2}{B^2} = 1$ at the point (x_1, y_1) is
$A^2(y - y_1)(y_1 - b) - B^2(x - x_1)(x_1 - a) = 0$.

CONSOLIDATION EXERCISES FOR CHAPTER 7

In questions **1–4**, classify the conic sections. For each circle find the radius and centre and for each ellipse find the axis-length and centre. In each case sketch the graph of the function without using a graphics calculator.

1 $x^2 - y^2 = 16$ **2** $x^2 + y^2 - 4x + 6y - 87 = 0$

3 $2x^2 + y^2 - 8x - 6y - 8 = 0$ **4** $y^2 - 2y - 4x = 7$

5 Find the equation of the tangent and normal to the curve with equation $x^2 + y^2 - 10x - 12y + 51 = 0$ at the point $(6, 3)$.

6 Find the range of values of m so that the line $y = mx$ and the circle $x^2 + y^2 - 6x - 8y + 24 = 0$
a) cut in two points,
b) touch at two points
c) do not intersect.

7 Show that an equation of the normal to the hyperbola with equation $xy = c^2$, at the point $\left(cp, \frac{c}{p}\right)$ is $y - \frac{c}{p} = xp^2 - cp^3$.

(ULEAC Question 3 (part), Paper 2, January 1994)

8   A spherical hot-air balloon has radius 30 feet. Cables join the balloon to the gondola which is cylindrical with diameter 6 feet and height 4 feet. The top of the gondola is 16 feet below the bottom of the balloon.

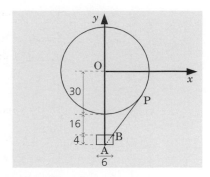

Coordinate axes are chosen as shown in the diagram. One of the cables is represented by PB and PBA is a straight line.

a) Find the equation of the cable PB.

b) State the equation of the circle representing the balloon.

c) Prove that this cable is a tangent to the balloon and find the coordinates of the point P.

(SEB Question 9, Paper II 1992)

9   A penny-farthing bicycle on display in a museum is supported by a stand at points A and C. A and C lie on the front wheel.

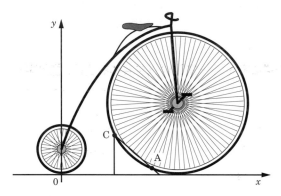

With coordinate axes as shown and 1 unit = 5 cm, the equation of the rear wheel (the small wheel) is $x^2 + y^2 - 6y = 0$ and the equation of the front wheel is $x^2 + y^2 - 28x - 20y + 196 = 0$.

a) **i)** Find the distance between the centres of the two wheels.

   ii) Hence calculate the clearance, i.e. the smallest gap, between the front and rear wheels. Give your answer to the nearest millimetre.

b) B(7, 3) is half-way between A and C, and P is the centre of the front wheel.

   i) Find the gradient of PB.

   ii) Hence find the equation of AC and the coordinates of A and C.

(SEB Question 4, Paper II, 1994)

10 The points (5, 5) and (–3, –1) are the ends of a diameter of the circle C with centre A. Write down the coordinates of A and show that the equation of C is $x^2 + y^2 - 2x - 4y - 20 = 0$.

The line L with equation $y = 3x - 16$ meets C at the points P and Q. Show that the x-coordinates of P and Q satisfy the equation $x^2 - 11x + 30 = 0$.

Hence find the coordinates of P and Q.

(WJEC Question 3, Specimen Paper A1, 1994)

11   Find the centre and radius of the circle with equation $x^2 + y^2 = 6x$.

The line $x + y = k$ is a tangent to this circle. Find the two possible values of the constant k, giving your answers in surd form.

(OCR Question 3, Specimen Paper P3)

12   **a)** Find in cartesian form an equation of the circle C with centre (1, 4) and radius 3.
   b) Determine, by calculation, whether the point (2.9, 1.7) lies inside or outside C.

(EDEXCEL Question 1, Specimen Paper P3)

13   The equation of a curve is $y \cos x = x + y^2$.
Find the gradient of the tangent to the curve at the point (0,1).

(AQA B Question 2, Specimen Paper P4)

14   Determine the coordinates of the centre C and the radius of the circle with equation:

$x^2 + y^2 + 4x - 10y + 13 = 0$.

Find the distance from the point P (2, 3) to the centre of the circle. Hence find the length of the tangents from P to the circle.

(AQA A Question 1, Specimen Paper P3)

Summary

The **conic sections** are the following curves:

- circle, centre (a, b), radius r, $(x - a)^2 + (y - b)^2 = r^2$
- ellipse, centre $(0, 0)$, major axis $2a$, minor axis $2b$, $\dfrac{x^2}{a^2} + \dfrac{y^2}{b^2} = 1$

- hyperbola, centre $(0, 0)$, slant asymptotes $y = \pm \dfrac{b}{a} x$, $\dfrac{x^2}{a^2} - \dfrac{y^2}{b^2} = 1$
- parabola, through $(0, 0)$, $y^2 = 4ax$

The **implicit form** of a function is a relation of the form $f(x, y) = 0$. To differentiate functions given in implicit form we use **implicit differentiation**.

PURE

8

Curves 2

In this chapter we shall introduce:

■ *an alternative method of describing the equation of a curve using a parameter,*

■ *the method of parametric differentiation.*

PARAMETRIC EQUATIONS

In Chapter 7, *Curves 1*, the equations of the conic sections were given as direct relationships between x and y. Sometimes it is more convenient to express x and y in terms of a third quantity called a **parameter**. The pair of equations for x and y given in terms of the parameter are called the **parametric** equations of the curve.

Exploration 8.1

Time as the parameter

A tennis player serves a tennis ball from a height of 2 metres above the ground with speed 30 m s^{-1}. The horizontal and vertical displacements of the ball at time t seconds after serving are:

$x = 30t$
$y = 2 - 5t^2$

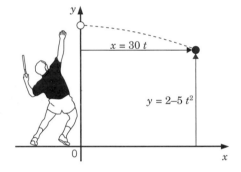

■ Eliminate t to find the equation of the path of the tennis ball $y = f(x)$.
■ Sketch the graph of $f(x)$.
■ Where does the ball first bounce?
■ When does the ball first bounce?

Interpreting the results

The equation of the path is $y = 2 - \frac{1}{180}x^2$ which is the equation of a parabola. The ball hits the ground when $y = 0$. Either reading off the x-value from the graph or solving $2 - \frac{1}{180}x^2 = 0$, we find that the ball hits the ground when $x = 19$ metres (correct to two significant figures).

This occurs after $\frac{19}{30} = 0.63$ seconds.

In this exploration, time is a parameter. The coordinates of the position of the tennis ball are functions of time. Eliminating time gives the path of the ball. This is a common method used in Mechanics. The equations $x = 30t$ and $y = 2 - 5t^2$ are the parametric equations of the path of the ball.

Exploration 8.2

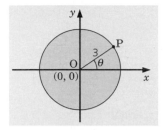

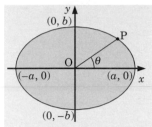

Circles and ellipses

The figure shows the circle centre (0, 0) and radius 3. The angle θ is the angle between OP and the x-axis.

■ Write down the coordinates of the point P in terms of θ:
$x = f(\theta), y = g(\theta)$.

■ Eliminate θ between f and g and show that the equation of the circle is $x^2 + y^2 = 9$.

■ Deduce the parametric equations of a circle centre (0, 0) and radius r.

■ Investigate the ellipse shown and propose parametric equations for an ellipse of major axis $2a$ and minor axis $2b$.

Interpreting the results

For a circle of radius r, centre (0, 0) the parametric equations are $x = r\cos \theta$ and $y = r\sin \theta$.

When we try to find the parametric equations of an ellipse, a simple geometrical approach does not give the answer as it did for a circle. Begin with the Cartesian equation:

$$\frac{x^2}{a^2} + \frac{y^2}{b^2} = 1$$

and compare it with the trigonometric identity $\cos^2 \theta + \sin^2 \theta \equiv 1$.

Now if we choose $\frac{x}{a} = \cos\theta$ and $\frac{y}{b} = \sin\theta$ then the parametric equations of the ellipse are $x = a\cos \theta$ and $y = b\sin \theta$.

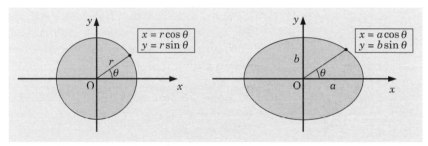

Example 8.1

Sketch the curve given by the parametric equations $x = 2t - 3$ and $y = t + 2$.

Solution
There are two methods of approach.
Using the values of the parameter
Draw up a table of values for t, x and y.

t	-2	0	2	4
$x\ (= 2t - 3)$	-7	-3	1	5
$y\ (= t + 2)$	0	2	4	6

Plotting a graph of y against x shows that in this case the parametric equations give a straight line.

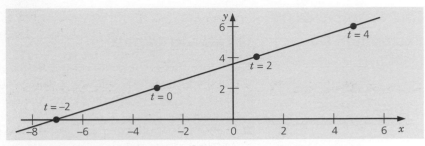

Eliminating the parameter *t*
The second method is to eliminate the parameter *t* to find the corresponding Cartesian equation. From $y = t + 2 \Rightarrow t = y - 2$.
Substitute for *t* into the *x*-equation:
$x = 2(y - 2) - 3 = 2y - 7$
$\Rightarrow 2y - x = 7$
This is the equation of a straight line with gradient $\frac{1}{2}$ and intercept (0, 3.5), which is the same as we drew (above) using the first method.

Example 8.2

Sketch the curve given by the parametric equations $y = 2t - 1$ and $x = t^2 - 4$.

Solution
Using the values of the parameter
We can choose a small number of values for the parameters but the problem is always deciding which values to choose. A useful approach is to find where the curve cuts the axes.
$y = 2t - 1 \Rightarrow y = 0$ when $t = \frac{1}{2} \Rightarrow x = t^2 - 4 = -3.75$

$x = t^2 - 4 \Rightarrow x = 0$ when $t = \pm 2 \Rightarrow y = 3$ or $y = -5$
The curve cuts the axes at the points (–3.75, 0), (0, 3) and (0, –5).
Choosing other values of *t* between –3 and + 3 will give a good idea of the graph.

t	–3	–1	0	1	3
$x(= t^2 - 4)$	5	–3	–4	–3	5
$y (= 2t - 1)$	–7	–3	–1	1	5

The graph of the function is shown in the figure. It is a parabola.

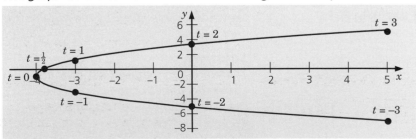

Eliminating the parameter *t*
From $y = 2t - 1 \Rightarrow t = \frac{1}{2}(y + 1)$.

Substituting for *t* into the *x*-equation:

$x = \left(\frac{1}{2}(y + 1)\right)^2 - 4 = \frac{1}{2}y^2 + y - 3.75$

$\Rightarrow 2x = y^2 + 2y - 7.5$

Drawing a graph of this equation will give a parabola as before. In many examples the parametric equations are easier to deal with and involve easier calculations.

EXERCISES

8.1 CLASSWORK

1 Find the Cartesian equation corresponding to the following pairs of parametric equations and hence classify the curves using the definitions of Chapter 7.

a) $x = 2\cos\theta$, $y = 2\sin\theta$ **b)** $x = 4\sin\theta$, $y = 3\cos\theta$

c) $x = 2t$, $y = \dfrac{1}{t}$ **d)** $x = t - 1$, $y = t^2 + 1$

e) $x = 1 + 3\cos\theta$, $y = 2 + 3\sin\theta$

2 The parametric equations of a curve are $x = 2\sec t$ and $y = 3\tan t$.
a) Starting from $\sin^2 t + \cos^2 t = 1$ show that $\sec^2 t = 1 + \tan^2 t$.
b) Find the Cartesian equation of the curve by eliminating the parameter t using the result in **a)**.
c) Classify the resulting curve.

3 Find the Cartesian equation of the straight line with parametric equations $x - 2t - 4$ and $y = t - 1$.
Given that the line can also be represented by the parametric

equations $x = \dfrac{a}{T-1}$ and $y = \dfrac{T}{T-1}$ where a is a constant, find:
a) the value of a,
b) the value of T at the point where $t = 4$.

(UCLES A/O Question 8 (part), Paper 2, November 1989)

4 Find the Cartesian equation and hence classify the curve with parametric equations $x = 5\sin^2 t$ and $y = \cos t$.

5 Sketch the curve given by the parametric equations $y = 3t^2 + 1$ and $x = 6t$.

6 Sketch the curve given by the parametric equations $x = \dfrac{1}{t}$ and $y = t - \dfrac{1}{t}$.

7 The straight line $2y = 3x - 11$ cuts the curve with parametric equations $x = t^2 + 3$ and $y = 3t - 1$ at the points A and B. Calculate the coordinates of A and B.

8 The parametric equations of a curve are $x = t^2 + 3$ and $y = 2t + 1$. Find the coordinates of the points of intersection of the curve and the straight line with parametric equations $x = T + 5$ and $y = 1 - 2T$.

EXERCISES

8.1 HOMEWORK

1 Find the Cartesian equation corresponding to the following pairs of parametric equations and hence classify the curves using the definitions of Chapter 7.

a) $x = 5\sin\theta$, $y = 5\cos\theta$ **b)** $x = 5t$, $y = \dfrac{2}{t}$

c) $x = 2t^2 - 1$, $y = 3t + 1$ **d)** $x = 2\cos\theta - 3$, $y = 5\sin\theta + 1$
e) $x = t + 1$, $y = t - 1$

2 The parametric equations of a curve are $x = e^t + e^{-t}$ and $y = e^t - e^{-t}$.
a) Eliminate t to find the Cartesian equation of the curve.
b) Classify the curve.

3 Find the Cartesian equation and hence classify the curve with parametric equations $x = 1 + \tan \theta$ and $y = 1 - \sec \theta$.

4 The parametric equations of a curve are $x = 2\cos \theta + \sin \theta$ and $y = \cos \theta - 2\sin \theta$.
  a) Write down expressions for $2x + y$ and $x - 2y$ in terms of θ.
  b) Hence determine the Cartesian equation of the curve.
  c) Classify the curve.

5 Sketch the curve given by the parametric equations $x = t^2 + 2t$ and $y = t^2 - 2t$.

6 Sketch the curve given by the parametric equations $x = 8t^3$ and $y = t^2$.

7 The parametric equations of a curve are $x = t^2 + 2$ and $y = 2t - 1$. Find the coordinates of the points of intersection of the curve and the straight line with Cartesian equation $2x + y = 7$.

8 The parametric equations of a curve are $x = 2t - \dfrac{1}{t}$ and $y = 2t + \dfrac{1}{t}$.
  a) Sketch the curve.
  b) A and B are points on the curve at which the values of t are 1 and $\frac{1}{2}$. Find the equation of the straight line through A and B.

PARAMETRIC DIFFERENTIATION

Exploration 8.3

Differentiating parameters

A curve is given by the parametric equations $x = 30t$ and $y = 2 - 5t^2$.
- By eliminating t find the Cartesian equation of the curve.
- Find the slope of the tangent, $\frac{dy}{dx}$, at any point on the curve.

- Find $\frac{dy}{dt}$ and $\frac{dx}{dt}$ and show that $\dfrac{dy}{dx} = \dfrac{\frac{dy}{dt}}{\frac{dx}{dt}}$.

Repeat the tasks for the curves with the following parametric equations.
  a) $x = t^2 + 4t, y = 3t - 1$ **b)** $x = 16t^3, y = 2t^2$

Interpreting the results

There are two methods of finding the equation of the tangent or normal to a curve given by parametric equations. We can either eliminate the parameter and differentiate in the normal way or work directly from the parametric equations. Exploration 8.3 should have demonstrated that using the parametric equations is more straightforward.

The chain rule provides the formula in the exploration. Let $y = u(t)$, $x = v(t)$ be the parametric equations of a curve and $y = f(x)$ be the Cartesian equation obtained by eliminating t. Then applying the chain rule:

$$\frac{dy}{dt} = \frac{dy}{dx} \times \frac{dx}{dt} \Rightarrow u'(t) = f'(x) \times v'(t)$$

The slope of the tangent to the curve is $f'(x) = \dfrac{u'(t)}{v'(t)}$.

In terms of x, y and t $\dfrac{dy}{dx} = \dfrac{\frac{dy}{dt}}{\frac{dx}{dt}}$

This is called **parametric differentiation**.

Example 8.3

Find the equations of the tangent and the normal, at the point (2, 2), to the curve with parametric equations $x = t^2 + 1$ and $y = t^2 + t$.

Solution

At the point (2, 2), $t^2 + 1 = 2$ and $t^2 + t = 2 \Rightarrow t = 1$. The slope of the tangent at (2, 2) is the value of $\frac{dy}{dx}$ when $t = 1$.

$$\frac{dy}{dx} = \frac{\frac{dy}{dt}}{\frac{dx}{dt}} = \frac{2t + 1}{2t}$$

When $t = 1$, $\frac{dy}{dx} = \frac{3}{2}$.

The equation of the tangent is $\dfrac{y - 2}{x - 2} = \dfrac{3}{2} \Rightarrow 2y = 3x - 2$.

The slope of the normal at (2, 2) is $-\frac{2}{3}$.

The equation of the normal is $\dfrac{y - 2}{x - 2} = -\dfrac{2}{3} \Rightarrow 3y = 10 - 2x$.

Example 8.4

A curve is defined parametrically by the equations $x = t^2 + 2t$ and $y = t^2 - 2t$. Find:

a) *the gradient of the chord joining the points A and B for which $t = 1$ and $t = 4$, respectively,*

b) *$\frac{dy}{dx}$ in terms of t,*

c) *the value of t at the point on the curve at which the tangent is parallel to AB. Find the equation of the tangent at this point.*

(Question 8 (part), UCLES (A/O) Paper 2, June 1989)

Solution

a) *$t = 1 \Rightarrow x = 3$ and $y = -1$*

$t = 4 \Rightarrow x = 24$ and $y = 8$

Points A and B are (3, -1) and (24, 8) respectively.

The chord joining the points A and B has gradient $\dfrac{8 - (-1)}{24 - 3} = \dfrac{9}{21} = \dfrac{3}{7}$.

b) *$\dfrac{dy}{dx} = \dfrac{\frac{dy}{dt}}{\frac{dx}{dt}} = \dfrac{2t - 2}{2t + 2}$*

c) *The tangent to the curve is parallel to the line AB when*

$$\frac{2t - 2}{2t + 2} = \frac{3}{7} \Rightarrow 14t - 14 = 6t + 6 \Rightarrow t = \frac{5}{2}$$

At $t = \dfrac{5}{2}$ we have $x = \dfrac{45}{4}$ and $y = \dfrac{5}{4}$

The equation of the tangent at this point is:

$$\frac{y - \frac{5}{4}}{x - \frac{45}{4}} = \frac{3}{7} \Rightarrow 7y = 3x - 25$$

Example 8.5

A curve is given parametrically by the equations $x = 1 + 2t$ and $y = t^2 + 4$.

Find the area of the finite region R bounded by the curve and the lines $x = 3$, $x = 6$ and the x-axis.

Solution

The region R of which the area is to be found is shown in the diagram.

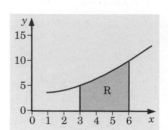

The area of the region R is given by the integral $\int_{x=3}^{x=6} y\,dx$ and we need to write x and y in terms of t.

We know that $x = 1 + 2t$ so $\dfrac{dx}{dt} = 1$.

Further, the limits of integration $x = 3$ and $x = 6$ can be written as $t = 1$ and $t = 2.5$ respectively.

The integral $\int y\,dx$ can be written as $\int y\dfrac{dx}{dt}\,dt$ using the chain rule for differentiation.

Now we substitute for $y = t^2 + 4$ and $\dfrac{dx}{dt} = 2$ to give:

$$\text{area of the region R} = \int_{1}^{2.5}\left(t^2 + 4\right)\times 2 \times dt = \int_{1}^{2.5} 2\left(t^2 + 4\right) dt = 21.75.$$

EXERCISES

8.2 CLASSWORK

In questions **1–6** find the equations of the tangent and normal to the curve at the point with the given value of t.

1. $x = t^2 - 1$, $y = t^2 + t$ at $t = 1$

2. $x = 3\cos t + 1$, $y = 3\sin t - 1$ at $t = \dfrac{\pi}{3}$

3. $x = \dfrac{4}{t}$, $y = 3t - 1$ at $t = 2$

4. $x = e^t - e^{-t}$, $y = e^t + e^{-t}$ at $t = 0$

5. $x = 1 + \tan t$, $y = 1 - \sec t$ at $t = \dfrac{\pi}{4}$

6. $x = \dfrac{t}{t+1}$, $y = \dfrac{t-1}{t}$ at $t = 2$

7.   Find and classify the stationary point of the curve given by the parametric equations $x = 2t^3$, $y = (t + 1)^2$. Sketch the curve. Find the area of the finite region between the curve, the x-axis, $x = 0$ and $x = 1$.

8.   Find and classify the stationary points of the curve given by the parametric equations $x = t$, $y = t^3 - t$. Sketch the curve.
Find the area of the finite region between the curve, the x-axis, $x = 1$ and $x = 3$.

EXERCISES

8.2 HOMEWORK

In questions **1–6** find the equations of the tangent and normal to the curve at the point with the given value of t.

1. $x = t^2$, $y = 4t$ at $t = -1$

2. $x = 5\sin t - 1$, $y = 5\cos t + 1$ at $t = \dfrac{\pi}{6}$

3. $x = 3\cos t - 2$, $y = 2\sin t + 3$ at $t = \dfrac{4\pi}{3}$

4. $x = \dfrac{1+t}{1-t}$, $y = \dfrac{1+2t}{1-2t}$ at $t = 0$

5. $x = e^t$, $y = \sin t$ at $t = 0$

6. $x = t - \cos t$, $y = \sin t$ at $t = \dfrac{\pi}{4}$

7   A curve is given by the parametric equations $x = \sin t$ and $y = \cos 2t$.
Find $\dfrac{dy}{dx}$ in terms of x and show that $\dfrac{d^2 y}{dx^2} = -4$.

8   The parametric equations of a curve are $x = 4t^2$ and $y = 2t + \dfrac{1}{t}$.

   a) Find $\dfrac{dy}{dx}$ when $t = \frac{1}{2}$ and hence find the equations of the tangent
   and normal at this point.
   b) Find if either the tangent or normal intersects the curve again.

9   A curve is given parametrically by the equations $x = 4t$ and $y = \dfrac{4}{t}$.

   Find the area of the finite region R bounded by the curve, the lines
   $x = 4$, $x = 16$ and the x-axis.

10   An ellipse is given parametrically by the equations
   $x = 3 \cos t, y = 2 \sin t, 0 \le t \le 2\pi$

   Find the area of the finite region bounded by the ellipse and the
   positive x- and y-axes.

CONSOLIDATION EXERCISES FOR CHAPTER 8

1   A particle orbits the origin so that its position at time t is given by the
equations $x = 2\cos t$ and $y = 2\sin t$, where t is in radians.
   a) Calculate the particle's position and speed when $t = \frac{1}{3}\pi$.

   b) Calculate the particle's direction of travel when $t = \frac{1}{3}\pi$.
   c) Find the Cartesian equation of the orbit.
   d) Confirm your answer to part **b)** by using your Cartesian equation.

(Oxford (Nuffield) Question 5, Specimen Paper 3, 1994)

2   The equation of a curve is given in terms of the parameter t by the
equations $x = 2t$ and $y = \dfrac{2}{t}$, where t takes positive and negative values.

   a) Sketch the curve.
   At the point on the curve with parameter t,
   b) show that the gradient of the curve is $-t^{-2}$,
   c) find and simplify the equation of the tangent.
   P and Q are the points where a tangent on this curve crosses the x-
   and y-axes, and O is the origin.
   d) Show that the area of the triangle OPQ is independent of t.

(MEI Question 2, Specimen Paper 3, 1994)

3   The parametric equations of a curve are $x = 4t, y = \dfrac{4}{t}$, where the
parameter t takes all non-zero values. The points A and B on the curve
have parameters t_1 and t_2 respectively.
   a) Write down the coordinates of the mid-point of the chord AB.
   b) Given that the gradient of AB is -2, show that $t_1 t_2 = \frac{1}{2}$.
   c) Show that the coordinates of the mid-point of any chord with
      gradient -2 may be expressed in the form: $x = 2T, y = 4T$,
      where T is a parameter, and hence state the equation of the line
      on which all such mid-points lie.
   d) Find the coordinates of the points on the curve at which the
      gradient of the tangent is -2.

(UCLES (Modular) Question 9, Specimen Paper 3, 1994)

4   The equation of a curve is given in terms of the parameter t by the equations $x = 4t$ and $y = 2t^2$ where t takes positive and negative values.
a) Sketch the curve.
P is the point on the curve with parameter t.
b) Show that the gradient at P is t.
c) Find and simplify the equation of the tangent at P.
The tangents at two points Q (with parameter t_1) and R (with parameter t_2) meet at S.
d) Find the coordinates of S.
e) In the case when $t_1 + t_2 = 2$ show that S lies on a straight line. Give the equation of the line.

(MEI Question 4, Paper 2, June 1993)

5   The diagram shows a sketch of the curve given parametrically in terms of t by the equations $x = 1 - t^2$, $y = 2t + 1$.
a) Show that the point Q (0, 3) lies on the curve, stating the value of t corresponding to this point.

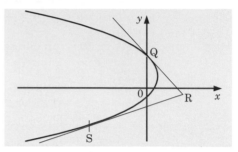

b) Show that, at the point with parameter t, $\dfrac{dy}{dx} = -\dfrac{1}{t}$.
c) Find the equation of the tangent at Q.
d) Verify that the tangent at Q passes through the point R (4, −1).
e) The other tangent from R to the curve touches the curve at the point S and has equation $3y - x + 7 = 0$. Find the coordinates of S.

(MEI Question 4, Paper 2, January 1995)

6   Show that an equation of the normal to the hyperbola with parametric equations $x = ct$, $y = \dfrac{c}{t}$, $t \neq 0$, at the point $\left(cp, \dfrac{c}{p} \right)$ is $y - \dfrac{c}{p} = xp^2 - cp^3$.

(ULEAC Question 3, Paper 2, January 1994)

7   The curve C shown in the diagram is given by $x = t + \dfrac{1}{t}$, $y = t - \dfrac{1}{t}$, $t > 0$, where t is a parameter.

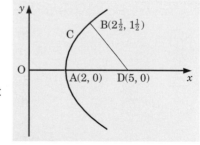

a) Find $\dfrac{dy}{dx}$ in terms of t and deduce that the tangent to C at the point A(2, 0) has equation $x - 2 = 0$.
b) For every point (x, y) on C, show that $x^2 - y^2 = 4$.
The point B has coordinates $(2\frac{1}{2}, 1\frac{1}{2})$ and the point D has coordinates (5, 0). The region R is bounded by the lines AD and BD and arc AB of the curve C. The region R is rotated through 2π radians about the x-axis to form a solid of revolution.
c) Find the volume of the solid, leaving your answer in terms of π.

(ULEAC Question 9, Paper 2, May 1994)

8   The curve shown in the diagram has parametric equations $x = t^2$, $y = t^3$, where $t \geq 0$ is a parameter. Also shown is part of the normal to the curve at the point where $t = 1$.

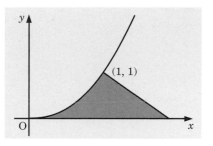

   a) Find an equation of this normal.

   b) Find the area of the finite region bounded by the curve, the x-axis and this normal.

(ULEAC Question 8, Paper 2, January 1995)

9   A curve is given parametrically by the equations $x = c(1 + \cos t)$, $y = 2c\sin^2 t$, $0 \leq t \leq \pi$, where c is a positive constant.

   a) Show that $\dfrac{\mathrm{d}y}{\mathrm{d}x} = -4 \cos t$.

   At point P on the curve, $\cos t = \dfrac{3}{4}$.

   b) Show that the normal to the curve at P has equation
   $24y - 8x - 7c = 0$.

   c) Sketch the curve for $0 \leq t \leq \pi$.

(ULEAC Question 10 (part), Paper 2, January 1992)

10   Show that the equation of the normal to the parabola $y^2 = 4x$ at the point $P(p^2, 2p)$ is $y + px = 2p + p^3$.
   Given that $p \neq 0$ and that the normal at P cuts the x-axis at the point $B(b, 0)$ obtain an expression for p^2 in terms of b. Deduce that $b > 2$.
   The normal at P meets the normal at $Q(q^2, 2q)$ at the point R. Show that the coordinates of R are $(2 + p^2 + pq + q^2, -pq\,(p + q))$.
   Given that $pq = 2$, show that these coordinates can be written in the form $(r^2, 2r)$ where r is a function of p. What does this result tell you about the point R?
   The normal at R meets the parabola again at the point $S(s^2, 2s)$. Find s in terms of r.

(WJEC Question 15, Specimen Paper A1, 1994)

11   The parametric equations of a curve are $x = a \sin \theta$, $y = a\,\theta\cos \theta$ where a is a positive constant and $0 < \theta < \dfrac{1}{2}\pi$. Find $\dfrac{\mathrm{d}y}{\mathrm{d}x}$ in terms of θ,

   and hence show that the gradient of the curve is zero where $\tan \theta = \dfrac{1}{\theta}$.

   By sketching a suitable pair of graphs, show that the equation $\tan \theta = \dfrac{1}{\theta}$ is satisfied by just one value of θ in the relevant range.

   Determine, with reasons, whether this value of θ is greater or less than $\dfrac{1}{4}\pi$.

(OCR Question 6, Specimen Paper P3)

12   A curve is given by the parametric equations
   $x = 4 \sin^3 t, y = \cos 2t, 0 \leq t \leq \dfrac{\pi}{4}$

   a) Show that $\dfrac{\mathrm{d}x}{\mathrm{d}y} = -3 \sin t$.

   b) Find an equation of the normal to the curve at the point where $t = \dfrac{\pi}{6}$.

(EDEXCEL Question 4, Specimen Paper P3)

13   For the ellipse shown in the diagram:
   a) find suitable parametric equations
   b) state any limitation on the values of
      the parameter.

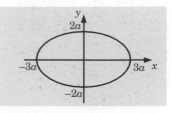

(AQA A Question 2, Specimen Paper P3)

14   A curve is defined parametrically by $x = (2t - 1)$, $y = t^3$ and P is the point on the curve when $t = 2$.

   a) Obtain an expression for $\dfrac{dy}{dx}$ in terms of t and calculate the gradient of the curve at P.

   b) Find $\dfrac{d^2 y}{dx^2}$ in terms of t, expressing your answer in its simplest form.

   c) Determine a Cartesian equation of the curve, expressing your answer in the form $y = f(x)$.

   d) Sketch the curve, showing clearly the values of the intercepts on the axes.

(AQA B Question 4, Specimen Paper P5)

Summary

■   The parametric equations of a curve are functions $x = u(t)$ and $y = v(t)$ in which the Cartesian coordinates of a point on the curve are given in terms of a third variable t called a parameter.

■   The Cartesian equation of the curve is found by eliminating t to give $y = f(x)$.

■   The slope of the tangent to the curve is given by parametric differentiation.

■ $$\frac{dy}{dx} = \frac{\frac{dy}{dt}}{\frac{dx}{dt}} = \frac{v'(t)}{u'(t)}$$

■   The area of the finite region between a curve, the x-axis $x = a$ and $x = b$ when given parametrically is:

$$\int_a^b y\,dx = \int_{t_1}^{t_2} v(t)u'(t)\,dt$$

where $a = u(t_1)$ and $b = u(t_2)$.

Differential equations

In this chapter we shall:

- *introduce the idea of differential equations and give examples of how they are used in problem-solving,*
- *explore the analytical methods of solving simple first-order differential equations,*
- *introduce Euler's numerical method for solving first-order differential equations.*

FORMING DIFFERENTIAL EQUATIONS

Throughout this book it has been clear that one of the reasons for studying mathematics is that it provides a precise language for modelling many of the physical laws and processes in the real world. Many real-life situations involve growth and/or decay. Therefore the mathematical models that we formulate will involve **derivatives** because differentiation describes rates of change. Equations involving derivatives are called **differential equations**. This chapter is about forming and solving equations involving first-order derivatives, and these are called **first-order differential equations**.

Exploration 9.1

Newton's law of cooling

Suppose that you are in a hurry to go out but you want to drink a cup of hot coffee before you go. The initial temperature of the coffee is 90°C and you can start to drink the coffee when its temperature is 45°C. The temperature of the room is 20°C. Formulate a model to find out how long you will have to wait.

What assumptions and simplifications have you made?

Interpreting the results

To formulate a model we need to know something about how a liquid cools. Experimental evidence shows that the rate at which the temperature changes is proportional to the difference in temperature between the liquid and the surrounding air. This is called **Newton's law of cooling**. If T is the temperature of the liquid at time t then in this case:

$$\frac{\mathrm{d}T}{\mathrm{d}t} = -k(T - 20)$$

where k is the constant of proportionality and the negative sign shows that the temperature is reducing. When the coffee is made its temperature is 90°C. So $T = 90$°C when $t = 0$.

In formulating this model we have assumed that
- the temperature throughout the coffee is uniform,
- the temperature of the surrounding air is constant,
- the rate of cooling of a body is proportional to the temperature of the body above that of the surrounding air.

Equation $\dfrac{dT}{dt} = -k(T - 20)$ is an example of a **first-order differential equation**. The solution for $T(t)$ will give the temperature distribution as a function of time. The statement $T = 90°C$ when $t = 0$ is called **the initial condition**.

Example 9.1

The graph of a function passes through the point (1, 3). The gradient function of the graph is $(x - 1)y^2$. Formulate a problem for finding the equation of the graph.

Solution
The gradient function of a graph is $\dfrac{dy}{dx}$. So we can write:

$$\frac{dy}{dx} = (x - 1)y^2$$

which is a first-order differential equation. Since the graph passes through the point (1, 3) the initial condition for this problem is $y = 3$ when $x = 1$.

Example 9.2

In the atmosphere the pressure decreases with height at a rate that is proportional to the pressure. At a height of 1 km the pressure is 6.7×10^4 Pa and the rate of change of pressure is -9000 Pa km^{-1}. At ground level the atmospheric pressure is 10^5 Pa.
Formulate a problem consisting of a differential equation and initial condition to model the pressure in the atmosphere. (The Pascal (Pa) is the unit of pressure.)

Solution
Let the pressure in the atmosphere be denoted by P. The quantity

$\dfrac{dP}{dh}$ *gives the rate at which the pressure is changing with height h.*
As the rate of change is proportional to pressure then:

$$\frac{dP}{dh} \propto P$$
$$\Rightarrow \frac{dP}{dh} = -kP$$

where k is a positive constant of proportionality and the negative sign shows that P is decreasing with height. When the pressure is 6.7×10^4 Pa the pressure change is 9000 Pa km^{-1}, then $k = \frac{9000}{6.7 \times 10^4} = 0.13$ (correct to two significant figures).
The differential equation for P is:

$$\frac{dP}{dh} = -0.13P$$

and the initial condition is $P = 10^5$ Pa when $h = 0$.

Mixing liquids

Example 9.3

A cylindrical tank A is filled with 800 litres of water containing a concentration of dye. A second tank B is partially filled with 200 litres of pure water. The liquid in tank A feeds into tank B at the rate of 20 litres per minute and is thoroughly mixed with the water in tank B. The mixed solution is drawn off tank B at a rate of 15 litres per minute.

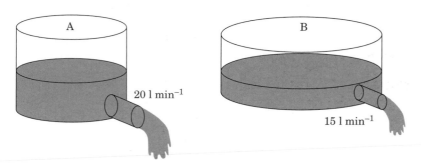

If the concentration of dye in tank A is 1 kg per litre, find an expression for the amount of dye in tank B at any time.

Solution

Let $q(t)$ be the total amount (i.e. mass) of dye in tank B at time t. The rate at which the dye is accumulating in tank B is given by:

$$\frac{dq}{dt} = \begin{array}{c} \textit{amount of dye} \\ \textit{entering per minute} \end{array} - \begin{array}{c} \textit{amount of dye} \\ \textit{leaving per minute} \end{array}$$

The amount of liquid entering tank B from tank A is 20 litres per minute. Since the concentration in tank A is 1 kg per litre:

$$\begin{array}{c} \textit{amount of dye} \\ \textit{entering per minute} \end{array} = \left(1\,\mathrm{kg\,l^{-1}}\right)\left(20\,\mathrm{l\,min^{-1}}\right) = 20\,\mathrm{kg\,min^{-1}}$$

The amount of liquid leaving tank B is 15 litres per minute so at any time the amount of liquid in tank B is increasing at the rate of $(20 - 15) = 5$ litres per minute.

The volume of liquid in tank B after t minutes is $(200 + 5t)$ litres.

The concentration of dye in tank B after t minutes is $\dfrac{q}{(200 + 5t)}\,\mathrm{kg\,l^{-1}}$.

$$\begin{array}{c} \textit{amount of dye} \\ \textit{leaving per minute} \end{array} = \left(\frac{q}{200 + 5t}\,\mathrm{kg\,l^{-1}}\right)\left(15\,\mathrm{l\,min^{-1}}\right) = \frac{15q}{200 + 5t}\,\mathrm{kg\,min^{-1}}$$

$$\Rightarrow \frac{dq}{dt} = 20 - \frac{15q}{(200 + 5t)}$$

Initially tank B contains pure water so the initial condition is $q = 0$ when $t = 0$.

The differential equation for $\dfrac{dq}{dt}$ with this initial condition can be solved to give the desired equation for the amount of dye in tank B.

EXERCISES

9.1 CLASSWORK

In the following problems *do not attempt to solve* the differential equations.

1   The slope of the tangent to a curve at the point (x, y) is given by $(x + y)$. The curve passes through the point (0, 1). Set up a problem

consisting of a differential equation and initial condition to find the equation of the curve.

2   An object moves so that its velocity is proportional to $\sqrt{1-x^2}$ where x is its position at time t. The object starts at the origin. Form a differential equation and initial condition to find the position as a function of time.

3   The rate of growth of a sunflower after germination is initially proportional to its height. The growth rate is 2.5 cm per day when its height is 10 cm. In modelling the growth it is assumed that the initial height is 2 cm.

   Formulate a problem consisting of the differential equation and initial condition to find the height of the sunflower at any time.

4   The rate at which the population of a colony of birds is increasing is proportional to its population. Currently the population is 100 000 and is increasing at a rate of 2000 per year. Form a differential equation for the population of the colony.

5   A cup of hot chocolate cools at a rate proportional to the temperature of the chocolate above that of the surrounding air. The chocolate is made from boiling milk and has an initial temperature of 90°C. It cools at the rate of 0.4°C per second in a room where the temperature is 20°C.

   Formulate a problem consisting of a differential equation and initial condition to model this situation.

6   The area, A, of a circular oil slick is increasing at a rate proportional to its radius, r.
   a) Write down an expression for $\dfrac{\mathrm{d}A}{\mathrm{d}t}$.

   b) Find an expression for $\dfrac{\mathrm{d}A}{\mathrm{d}r}$ in terms of r.

   c) Use the chain rule to find a differential equation involving $\dfrac{\mathrm{d}r}{\mathrm{d}t}$.

7   Air is escaping from a spherical balloon at a rate that is proportional to its surface area. If the air is escaping at 2.5 cm³ s⁻¹ when its radius is 6 cm, formulate a differential equation for the rate of change of the radius.

8   A tank made of porous material has a square base of side 2 m and vertical sides. The tank contains water which seeps out through the base and sides at a rate proportional to the total area in contact with the water. When the depth is 3 m it is observed that the level of the water is falling at a rate of 0.2 m h⁻¹. Formulate a differential equation model to describe the depth of water in the tank as a function of time.

9   When drugs are injected into the bloodstream they lose effectiveness as they pass out of the system. A simple model assumes that the rate of decay in concentration of the drug is proportional to the present concentration. Set up a differential equation model for the drug concentration for a drug for which the rate of decay is 0.02 g cm⁻³ s⁻¹ when the concentration is 0.1 g cm⁻³.

10 A water storage tank has a rectangular cross-section. Its base is 1 m by 1.25 m and its depth is 1 m. Water flows into the tank at a constant rate of 0.005 m³ s⁻¹. Water flows out of the tank at a rate that is proportional to the depth of water in the tank; the constant of proportionality is 0.001 m² s⁻¹. The tank is initially half full of water. Formulate a differential equation and initial condition to describe how the depth of water changes with time. Deduce from the differential equation whether the tank fills or empties.

EXERCISES

9.1 HOMEWORK

In the following problems *do not attempt to solve* the differential equations.

1 As a radioactive substance decays it loses its mass at a rate proportional to its mass at the present time. Write down a differential equation to model this statement.

2 The population of a colony of rabbits in a park increases at a rate proportional to the population. Initially there are ten rabbits in the park. When the population is 100 rabbits the colony is increasing at a rate of seven rabbits per month. Set up a problem consisting of a differential equation and initial condition to model this situation.

3 A curve has equation $y = f(x)$. The function $f(x)$ is not known but the slope of the tangent to the curve at any point (x, y) is given by $x^2 - y^2$. We know that the curve goes through the point (1, 1). Set up a problem consisting of a differential equation and initial condition to find the function $f(x)$.

4 A cold can of cola is removed from a refrigerator where it had a temperature of 2°C and placed in a warm room which is at a temperature of 20°C. The cola warms so that the rate of increase in temperature is proportional to the difference between its temperature and the temperature of the surroundings. The rate of increase is 3°C per minute when the temperature is 10°C. Formulate a problem consisting of a differential equation and initial condition to model this situation.

5 Air is escaping from a spherical balloon at a rate that is proportional to the volume of air left in the balloon. When the radius of the balloon is 15 cm the air is leaving at a rate of 10 cm³ s⁻¹. The initial radius of the balloon is 20 cm.
  a) Form a differential equation for the volume, V.
  b) Set up a problem consisting of a differential equation and initial condition involving the radius, r, of the balloon.

6 The volume of a balloon is increasing at a constant rate of 20 cm³ s⁻¹ as air is pumped in. Form a differential equation for the radius of the balloon.

7 Living tissue contains 10^{-22} g of carbon-14 in every gram of carbon. A sample of dead wood is estimated to contain 3.5×10^{-23} g of carbon-14 in every gram of carbon. It is assumed that the proportion of carbon-14 in carbon in living tissue was the same when the wood died as it is in living tissue today. The rate of decay of carbon-14 is assumed to be proportional to the amount of carbon-14 present.

Formulate a differential equation and initial condition to model this situation.

8   In a electrical circuit, the current is reducing at a rate which is proportional to the current flowing at that time. When the current is 40 milliamps, it is falling at a rate of 0.5 milliamps per second. Set up a differential equation which models this situation.

9   Water is pumped into a cone shaped tank at a constant rate of 30 cm^3 s^{-1}. The cone has dimensions shown in the diagram.
The water leaks from a hole in the base of the cone at a rate proportional to the depth of water in the tank. The constant of proportionality is 0.5 cm^2 s^{-1}. Initially the water in the cone has a depth of 0.5 m.
Formulate a differential equation and initial condition to describe how the depth of water changes with time. Deduce from the differential equation whether the cone initially fills or empties. Is there a constant depth for the water?

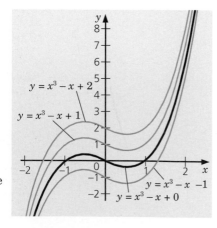

10 An individual in a population of 1500 people working in a company becomes infected with a virus. It is assumed that the rate at which the virus spreads throughout the company is proportional to the number of people infected, P, and to the number of people not infected. Form a differential equation to model the number of people infected as a function of time.

SOLVING DIFFERENTIAL EQUATIONS

Exploration 9.2

Method of direct integration

We have solved differential equations of the type $\frac{dy}{dx} = f(x)$ in the work on integration. The solution of $\frac{dy}{dx} = f(x)$ is found simply by integrating.

■ Solve the differential equation $\frac{dy}{dx} = 3x^2 - 1$ by direct integration.

■ Sketch several solution curves.

■ Sketch the solution curve that passes through the point (1, 0).

Interpreting the results

Integrating $\frac{dy}{dx} = 3x^2 - 1$ gives

$y = x^3 - x + c$ where c is a constant of integration. The diagram shows some of the solution curves for different values of c.

The curve through the point (1, 0) is the bold curve for $c = 0$.

The solution $y = x^3 - x + c$ is called the **general solution** of the differential equation. It contains one unknown

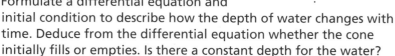
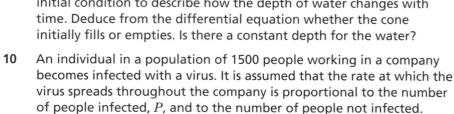

constant. When we solve a differential equation we obtain a **family of solutions**. Each value of c gives a different member of the family.

The solution through the point $(1, 0)$ for which $c = 0$ is one member of that family. It is called **the particular solution** of the differential equation.

We usually find the value of the constant for the particular solution using algebra. For example, in this case the general solution is $y = x^3 - x + c$ and $y = 0$ when $x = 1$.

Substituting for $y = 0$ and $x = 1$ into the general solution gives:
$$0 = 1 - 1 + c \Rightarrow c = 0$$

The particular solution is:
$$y = x^3 - x$$

Example 9.4

Find the particular solution of the differential equation $\dfrac{dy}{dx} = \dfrac{1}{x(x-1)}$ *for which $y = 3$ when $x = 2$.*

Solution
By direct integration:
$$y = \int \frac{1}{x(x-1)}\,dx$$

$$y = \int \left(\frac{1}{x-1} - \frac{1}{x} \right) dx \quad \textit{(using partial fractions)}$$

$$y = \ln(x-1) - \ln x + c$$

This is the general solution. When $x = 2$, $y = 3$
$$\Rightarrow 3 = \ln 1 - \ln 2 + c$$
$$\Rightarrow c = 3 + \ln 2$$
So the particular solution is:
$$y = \ln(x-1) - \ln x + 3 + \ln 2$$
which can be simplified to:
$$y = \ln\left(\frac{2(x-1)}{x} \right) + 3$$

Exploration 9.3

Growth and decay problems

Many quantities, such as population growth and radioactive decay, vary in such a way that the rate of change of the quantity is proportional to the quantity itself. In such models the differential equation is:
$$\frac{dy}{dx} = ky$$

where k is a constant of proportionality.

■ Solve the differential equation $\dfrac{dy}{dx} = 2y$ by dividing both sides by y and integrating.

■ Write the general solution in the form $y = \dots$.

Interpreting the results

The function $\dfrac{dy}{dx} = 2y$ cannot be solved directly by integration because the right-hand side is a function of y. However if we divide both sides by y we get:

$$\frac{1}{y}\frac{dy}{dx} = 2$$

and integrating both sides:

$$\int \frac{1}{y}dy = \int 2dx$$

Now both sides can be integrated.

$$\ln y = 2x + c$$

Raising e to a power equal to the left or right-hand side (remember $e^{\ln y} = y$)

$$y = e^{2x+c} = e^{2x}e^{c}$$

This expression can be made simpler by replacing e^c with a new constant A, so the general solution is:

$$y = Ae^{2x}$$

Example 9.5

A model for the pressure in the atmosphere P is:

$$\frac{dP}{dh} = -0.13P$$

where h is the height above sea level. When h = 0, P = 10^5 Pa (see Example 9.2).

Solution
Divide by P and integrate.

$$\int \frac{1}{P}dP = \int -0.13\,dh$$
$$\ln P = -0.13h + c$$

Raising e to a power equal to the left or right-hand side:

$$P = e^{-0.13h+c} = e^{-0.13h}e^{c} = Ae^{-0.13h}$$

where $e^c = A$.

This is the general solution. When h = 0, P = 10^5.

$$10^5 = Ae^0 = A \quad \text{So the particular solution is } P = 10^5 e^{-0.13h}.$$

Method of separation of variables

Exploration 9.3 and Example 9.5 are special cases of **the method of separation of variables**. Consider a general first-order differential equation which may be written as:

$$\frac{dy}{dx} = u(x)v(y)$$

The special feature of this equation is that the right-hand side **separates** into the product of two functions. One is a function of x only and the other is a function of y only. Dividing both sides by $v(y)$ and multiplying by dx leads to:

$$\frac{1}{v(y)}dy = u(x)dx$$

This process is called **separating the variables**. Once the variables are separated, the general solution is obtained by integrating both sides.

$$\int \frac{1}{v(y)}dy = \int u(x)dx + c$$

Example 9.6

Find the particular solution of the differential equation $\dfrac{dy}{dx} = -xy^3$
that satisfies the initial condition $y = 1$ *when* $x = 1$.

Solution

The differential equation is written in the separated form.

$$\frac{dy}{dx} = (\quad -x \quad)(\quad y^3 \quad)$$

function of
x only   function of
y only

Separating the variables:

$$\frac{1}{y^3}\, dy = -x\, dx$$

Integrating both sides:

$$\int \frac{1}{y^3}\, dy = \int -x\, dx + c \;\Rightarrow\; -\frac{1}{2y^2} = -\frac{1}{2}x^2 + c$$

This is the general solution.
When $x = 1$, $y = 1$ *so:*

$$-\tfrac{1}{2} = -\tfrac{1}{2} + c \Rightarrow c = 0$$

The particular solution is $y^2 = \dfrac{1}{x^2}$ *or* $y = \pm\dfrac{1}{x}$.

A unique solution is obtained by recalling that $y = 1$ *when* $x = 1$ *so the
solution* $y = \dfrac{1}{x}$ *must be selected in order to fit the initial condition.*

Example 9.7

A curve passes through the point $(0, -\tfrac{1}{2})$ *and its gradient function is*
$y^2 \cos x$. *Find the equation of the curve.*

Solution

The quantity $\dfrac{dy}{dx}$ is the gradient so the differential equation for the
curve is:

$$\frac{dy}{dx} = y^2 \cos x$$

Separating the variables:

$$\frac{1}{y^2}\, dy = \cos x\, dx$$

Integrating both sides:

$$\int \frac{1}{y^2}\, dy = \int \cos x\, dx + c \;\Rightarrow\; -\frac{1}{y} = \sin x + c$$

This is the general solution.
Since the curve passes through the point $\left(0, -\tfrac{1}{2}\right)$:

$$-\frac{1}{\left(-\tfrac{1}{2}\right)} = \sin 0 + c \Rightarrow c = 2$$

The particular solution is $y = \dfrac{-1}{2 + \sin x}$.

EXERCISES

1 Find the general solution of the following differential equations by integrating.

a) $\dfrac{dy}{dx} = x^2$

b) $\dfrac{dy}{dx} = \sin x$

c) $\dfrac{dy}{dx} = e^{-2x}$

d) $\dfrac{dy}{dx} = \dfrac{1}{x(x+1)}$

e) $\dfrac{dy}{dt} = \sqrt{t}$

f) $\dfrac{ds}{dt} = 4t^{\frac{3}{2}}$

2 Find the general solution of the following differential equations by the method of separation of variables.

a) $\dfrac{dy}{dx} = \dfrac{x}{y}$

b) $\dfrac{dy}{dx} = xy^2$

c) $\dfrac{dy}{dx} = \dfrac{\sin x}{y}$

d) $\dfrac{dy}{dx} = xe^{-4y}$

e) $\dfrac{dy}{dx} = y \cos x$

f) $\dfrac{dy}{dx} = (1+y)(1-y)$

3 Find the particular solution of the following differential equations using the given conditions.

a) $\dfrac{dy}{dx} = x^2 + 1$ and $y = 4$ when $x = 3$

b) $\dfrac{dy}{dx} = 2y(1+x)$ and $y = 1$ when $x = 0$

c) $\dfrac{dy}{dx} = y^2 \sin x$ and $y = 1$ when $x = 0$

d) $\dfrac{dx}{dt} = 2t(x^2 - 1)$ and $x = 2$ when $t = 1$

e) $\dfrac{dP}{dt} = 3P(1-P)$ and $P = 0.5$ when $t = 0$

f) $\dfrac{dx}{dt} = e^{-2x} \sin 3t$ and $x = 0$ when $t = 0$

g) $\dfrac{dy}{dx} = \dfrac{(3+x)(1+y^2)}{(1-x^2)y}$ and $y = \sqrt{3}$ when $x = 0$

h) $\dfrac{y}{x} \dfrac{dy}{dx} = \dfrac{y^2 - 1}{x^2 - 1}$ and $y = 3$ when $x = 2$

4 A curve passes through the point (0, 2) and its gradient function is $2y - 1$. Find the equation of the curve and use a graphical calculator to sketch the curve.

5 A curve passing through point (–3, 1) has gradient function $\dfrac{y+1}{x^2 - 1}$. Find the equation of the curve and use a graphics calculator to sketch the curve.

6 The tangent to a curve at any point (x, y) has slope inversely proportional to x^2. The curve passes through the two points (1, 1) and (2, 3). Find the equation of the curve.

7 Solve problems **3–10** from Exercises 9.1 CLASSWORK on pages 166–7. Use your solutions to answer each of the following questions
Problem 3 Sketch a graph of the height of a sunflower against time. Is this a good model of sunflower growth? Describe how you would expect the graph to look.
Problem 5 How many seconds does it take for the temperature to reach 30°C?
Problem 8 If the initial depth of the water is 4 m, how long does it take to half empty the tank?
Problem 9 How long does it take for the drug to decay to 25 per cent of the initial dose?
Problem 10 Find how long it takes for the tank to overflow.

EXERCISES

9.2 HOMEWORK

1 Find the general solution of the following differential equations by integration.

a) $\dfrac{dy}{dx} = x^3$

b) $\dfrac{dy}{dx} = \cos x - 1$

c) $\dfrac{dy}{dx} = e^{4x}$

d) $\dfrac{ds}{dt} = \dfrac{1}{(t+1)(t+2)}$

e) $\dfrac{dP}{dt} = te^t$

f) $\dfrac{dv}{ds} = -4s^{\frac{5}{4}}$

2 Find the general solution of the following differential equations by the method of separation of variables.

a) $\dfrac{dy}{dx} = \dfrac{y}{x^2}$

b) $\dfrac{dP}{dt} = 2P(3-P)$

c) $\dfrac{dy}{dx} = \dfrac{x+2}{y}$

d) $r\dfrac{dr}{d\theta} = \sin^2\theta$

e) $\dfrac{dy}{dx} = \dfrac{(1+y)(3+2y)}{1-x}$

f) $v\dfrac{dv}{ds} = 3 - 2v^2$

3 Find the particular solution of the following differential equations using the given conditions.

a) $\dfrac{dy}{dx} = 3x^2 - 2x + 1$ and $y = 2$ when $x = 1$

b) $\dfrac{dy}{dx} = y\sin x$ and $y = 1$ when $x = 0$

c) $\dfrac{dy}{dx} = \sqrt{y}e^{-x}$ and $y = 4$ when $x = 0$

d) $(1+x)\dfrac{dy}{dx} - y(y+1) = 0$ and $y = 1$ when $x = 1$

e) $\dfrac{dT}{dt} = 2(20 - T)$ and $T = 5$ when $t = 0$

f) $v\dfrac{dv}{ds} = 10 - 3v$ and $v = 1$ when $s = 0$

g) $\dfrac{ds}{dt} = e^{-2s}\sin 3t$ and $s = 0$ when $t = 0$

h) $\dfrac{dv}{dt} = -0.2(v + v^2)$ and $v = 40$ when $t = 0$

4 Water leaks from a tank so that the rate of change of depth of water h m is modelled by:
$$\dfrac{dh}{dt} = -\dfrac{3h^2}{4}$$
where t is time in minutes. The initial depth of water in the tank is 1 m.
a) Find the particular solution of the differential equation.
b) How long does it take for the depth of the water in the tank to decrease to 10 cm?

5 A curve passes through the point (3, 2) and its gradient function is $\dfrac{y+2}{x-2}$. Find the equation of the curve.

6 The tangent to a curve at any point (x, y) has slope proportional to $\sqrt{y}$. The curve passes through the two points (0, 4) and (2, 9). Find the equation of the curve.

7 Solve problems **2, 4–10** from Exercise 9.1 HOMEWORK on pages **167–8**. Use your solutions to answer each of the following questions.
Problem 2 Sketch a graph of the size of the colony of rabbits against time. Is this a good model? Describe how you would expect the graph to look.

Problem 4 Andrew likes to drink cola at a temperature of 10°C. How long does he have to wait after removing the cola from the refrigerator to be able to drink the cola?

Problem 5 How long does it take for the radius of the balloon to reduce to 10 cm?

Problem 7 How old is the sample of dead wood?

EULER'S NUMERICAL STEP-BY-STEP METHOD

The methods of the last section provide exact solutions in the form $y = f(x)$. These are called **analytical solutions**. The differential equation $\dfrac{dy}{dx} = x + y^2$ cannot be solved exactly. In such cases we have to adopt methods for estimating solutions. These are called **numerical methods**. Here we shall introduce one simple method to illustrate the ideas.

For a first order differential equation $\dfrac{dy}{dx} = f(x, y)$, the gradient function $f(x, y)$ gives the slope of the tangent at any point on a solution curve. If we do not know the actual solution curve, then a sequence of straight line segments is used as an approximation. The slopes of these straight line segments are given by the gradient function $f(x, y)$. The diagram illustrates the idea. Suppose the differential equation is $\dfrac{dy}{dx} = x + y^2$ with initial condition (1, 2).

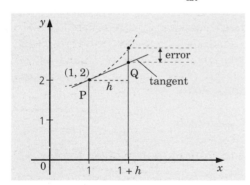

The gradient function tells us in which direction to leave the point (1, 2). When $x = 1$ and $y = 2$ the slope of the tangent is $f(1, 2) = 5$. We choose a step size h so that the tangent arrives at point Q. At Q we form another line segment by recalculating the gradient function with the coordinates of Q. Gradually we build up a sequence of line segments. The method is attributed to a famous 18th-century mathematician Leonhard Euler and is called **Euler's numerical step-by-step method** (or often just 'Euler's method').

Exploration 9.4

A formula for Euler's method

Use graph paper for this exploration, choosing large scales on the x-axis. Look at the differential equation $\dfrac{dy}{dx} = 3x^2 + 1$ with initial condition (1, 2).

■ On your graph paper, draw a sketch of the figure above using gradient function $3x^2 + 1$ with initial condition (1, 2).

■ Choosing $h = 0.2$ find the coordinates of point Q using gradient function $3x^2 + 1$ to form the line PQ.

■ Using the coordinates of Q, draw in the next line segment. Find the coordinates of the next point R using a step size 0.2.

■ Repeat the process forming five line segments.

■ Find the exact solution of the problem and draw the exact solution curve between $x = 1$ and $x = 2$.

- Form a table showing the estimated values and exact values for y for each step, i.e. $y(1.2)$, $y(1.4)$, $y(1.6)$, ...
- Comment on how you might improve the accuracy of the numerical method.

Interpreting the results

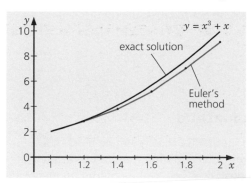

For this problem we can find an exact solution by direct integration. The general solution is $y = x^3 + x + c$. With $y = 2$ when $x = 1$ the constant of integration $c = 0$. The particular solution is $y = x^3 + x$.

You should have drawn the graph on the left, which shows the line segments and exact solution.

The following table compares the answers.

	$y(1.2)$	$y(1.4)$	$y(1.6)$	$y(1.8)$	$y(2.0)$
Analytical solution	2.928	4.144	5.696	7.632	10
Numerical solution	2.8	3.864	5.24	6.976	9.12

The error after five steps is 8.8 per cent. Euler's method is easy to use but may produce errors. One way to improve the accuracy of this method is to reduce the step size h. For example, with a step size of 0.1 the error after ten steps is 4.45 per cent. In Exploration 9.4 we chose a differential equation with an analytical solution so that the error could be identified. In practice we would only use a numerical method for a differential equation that could not be solved analytically.

Exploration 9.5

Improving the estimate

A computer package was used to estimate the value of $y(2.0)$ given by Euler's method when solving the differential equation $\dfrac{dy}{dx} = \sqrt{x + y}$ with initial condition $y = 1$ when $x = 1$. The following table shows the results for different step sizes.

Step size	Estimate to $y(2.0)$
0.2	2.726 79
0.1	2.770 11
0.05	2.792 12
0.01	2.809 89
0.005	2.812 12

- Plot a graph of these estimates to $y(2.0)$ against the step size h.
- Comment on how good a straight line graph would be.
- Use your graph to estimate the true value of $y(2.0)$ correct to four decimal places.

Interpreting the results

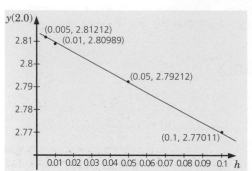

The graph shows that the estimates to $y(2.0)$ obtained using Euler's method depends reasonably linearly on the step size. The graph can be used to estimate the exact value by taking the intercept on the vertical axis of the best straight line through the plotted points. The answer is 2.814 (correct to three decimal places).

A formula for Euler's method

The real power of a numerical method is that it can be used in a calculator or computer program, thus avoiding many long-winded calculations. The first step in writing a program is to find an algebraic formula to define the sequence of estimates.

Consider the initial value problem $\dfrac{dy}{dx} = f(x, y)$ with initial condition $y(x_0) = y_0$. With a step size h the figure shows the first straight line segment that estimates the value of y at $x = x_0 + h$. The values of x and y at Q are labelled (x_1, y_1).

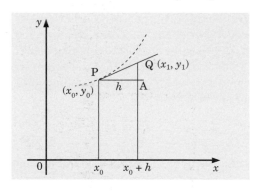

From triangle PAQ:

$$\frac{AQ}{AP} = \text{slope of tangent to solution curve at P} = f(x_0, y_0)$$

$$\Rightarrow \qquad \frac{y_1 - y_0}{h} = f(x_0, y_0)$$

$$\Rightarrow \qquad y_1 = y_0 + hf(x_0, y_0)$$

This formula can be used to form a sequence of estimates for y as x increases.

Exploration 9.6

A general formula for the nth step

- Show that after two steps $y_2 = y_1 + hf(x_1, y_1)$
- Show that after three steps $y_3 = y_2 + hf(x_2, y_2)$
- Formulate a general formula $y_{n+1} = \ldots$ to generate the sequence $y_1, y_2, y_3, \ldots$

Interpreting the results

The formula for the sequence generated by Euler's method is:
$$y_{n+1} = y_n + hf(x_n, y_n).$$

Example 9.8

Solve the differential equation $\dfrac{dy}{dx} = x + y^3$ with initial condition $y = 1$ when $x = 0$.

Write down the sequence for Euler's numerical method applied to the above problem. Use the sequence with step length $h = 0.1$ to estimate the solution to $y(0.5)$ giving the answer correct to four decimal places.

Solution

The general formula for y_{n+1} from Exploration 9.6 is:

$$y_{n+1} = y_n + h\left(x_n + y_n^3\right)$$

Starting with $x_0 = 0$, $y_0 = 1$, and $h = 0.1$. The following table shows the sequence for y_1, y_2, ... The layout of the table includes all the calculations as they occur.

n	x_n	y_n	$x_n + y_n^3$	$h\left(x_n + y_n^3\right)$	$y_{n+1} = y_n + h\left(x_n + y_n^3\right)$
0	0	1	1	0.1	1.1
1	0.1	1.1	1.431	0.1431	1.2431
2	0.2	1.2431	2.120 95	0.212 095	1.455 19
3	0.3	1.455 19	3.381 47	0.338 147	1.793 33
4	0.4	1.793 33	6.167 40	0.616 74	2.410 06
5	0.5	2.410 06			

The estimate of y when $x = 0.5$ is $y(0.5) = 2.4101$ correct to four decimal places.

CALCULATOR ACTIVITY

Exploration 9.7

Using Euler's method

The program generates the x-values and y-values using Euler's numerical method to estimate the solution of a first-order differential equation. Values for the initial values of x and y are stored as X and Y. The step size is stored as H and the final x-value as Z. Use the program to check estimates in Exploration 9.5. Before using the program you need to store the function $f(x, y)$ as $\sqrt{x + y}$ within the program.

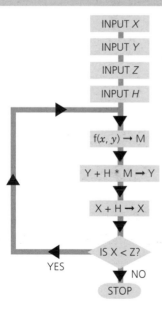

Example 9.9

Solve the differential equation $\dfrac{dy}{dx} = (1 + x)y$ with initial condition $y = 1$ when $x = 2$.

a) Use the program to estimate the solution to $y(3)$ correct to four decimal places with step sizes $h = 0.1$, $h = 0.05$, $h = 0.01$, $h = 0.005$, $h = 0.001$.

b) Plot a graph of these estimates to $y(3)$ against the step size h and use your graph to estimate the true value of $y(3)$, correct to two significant figures.

c) Find the analytical solution to the problem and compare the exact value of $y(3)$ with your estimate in part b).

Solution

a) The program generates the following estimates for $y(3)$.

Step size h	0.1	0.05	0.01	0.005	0.001
Estimate to $y(3)$	19.3300	24.5956	31.0290	32.0247	32.8960

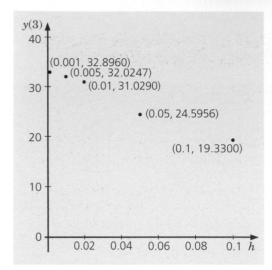

b) The diagram shows the graph of $y(3)$ against h. As $h \to 0$, the graph suggests that $y(3) \to 33$ (correct to two significant figures). For small values of h, the relationship between $y(3)$ and h is approximately linear. However, the analysis of these ideas is beyond the scope of this book.

c) The differential equation $\dfrac{dy}{dx} = (1+x)y$ can be solved analytically using the method of separation of variables.

$$\int \frac{1}{y}\,dy = \int (1+x)\,dx$$

$$\Rightarrow \ln y = x + \tfrac{1}{2}x^2 + c$$

The initial condition $y = 1$ when $x = 2 \to c = -4$, so:

$$y = e^{x + \frac{1}{2}x^2 - 4}$$

When $x = 3$, the analytical solution for $y(3)$ is:

$y(3) = e^{3 + \frac{1}{2}3^2 - 4} = e^{3.5} = 33.1155$, correct to four decimal places. The percentage errors in the estimates from part b) are summarised in this table.

Step size h	0.1	0.05	0.01	0.005	0.001
Estimate to $y(3)$	19.3300	24.5956	31.0290	32.0247	32.8960
Percentage error	41.6	25.7	6.3	3.3	0.7

You can see that by reducing the step size considerably the percentage error in the estimate is also reduced to an acceptable level.

EXERCISES

9.3 CLASSWORK

For questions **1–3**, use Euler's method by hand to find the solution for each differential equation with the given initial condition and step length h.

1 $\dfrac{dy}{dx} = x^2 - y^2$ initial condition $y = 0$ when $x = 1$, and $h = 0.1$
Estimate $y(1.2)$.

2 $\dfrac{dy}{dx} = (x - y)^2$ initial condition $y = 0.5$ when $x = 1$, and $h = 0.1$
Estimate $y(0.5)$.

3 $v\dfrac{dv}{ds} = 10 - 3v^{\frac{3}{2}}$ initial condition $v = 10$ when $s = 0$, and $h = 0.1$
Estimate $v(0.5)$.

In questions **4** and **5** the tables show Euler's numerical solutions to the given differential equation. Use an appropriate graph to estimate the exact value correct to five significant figures.

4 $\dfrac{dy}{dx} = x^2 - y^2$ initial condition $y = 0$ when $x = 1$

Step size h	0.1	0.05	0.025	0.01
Estimate to $y(2)$	1.563 85	1.565 09	1.565 65	1.565 98

5 $v\dfrac{dv}{ds} = 10 - 3v^{\frac{3}{2}}$ initial condition $v = 10$ when $s = 0$

Step size h	1	0.5	0.2	0.1	0.05
Estimate to $v(5)$	10.6536	2.232 96	2.231 45	2.231 45	2.231 45

Explain what is happening in this problem.

6 Solve the differential equation $\dfrac{dy}{dx} = -x^2 y^2$ with initial condition $y = 0.5$ when $x = 0$.

a) Use the program for Euler's method to estimate the solution to $y(2)$ correct to four decimal places with step sizes $h = 0.2$, $h = 0.1$, $h = 0.05$, $h = 0.02$.

b) Plot a graph of these estimates for $y(2)$ against step size h and use your graph to estimate the true value $y(2)$ correct to three decimal places.

c) Find the analytical solution to the problem and compare the exact value of $y(2)$ with your estimate in part **b)**.

EXERCISES

9.3 HOMEWORK

For questions **1–3**, use Euler's method by hand to find the solution for each differential equation with the given initial condition and step length h.

1 $\dfrac{dy}{dx} = 2x - y^2$ initial condition $y = 1$ when $x = 0$, and $h = 0.1$
Estimate $y(0.5)$.

2 $\dfrac{dy}{dx} = 1 + x \sin y$ initial condition $y = 0.5$ when $x = 0$, and $h = 0.1$
Estimate $y(0.5)$.

3 $\dfrac{dv}{dt} = 10 - 0.1v^2$ initial condition $v = 15$ when $t = 0$, and $h = 0.2$
Estimate $v(2)$.

In questions **4** and **5** the tables show Euler's numerical solutions to the given differential equation. Use an appropriate graph to estimate the exact value correct to five significant figures.

4 $\dfrac{dy}{dx} = 2x - y^2$ initial condition $y = 1$ when $x = 0$

Step size h	0.2	0.1	0.05	0.01
Estimate to $y(2)$	1.84774	1.84396	1.84264	1.84184

5 $\dfrac{dy}{dx} = 1 + x \sin y$ initial condition $y = 0.5$ when $x = 0$

Step size h	0.2	0.1	0.05	0.01
Estimate to $v(5)$	1.860 69	1.910 62	1.934 95	1.954 01

6 The graph of a function passes through the point (1, 0.5). The gradient function of the graph is $\sqrt{x} + \sqrt{y}$. Use the program for

Euler's method to estimate the solution correct to one decimal place at $x = 2$, $x = 3$, $x = 4$, $x = 5$. Sketch the graph of the function for $1 \leq x \leq 5$ using your estimates.

You may need to choose different h values within each interval (1, 2), (2, 3), (3, 4), (4, 5) to give an accuracy of two decimal places.

MATHEMATICAL MODELLING ACTIVITY

Problem statement

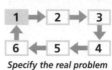

Specify the real problem

Yogurt can be made at home by placing a small amount of commercially made yogurt into warm milk and leaving it in a warm place. The bacteria in the yogurt thrive in the warm milk and multiply. By this process the milk is turned into yogurt.

■ Formulate a model describing the growth of the population of yogurt bacteria. Use the model to find the time it takes to make yogurt.

Set up a model

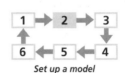

Set up a model

As described above, the problem is described in vague terms, so the first step is to find out about the biological process of turning milk into yogurt. Essentially what happens is that the *Lactobacillus bulgaris* bacteria present in a small batch of yogurt ferment in the warm milk producing lactic acid from the fermentation of the carbohydrates. Gradually, if the correct temperature of approximately 45°C is maintained, the milk becomes yogurt. Typically 10 grams of yogurt should be placed in 500 ml of warm milk. Experiments show that under ideal conditions the amount of yogurt doubles approximately every 30 minutes. To proceed we make the following assumptions.

■ The mixture of milk and yogurt is kept in ideal conditions.
■ The yogurt increases so that its growth rate is proportional to the amount present which leads to an exponential model.

Mathematical model

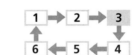

Formulate the mathematical problem

The assumptions lead to the following relationship between the amount of yogurt present P, measured in grams, at time t, measured in hours.

$$\frac{dP}{dt} = kP \text{ or } P = P_0 e^{kt} \qquad (1)$$

where P_0 is the initial amount of yogurt and k is a constant describing the growth rate. The initial problem is to find the value of k.

Mathematical solution

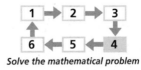

Solve the mathematical problem

Under ideal conditions the amount of yogurt doubles every half-hour. Hence $P = 2P_0$ when $t = 0.5$.

Substitution into (1) gives:

$$2P_0 = P_0 e^{0.5k}$$

and solving for k:

$$k = 2\ln(2) \approx 1.39 \qquad \text{(correct to two decimal places)}$$

The model of the growth of yogurt is:

$$P = P_0 e^{1.39t}$$

Interpret the solution

Interpretation

Suppose that we start with 10 grams of yogurt. Then the figure shows the growth of the yogurt in the milk.

After four hours we have a lot of yogurt! If we assume that the density of yogurt is the same as that of water, then 2598 grams of yogurt is 2.598 litres (just over 4 pints). According to a recipe book, it takes between four and six hours for 10 grams of yogurt culture to turn 500 grams of milk into yogurt.

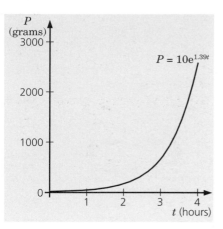

Criticism of the model

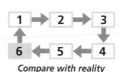

Compare with reality

The pitfall in our model is the assumption that the bacteria will continue to grow indefinitely according to the exponential model. The basic assumption underlying the exponential model is that the growth rate is proportional to the amount of yogurt present, i.e:

$$\frac{\mathrm{d}P}{\mathrm{d}t} = kP$$

The growth of the yogurt will be approximately exponential at the start but the growth rate will decline as the milk is being used up. If we start with 500 grams of milk then the limiting amount of yogurt is 500 grams.

Refinement of the model

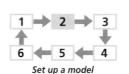

Set up a model

We shall still assume that the mixture of milk and yogurt is kept under ideal conditions of approximately 45°C, but we change the second assumption.
- The growth rate of the yogurt increases initially and then decreases to zero as the amount of yogurt increases.

Set up an improved model

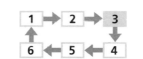

Formulate the mathematical problem

A quadratic function satisfies this new assumption. We have:

$$\frac{\mathrm{d}P}{\mathrm{d}t} = aP(M - P) \qquad (2)$$

where M is called the equilibrium population and a is a constant. In our problem M is the amount of milk at the start of the yogurt-making process. When $P = M$ there is no more milk to be turned into yogurt, and the bacteria stop growing.

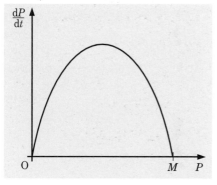

Mathematical solution

Solve the mathematical problem

Equation (2) is a differential equation with separable variables. To solve it, we rearrange it in the form:

$$\int \frac{1}{P(P - M)} \, \mathrm{d}P = \int a \, \mathrm{d}t$$

The left-hand side can be integrated by first using partial fractions. The solution for P is:

$$P = \frac{P_0 M}{P_0 + (M - P_0)e^{-aMt}} \qquad (3)$$

(This is left as an activity for you to do.)

Interpretation

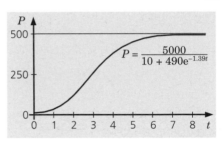

Interpret the solution

At first sight this looks a complicated formula for P. However if we choose some values of the constants and draw a graph of P against t then we can see that this model has all the ingredients of the real situation.

Let $P_0 = 10$, $M = 500$, and $aM = 1.39$.

Equation (3) becomes:

$$P = \frac{5000}{10 + 490e^{-1.39t}} \qquad (4)$$

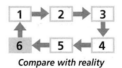

A graph of this function is shown in the diagram.

This is known as the **logistic curve**. The yogurt grows rapidly at the start with the same form as the exponential model. But as time increases, the amount of yogurt levels off towards the maximum amount of 500 grams.

Answer to the problem

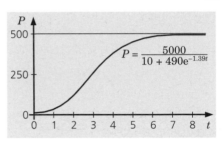

Compare with reality

The initial statement asked for the time required to make yogurt. According to equation (4) it would take an infinite time to turn 500 grams of milk into yogurt. However we would probably be satisfied with, say, 90 per cent of the milk becoming yogurt. Equation (4) can be used to find the value of t for $P = 0.9 \times 500 = 450$. We need to solve for t.

$$450 = \frac{5000}{10 + 490e^{-1.39t}}$$

$$t = 4.38$$

This model predicts that it takes almost $4\frac{1}{2}$ hours to make 450 grams (i.e. half a litre) of yogurt, using 10 grams of culture. This agrees with a cookery book which suggests removing the yogurt to a refrigerator after four to six hours so that the yogurt does not become too thick and the acid flavour does not become too strong.

Activities

- Show that equation (3) is the general solution to the differential equation (2).
- Explain why we chose $aM = k = 1.39$.

CONSOLIDATION EXERCISES FOR CHAPTER 9

1 The body of a murder victim was discovered in the early hours of the morning at 2.00 a.m. The police doctor arrived at 2.30 a.m. and immediately took the temperature of the body, which was 34.8°C. One hour later the temperature of the body was 34.1°C. The room temperature was constant at 32.2°C. (The normal body temperature is 37°C.)

   a) Formulate a differential equation model for the temperature of the body as a function of time. State your assumptions clearly.

   b) Solve the differential equation and use the given information to find any unknown constants in the general solution.

   c) Use your solution to estimate the time of death.

2 The slope of the tangent to a curve at the point (x, y) is given by $x + y^2$. The curve passes through the point (0, 1).

   a) Set up a problem consisting of a differential equation and an initial condition to find the equation of the curve.

   b) Write down the sequence for Euler's numerical method applied to the above problem.

   c) Use this sequence with a step length 0.2 to estimate the curve between $x = 0$ and $x = 1$.

   d) Improve your solution by choosing a smaller step length.

3 Radium is a radioative substance. You can model its decay by the differential equation $\frac{dR}{dt} = -kR$ where t is the time in years, R is the amount of radium in grams present at time t, and k is a positive constant. Suppose that when $t = 0$, 10 g of radium are present.

   a) Solve the equation $\frac{dR}{dt} = -kR$ to find R in terms of t and k.

   b) It is known that the amount of radium will have halved after about 1600 years. Use this information to show that $k = \frac{\ln 2}{1600}$.

   c) According to this model, how many grams of radium will be left after 100 years?

   (Oxford (Nuffield) Question 9, Specimen Paper 2, 1994)

4 Find:

   a) $\int x \cos x \, dx,$ **b)** $\int \cos^2 y \, dy$.

   Hence find the general solution of the differential equation
   $$\frac{dy}{dx} = x \cos x \sec^2 2y, \quad 0 < y < \frac{\pi}{4}.$$
   (ULEAC Question 9, Specimen Paper 2, 1994)

5 **a)** Write $\dfrac{1}{y(3-y)}$ in partial fractions.

   b) Find $\displaystyle\int \frac{1}{y(3-y)} \, dy$.

   c) Solve the differential equation $x\dfrac{dy}{dx} = y(3-y)$ where $x = 2$ when $y = 2$, giving y as a function of x.

   (MEI Question 4, Specimen Paper 3, 1994)

6 If left undisturbed, the population, P, of mice on a small island would increase at two per cent of its current value every day. However, it is estimated that the number of mice killed each day by predators is $0.8\sqrt{P}$. These facts can be summarised in a differential equation.
   $$\frac{dP}{dt} = 0.02P - 0.8\sqrt{P}$$

   [In this model, P and t are to be treated as continuous variables.]

a) If when $t = 0$ the population is 1000 mice, use a step-by-step method to estimate how it will change over the next 20 days. Use a step-length of $\delta t = 10$, and work to the nearest whole number of mice at each step.

b) Use the differential equation to show that, if P exceeds a certain critical value, then the population will increase, but that if P is below that value, the population will decrease. State the value of this critical number.

c) Explain why, if the population is larger than the critical number found in **b)**, then it will go on increasing indefinitely, but that if it is less than the critical value, it will go on decreasing (until it is wiped out).

(Oxford and Cambridge Question 1, Specimen Paper 1, 1994)

7 Water flows out of a tank through a pipe at the bottom, and at time t minutes the depth of the water in the tank is x metres. The rate at which the depth of water remaining in the tank is decreasing at any instant is proportional to the square root of the depth at that instant.

a) Explain how the above information leads to the differential equation:

$$-\frac{dx}{dt} = k\sqrt{x} \text{ where } k \text{ is a positive constant.}$$

b) Find the general solution of the differential equation in part **a)**.

c) At time $t = 0$ the depth of the water in the tank is 2 m. After 10 minutes the depth is 1.5 m. Find, to the nearest minute, the time at which the depth is 1 m.

(UCLES (Linear) Question 14, Specimen Paper 1, 1994)

8 A canal lock is modelled as a tank with a rectangular base area of 50 m^2 which is filled by letting water run in. The height of the water surface above its lowest level is h m at time t, where t is the number of seconds after the lock starts to fill.

In the model, h satisfies the differential equation:

$$\frac{dh}{dt} = k(2.5 - h)$$

where k is constant.

Initially, when $t = 0$, water flows into the lock at 2 m^3 s^{-1}.

a) Show that initially $\frac{dh}{dt} = 0.04$ m s^{-1} and hence that $k = 0.016$.

b) Solve the original differential equation for t in terms of h.

The lock is full when $h = 2.5$.

c) What does your solution to the differential equation predict about the time required to fill the lock?

d) How long would it take for the water to rise to within 2 mm of the lock being full?

(In practice, the lock gates can be opened before the lock is completely full.)

(MEI Paper 9, Mechanics 3, January 1994)

9 A cylindrical container has a height of 200 cm. The container was initially full of a chemical but there is a leak from a hole in the base. When the leak is noticed, the container is half full and the level of the chemical is dropping at a rate of 1 cm per minute. It is required to find for how many minutes the container has been leaking. To model the situation it is assumed that, when the depth of the chemical remaining is x cm, the rate at which the level is dropping is proportional to $\sqrt{x}$. Set up and solve an appropriate differential equation, and hence show that the container has been leaking for about 80 minutes.

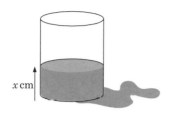

(OCR Question 8, Specimen Paper P3)

10 A cylindrical tank with a horizontal circular base is leaking. At time t minutes the depth of oil in the tank is h metres. It is known that $h = 10$ when $t = 0$ and that $h = 5$ when $t = 40$.
Alan assumes that the rate of change of h with respect to t is constant.
a) Find an expression for h in terms of t.
Bhavana assumes that the rate of change of h with respect to t is proportional to h.
b) Form a differential equation and, using the conditions given, solve it to find Bhavana's expression for h in terms of t.
c) Find, in each case, the value of h when $t = 0$.
d) Briefly explain which assumption you would use.

(EDEXCEL Question 7, Specimen Paper P3)

11 The rate at which a rumour spreads in a crowd of people can be modelled with the differential equation:

$$\frac{dn}{dt} = 0.0002n(N - n)$$

where N is the number in the crowd and n the number who have heard the rumour at time t minutes.

There are 5000 people in the crowd and initially 10 of them have heard the rumour.

a) Copy and complete the table below for a step-by-step solution of the differential equation and estimate the number of people who have heard the rumour after 10 minutes.

n	t	$\frac{dn}{dt}$	dt	dn
10	0		5	
	5		5	
	10			

b) State a means by which your estimate could be improved.

(AQA A Question 3, Specimen Paper P3)

12 A solid steel cylinder is reshaped so that its volume, V cm^3, remains constant and its shape remains cylindrical while its height, h cm, and its radius, r cm, change in value.
a) Show that $\dfrac{dh}{dr} = -\dfrac{2V}{\pi r^3}$.

b) At the instant when the height is 10 cm and the radius is 15 cm, the rate of decrease in height is 0.2 cm per second. Find the rate of increase in the radius at this instant.

(AQA A Question 5, Specimen Paper P3)

13   Solve the differential equation $\dfrac{dy}{dx} = \sqrt{y}\,\sec^2 3x$

given that $y = 1$ when $x = 0$, expressing your answer in the form $y = f(x)$.

(AQA B Question 3, Specimen Paper P5)

Summary

- A differential equation is an equation involving derivatives.

- A first order differential equation only involves a first derivative. The general form of a first order differential equation is:
  $$\frac{dy}{dx} = f(x, y).$$

- If $f(x, y)$ is a function of x only then the differential equation can be solved by direct integration.

- If $f(x, y)$ is in the form $u(x)v(y)$ then we say that the variables have separated and the method of separation of variables can be used to give:
  $$\int \frac{1}{v(y)}\,dy = \int u(x)\,dx$$

- Euler's numerical step-by-step method gives the following sequence for estimating a solution:
  $$y_{n+1} = y_n + h f(x_n, y_n)$$

- The general solution of a first-order differential equation contains one unknown constant and represents a 'family of solution curves'.

- A particular solution is one member of the family of solutions.

MECHANICS 10

Projectiles

- *In mechanics, any unpowered object that is launched into the air, for example a tennis ball hit by a racquet is called a projectile.*

- *In this chapter, equations modelling the motion of a projectile are developed.*

- *In order to keep things simple, we have assumed that there is no air resistance to the motion of a projectile.*

THE MOTION OF A PROJECTILE

When a particle is launched into the air, its motion follows mathematical rules and patterns. In this chapter we shall explore these patterns and establish some of the basic rules.

Exploration 10.1

Simplifications and assumptions

When trying to describe the path of a ball in flight mathematically it is necessary for us to ignore certain aspects of its motion, so that we can formulate a simple model.

- Air resistance could be ignored. Are there any other assumptions that it may be advisable to make? You may wish to identify specific assumptions for balls used in different sports.
- How do you think the speed of a projectile, for example a golf ball, varies during its flight? Looking at this diagram may give some clues.

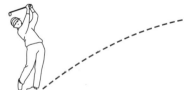

Assumptions

In some ball games, the spin of the ball affects its flight by generating a lift force. In this chapter we shall model projectiles as particles that do not spin, and are influenced only by gravity. This allows us to draw up a very simple model.

The speed of a cricket ball decreases as it gains height, reaching a minimum at the ball's highest point, before gaining speed again as the ball returns to the ground. It is useful to compare this situation with a ball that is thrown straight up and then falls straight down again in the air. The speed decreases to zero on the way up and increases again on the way down.

Exploration 10.2

The path of a projectile

■ Set up the apparatus shown in the diagram. The plastic tube should be fixed to a retort stand with a clamp. It is used to provide a consistent way of launching the ball or marble. Provided the angle of the tube to the vertical is not altered, the speed at which the ball leaves the tube will always be the same. The sloping table provides a means of slowing down the motion of the projectile. Imagine that the table top is in a vertical plane, and that you are seeing a ball move in slow motion.

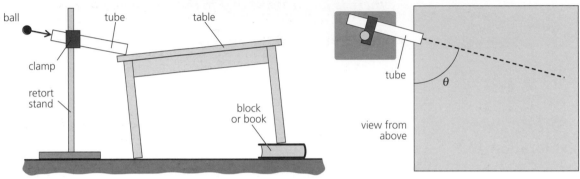

■ Begin by launching the ball straight up the table. It should return to the tube! Now vary the angle the tube makes with the edge of the table. What angle will give you the maximum range?
■ Change the launch speed and repeat the last step. How does the path of the ball change?
■ Place a target somewhere on the table top (a pencil sharpener or small object that the ball can knock over is ideal). By changing the angle of launch and the launch speed, try to find different ways of hitting the target.

The path of a projectile

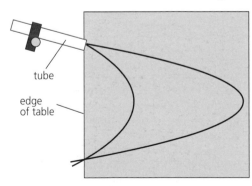

The distance travelled by the ball on the table top increases as the launch speed is increased. The angle that the table makes with the edge of the tube is also very important. When it is 45° the ball will travel the greatest distance. The same point on the edge of the table can be reached by two different paths, one launched with a small angle, less than 45°, and the other with a large angle, greater than 45°, as shown in the diagram. The path that the ball describes is a **parabola**.

The worked examples that follow show how to find the position vector for a projectile and to determine some of the features of the motion.

CALCULATOR ACTIVITY

Exploration 10.3

1 First select parametric plotting mode and degree mode. Then set the range or window values to be

$$x_{min} = 0; \qquad x_{max} = 5; \qquad x_{scl} = 1$$
$$y_{min} = 0; \qquad y_{max} = 2; \qquad y_{scl} = 1$$
$$T_{min} = 0 \qquad T_{max} = 2 \qquad T_{step/pitch} = 0.1$$

2 The path of a particular projectile is modelled by:
$$\mathbf{r} = (6t\cos 30°)\mathbf{i} + (6t\sin 30° - 5t^2)\mathbf{j}$$

where $\mathbf{i}$ and $\mathbf{j}$ are the unit vectors in the horizontal and vertical directions, as usual. Enter this in the form:
$$x = (6t\cos 30°) \quad \text{and} \quad y = (6t\sin 30° - 5t^2)$$

Is the path plotted what you may expect for a projectile?

3 In the equations above, 30° is the **angle of projection**. Use some different values for this angle. Sketch a graph to show that the **range** (horizontal distance travelled) varies with the angle. What angle gives the maximum range?

4 In the equations above, 6 represents the speed of projection. Use some different values for this speed in the equations. How does the speed affect the range?

Modelling the path of a projectile

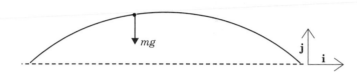

To model the path of a projectile we assume that the only force acting on the projectile is its weight. This force can be expressed as $-mg\mathbf{j}$. Then, by using Newton's second law we can show that the acceleration of the projectile is $-g\mathbf{j}$.

As we are assuming that the acceleration of the projectile is constant, we can apply the results $\mathbf{v} = \mathbf{u} + \mathbf{a}t$ and $\mathbf{r} = \mathbf{u}t + \frac{1}{2}\mathbf{a}t^2$ to solve problems. The use of these results is illustrated in the following worked examples.

Example 10.1

A golf ball is struck so that its initial velocity is $20\,\text{m s}^{-1}$ at an angle of 40° above the horizontal. Use the unit vectors $\mathbf{i}$ and $\mathbf{j}$, directed horizontally and vertically respectively.

a) Express the acceleration of the ball in terms of the unit vectors $\mathbf{i}$ and $\mathbf{j}$.

b) Express the initial velocity in terms of the unit vectors $\mathbf{i}$ and $\mathbf{j}$.

c) Find an expression for the position of the ball, assuming that it starts at the origin.

d) Find how far the ball is from the origin when it hits the ground.

e) What factors about the ball's motion have been ignored?

Solution

a) If the ball is modelled as a particle that is acted on by only the force of gravity, then the acceleration will simply be the acceleration due to gravity, so:
$$\mathbf{a} = -g\mathbf{j} = -9.8\mathbf{j}$$

b) The initial velocity of the ball is: $u = 20\cos 40°\mathbf{i} + 20\cos 50°\mathbf{j}$
$$= 20\cos 40°\mathbf{i} + 20\sin 40°\mathbf{j}$$

(Note: When modelling projectiles it is best to express the initial velocities in the form $V\cos\alpha\mathbf{i} + V\sin\alpha\mathbf{j}$.)

c) Using the formula $\mathbf{r} = \mathbf{u}t + \frac{1}{2}\mathbf{a}t^2$ with $\mathbf{u}$ and $\mathbf{a}$ from above gives:
$$\mathbf{r} = (20\cos 40°\mathbf{i} + 20\sin 40°\mathbf{j})t + \frac{1}{2}(-g\mathbf{j})t^2$$
$$= 20\cos 40°t\mathbf{i} + (20\sin 40°t - \frac{gt^2}{2})\mathbf{j}$$

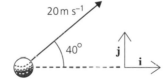

189

d) When the ball hits the ground the vertical component of the position vector will be zero, giving:

$$20\sin 40°t - \frac{gt^2}{2} = 0$$

$$\left(20\sin 40° - \frac{gt}{2}\right)t = 0$$

$$t = 0 \text{ or } t = \frac{2\times 20\sin 40°}{g} = 2.624\,\text{s}$$

The first solution, $t = 0$, corresponds to the instant that the ball leaves the ground and the second, $t = 2.624$, corresponds to the instant when the ball hits the ground. The time that the ball is in the air is often referred to as the **time of flight**.
Substituting $t = 2.624$ into the horizontal component of the position vector gives: $x = 20\cos 40° \times 2.624$

$$= 40.2\,\text{m}$$

So the ball hits the ground 40.2 m from the point where it began its flight. This distance is known as the **range** of the projectile.

e) Golf balls are designed so that as they spin they experience an aerodynamic lift force that increases their range. This factor has been completely ignored, as has any air resistance. It has also been assumed that there is no wind present.

Example 10.2

An archer shoots an arrow so that its initial velocity is 40 m s⁻¹ at an angle of 60° to the horizontal.

a) Find the initial velocity of the arrow in terms of the unit vectors **i** and **j**.

b) Find the position and velocity vectors for the arrow.

c) Find the maximum height reached by the arrow.

Solution

a) The initial velocity is:

$$40\cos 60°\mathbf{i} + 40\sin 60°\mathbf{j}$$

b) Assuming that the only force acting is gravity gives the acceleration as:

$$\mathbf{a} = -g\mathbf{j} = -9.8\mathbf{j}$$

We shall assume that the arrow is launched from ground level. Using the formula $\mathbf{r} = \mathbf{u}t + \frac{1}{2}\mathbf{a}t^2$ with **u** and **a** from above gives:

$$\mathbf{r} = (40\cos 60°\mathbf{i} + 40\sin 60°\mathbf{j})t + \frac{1}{2}(-g\mathbf{j})t^2$$

$$= 40\times\frac{1}{2}t\mathbf{i} + \left(40\times\frac{\sqrt{3}}{2}t - \frac{gt^2}{2}\right)\mathbf{j}$$

$$= 20t\mathbf{i} + \left(20t\sqrt{3} - \frac{gt^2}{2}\right)\mathbf{j}$$

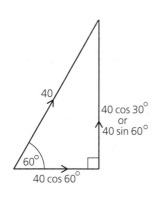

Note the use of the surd forms for the trigonometric values.
The result **v** = **u** + **a**t can be used to find the velocity.

$$\mathbf{v} = (40 \cos 60°\mathbf{i} + 40 \sin 60°\mathbf{j}) + (-g\mathbf{j})t$$

$$= 40\frac{1}{2}\mathbf{i} + \left(40 \times \frac{\sqrt{3}}{2} - gt\right)\mathbf{j}$$

$$= 20\mathbf{i} + \left(20\sqrt{3} - gt\right)\mathbf{j}$$

c)

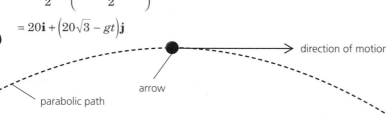

arrow

parabolic path

At the highest position of the arrow it is for an instant moving horizontally, so the vertical component of its velocity is zero. This gives the equation:

$$20\sqrt{3} - gt = 0$$

$$t = \frac{20\sqrt{3}}{g} = 3.53\,\text{s}$$

So the arrow reaches its maximum height when $t = \frac{20\sqrt{3}}{g}$.

Substituting this into the vertical component of the position vector

gives: $y = 20\sqrt{3} \times \frac{20\sqrt{3}}{g} - \frac{1}{2}g\left(\frac{20\sqrt{3}}{g}\right)^2$

$$= \frac{1200}{g} - \frac{600}{g}$$

$$= \frac{600}{g} = 61.2 \text{ m}$$

So the maximum height reached by the arrow is 61.2 m.

The examples above have considered specific cases of projectile motion. The next example involves a general projectile. This approach allows results for the range, height and time of flight to be formulated.

Example 10.3

A projectile is launched with an initial speed V at an angle α above the horizontal.

a) *Find the initial velocity of the projectile.*
b) *Find the position vector and the velocity of the projectile.*
c) *Find the range of the projectile.*
d) *Find the maximum height reached by the projectile.*

Solution
a) *The initial velocity is:*
   $V \cos \alpha\,\mathbf{i} + V \sin \alpha\,\mathbf{j}$
b) *If gravity is assumed to be the only force then the acceleration will be* **a** = –g**j**.
   We shall assume that the arrow is launched from ground level.
   Using the formula **r** = **u**t + $\frac{1}{2}$**a**t² *with the initial velocity and this*

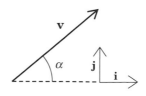

   acceleration gives: $\mathbf{r} = (V \cos \alpha\mathbf{i} + V \sin \alpha\mathbf{j})t + \frac{1}{2}(-g\mathbf{j})t^2$

$$= Vt \cos \alpha\,\mathbf{i} + \left(Vt \sin \alpha - \frac{1}{2}gt^2\right)\mathbf{j}$$

The result $\mathbf{v} = \mathbf{u} + \mathbf{a}t$ can be used to find the velocity.

$$\mathbf{v} = (V\cos\alpha\,\mathbf{i} + V\sin\alpha\,\mathbf{j}) + (-gt\mathbf{j})$$
$$= V\cos\alpha\,\mathbf{i} + (V\sin\alpha - gt)\mathbf{j}$$

c) The time of flight is found by considering when the projectile returns to the level from which it was launched. When this is the case the vertical component of the position vector, $Vt\sin\alpha - \frac{1}{2}gt^2$, is zero, giving:

$$Vt\sin\alpha - \tfrac{1}{2}gt^2 = 0$$

As t is a factor, this can be expressed as:

$$t\left(V\sin\alpha - \tfrac{1}{2}gt\right) = 0$$

Solving this equation gives:

$$t = 0 \ \ or \ \ \left(V\sin\alpha - \tfrac{1}{2}gt\right) = 0 \Rightarrow \ \ t = 0 \ \ or \ \ t = \frac{2V\sin\alpha}{g}$$

and the time of flight is given by $\dfrac{2V\sin\alpha}{g}$.

d) The range is given by the horizontal component of the position vector, $Vt\cos\alpha$, when the projectile hits the ground.

Substituting $t = \dfrac{2V\sin\alpha}{g}$ and using the trigonometric identity,

$2\sin\alpha\cos\alpha = \sin 2\alpha$ gives:

$$\text{range} = V\cos\alpha\,\frac{2V\sin\alpha}{g} = \frac{V^2\,2\sin\alpha\cos\alpha}{g} = \frac{V^2\sin 2\alpha}{g}$$

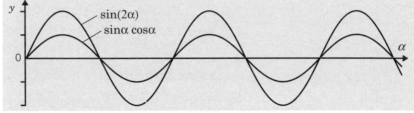

Note: By using Pure Mathematics as well as Mechanics, you should recognise the identity $2\sin\alpha\cos\alpha = \sin 2\alpha$. If you do not, try plotting, $\sin\alpha\cos\alpha$ and $\sin 2\alpha$ and comparing the curves.

e) The maximum height is reached when the vertical component of the velocity, $V\sin\alpha - gt$ is zero. At this point:

$$V\sin\alpha - gt = 0$$

so that

$$t = \frac{V\sin\alpha}{g}$$

Note that this is half the time of flight.

Substituting the time into the vertical component of the position vector, $V\sin\alpha\,t - \frac{1}{2}gt^2$, gives:

$$\text{maximum height} = V\sin\alpha\,\frac{V\sin\alpha}{g} - \frac{g}{2}\left(\frac{V\sin\alpha}{g}\right)^2$$
$$= \frac{V^2\sin^2\alpha}{g} - \frac{V^2\sin^2\alpha}{2g} = \frac{V^2\sin^2\alpha}{2g}$$

Summarising the results so far

The results produced in Example 8.3 can be very useful for dealing with projectile problems. They are summarised below.

$$\mathbf{r} = Vt\cos\alpha\,\mathbf{i} + \left(Vt\sin\alpha - \tfrac{1}{2}gt^2\right)\mathbf{j}$$

$$\text{Range} = \frac{V^2\sin 2\alpha}{g}$$

$$\text{Time of flight} = \frac{2V\sin\alpha}{g}$$

$$\text{Maximum height} = \frac{V^2\sin^2\alpha}{2g}$$

However, it is important that problems can be solved by finding the position vector for that situation, as well as using standard formulae.

EXERCISES

10.1 CLASSWORK

1 A cricket ball is hit so that it leaves ground level with a speed of $4\,\text{m s}^{-1}$ and moving at an angle of 20° above the horizontal.
   a) Express the initial velocity of the ball in terms of the unit vectors **i** and **j** which are horizontal and vertical respectively.
   b) State the acceleration of the ball, in terms of **i** and **j**.
   c) If the ball has been in motion for t seconds, find the velocity of the ball in terms of t.
   d) Find the position vector of the ball, in terms of t, stating a suitable origin.

2 A kangaroo hops so that it leaves the ground moving at $5\,\text{m s}^{-1}$ and at an angle of 15° to the horizontal.
   a) Express the initial velocity of the kangaroo in terms of the unit vectors **i** and **j** which are horizontal and vertical respectively.
   b) Find the position vector of the kangaroo in terms of t, where t is the time, in seconds, the kangaroo has been in motion.
   c) For how long is the kangaroo in the air during one hop?
   d) How much ground does the kangaroo cover during one hop?
   e) What is the greatest height reached by the kangaroo?

3 An athlete competing in a long jump event claims that he can take off at $10\,\text{m s}^{-1}$. Assume that he initially moves at 25° to the horizontal.
   a) Find the distance that the athlete would jump.
   b) Do you think that the claim is reasonable? Explain why.

4 A tennis ball is launched from ground level so that it initially moves at $15\,\text{m s}^{-1}$ at 39° to the horizontal.
   a) Find the range of the ball.
   b) Would it make any difference to your answer if it was a cricket ball?
   c) If you were to include air resistance in the problem, which ball would be affected more?

5 An archer shoots an arrow at a target, hitting it dead centre. Assume that the arrow is launched from the same height as the centre of the target, at an initial speed of $25\,\text{m s}^{-1}$ and at 25° to the horizontal.
   a) Find the distance of the target from the archer.
   b) Show that if the arrow were fired at the same speed but at 65° to the horizontal it would hit the target in the same place.

c) Find the speeds of the arrows when they hit the target in each case.
d) Comment on which angle the archer would prefer to use, giving reasons to support your conclusion.

6 In a school sports day a student jumps 1.8 m in the long jump event.
   a) Assuming that the student initially moves at 18° to the horizontal find their initial speed.
   b) What angle of projection would give the greatest range?
   c) If the angle of the initial velocity was unknown, find the minimum initial speed that would be needed to travel 1.8 m.

7 A shot putt is thrown with an initial speed of 8 m s^{-1} and travels 4.8 m.
   a) Find the angle at which the shot putt was projected.
   b) If a lighter shot putt were launched with the same initial velocity, how would its range compare to the heavier one?
   c) Explain why an athlete can achieve a greater range with a lighter shot putt.

8 A crate of relief supplies is dropped from an aeroplane travelling horizontally at 75 m s^{-1}. It falls for three seconds before a parachute attached to it opens automatically. The unit vectors **i** and **j** are horizontal and vertical respectively.
   a) Explain why the initial velocity of the crate is 75**i**.
   b) Find an expression for the position vector of the crate relative to its point of release.
   c) Find the position of the crate when the parachute opens.
   d) Find the speed of the crate when the parachute opens.
   e) Draw a diagram to show the path of the crate and the aeroplane, assuming that the aeroplane maintains a constant velocity.

9 A footballer heads a ball giving it an initial velocity of 6 m s^{-1} at 70° to the horizontal. The ball is initially at a height of 2 m.
   a) Using a suitable origin, find a position vector for the ball.
   b) Find the maximum height reached by the ball.
   c) Find the time that the ball is in the air and the distance it travels horizontally.

10 A basketball player throws a ball from a height of 1.8 m with an initial velocity of 8 m s^{-1} at 38° to the horizontal. The basket is 3 m above ground level.
   a) Find the position vector of the ball relative to the player's feet.
   b) The basket is situated 4 m from the player. Find the time it takes the ball to travel a horizontal distance of 4 m.
   c) What is the height of the ball when it has travelled 4 m horizontally?
   d) Suggest how the player could improve the chance of the ball going in the basket.

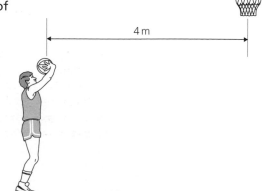

EXERCISES

10.1 HOMEWORK

1   A football is kicked from the ground so that it leaves the ground with a speed of $7\,m\,s^{-1}$ at an angle of 30° above the horizontal.
   a) Express the initial velocity of the ball in terms of the unit vectors **i** and **j** which are horizontal and vertical respectively.
   b) State the acceleration of the ball in terms of **i** and **j**.
   c) Find the velocity of the ball in terms of t, if the ball has been in motion for t seconds.
   d) Find the position vector of the ball in terms of t, using a suitable origin.

2   During a sack race, a girl jumps so that she leaves the ground moving at $2\,m\,s^{-1}$ and at an angle of 20° to the horizontal.
   a) Express the initial velocity of the girl in terms of the unit vectors **i** and **j** which are horizontal and vertical respectively.
   b) Find a position vector to describe the position of the girl in terms of t, if t is the amount of time in seconds she has been in motion.
   c) For how long is the girl in the air for each jump?
   d) How much ground does she cover during each jump?
   e) What is the greatest height reached by the girl?

3   A rugby player claims to be able to kick a rugby ball from the ground at $12\,m\,s^{-1}$. Assume that the ball initially moves in a direction 35° above the horizontal.
   a) Find the distance that the rugby player can kick the ball.
   b) Do you think that the claim is reasonable? Explain why.

4   A tennis ball is launched from ground level so that initially it moves at $14\,m\,s^{-1}$ at 42° to the horizontal.
   a) Find the range of the ball.
   b) Would it make any difference to your answer if it were a table tennis ball?
   c) If you were to consider the effects of air-resistance in the problem, how would the motion of the balls compare with your earlier answers?

5   During a darts match a darts player hits the bulls eye. Assume that the dart is thrown from the same height as the bulls eye at an initial speed of $8\,m\,s^{-1}$ and at 10° above the horizontal.
   a) Find how far from the dart board the player is standing.
   b) Show that if the dart had been thrown with the same speed but at 80° above the horizontal it would also have hit the bulls eye.
   c) Find the speed of the dart when it hits the target in each case.
   d) Which would be the best angle to throw the dart?
      Give reasons for your choice.

6   A motorcycle stunt rider jumps a distance of 24 metres.
   a) Assuming the rider and bike initially move at 20° to the horizontal, find the initial speed.
   b) What angle of projection would give the greatest range?
   c) If the angle of the initial velocity was unknown, find the minimum initial speed that would be needed to travel 24 metres.

7 During a game of tiddly-winks, counters initially travel at $1\,\text{ms}^{-1}$.
   a) What is the maximum range of a counter?
      The counters are projected at an angle of 60° to the horizontal.
   b) If a circular cup of radius 4 cm and height 3 cm is placed on the table to collect the counters, what is the maximum distance from the centre of the cup a counter can be projected to land in the cup?
   c) What is the minimum distance?
   d) How would the radius and height of the circular cup affect your results?

8 A child drops an apple core from the open window of a moving car, travelling on a horizontal road at a constant velocity V.
   a) Explain why, when the apple core hits the road, it is still below the child's hand vertically.
   b) If t is the time in seconds from the moment the apple core is released, find an expression for the position vector of the apple core relative to its point of release.
   c) If the apple core hits the road when $t = 0.6$, find the speed of the apple core at this time if the speed of the car is a constant $20\,\text{ms}^{-1}$.

9 A shot-putter is able to project a shot with a speed of $6\,\text{ms}^{-1}$ at an angle above the horizontal of 35° from a point 1.7 m vertically above the ground.
   a) Using a suitable origin, find a position vector for the shot.
   b) Find the time that the shot is in the air and the distance that it travels horizontally.
   c) Draw a sketch of the trajectory of the shot as seen from one side.
   d) Explain why considering air resistance would not change the path of the ball appreciably.

10 An enterprising golf enthusiast decides to stake a claim to build the first golf course on the moon to provide a facility for those who will eventually live and work there. The length of a typical golf drive on Earth is 180 m. Assume that an average golfer hits the ball at 35° to the horizontal.
   a) Find the initial speed of the ball.
   b) What range would be reached using the same initial velocity on the moon? (Assume $g = 1.6\,\text{ms}^{-2}$ on the moon.)
   c) Give brief advice to the enthusiast about the design of his new course.

THE EQUATION OF THE PATH OF A PROJECTILE

Sometimes, when solving problems involving projectiles, it is helpful to find an equation for the path of a projectile that does not involve time. The height of the projectile is then expressed in terms of the horizontal distance travelled. This is useful, for example, when a rugby player is trying to decide how to kick the ball, to obtain a conversion.

The following exploration demonstrates that the path of a projectile can be described in two different ways, one of which is independent of time.

Exploration 10.4

1 A projectile has a position vector:

$$\mathbf{r} = 15t\mathbf{i} + (10t - 5t^2)\mathbf{j}$$

Set your calculator to parametric plotting mode and to the range/window values below.

$x_{\min} = 0$; $x_{\max} = 40$; $x_{scl} = 10$
$y_{\min} = 0$; $y_{\max} = 10$; $y_{scl} = 10$
$T_{\min} = 0$; $T_{\max} = 2$; $T_{step/pitch} = 0.1$

Find the range and maximum height of the projectile.

2 Repeat **1** for the projectile with position vector

$$\mathbf{r} = 12t\mathbf{i} + (12t - 5t^2)\mathbf{j}$$

3 Change the Function mode (Texas) or Rec mode (Casio).

Plot $y = \dfrac{x(30 - x)}{45}$

Is the shape similar to the path of the projectile drawn in **1**? Use Trace to verify that the range and the maximum height are the same.

4 Now plot $y = \dfrac{x(28.8 - x)}{28.8}$ and compare with the projectile path in **2**.

5 The equation of the path is in fact given by:

$$y = \dfrac{4hx(R - x)}{R^2}$$

where h is the maximum height and R the range. Verify that this gives the equation of the path for some other projectiles.

The path of a projectile as a quadratic equation

It is possible to express the path of the projectile where

$$\mathbf{r} = x\mathbf{i} + y\mathbf{j}$$

in the form

$$y = ax^2 + bx + c.$$

The method of obtaining this result, without the range or maximum height, is demonstrated in the following examples.

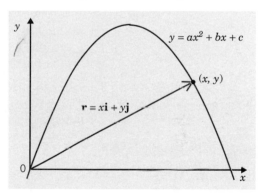

Example 10.4

A projectile moves with position vector $\mathbf{r} = 8t\mathbf{i} + (4t - 4.9t^2)\mathbf{j}$.
a) *If $\mathbf{r}$ is considered as $\mathbf{r} = x\mathbf{i} + y\mathbf{j}$, express y in terms of x.*
b) *Factorise the result and hence find the range.*

Solution

a) *Comparing* $\mathbf{r} = 8t\mathbf{i} + (4t - 4.9t^2)\mathbf{j}$
and $\mathbf{r} = x\mathbf{i} + y\mathbf{j}$
gives $x = 8t$ *and* $y = 4t - 4.9t^2$.

From the first of these equations, $t = \dfrac{x}{8}$. This can then be substituted into the second equation to give:

$$y = 4t - 4.9t^2 = 4 \times \left(\frac{x}{8}\right) - 4.9 \times \left(\frac{x}{8}\right)^2 = \frac{x}{2} - \frac{4.9x^2}{64} = \frac{x}{2} - \frac{49x^2}{640}$$

b) The result above can be factorised to give $y = x\left(\dfrac{1}{2} - \dfrac{49x}{640}\right)$.
To find the range we require $y = 0$, so:

$$0 = x\left(\dfrac{1}{2} - \dfrac{49x}{640}\right) \implies x = 0 \quad \text{or} \quad \dfrac{1}{2} - \dfrac{49x}{640} = 0$$

$$\implies x = 0 \quad \text{or} \quad x = \dfrac{640}{98} = 6.53\,\text{m}$$

So the range is 6.5 m, correct to 2 significant figures.

Example 10.5

A footballer is 10 m from an open goal when he kicks the football with a speed of $20\,\text{ms}^{-1}$ at 38° to the horizontal.
a) Express the path of the ball in the form $y = \mathrm{f}(x)$.
b) Find the height of the ball when it crosses the goal line. Do you think a goal is scored?

Solution

a) The position vector of the ball is:

$$\mathbf{r} = 20t\cos 38°\mathbf{i} + \left(20t\cos 52° - 4.9t^2\right)\mathbf{j}$$

This could be expressed as $\mathbf{r} = x\mathbf{i} + y\mathbf{i}$ so that:

$$x = 20t\cos 38° \quad \text{and} \quad y = 20t\cos 52° - 4.9t^2$$

From the equation for x:

$$t = \dfrac{x}{20\cos 38°}$$

This can be substituted into the expression for y to give:

$$y = 20 \times \dfrac{x}{20\cos 38°}\cos 52° - 4.9\left(\dfrac{x}{20\cos 38°}\right)^2 = 0.7813x - 0.0197x^2$$

b) The height is given by y, so when $x = 10$:
$$y = 0.7813 \times 10 - 0.0197 \times 10^2 = 5.84\,\text{m}$$
The ball goes way over the top of the goal.

In the last two examples, projectiles were launched from ground level. The next example shows how to obtain an equation for all projectiles launched in this way.

Example 10.6

A projectile moves with position vector $\mathbf{r} = Vt\cos\alpha\,\mathbf{i} + (Vt\sin\alpha - \frac{1}{2}gt^2)\mathbf{j}$.
If $\mathbf{r} = x\mathbf{i} + y\mathbf{i}$, express y in terms of x.

Solution

Comparing $\mathbf{r} = Vt\cos\alpha\,\mathbf{i} + (Vt\sin\alpha - \frac{1}{2}gt^2)\mathbf{j}$ and $\mathbf{r} = x\mathbf{i} + y\mathbf{j}$ gives:

$$x = Vt\cos\alpha \quad \text{and} \quad y = Vt\sin\alpha - \tfrac{1}{2}gt^2$$

From the expression for x, t can be expressed as:

$$t = \dfrac{x}{V\cos\alpha}$$

This can be substituted into the above expression for y to give:

$$y = V \times \dfrac{x}{V\cos\alpha}\sin\alpha - \dfrac{1}{2}g\left(\dfrac{x}{V\cos\alpha}\right)^2$$

$$= x\tan\alpha - \dfrac{gx^2}{2V^2\cos^2\alpha} = x\tan\alpha - \dfrac{gx^2\sec^2\alpha}{2V^2}$$

Projectiles launched from points not at ground level

Not all projectiles are launched from ground level. In a game of football the ball is often kicked from ground level, so the ball can be modelled as a particle that is projected from ground level and returns to ground level. However, if the ball is headed rather than kicked, then the height at which it is projected becomes significant and must be taken into account. The next example illustrates one approach to dealing with this problem by taking the point of release as the origin.

Example 10.7

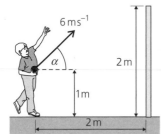

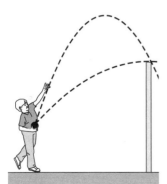

A disruptive pupil is hoping to throw a tennis ball over the school fence, as shown in the diagram. He can throw the ball at $6\,ms^{-1}$. At what angle α should he throw the ball to get it over the fence?

Solution

The position vector for the ball is given by:
$$\mathbf{r} = 6t\cos\alpha\,\mathbf{i} + \left(6t\sin\alpha - 4.9t^2\right)\mathbf{j}$$

where the point of release is taken as the origin.
The path can then be found since:
$x = 6t\cos\alpha$ *and* $y = 6t\sin\alpha - 4.9t^2$
Eliminating t gives:
$y = x\tan\alpha - 0.136x^2\sec^2\alpha$
The ball just passes over the fence if $x = 2$ and $y = 1$, so substituting these values gives: $1 = 2\tan\alpha - 0.54\sec^2\alpha$
but $\sec^2\alpha = 1 + \tan^2\alpha$ *giving:* $1 = 2\tan\alpha - 0.54(1 + \tan^2\alpha)$
Rearranging gives a quadratic equation:
$0.54\tan^2\alpha - 2\tan\alpha + 1.54 = 0$
and solving this quadratic for $\tan\alpha$ gives:

$$\tan\alpha = \frac{2 \pm \sqrt{2^2 - 4 \times 1.54 \times 0.54}}{2 \times 0.54} = \frac{2 \pm 0.821}{1.08} = 2.61 \text{ or } 1.08$$

Now $\tan\alpha = 2.61$ gives $\alpha = 69°$ and $\tan\alpha = 1.08$ gives $\alpha = 47°$. Using either angle will have the required result. The diagram shows the two different paths.

EXERCISES

10.2 CLASSWORK

1. For each position vector given below, express the path followed in the form $y = f(x)$ and use this to find the range.
   a) $\mathbf{r} = 40t\mathbf{i} + (40t - 4.9t^2)\mathbf{j}$ **b)** $\mathbf{r} = 10t\mathbf{i} + (20t - 4.9t^2)\mathbf{j}$
   c) $\mathbf{r} = 12t\mathbf{i} + (18t - 4.9t^2)\mathbf{j}$ **d)** $\mathbf{r} = 6t\mathbf{i} + (4t - 4.9t^2 + 3)\mathbf{j}$

2. A projectile on the moon has position vector $\mathbf{r} = 4t\mathbf{i} + (2t - 0.8t^2)\mathbf{j}$
   Express the path of the projectile in the form $y = f(x)$.

3. A golf ball is 20 m from some trees. The player then hits the ball with an initial speed of $45\,ms^{-1}$ at an angle of 30° to the horizontal.

   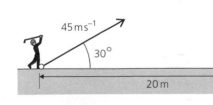

   a) Find the position vector of the golf ball at time t seconds.
   b) Express the path of the ball in the form $y = f(x)$.
   c) If the ball just clears the trees, find the height of the trees.

4 A footballer is about to take a free kick. He kicks the ball so that it initially moves at 18 m s⁻¹ at 30° to the horizontal.

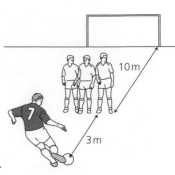

a) Write down an expression for the position vector of the ball at time t seconds.

b) If this can be expressed as $\mathbf{r} = x\mathbf{i} + y\mathbf{j}$, where $\mathbf{i}$ and $\mathbf{j}$ are horizontal and vertical unit vectors, find y in terms of x.

c) What is the height of the ball when it reaches the wall of defenders?

d) Is it possible for a goal to be scored?

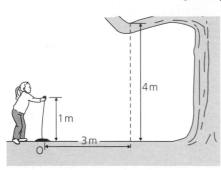

5 A child is trying to throw a stone, tied to a piece of light string, over a branch, to make a rope swing. The diagram shows the positions of the child and the branch. Assume that the stone is thrown with speed v m s⁻¹ at 70° to the horizontal.

a) Write down the position vector of the stone at time t seconds, relative to the point O.

b) Find the equation of the path of the stone in terms of x and v.

c) At what speed must the stone be thrown if it is to go over the branch?

6 A shuttlecock is hit when it is in the position shown in the diagram. It is hit so that it initially moves at v m s⁻¹ and at an angle of 60° above the horizontal.

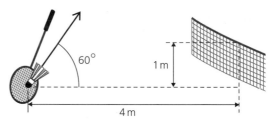

a) Find the equation of the path of the shuttlecock in terms of x and v, relative to its initial position.

b) For what values of v will the shuttlecock just clear the net?

c) Is it reasonable to model a shuttlecock as a particle moving under gravity alone? Explain why.

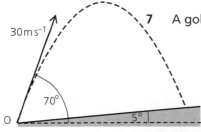

7 A golf ball is hit at a speed of 30 m s⁻¹ at 70° to the horizontal on a slope.

a) Find the equation of the path of the ball.

b) Find the equation of the slope.

c) Use the two equations above to find where the ball lands by eliminating y from the equations.

d) How far from O does the ball land?

8 A child stands at the top of a bank and throws a ball horizontally at 5 m s⁻¹ from the position shown.

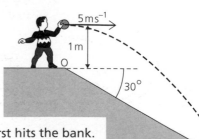

a) Find the equation of the path of the ball relative to the point O.

b) Find the equation of the bank.

c) Find where and when the ball first hits the bank.

9 A motorcyclist intends to ride off a ramp at A and attempt to clear a wall at B.

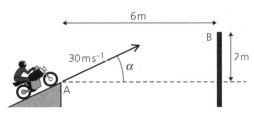

a) Find the equation of the path of the motorcyclist, in terms of x, the horizontal displacement from A, and α, the angle of the ramp, if the take-off speed is $30\,\text{m s}^{-1}$.

b) Use the result $\sec^2\alpha = 1 + \tan^2\alpha$ to produce a quadratic equation in $\tan\alpha$, if he just clears the wall.

c) Solve this equation to find two possible values of α.

d) What would you recommend and why?

10 A tennis player can serve a ball at a speed of $20\,\text{m s}^{-1}$, with the ball at an initial height of $2\,\text{m}$. The diagram shows the dimensions of the net and court.

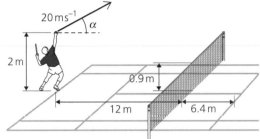

a) Find the equation of the path of the ball, assuming that it starts at the origin, O, in terms of x, the horizontal displacement of the ball from its initial position, and α, the angle of elevation of the path.

b) Find the possible values of α if the ball just clears the net.

c) Which would you recommend and why?

EXERCISES

10.2 HOMEWORK

1 For each position vector given below, express the path followed in the form $y = \text{f}(x)$ and use this to find the range.

a) $\mathbf{r} = 21t\mathbf{i} + (21t - 4.9t^2)\mathbf{j}$

b) $\mathbf{r} = 60t\mathbf{i} + (80t - 4.9t^2)\mathbf{j}$

c) $\mathbf{r} = 0.7t\mathbf{i} + (2.1t - 4.9t^2)\mathbf{j}$

d) $\mathbf{r} = ut\cos\beta\,\mathbf{i} + \left(ut\sin\beta - \dfrac{gt^2}{2}\right)\mathbf{j}$

Sketch the trajectory of the projectile in each case.

2 A projectile on the moon has position vector $\mathbf{r} = 5\sqrt{3}\,t\mathbf{i} + \left(5t - \frac{4}{5}t^2\right)\mathbf{j}$. Express the path of the projectile in the form $y - \text{f}(x)$.

3 A rugby ball is $26\,\text{m}$ from the goal post. It is kicked with an initial speed of $17\,\text{m s}^{-1}$ at an angle of $45°$ to the horizontal.

a) Find the position vector of the rugby ball relative to its starting point, using suitable unit vectors.

b) Express the path of the ball in the form $y = \text{f}(x)$.

c) If the ball just clears the bar, find the height of bar.

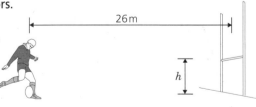

4 A golf ball is $5\,\text{m}$ from some bushes. The player hits the ball with an initial speed of $10\,\text{m s}^{-1}$ at an angle of $30°$ to the horizontal.

a) Write down an expression for the position vector of the ball, relative to its original position in terms of t, $\mathbf{i}$ and $\mathbf{j}$, where $\mathbf{i}$ and $\mathbf{j}$ are horizontal and vertical unit vectors respectively.

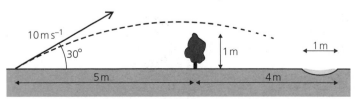

b) If this can be expressed as $\mathbf{r} = x\mathbf{i} + y\mathbf{j}$ find y in terms of x.

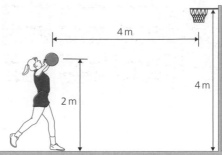

10 *Projectiles*

c) How much clearance is there when the ball passes over the bushes, if they have a height of 1 m?

d) Does the ball land in the bunker?

5 A netball is thrown with an initial speed of V m s⁻¹ at an angle of 60° to the horizontal. The netball leaves the hands of the player 2 m from the ground at a horizontal distance of 4 m from the net.

a) Find the position vector of the ball, using appropriate unit vectors and origin.

b) Find the equation of the path of the ball in terms of x and y.

c) Find the value of V if the ball is to go into the net.

6 An office worker lobs a screwed up piece of paper at an angle of 50° to the horizontal so as to clear a partition and hit the office worker behind, as shown in the diagram.

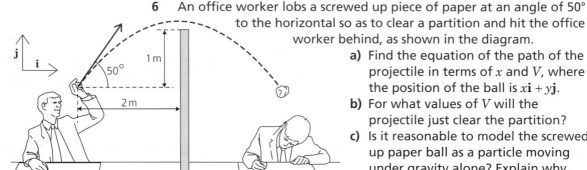

a) Find the equation of the path of the projectile in terms of x and V, where the position of the ball is $x\mathbf{i} + y\mathbf{j}$.

b) For what values of V will the projectile just clear the partition?

c) Is it reasonable to model the screwed up paper ball as a particle moving under gravity alone? Explain why.

7 A football is kicked up a bank with a speed of 20 m s⁻¹ at 60° to the horizontal as shown.

a) Find the equation of the path of the ball.

b) Find the equation of the slope.

c) Use the two equations above to find where the ball lands, by eliminating y from the equations.

d) How far from O does the ball land?

8 A stunt car speeds off a horizontal ramp at 30 m s⁻¹ as shown.

a) Find the equation of the path of the car, taking the point O as the origin.

b) Find the equation of the inclined plane, taking the point O as the origin.

c) Find where the car hits the inclined plane.

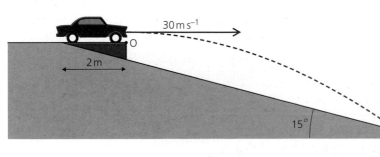

9 A motorcyclist intends to clear a row of buses by riding off a ramp as shown.

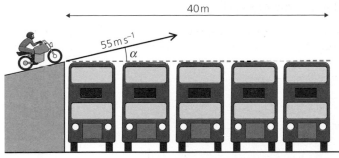

40 m

55 m s⁻¹

α

a) Find the equation of the path of the motorcyclist in terms of x and α, if the take-off speed is $55\,\text{m s}^{-1}$.

b) Use the result $\sec^2\alpha = 1 + \tan^2\alpha$ to produce a quadratic equation in $\tan\alpha$ if the rider just clears the buses.

c) Solve the equation to find two possible values of α.

d) Which would you recommend and why?

10 A tennis player serves with a speed V at an angle α to the horizontal. The diagram shows the dimensions of the net and court.

a) Find the equation of the path of the ball, assuming that it starts at the origin, in terms of x, y and V. (Take g to be $10\,\text{m s}^{-2}$.)

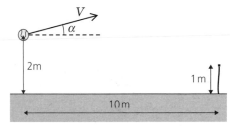

V

α

2 m

1 m

10 m

b) If the ball just clears the net, write down a quadratic equation in $\tan\alpha$.

c) From your equation in $\tan\alpha$, prove that if the ball just clears the net then $V \geq 9.51\,\text{m s}^{-1}$.

CONSOLIDATION EXERCISES FOR CHAPTER 10

1 A cricket ball is hit from a height of 0.8 m above horizontal ground with a speed of $26\,\text{m s}^{-1}$ at an angle α above the horizontal where $\tan\alpha = \frac{5}{12}$. The motion of the ball is modelled as that of a particle moving freely under gravity.

a) Find, to two significant figures, the greatest height above the ground reached by the ball.

When the ball has travelled a horizontal distance of 36 m, it hits a window.

b) Find, to two significant figures, the height above the ground at which the ball hits the window.

c) State one physical factor which could be taken into account in any refinement of the model which would make it more realistic.

(EDEXCEL Question 6, Specimen Paper M2)

2 A golfer hits a ball from a point O, with an initial velocity of $28\,\text{m s}^{-1}$ and at an angle θ above the horizontal. The ball clears an electricity pylon. The height of the pylon is 27.5 m and it is at a horizontal distance of 20 m from O.

a) State one assumption that it is important to make about the motion of the ball in order to model the motion of the ball.

b) Find the range of possible values of θ.

c) Find an expression for the range of the ball in terms of θ.

d) If the ground is horizontal, explain which value of θ gives:

i) the shortest time of flight,

ii) the maximum range.

(AQA B Question 7, Specimen Paper M1)

3

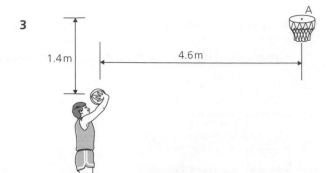

During a practice session, a basketball player throws a ball towards a horizontal ring of centre A. In a simple model, this ball is treated as a particle.

a) The ball is first projected at a speed of $8\,\text{ms}^{-1}$ and at an angle of 40° to the horizontal, from a point at a horizontal distance of 4.6 m from A and 1.4 m below A.

   i) Find the time taken for the ball to travel a horizontal distance of 4.6 m, giving your answer correct to two significant figures.

   ii) Taking $g = 9.8\,\text{ms}^{-2}$, show that the ball passes below A.

b) The player throws again from the same point as before. He projects the ball at an angle of 40° to the horizontal but increases the speed of projection to $V\,\text{ms}^{-1}$.

   i) Determine the value of V for which the ball passes through A.

   ii) Show that, for this value of V, the ball is descending as it passes through A.

(AQA A Question 8, Specimen Paper M1)

4

A shell is fired from a stationary ship O which is at a distance of 1000 m from the foot of a vertical cliff AB of height 100 m. The shell passes vertically above B and lands at a point C on horizontal ground, level with the top of the cliff (see diagram above). The shell is fired with speed $300\,\text{m s}^{-1}$ at angle of elevation θ, and air resistance to the motion of the shell may be neglected.

a) Given that $\theta = 30°$, find the time of flight of the shell and the distance BC.

b)

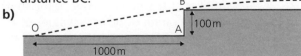

Given instead that the shell *just* passes over B, as shown in this diagram, find the value of θ, correct to the nearest degree.

(OCR Question 7, Specimen Paper M2)

5 A particle is projected with speed u at an angle α *below* the horizontal and moves freely under gravity alone. When the particle has moved a horizontal distance x, it has moved a vertical distance y.

a) Show that $y = x\tan\alpha + \dfrac{gx^2}{2u^2\cos^2\alpha}$.

An archer sits on top of a vertical tower which stands on level ground. He sees a rabbit sitting at a point on the ground which is a horizontal distance of 20 m from the base of the tower. The archer fails to allow for any effect of gravity and aims an arrow directly at the point on the ground where the rabbit is sitting. The height of the arrow is initially 10 m above the ground, and the initial speed of the arrow is 28 m s^{-1}. By modelling the arrow as a particle moving freely under gravity alone,

b) find the distance by which the arrow falls short of the rabbit.

(EDEXCEL Question 8, M1 Paper Jan 1998)

6

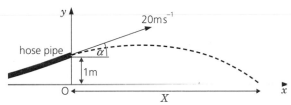

Take $g = 10\,\text{m s}^{-2}$.

A high pressure hose is used to water a horizontal field. The jet of water is modelled as a stream of small droplets (i.e. particles) projected at 20 m s^{-1} at an angle α to the horizontal from a point 1 m above the field. Air resistance may be neglected.

The diagram shows this situation as well as the origin O and x- and y-axes. The unit of each axis is the metre.

a) Write down the horizontal and vertical components of the initial velocity of a droplet.

b) Show that the vertical height of a droplet at time t is given by:
$y = 1 + 20t\,\cos\alpha - 5t^2$
Write down the corresponding equation for the horizontal distance. The horizontal range of a droplet projected at angle α is X m, as shown in the diagram.

c) Use your answers from part **b)** to deduce that
$5X^2\tan^2\alpha - 400X\tan\alpha + 5X^2 - 400 = 0$.

d) Show that it is possible to adjust the angle of projection so that the water lands on the point (40, 0) but that the point (50, 0) is out of range.

e) Does the maximum value of X occur when $\alpha = 45°$? Explain your answer briefly.

(OCR MEI Question 1, M1 Specimen Paper)

MATHEMATICAL MODELLING ACTIVITY

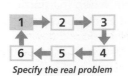

Specify the real problem

Problem statement

Many sports involve hitting, kicking or throwing balls. It is often easy to measure the distance that a ball travels and the time it is in the air, but it is more difficult to find the speed at which it was projected. Find a method for determining the speed at which a football has been kicked.

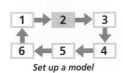

Set up a model

Set up a model

Make a list of the key features that should be considered in solving this problem. In order to solve the problem the following set of assumptions will be made.

- The ball is a particle.
- The only force acting is gravity.
- The ball is launched from ground level.
- The ball is projected at 45° to the horizontal.
- It is possible to record the distance travelled by the ball and the time of flight.

Comment on this set of assumptions, in particular add any further assumptions that you feel are appropriate.

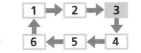

Formulate the mathematical problem

Formulate a mathematical problem

Assume a ball is projected at speed V at 45° to the horizontal and travels a distance R. Express V in terms of R the range of the ball.

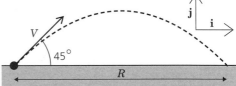

Mathematical solution

Solve the mathematical problem

The position vector $\mathbf{r}$ of the ball at time t, is $\mathbf{r} = \dfrac{Vt}{\sqrt{2}}\mathbf{i} + \left(\dfrac{Vt}{\sqrt{2}} - 4.9t^2\right)\mathbf{j}$.

Show that $V = \sqrt{9.8R}$.

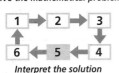

Interpret the solution

Interpretation

The result above shows how the speed of projection is related to the range. It is interesting to note that $R \propto V^2$ so that an increase in V gives a greater increase in R provided $V > 1$.

The speed of projection of a projectile can be found by measuring the range and using the result $V = \sqrt{9.8R}$.

The three factors that his solution does not address are that the ball may not have been launched at 45°, it may not have been launched at ground level and no account has been taken of air resistance.

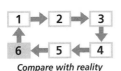

Compare with reality

Compare with reality

Conduct an experiment with a football to determine the speed of projection. Comment on your results. If you are unable to conduct the experiment find the speed at which a football must be kicked if it travels a distance of between 60 to 70 m, which could be done by a good player.

Refining the model

Apply one or both of the revisions outlined below and conduct a further experiment. Also state which sport you are considering and why that revision is appropriate.

Three criticisms have been made of the model. Make at least one further criticism of this model.

The criticisms outlined above are now considered.

1   The effect of the air resistance is that the ball will be slowed down during its flight, reducing the range. So the air resistance will cause the initial speed of the football to be under estimated.

2   Assume that the angle of projection is now α, and not fixed at 45°. Show that:

$$\tan \alpha = \frac{gT^2}{2R}$$

where T is the time of flight and that:

$$V = \frac{R}{T \cos \alpha}$$

Using the time of flight, the angle of projection can be calculated and then the speed of projection found.

Comment on the value of the original model based on the 45° angle of projection.

3   Assume that the ball is launched from a height h, at 45° to the horizontal, show that:

$$V = \sqrt{\frac{R^2 g}{R + h}}$$

Consider two cases, first where a drop kick takes place and secondly where a ball is headed rather than being kicked.

Calculate the speed of projection with and without taking account of the height at which the ball is projected. Is it important to take account of the height of projection?

POSSIBLE MODELLING TASKS

1   By measuring the range and time of flight of a golf ball (or a ball used in some other sport), estimate its speed of projection.

2   Find the optimum angle of projection for a shot putt, taking into account the height of release. The speed of launch is about $13\,\mathrm{m\,s^{-1}}$ for a strong athlete. Should athletes concentrate on gaining the maximum speed of release or the most accurate angle of projection?

3   Estimate the speed of a tennis ball that has been served by one of your fellow students. (Investigate how they should hit the ball when they serve.)

4   Investigate how the wind speed may affect the path of a projectile.

5   Consider a set of golf clubs. Investigate how the different clubs have been designed to achieve different ranges when used.

Summary

After working through this chapter you should:

■ be able to find the position vector, time of flight, maximum height and range of a projectile

■ be aware of the key results listed below:

$$\text{range} = \frac{V^2 \sin 2\alpha}{g}$$

$$\text{time of flight} = \frac{2V \sin \alpha}{g}$$

$$\text{maximum height} = \frac{V^2 \sin^2 \alpha}{2g}$$

$$\text{position vector } \mathbf{r} = Vt \cos \alpha \mathbf{i} + \left(Vt \sin \alpha - \tfrac{1}{2}gt^2\right)\mathbf{j}$$

■ be able to express the path of a projectile as an equation in terms of x and y and, in particular, obtain the result:

$$y = x \tan \alpha - \frac{gx^2 \sec^2 \alpha}{2V^2}$$

for a projectile launched from ground level.

MECHANICS
11

Kinematics with calculus

■ *You will be familiar with the constant acceleration equations. These cannot be used in all situations.*

■ *In reality some forces vary in magnitude and direction and so produce variable accelerations.*

Exploration 11.1

Forces acting on an object

Describe what happens to the forces acting on each object described below.

■ A mass vibrating on the end of a spring.
■ A ball that is hit by a racquet or bat.
■ A pendulum.

Would it be reasonable to model any of the forces above as constant forces?

Try to describe some situations where variable forces act. Is it reasonable to model any of these forces as constant forces?

VELOCITY AND ACCELERATION

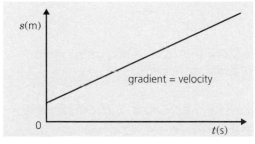

In earlier work you studied velocity and acceleration by looking at the gradients of displacement–time and speed–time graphs. All the examples that you considered were restricted to the special case where acceleration was constant.

Using the notation of calculus, we can extend these ideas to a more general format that is not restricted to constant acceleration.

As the gradient of a displacement–time graph is $\dfrac{\mathrm{d}s}{\mathrm{d}t}$, we can write $v = \dfrac{\mathrm{d}s}{\mathrm{d}t}$.

Similarly the acceleration can be expressed as:

$$a = \frac{\mathrm{d}v}{\mathrm{d}t} \text{ or } a = \frac{\mathrm{d}^2 s}{\mathrm{d}t^2}.$$

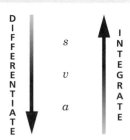

We can then find speeds and accelerations by **differentiating** expressions for displacement. Displacements and speeds can also be found by **integrating** expressions for acceleration.

Example 11.1

A bullet is fired vertically from a rifle. The height, in metres, of the bullet at time t seconds is given by $h = 147t - 4.9t^2 + 1.5$.
a) Show that the acceleration of the bullet is constant.
b) Find the maximum height of the bullet.

Solution
a) The velocity and acceleration can be found by differentiating.

$$v = \frac{dh}{dt}$$
$$= 147 - 9.8t$$
and
$$a = \frac{dv}{dt}$$
$$= -9.8$$

Hence the acceleration is constant.

b) The maximum height will be achieved when the velocity of the bullet is zero. This gives the equation below.

$$0 = 147 - 9.8t$$
$$t = \frac{147}{9.8} = 15\,\text{s}$$

This value for t can now be substituted into the expression for h to give the maximum height.
$$h_{max} = 147 \times 15 - 4.9 \times 15^2 + 1.5$$
$$= 1104\,\text{m}$$

Example 11.2

The distance, in metres, travelled, along a straight road, by a cyclist at time t seconds is modelled by:
$$s = \frac{t^2}{2} - \frac{t^4}{1200} \text{ for } 0 \le t \le 17.3\,\text{s}$$

a) Find expressions for the velocity and acceleration of the cyclist.
b) When does the cyclist begin to slow down?

Solution
a) The velocity and acceleration can be found by differentiating the expression for s with respect to t.

$$v = \frac{ds}{dt} = t - \frac{t^3}{300}$$
and
$$a = \frac{dv}{dt} = 1 - \frac{t^2}{100}$$

b) For the cyclist to be slowing down $a < 0$ so:
$$1 - \frac{t^2}{100} < 0 \quad \Rightarrow \quad 1 < \frac{t^2}{100} \quad \Rightarrow \quad 100 < t^2 \quad \Rightarrow \quad 10 < t$$

So the cyclist begins to slow down after 10 seconds.

Example 11.3

The distance, s metres, fallen by a parachutist, t seconds after she has opened her parachute is given by $s = 10t + 40e^{-0.2t}$.

Obtain expressions for the velocity and acceleration of the parachutist at time t and sketch an acceleration–time graph for the parachutist.

Solution

The velocity and acceleration can be found by differentiating.

$$v = \frac{ds}{dt}$$
$$= 10 + (-0.2) \times 40e^{-0.2t}$$
$$= 10 - 8e^{-0.2t}$$

and

$$a = \frac{dv}{dt}$$
$$= (-0.2) \times 8e^{-0.2t}$$
$$= -1.6e^{-0.2t}$$

The graph shows how the acceleration varies with time from its initial value of -1.6 m s^{-2}.

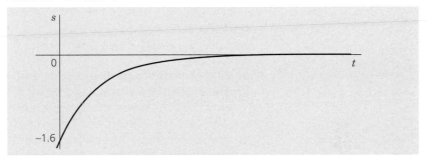

EXERCISES

11.1 CLASSWORK

1   At time t seconds the velocity of a car, moving in a straight line, is $t(t - 10) \text{ m s}^{-1}$. Find the acceleration of the car at time t seconds.

2   The distance, s m, travelled by a cyclist along a straight line in t seconds is modelled by:
$$s = t^2 - \frac{t^3}{240}$$
   a) Show that the cyclist starts at rest.
   b) Find the time when the acceleration becomes zero.
   c) Find the distance travelled and the velocity of the cyclist when his acceleration becomes zero.

3   The height, h m, at time t seconds, of a ball thrown up into the air is modelled by:
$$h = 16t - 4.9t^2 + 2$$
   a) Find an expression for the velocity of the ball.
   b) Find the maximum height reached by the ball.
   c) Find the acceleration of the ball.

4   The distance, s, travelled along a straight line, by a dragster at time t seconds, is modelled by:
$$s = 4t^2 - \frac{t^3}{15} \text{ while the dragster is accelerating.}$$
   a) Find when the acceleration of the dragster becomes zero.
   b) Hence find the maximum speed attained by the dragster and the distance it travels while accelerating.

5 The height, h m, of a hot air balloon at time t seconds is given by:
$$h = \frac{t^2\left(400 - t^2\right)}{400} \text{ for } 0 \le t \le 20$$
a) Find expressions for the velocity and acceleration of the hot air balloon at time t.
b) Find the maximum speed of the balloon in this period.
c) Sketch an acceleration–time graph for the balloon.

6 The speed, v m s⁻¹ at time t seconds, of a car that starts from rest is modelled by:
$$v = 2\sqrt{t} \text{ for } 0 \le t \le 100$$
a) Find the speed of the car when $t = 100$.
b) Find an expression for the acceleration of the car.
c) Find the acceleration of the car when $t = 100$.

7 The height, h m, at time t seconds, of a rocket fired vertically upwards is given by:
$$h = 10t^2 - \frac{5t^3}{3}$$
a) Find expressions for the velocity and acceleration of the rocket.
b) The expressions above are only valid while the acceleration, $a \ge 0$. Find the time when the acceleration of the rocket becomes zero. Calculate the velocity and height at this time.
c) The rocket then moves under the influence of gravity with an acceleration of -10 m s⁻². Find the maximum height reached by the rocket.

8 A ball is released from rest at the top of a tall building, of height 20 m. The ball has fallen a distance, s m, at time t seconds where:
$$s = 7t + 5e^{-1.4t} - 5$$
a) Show that the ball hits the ground when $t \approx 3.57$ s.
b) Find the speed of the ball when it hits the ground.
c) Find an expression for the acceleration of the ball at time t seconds.
d) Sketch graphs to show how the velocity and acceleration vary with time.

9 A particle moves along a straight line, so that its displacement from its starting point at time t seconds is s m, where:
$$s = 5\sin\left(\frac{t}{40\pi}\right)$$
a) Find expressions for the velocity and acceleration of the particle at time t.
b) Find the maximum speed of the particle.
c) Show that $\frac{d^2s}{dt^2} = -ks$ and state the value of k.
d) Sketch graphs to show how the displacement, velocity and acceleration vary with time.

10 A ball is thrown so that it moves vertically upwards. As the ball is rising its height, h m, at time t seconds is given by:
$$h = 245 - 245e^{-0.2t} - 40t$$
a) Find the maximum height of the ball.
b) Describe how the acceleration of the ball varies as it rises.

EXERCISES

11.1 HOMEWORK

1 A rocket is fired vertically, so that at time t seconds its velocity is $v \, \mathrm{ms}^{-1}$, where:

$v = 2t - 0.5t^2 \quad 0 \le t \le 4$

a) Find an expression for the acceleration of the rocket at time t.
b) Find the maximum speed of the rocket.
c) Sketch an acceleration–time graph for the rocket.

2 A diver dives from a high board into a pool of water. The depth, $d \, \mathrm{m}$, of the diver in the water, at time t seconds is modelled as:

$d = t^3 - 4t^2 + 4t$

a) Find an expression for the velocity of the diver while she is in the water.
b) What is the greatest depth that the diver reaches?
c) What is the velocity of the diver when she returns to the surface?
d) An alternative model for d is:

$$d = \frac{32t(2-t)}{27}$$

Show that the diver still reaches the same maximum depth and find the speed at which the diver returns to the surface.
e) Explain which is the more realistic model.

3 The distance, $s \, \mathrm{m}$, travelled by a cyclist along a straight road at time t seconds is modelled as:

$s = 0.8t^2$ for $0 \le t \le 5$

a) Find the velocity and acceleration of the cyclist at time t.
b) Describe what happens to the velocity and acceleration of the cyclist in reality, using sketch graphs to help.
c) Suggest how the cycle moves for $t > 5$.

4 When a large rocket takes off it is suggested that the height, $h \, \mathrm{m}$, of the rocket at time t seconds is given by:

$h = kt^6$

where k is a constant. If the acceleration of the rocket is $30 \, \mathrm{ms}^{-2}$ after 10 seconds, find the value of k.

5 A particle moves along a straight line, so that at time t seconds its displacement, $s \, \mathrm{m}$, is given by:

$s = t^3 - 30t^2 + 225t$ for $0 \le t \le 15$

a) Find the times when the particle comes to rest.
b) Find the particle's initial speed and maximum speed.
c) Sketch a velocity–time graph for the particle.

6 The displacement, $s \, \mathrm{m}$, at time t seconds of a car that starts from rest is given by:

$$s = \frac{t^2}{2} - \frac{t^4}{400} \quad \text{for } 0 \le t \le 10$$

a) Find the maximum speed of the car.
b) Find the initial and final speeds of the car.
c) Find the initial and final accelerations of the car.
d) Sketch velocity–time and acceleration–time graphs for the car.

7 A child descends a slide, with displacement, s at time t seconds, modelled by:

$$s = 0.66t + 0.52t^2$$

a) Find the velocity and acceleration of the child.
b) Describe the initial motion of the child.
c) The slide is at 45° to the horizontal and straight. What assumptions have been made about the coefficient of friction between the child and the slide?

8 A bag of sand is dropped from a hot air balloon. The height, h m, of the bag of sand at time t seconds is modelled by:

$$h = 738 - 20t - 62e^{-0.4t}$$

a) Find the initial velocity of the sand bag and describe how the balloon is moving when the sand bag is dropped.
b) Verify that the sand bag hits the ground when $t \approx 36.9$ seconds.
c) Find the speed of sand bag when it hits the ground.
d) Find the initial acceleration of the bag and state, with reasons, whether or not this is a reasonable value.

9 The tip of the blade of a jigsaw moves so that the displacement, s m, of the tip of the blade from its lowest position at time t seconds is modelled as $s = 0.03 + 0.03 \sin(80\pi t)$.
a) Find the maximum speed of the blade.
b) Find the maximum magnitude of the acceleration of the blade.

10 A model for the displacement, s m, at time t seconds of a stone that is catapulted vertically upwards is $s = A - Be^{-0.4t} - Ct$.
The stone is assumed to start so that $s = 0$, with an initial velocity of $20\,\text{m s}^{-1}$ and an initial acceleration of $-10\,\text{m s}^{-2}$.

Find the values of A, B and C.

VARIABLE ACCELERATION

So far we have discussed situations in which the acceleration was taken to be constant. In real life, this rarely happens, so now we need to consider what is more likely to happen in 'everyday' situations.

We have already seen that differentiation can be used to move from displacement to velocity and from velocity to acceleration. To move from acceleration to velocity or from velocity to displacement we must integrate with respect to time.

$$v = \int a\,\mathrm{d}t$$

$$s = \int v\,\mathrm{d}t$$

Example 11.4

A spaceship that travels in a straight line experiences an acceleration, $a\,\text{m s}^{-2}$, that increases so that at time t seconds:

$$a = \frac{3t}{400} \quad \text{for} \quad 0 \le t \le 20$$

Find the speed reached by the spaceship in the first 20 seconds of its motion and the distance it travels if it initially has velocity $0.3\,\text{m s}^{-1}$.

Solution

The velocity can be found by integrating the expression for the acceleration.

$$v = \int a\,dt = \int \frac{3t}{400}\,dt = \frac{3t^2}{800} + c$$

We now need to find the value of the constant of integration. When $t = 0$, $v = 0.3$, so:

$$0.3 = 0 + c$$

giving the constant $c = 0.3$. In this case, the constant represents the initial velocity of the spaceship. Thus the velocity is:

$$v = \frac{3t^2}{800} + 0.3$$

so at the end of the 20-second period:

$$v = \frac{3 \times 20^2}{800} + 0.3 = 1.8 \text{ m s}^{-1}$$

The distance travelled by the ship is given by:

$$s = \int v\,dt = \int \left(\frac{3t^2}{800} + 0.3 \right)dt = \frac{t^3}{800} + 0.3t + c$$

Assuming that the motion begins at the origin, then $s - 0$ when $t = 0$, so $c = 0$, giving:

$$s = \frac{t^3}{800} + 0.3t$$

After 20 seconds, the distance travelled is given by:

$$s = \frac{20^3}{800} + 0.3 \times 20 = 16 \text{ m}$$

Example 11.5

When a ball bounces on the ground it is in contact with the ground for 0.5 seconds and at time t seconds experiences an acceleration, a ms^{-1}, that is modelled by:

$$a = 200t - 400t^2 - 10 \quad \text{for} \quad 0 \le t \le 0.5$$

a) *Calculate the magnitude of the acceleration when $t = 0$, 0.25 and 0.5. Use this to sketch a graph of the acceleration against time.*

b) *If initially the velocity of the ball is $-\frac{5}{3}$ ms^{-1} find an expression for v, the velocity of the ball.*

c) *Find the velocity of the ball when it leaves the ground at $t = 0.5$.*

d) *What criticisms could be made about this model?*

Solution

a) *The acceleration can be found by substituting the values of t into the expression to give:*

$t = 0 \qquad a = -10$

$t = 0.25 \qquad a = 15$

$t = 0.5 \qquad a = -10$

These three points are represented by the points on the diagram. As the acceleration is a quadratic, it must have the shape shown.

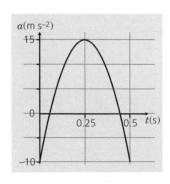

b) *The velocity can be found by integrating the acceleration.*

$$v = \int a\,dt = \int (200t - 400t^2 - 10)\,dt = 100t^2 - \frac{400t^3}{3} - 10t + c$$

As the velocity is $-\frac{5}{3}$ when $t = 0$, we have: $-\frac{5}{3} = 0 + c \implies c = -\frac{5}{3}$

thus the velocity is given by: $v = 100t^2 - \dfrac{400t^3}{3} - 10t - \dfrac{5}{3}$

c) The velocity of the ball when $t = 0.5$ is:

$$v = 100 \times 0.5^2 - \frac{400 \times 0.5^3}{3} - 10 \times 0.5 - \frac{5}{3} = \frac{5}{3}$$

d) The ball rebounds at the same speed as it hits the ground. It is very unlikely that this will happen in reality.

Example 11.6

A possible model for the acceleration, a, of a car at time t seconds after it starts to move from rest along a straight line is:

$$a = 2\sin\left(\frac{\pi t}{40}\right) \text{m s}^{-2} \quad \text{for } 0 \le t \le 40$$

a) Find the velocity of the car at time t seconds.
b) Find the displacement of the car from its starting position at time t seconds.
c) Find the distance travelled in 40 seconds.

Solution
a) We must integrate the acceleration to find the velocity.

$$v = \int 2\sin\frac{\pi t}{40}\,dt$$

$$= \frac{-80}{\pi}\cos\frac{\pi t}{40} + c_1$$

As the car starts at rest we can substitute $v = 0$ and $t = 0$ to find c_1.

$$0 = -\frac{80}{\pi}\cos 0 + c_1$$

$$c_1 = \frac{80}{\pi}$$

Hence the velocity is:

$$v = \frac{80}{\pi}\left(1 - \cos\frac{\pi t}{40}\right)$$

The velocity can now be integrated to give the displacement.

$$s = \int \frac{80}{\pi}\left(1 - \cos\frac{\pi t}{40}\right)dt$$

$$= \frac{80}{\pi}t - \frac{3200}{\pi^2}\sin\left(\frac{\pi t}{40}\right) + c_2$$

As the displacement is relative to the starting point of the car we can substitute $s = 0$ and $t = 0$ to find c_2.

$$0 = \frac{80}{\pi} \times 0 - \frac{3200}{\pi^2}\sin 0 + c_2$$

$$c_2 = 0$$

Hence:

$$s = \frac{80}{\pi}t - \frac{3200}{\pi^2}\sin\frac{\pi t}{40}$$

Now substituting $t = 40$ will give the total distance travelled.

$$s = \frac{80}{\pi} \times 40 - \frac{3200}{\pi^2}\sin\frac{40\pi}{40}$$

$$= 1020\,\text{m (to 3 s.f.)}$$

EXERCISES

11.2 CLASSWORK

1 At time t seconds the acceleration, a, of a cyclist, moving in a straight line, is modelled by:

$$a = 1 - \frac{t}{40} \, \mathrm{m\,s^{-2}}$$

The cyclist starts at rest at the origin.
  a) Find an expression for the velocity of the cyclist at time t seconds.
  b) Find an expression for the distance travelled by the cyclist after t seconds.
  c) Find the time when the cyclist's acceleration becomes zero.
  d) Find the distance travelled by the cyclist at this time.

2 As a ship begins to move, it experiences an acceleration that decreases linearly from $0.5\,\mathrm{m\,s^{-2}}$ to 0 over a 30-second period.
  a) Write down an expression for the acceleration of the ship in terms of time, t, that is valid for $0 \le t \le 30$.
  b) Find an expression for the speed of the ship if it starts at rest and find the speed reached at the end of the 30 seconds.
  c) Find an expression for the distance travelled by the ship and the distance covered in the 30-second period.

3 A cyclist is initially at rest and accelerates at $0.4\,\mathrm{m\,s^{-2}}$ but this decreases uniformly to 0 over 20 seconds. The cyclist then continues at a constant speed.
  a) Write down an expression for the acceleration of the cyclist at time t seconds.
  b) Find the maximum speed reached by the cyclist.
  c) How far does the cyclist travel in the 20-second period?

4 At time t seconds the velocity of a car, moving in a straight line, is $t(15 - t)\,\mathrm{m\,s^{-1}}$.
  a) Find the displacement of the car, from its starting position, at time t seconds.
  b) Find the distance travelled by the car before its speed becomes zero.

5 A car that moves along a straight line experiences an initial acceleration of $3\,\mathrm{m\,s^{-2}}$ but this decreases uniformly. The car reaches a maximum speed of $30\,\mathrm{m\,s^{-1}}$ and stops accelerating after 20 seconds. Find the distance travelled by the car while it is accelerating.

6 A car starts off from rest and travels along a straight line. The acceleration, $a\,\mathrm{m\,s^{-2}}$, of the car at time t seconds is modelled as:

$$a = \frac{t^2(25 - t)^2}{2000}$$

The car stops accelerating when $t = 25$. Find the speed of the car at this time and the distance that it has travelled.

7 The acceleration of a piston in an engine is modelled as $a = -10t$. The piston is initially at the mid-point of its path and moving at $20\,\mathrm{m\,s^{-1}}$.
  a) Find the time taken for the piston to come to rest.
  b) Sketch a graph of the displacement of the piston against time.
  c) State the range of values for which the model could be considered reasonable.
  d) Suggest how the model for the acceleration could be refined.

8   A particle moves from rest along a straight line. At time t seconds the acceleration, a ms^{-2}, of the particle is given by:

$$a = 2\cos\frac{\pi t}{8}$$

a) Find the maximum speed of the particle.
b) Find the maximum distance of the particle from its initial position.

9   A possible model for the velocity, v ms^{-1}, at time t seconds, of an athlete who sprints along a straight line is given as:

$$v = U\left(1 - e^{-0.5t}\right) \text{ where } U \text{ is a constant.}$$

a) Find U if the athlete starts at rest and completes a 100 m sprint in 14 seconds.
b) Find the initial acceleration of the athlete.

10   The graph shows how the magnitude of the acceleration of the car varies during an emergency stop.

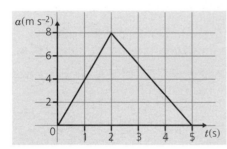

a) What is the direction of the acceleration?
b) Find $\int_0^5 a\,dt$.
c) What was the initial speed of the car?
d) Sketch a graph of speed against time.
e) What was the speed of the car after 2 seconds?
f) Give reasons why the acceleration graph has the shape illustrated.

EXERCISES

11.2 HOMEWORK

1   A particle moves along a straight line, so that its velocity is v ms^{-1}, at time t seconds, where $v = 8 - 2t$ for $0 \leq t \leq 6$.
a) Show that the acceleration of the particle is constant.
b) The particle starts at the origin. Find the distance of the particle from the origin when $t = 6$.

2   As a car moves away from rest it accelerates to its maximum speed in 10 s. A model for its acceleration, a ms^{-2}, at time t seconds during this period is $a = 10 - t$.
a) Find the maximum speed of the car.
b) Find the distance the car travels while accelerating.

3   A cyclist who starts from rest accelerates for 20 seconds along a straight line. A model for the acceleration, in ms^{-2}, of the cyclist at time t seconds is:

$$a = \frac{20 - t}{20}$$

a) Find the speed of the cyclist at the end of the 20 seconds.
b) Find the total distance travelled.

4   The acceleration, a ms^{-2}, of an aeroplane on a runway at time t seconds is modelled as:

$$a = \frac{\sqrt{t}}{2}$$

The aeroplane takes off when it reaches a speed of 72 ms^{-1}. Find the time that the aeroplane accelerates before take-off and the distance travelled before take-off.

5 A lorry is travelling at $20\,\mathrm{m\,s^{-1}}$, when it applies its brakes. The lorry travels along a straight line until it comes to rest 10 seconds later. The acceleration, $a\ \mathrm{m\,s^{-2}}$, of the lorry t seconds after the brakes have been applied is $a = \alpha t - 2.5$.
   a) By considering the velocity of the lorry, find α.
   b) How far does the lorry travel before it stops?

6 A car moves along a straight line, so that its acceleration, $a\ \mathrm{m\,s^{-2}}$, at time t seconds is given by $a = \alpha - \beta t$.

   The car starts at rest and travels a distance of 675 m in 30 seconds, reaching a speed of $37.5\ \mathrm{m\,s^{-1}}$. Find the values of α and β.

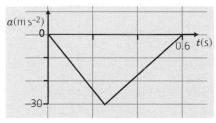

7 The mass attached to a spring at time t seconds is given an initial velocity of $2\,\mathrm{m\,s^{-1}}$. The acceleration of the mass is modelled as $a = -\frac{1}{2}t$.
   a) Find an expression for the displacement of the mass from its initial position.
   b) When does the mass come to rest for the first time?
   c) For what range of values of t could the model be reasonable?
   d) Suggest how to find an alternative model for the acceleration.

8 A skydiver is falling vertically at $60\,\mathrm{m\,s^{-1}}$, when he opens his parachute. After his parachute has been open for 10 seconds his speed has dropped to $5\,\mathrm{m\,s^{-1}}$. His deceleration at time t seconds is modelled as having magnitude Ae^{-t}, where A is a constant.
   a) Find A.
   b) Find the distance travelled by the skydiver in the 10 seconds.

9 A particle starts from rest at the origin and moves on a straight line. At time t seconds it experiences an acceleration, $a\ \mathrm{m\,s^{-2}}$, as given below.
$$a = 1 - 2\sin\frac{\pi t}{10}$$

   Find expressions for the velocity and displacement of the particle at time t seconds.

10 A ball hits a wall travelling at $5\,\mathrm{m\,s^{-1}}$. It experiences an acceleration that can be modelled as shown in the graph.
   a) Use the graph to find $\int_0^{0.6} a\,\mathrm{d}t$.
   b) If u is the impact speed and v the rebound speed, explain why $u - v = \int_0^{0.6} a\,\mathrm{d}t$
   c) Find the rebound speed.

CALCULUS IN TWO AND THREE DIMENSIONS

The principle of using calculus in one dimension can be extended to two or three dimensions. If the position vector is defined as:
$$\mathbf{r} = x\mathbf{i} + y\mathbf{j} + z\mathbf{k}$$
then:
$$\mathbf{v} = \frac{\mathrm{d}\mathbf{r}}{\mathrm{d}t} = \frac{\mathrm{d}x}{\mathrm{d}t}\mathbf{i} + \frac{\mathrm{d}y}{\mathrm{d}t}\mathbf{j} + \frac{\mathrm{d}z}{\mathrm{d}t}\mathbf{k}$$

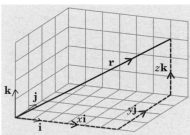

Note: Each component of the position vector is differentiated in turn. To find the acceleration, the velocity is differentiated in the same way.

$$\mathbf{a} = \frac{d\mathbf{v}}{dt} = \frac{d^2x}{dt^2}\mathbf{i} + \frac{d^2y}{dt^2}\mathbf{j} + \frac{d^2z}{dt^2}\mathbf{k}$$

In two dimensions the **k** term is simply omitted.

Example 11.7

As a car travels round a bend its position vector is modelled by:

$$\mathbf{r} = (2t + 4)\mathbf{i} + \tfrac{1}{4}t^3\mathbf{j}$$

After four seconds the car leaves the bend and the expression above no longer applies.

a) *If you have a graphics calculator, or software, plot the path of the car.*

b) *Calculate the position of the car when t = 0, 1, 2, 3 and 4. Use this information to plot the path of the car.*

c) *Find an expression for the velocity of the car. Calculate the velocity of the car when t = 0, 1, 2, 3 and 4. Draw vectors on your diagram to represent the velocity of the car at t = 0, 1, 2, 3 and 4.*

d) *Find an expression for the acceleration of the car. Calculate the acceleration when t = 0, 1, 2, 3 and 4 and draw vectors on the diagram to illustrate these.*

e) *Describe what happens to the acceleration of the car. Is this realistic?*

Solution

a) *See the graph on the left.*

b) *Substituting the values of t into the position vector gives:*

$t = 0 \Rightarrow \mathbf{r} = 4\mathbf{i} + 0\mathbf{j} = 4\mathbf{i}$

$t = 1 \Rightarrow \mathbf{r} = 6\mathbf{i} + 0.25\mathbf{j}$

$t = 2 \Rightarrow \mathbf{r} = 8\mathbf{i} + 2\mathbf{j}$

$t = 3 \Rightarrow \mathbf{r} = 10\mathbf{i} + 6.75\mathbf{j}$

$t = 4 \Rightarrow \mathbf{r} = 12\mathbf{i} + 16\mathbf{j}$

These points have been plotted on the diagram.

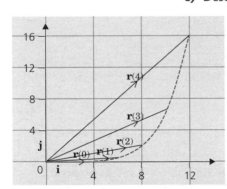

c) *The velocity of the car is given by:*

$$\mathbf{v} = \frac{d\mathbf{r}}{dt} = 2\mathbf{i} + \tfrac{3}{4}t^2\mathbf{j}$$

Substituting the values of t into the expression for the velocity gives:

$t = 0 \Rightarrow \quad \mathbf{v} = 2\mathbf{i} + 0\mathbf{j} = 2\mathbf{i}$

$t = 1 \Rightarrow \quad \mathbf{v} = 2\mathbf{i} + 0.75\mathbf{j}$

$t = 2 \Rightarrow \quad \mathbf{v} = 2\mathbf{i} + 3\mathbf{j}$

$t = 3 \Rightarrow \quad \mathbf{v} = 2\mathbf{i} + 6.75\mathbf{j}$

$t = 4 \Rightarrow \quad \mathbf{v} = 2\mathbf{i} + 12\mathbf{j}$

The diagram shows the path with the velocity vectors superimposed, note that the velocity vectors are at tangents to the path.

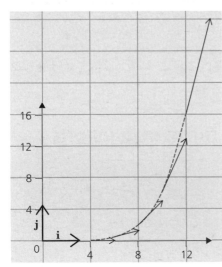

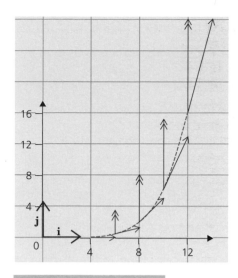

d) *The acceleration is obtained by differentiating the velocity.*

$$\mathbf{a} = \frac{d\mathbf{v}}{dt} = 0\,\mathbf{i} + \frac{3}{2}t\mathbf{j} = \frac{3}{2}t\mathbf{j}$$

Substituting values for t gives:

$t = 0 \Rightarrow \mathbf{a} = 0\mathbf{j} = 0 \qquad t = 1 \Rightarrow \mathbf{a} = 1.5\mathbf{j} \qquad t = 2 \Rightarrow \mathbf{a} = 3\mathbf{j}$

$t = 3 \Rightarrow \mathbf{a} = 4.5\mathbf{j} \qquad t = 4 \Rightarrow \mathbf{a} = 6\mathbf{j}$

The diagram shows the path with both the velocity and acceleration vectors superimposed.

e) *The acceleration is always in the $\mathbf{j}$-direction and increases in magnitude from 0 to $6\,\mathrm{m\,s^{-2}}$. It is very unlikely in reality that a normal car can produce an acceleration of $6\,\mathrm{m\,s^{-2}}$, a car that accelerates from 0 to 60 mph in 6 seconds has an acceleration of $4.5\,\mathrm{m\,s^{-2}}$.*

Example 11.8

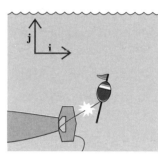

A buoy is snagged by a submarine and dragged down under the water. It becomes detached from the submarine which is moving horizontally at $2\,\mathrm{m\,s^{-1}}$. As the buoy rises, it experiences an upward acceleration of $5 - \frac{1}{2}t$. Find expressions for the velocity and position of the buoy relative to its point of release.

If the acceleration of the buoy is zero when it reaches the surface, find the depth to which it was dragged.

Solution

In terms of the unit vectors shown on the diagram, the acceleration of the buoy is: $\mathbf{a} = \left(5 - \frac{1}{2}t\right)\mathbf{j}$

The velocity can be found by integrating this expression.

$$\mathbf{v} = \int \mathbf{a}\,dt = \int\left(5 - \frac{t}{2}\right)dt\,\mathbf{j} = c_1\mathbf{i} + \left(5t - \frac{t^2}{4} + c_2\right)\mathbf{j}$$

Note that it is necessary to introduce the horizontal component of velocity. The initial velocity of the ball was $-2\mathbf{i} + 0\mathbf{j}$, so the values of the two constants are $c_1 = -2$ and $c_2 = 0$, which gives:

$$\mathbf{v} = -2\mathbf{i} + \left(5t - \frac{t^2}{4}\right)\mathbf{j}$$

This expression can now be integrated to give the position vector.

$$\mathbf{r} = \int \mathbf{v}\,dt = \int -2dt\,\mathbf{i} + \int\left(5t - \frac{t^2}{4}\right)dt\,\mathbf{j} = (-2t + c_3)\mathbf{i} + \left(\frac{5t^2}{2} - \frac{t^3}{12} + c_4\right)\mathbf{j}$$

If the initial position of the buoy is $0\mathbf{i} + 0\mathbf{j}$ then $c_3 = 0$ and $c_4 = 0$ so that the position vector is:

$$\mathbf{r} = -2t\,\mathbf{i} + \left(\frac{5t^2}{2} - \frac{t^3}{12}\right)\mathbf{j}$$

At the surface, the acceleration is zero so:

$$5 - \frac{t}{2} = 0 \quad \text{or} \quad t = 10 \text{ s}$$

When $t = 0$, the position is:

$$\mathbf{r} = (-2 \times 10)\mathbf{i} + \left(\frac{5 \times 10^2}{2} - \frac{10^3}{12}\right)\mathbf{j} = -20\mathbf{i} + 167\mathbf{j}$$

So the buoy must have been dragged to a depth of 167 m.

EXERCISES

1   The position vector, in metres, at time t seconds, for a ball thrown by a child is given by:
$$\mathbf{r} = 5t\mathbf{i} + \left(1 + 6t - 4.9t^2\right)\mathbf{j}$$
where $\mathbf{i}$ and $\mathbf{j}$ are horizontal and vertical unit vectors respectively.
a) Find an expression for the velocity of the ball at time t.
b) Show that the acceleration of the ball is constant and state its magnitude and direction.

2   At time t seconds an aeroplane has the position vector, in metres, of:
$$\mathbf{r} = \frac{t^3}{30}\mathbf{i} + \frac{t^4}{120}\mathbf{j} + 5t\mathbf{k}$$
The unit vectors $\mathbf{i}$ and $\mathbf{j}$ are horizontal and perpendicular and $\mathbf{k}$ is vertical.
a) Find expressions for the velocity and acceleration of the aeroplane at time t.
b) At what rate is the aeroplane gaining height?
c) What can be deduced about the direction of the acceleration of the plane?

3   The position, in metres, of a javelin at time t seconds is modelled by:
$$\mathbf{r} = \left(18t - 3t^2\right)\mathbf{i} + \left(14t - 4.9t^2\right)\mathbf{j}$$
where $\mathbf{i}$ and $\mathbf{j}$ are horizontal and vertical unit vectors respectively.

Find the length of the throw and the velocity of the javelin when it hits the ground.

4   As a car travels round a bend its position vector at time t seconds is:
$$\mathbf{r} = 5t\mathbf{i} + \frac{t^2}{6}\mathbf{j} \text{ for } 0 \le t \le 4$$
where $\mathbf{i}$ and $\mathbf{j}$ are perpendicular, horizontal unit vectors.
a) Find expressions for the velocity and acceleration of the car while it is on the bend.
b) Find the speed of the car as it enters the bend when $t = 0$ and leaves the bend when $t = 4$.
c) Describe what happens to the acceleration of the car as it rounds the bend.

5   The position of a rider on a helter-skelter at time t seconds is given by:
$$\mathbf{r} = 2\sin t\,\mathbf{i} + 2\cos t\,\mathbf{j} + \left(10 - 0.5t\right)\mathbf{k}$$
The unit vectors $\mathbf{i}$ and $\mathbf{j}$ are horizontal and perpendicular. The unit vector $\mathbf{k}$ is directed vertically upwards.
a) Find expressions for the velocity and acceleration of the rider.
b) Show that the speed of the rider is constant and find its magnitude.
c) Describe the acceleration of the rider.

6   A rocket launched at a fireworks display moves so that at time t seconds its position vector is:
$$\mathbf{r} = 10t\mathbf{i} + \left(2t^3 - 18t^2 + 54t\right)\mathbf{j} \quad \text{for} \quad 0 \le t \le 3$$
The unit vectors $\mathbf{i}$ and $\mathbf{j}$ are horizontal and vertical respectively.
a) Find the velocity of the rocket.
b) Find the acceleration of the rocket.
c) Find the velocity and position of the rocket when $t = 3$.
d) When $t = 3$, the rocket explodes and the shell of the rocket returns to Earth with a downward acceleration of $9.8\,\text{ms}^{-2}$. Find, by integrating,

expressions for the velocity and position of the shell of the rocket after it has exploded. (Let t be the time since the explosion.)

e) How far does the shell land from the point where the rocket was launched?

7 An object moves so that at time t seconds its position vector, in metres, is given by:

$$\mathbf{r} = \left(6t^2 - 5\right)\mathbf{i} + \left(5t^2 - 3t + 8\right)\mathbf{j}$$

where $\mathbf{i}$ and $\mathbf{j}$ are perpendicular unit vectors.

a) Find the acceleration of the object.

b) Find the velocity and speed of the object when $t = 3$.

c) When does the object have position vector $\mathbf{r} = 145\mathbf{i} + 118\mathbf{j}$?

8 In each case below find an expression for the position of the object at time t using the given acceleration, $\mathbf{a}$, initial velocity, $\mathbf{u}$, and initial position $\mathbf{r}_0$.

a) $\mathbf{a} = -10\mathbf{j}$ $\mathbf{u} = 4\mathbf{i} + 2\mathbf{j}$ $\mathbf{r}_0 = 2\mathbf{j}$

b) $\mathbf{a} = 4\mathbf{i} + t\mathbf{j}$ $\mathbf{u} = 3\mathbf{i} - 2\mathbf{j}$ $\mathbf{r}_0 = 0\mathbf{i} + 0\mathbf{j}$

c) $\mathbf{a} = t^2\mathbf{i} - t^3\mathbf{j}$ $\mathbf{u} = 0\mathbf{i} + 0\mathbf{j}$ $\mathbf{r}_0 = 10\mathbf{i} - 20\mathbf{j}$

9 A car has velocity $30\mathbf{i}\,\mathrm{m\,s}^{-1}$ when it enters a bend. While on the bend its acceleration is $(0.2\mathbf{i} + 0.1t\mathbf{j})\,\mathrm{m\,s}^{-2}$ where t is the time in seconds since the car entered the bend. The unit vectors $\mathbf{i}$ and $\mathbf{j}$ are perpendicular and both horizontal.

a) Find expressions for the velocity and position of the car while on the bend.

b) Sketch the path of the car for $0 \le t \le 5$.

10 The acceleration, in $\mathrm{m\,s}^{-2}$, of a jet-ski at time t seconds is modelled by:

$$\mathbf{a} = 2\mathbf{i} - \frac{t}{4}\mathbf{j}$$

where $\mathbf{i}$ and $\mathbf{j}$ are perpendicular unit vectors. The initial velocity of the jet-ski is $4\mathbf{j}\,\mathrm{m\,s}^{-1}$. Plot the path of the jet-ski for the 10 seconds that the acceleration is present.

EXERCISES

11.3 HOMEWORK

1 A football is kicked so that its position, in metres, at time t seconds is modelled by:

$$\mathbf{r} = 10t\mathbf{i} + \left(12t - 4.9t^2\right)\mathbf{j}$$

where $\mathbf{i}$ and $\mathbf{j}$ are horizontal and vertical unit vectors respectively. Show that the acceleration of the football is constant, stating clearly its direction and magnitude.

2 A hockey ball is hit on a sloping pitch, so that its position, in metres, at time t seconds is modelled as:

$$\mathbf{r} = 5t\mathbf{i} + \left(12t - 0.1t^3\right)\mathbf{j}$$

The unit vectors $\mathbf{i}$ and $\mathbf{j}$ are perpendicular and lie in the plane of the pitch.

a) Find the velocity and acceleration of the ball.

b) Sketch the path of the ball and indicate the direction of the acceleration of the ball.

c) Describe the slope of the pitch.

3 A 'demon-drop' slide at an adventure centre is such that at time t seconds, users move with position vector:

$$\mathbf{r} = \frac{t^4}{5}\mathbf{i} + \left(8 - 2t^2\right)\mathbf{j}$$

where $\mathbf{i}$ and $\mathbf{j}$ are horizontal and vertical unit vectors respectively and $\mathbf{r}$ is in metres. The model is only valid while the vertical component is greater than or equal to zero. After this, the riders all travel on a horizontal surface.

a) Find the range of values for which the model is valid.

b) What are the velocity and acceleration of the riders when they are about to reach the level surface?

c) Do you think that this ride is safe?

4 The path of an object is modelled with position vector $\mathbf{r}$ metres at time t seconds as:

$$\mathbf{r} = \sqrt{t}\,\mathbf{i} + \frac{1}{\sqrt{t}}\,\mathbf{j}$$

where $\mathbf{i}$ and $\mathbf{j}$ are perpendicular unit vectors. Find the velocity and acceleration of the object when $t = 4$.

5 A car on a bend moves so that at time t seconds its position vector is:

$$\mathbf{r} = \left(4t\,\mathbf{i} + 0.2t^3\,\mathbf{j}\right) \text{ for } 0 \leq t \leq 5$$

in metres, where $\mathbf{i}$ and $\mathbf{j}$ are perpendicular unit vectors. The car moves with a constant velocity once it has left the bend.

a) Sketch the path of the car and indicate the direction of the acceleration of the car.

b) Find the speed of the car when it enters the bend at $t = 0$ and when it leaves the bend at $t = 5$.

c) Find the position of the car when $t = 10$.

6 In each case below, the acceleration, $\mathbf{a}$, and initial velocity, $\mathbf{u}$, of an object are given. Initially the object was at the origin. Find an expression for the position vector of the object at time t.

a) $\mathbf{a} = \frac{t}{2}\mathbf{i} + \frac{t}{3}\mathbf{j}$ $\qquad \mathbf{u} = 4\mathbf{i}$ $\qquad$ b) $\mathbf{a} = 3t\mathbf{i} - 2t\mathbf{j}$ $\qquad \mathbf{u} = 20\mathbf{i} - 18\mathbf{j}$

c) $\mathbf{a} = \sqrt{t}\,\mathbf{i} + 2\sqrt{t}\,\mathbf{j}$ $\quad \mathbf{u} = 10\mathbf{i} - 2\mathbf{j}$

7 As a car accelerates from rest its acceleration at time t seconds is

$$\left(\frac{20-t}{5}\mathbf{i} + \frac{20-t}{10}\mathbf{j}\right) \text{m s}^{-2}$$ where $\mathbf{i}$ and $\mathbf{j}$ are perpendicular unit vectors.

a) Find the velocity of the car.

b) Show that when $t = 20$, the speed is a maximum.

c) When does the car come to rest?

d) Find the displacement of the car from its starting point when it comes to rest.

8 A ball is thrown so that its acceleration, $\mathbf{a}$ m s^{-2}, including some of the effects of air resistance, has been modelled at time t seconds as:

$$\mathbf{a} = -\frac{t}{20}\mathbf{i} - 10\mathbf{j}$$

where $\mathbf{i}$ and $\mathbf{j}$ are horizontal and vertical unit vectors respectively.

a) Find an expression for the velocity of the ball if its initial velocity is $8\mathbf{i} + 2\mathbf{j}$.

b) Find the position vector of the ball relative to its starting point at ground level.

c) Where does the ball hit the ground?

9 The acceleration of a jet-ski at time t seconds is modelled as:

$$\left(\frac{\sqrt{t}}{2}\mathbf{i} - \frac{\sqrt{t}}{4}\mathbf{j}\right) \mathrm{m\,s^{-2}}$$ where $\mathbf{i}$ and $\mathbf{j}$ are perpendicular unit vectors.

  a) If the jet-ski is initially at rest, at the origin, find its position vector after 16 seconds.

  b) Describe the path of the jet-ski.

10 The acceleration of a person on a free-fall slide at time t seconds is modelled as:

$$\left(0.5\mathbf{i} - \frac{(t-4)^2}{2}\mathbf{j}\right) \mathrm{m\,s^{-2}}$$

where $\mathbf{i}$ and $\mathbf{j}$ are horizontal and vertical unit vectors respectively. Initially the person is at rest at the origin.

  a) Find the expressions for the velocity and position of the person on the slide.

  b) When does the motion become horizontal?

  c) The acceleration from this point on is $-5\mathbf{i}$. How far does the person travel on the horizontal section at the bottom of the slide?

CONSOLIDATION EXERCISES FOR CHAPTER 11

1 A moving particle P travels in a straight line. At time t seconds after starting from the point O on the line, the velocity of P is $v\,\mathrm{m\,s^{-1}}$, where $v = t^2(6 - t)$.

Show that the acceleration of P is zero when $t = 4$.

After a certain time, P comes instantaneously to rest at the point A on the line. State the time taken for the motion from O to A, and find the distance OA.

(OCR A Question 4, Specimen Paper M1)

2 At time t seconds, a particle P has position vector $\mathbf{r}$ metres relative to a fixed origin O, where $\mathbf{r} = (t^3 - 3t)\mathbf{i} + 4t^2\mathbf{j}$, $t \geq 0$.
Find:

  a) the velocity of P at time t seconds,

  b) the time when P is moving parallel to the vector $\mathbf{i} + \mathbf{j}$.

(EDEXCEL Question 3, M2 Specimen Paper)

3 With respect to a fixed origin O, the velocity $\mathbf{v}\,\mathrm{m\,s^{-1}}$ of a particle P at time t seconds is given by $\mathbf{v} = t^2\mathbf{i} + (5 - 4t)\mathbf{j}$.

  a) Find the acceleration of P at time t seconds, giving your answer as a vector.

  b) Find the value of t when P is moving parallel to the vector $\mathbf{i}$.
    When $t = 0$, P is at the point with position vector $-3\mathbf{i}$ metres.

  c) Find, to three significant figures, the distance OP when $t = 3$.

(EDEXCEL Question 4, M2 June 98)

4 A possible model for the position of a car, at time t seconds, while it is travelling over a small hill is:

$$\mathbf{r} = 25t\mathbf{i} + \frac{50}{\pi}\left(1 - \cos\frac{\pi t}{10}\right)\mathbf{j}$$

where $\mathbf{i}$ and $\mathbf{j}$ are horizontal and vertical unit vectors respectively and the distances are in metres. The model is valid for $0 \leq t \leq 20$. The diagram shows the path of the car. Initially the car is at O, at time $t = 0$.

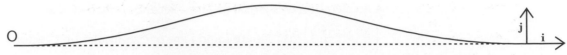

a) Find the velocity of the car at time t.
b) Find an expression for the speed of the car, at time t.
c) Find the times when the car has its minimum and maximum speeds and describe what happens to the speed of the car as it travels over the hill.
d) Comment on how your answer to part c) agrees or disagrees with the way that you would expect the speed of a car to change while going over a hill.

(AQA B Question 5, Specimen Paper M2)

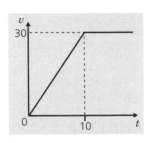

5 A car is moving in a straight line. At time t seconds, its speed is $v\,\text{m s}^{-1}$. It accelerates from rest at time $t = 0$ and reaches a maximum speed of $30\,\text{m s}^{-1}$ when $t = 10$, and maintains that speed thereafter. In an initial model of the situation, it is assumed that the acceleration is uniform for $0 \le t \le 10$, with the speed–time graph as shown in the top diagram. Using this model:

a) find the distance travelled by the car while it is accelerating,
b) sketch the graph of acceleration against time for the period $t \ge 0$.

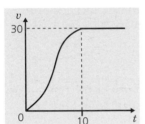

The model is refined to allow for the fact that when the car initially accelerates from rest, the magnitude of its acceleration increases gradually from zero, and as it approaches its maximum speed, the magnitude of its acceleration decreases gradually to zero. The speed $v\,\text{m s}^{-1}$ is now given by:

$$v = \begin{cases} \frac{3}{50}\left(15t^2 - t^3\right), & 0 \le t \le 10, \\ 30, & t > 10, \end{cases}$$

with the speed–time graph as shown in the lower diagram. Using this refined model:

c) show that the distance travelled by the car while it is accelerating is the same as in the previous model,
d) find the maximum acceleration of the car for $0 \le t \le 10$.
e) sketch the graph of acceleration against time for the period $0 \le t \le 10$.

(EDEXCEL Question 9, M1 June 98)

MATHEMATICAL MODELLING ACTIVITY

Problem statement

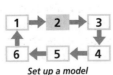

Specify the real problem

It has been suggested that a sprinter will reach their top speed in 4 s and maintain that speed for the rest of the sprint. Develop a model that describes how a sprinter moves during the first four seconds.

Set up a model

Set up a model

A simple first model can be developed from the assumptions listed below.

■ The sprinter is modelled as a particle travelling along a straight line.
■ The acceleration decreases linearly during the first four seconds and is then zero,
i.e. $a = p - qt$ for $t \le 4$.
■ The sprinter reaches a speed of $6.5\,\text{m s}^{-1}$. (This figure has been chosen as it relates to data that can be used later.)

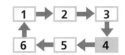

Formulate the mathematical problem

Formulate a mathematical problem

If the sprinter has acceleration $a = p - qt$, for $0 \le t \le 4$, and reaches a maximum speed of $6.5\,\mathrm{m\,s^{-1}}$ find the values of p and q.

Solve the mathematical problem

Mathematical solution

First consider the fact that the acceleration is zero when $t = 4$.
This gives the equation:
$$0 = p - (q \times 4) \Rightarrow p = 4q$$

Now to consider the velocity of the sprinter, which can be obtained by integration.
$$v = \int a\,\mathrm{d}t = \int (p - qt)\,\mathrm{d}t = pt - \frac{qt^2}{2} + c$$

When $t = 0$, $v = 0$ so the constant c is zero and $v = pt - \frac{qt^2}{2}$.

When $t = 4$, $v = 6.5\,\mathrm{m\,s^{-1}}$, and so $6.5 = 4p - 8q$.
But $p = 4q$, so $6.5 = 16q - 8q = 8q$
$$q = \frac{6.5}{8} = 0.8125$$

Using this gives $p = 3.25$.

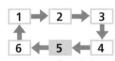

Interpret the solution

Interpretation

The acceleration can be modelled as: $a = 3.25 - 0.8125t$
and the velocity can be modelled as: $v = 3.25t - 0.40625t^2$
Show that the distance travelled by the sprinter can be modelled as:
$$s = 1.625t^2 - 0.135\,416t^3$$
Also find the distance travelled by the sprinter in the four seconds.

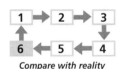

Compare with reality

Compare with reality

The table below gives a set of observed velocities recorded with an electronic measuring device.

t (s)	0	0.5	1.0	1.5	2.0	2.5	3.0	3.5	4.0
v ($\mathrm{m\,s^{-1}}$)	0	1.52	2.87	3.90	4.69	5.24	5.67	6.10	6.50

Compare the actual results with the model's predictions and comment on the quality of the model.

Refinement of the model

Suggest possible ways in which the model could be refined.

POSSIBLE MODELLING TASK

Many real situations involve variable forces. Choose a situation where an object begins to move from rest, such as a car or cyclist. Record how far the object travels over short periods of time. Use this to investigate how the resultant force on the object varies with time.

Summary

After working through this chapter you should:

■ be able to use differentiation to find velocity and acceleration from a given position vector

■ be able to use integration to find velocity and position from an acceleration

■ be able to work in two or three dimensions.

MECHANICS
12

Energy, work and power

- *The ideas of energy can be derived from the basic equations of motion, to provide an alternative approach to solving problems involving energy, work and power.*

- *This chapter concentrates on the energy associated with moving objects.*

FORMS OF ENERGY

Exploration 12.1

What is energy?

What do you understand by the word **energy**? Try to identify some situations that involve or are associated with energy. Decide where that energy may have come from and where it may go.

For example:
- a car that starts at rest, gains speed and then stops, using the brakes
- a carriage moving on a ride such as the famous Alton Towers corkscrew
- an athlete competing in a pole vault event.

Kinetic energy and potential energy

There are basically two kinds of energy: **kinetic** and **potential**. Kinetic energy is the energy associated with a moving object. The kinetic energy of an object is determined by the speed or velocity with which it is moving, and its mass. The faster an object moves, the more kinetic energy it has. A heavy moving object will have more kinetic energy than a lighter object moving at the same speed.

Potential energy, considered in its simplest form, is energy that has been stored in some way, but can be released and converted into potential energy. Potential energy can be stored in a compressed spring or in an object held above the ground. If the spring expands or the object falls, the stored potential energy is converted to kinetic energy.

Other 'forms' of energy are often talked about, but can always be related to these first simple – and more accurate – origins. For example, 'heat' energy (the hotter something is, the faster the atoms move about within the object) is kinetic energy. Heat is often released when energy is converted from one form to another. For example, when the brakes are applied in a car, some of the kinetic energy of the car is lost as heat in the brake pads. 'Chemical' energy can most accurately be thought of as potential energy. The atoms within a substance can be said to have energy because of their positions within the electrical fields. Any energy that an object has because of a field effect is called potential energy.

A basic rule of science is that 'energy cannot be created or destroyed', This is called **conservation of energy**. When energy is transferred from one form to another, it may manifest itself in different ways: heat, light, sound for example, but the total amount present stays the same.

EXERCISES

12.1 CLASSWORK

1   Describe examples of situations where:
    a) electricity is converted to kinetic energy or vice versa,
    b) potential energy stored in a spring is converted to kinetic energy.

2   Describe some situations where unwanted heat is converted from one form of energy to another.

3   Describe the energy changes that take place when an athlete takes part in a high jump contest at an athletics event.

4   Electricity is produced at a hydroelectric power station. From what form of energy is electricity obtained?

5   Describe the energy changes that take place during a bungee jump.

EXERCISES

12.1 HOMEWORK

1   Describe examples of situations where:
    a) kinetic energy is converted to potential energy,
    b) chemical potential energy is converted to kinetic energy.

2   Describe the energy changes that take place as a pendulum swings in a grandfather clock. Why does a grandfather clock need to be wound up?

3   Describe the energy changes that take place during a pole vault.

4   A wind farm has several windmills that are used to produce electricity. Describe the energy changes that take place as the electricity is produced. What is the original source of the energy that is produced?

5   Describe the energy changes that take place as a squash ball is hit.

KINETIC ENERGY

All moving objects have some energy associated with their motion, the faster they move the greater the energy. For example much more energy would be associated with the motion of a racing car than an average family car. Similarly, more energy would be associated with the motion of a heavy goods vehicle than a car moving at the same speed. The kinetic energy of an object is the energy that it has due to its motion and depends both on its mass and its speed.

The kinetic energy, KE, of an object is defined as:

$$KE = \frac{1}{2}mv^2$$

where m is the mass and v the speed of the object in question. Note this does not depend on the direction of motion, only the speed. The units of energy are joules, J, when ms^{-1} and kg are used for v and m respectively.

Example 12.1

A car of mass 1200 kg is initially moving at 13 m s^{-1} (30 mph). Later, its speed has increased to 15 m s^{-1} (34 mph).
a) Find the initial kinetic energy of the car.
b) Find the gain in kinetic energy of the car when the speed has increased.

Solution
a) Here $m = 1200\,kg$ and $v = 13\,m\,s^{-1}$, so:
$$KE = \tfrac{1}{2}mv^2 = \tfrac{1}{2} \times 1200 \times 13^2 = 101\,400 \text{ J}$$

b) When the speed has increased:
$$KE = \tfrac{1}{2} \times 1200 \times 15^2 = 135\,000 \text{ J}$$

Now the gain in kinetic energy can be calculated.
Gain in $KE = 135\,000 - 101\,400 = 33\,600\,\text{J}$

Example 12.2

A middle-distance runner of mass 68 kg can run at a steady 5 m s^{-1} or sprint for short distances at 10 m s^{-1}.
a) Find the KE at steady 5 m s^{-1}.
b) Find the KE at sprint speed of 10 m s^{-1}.
c) Compare your answers and comment on them.

Solution
a) Here $m = 68\,kg$ and $v = 5\,m\,s^{-1}$, so:
$$KE = \tfrac{1}{2}mv^2 = \tfrac{1}{2} \times 68 \times 5^2 = 850 \text{ J}$$

b) Now v has increased to 10 m s^{-1} and so:
$$KE = \tfrac{1}{2} \times 68 \times 10^2 = 3400 \text{ J}$$

c) Much more energy is needed for a speed of 10 m s^{-1}. If the speed is doubled, the kinetic energy increases by a factor of 4.

EXERCISES

12.2 CLASSWORK

1 Find the kinetic energy of each object described below.
a) A car of mass 900 kg moving at 30 m s^{-1}.
b) An iron of mass 3 kg moving at 0.5 m s^{-1}.
c) A squash ball of mass 24 grams moving at 5 m s^{-1}.
d) A swimmer of mass 64 kg moving at 0.8 m s^{-1}.

2 A cyclist of mass 60 kg on a cycle of mass 10 kg increases speed from 6 m s^{-1} to 9 m s^{-1}. Find the gain in kinetic energy.

3 A train of mass 50 tonnes is moving at a speed of 0.1 m s^{-1} when it is brought to rest by a spring buffer.
a) Find the initial kinetic energy of the train.
b) Find the energy that is stored in the buffer when the train comes to rest.
c) The buffer in fact returns 85% of the energy it gains to the train. Find the speed of the train as it bounces back off the buffer.

4 When a squash ball bounces off a wall it is estimated that it loses 20% of its kinetic energy. A squash ball has a mass of 24 grams and hits a wall at 4 m s^{-1}.
a) Find the kinetic energy of the ball when it hits the wall.
b) What is the speed of the ball when it rebounds?
c) Where could the energy that has been lost have gone?

5 The diagram shows a sprung device that can be used for launching balls into the air. When compressed, the energy stored in the spring is 80 J, which is all transferred to the ball.
a) Find the speed at which a 50 gram ball will be launched.
b) Find the speed at which a 120 gram ball would be launched.
c) A ball is launched at $8\,\text{m s}^{-1}$. What is its mass?

6 The diagram shows a spring-powered launcher that is part of a pin ball machine. The plunger has mass 200 grams and the ball has mass

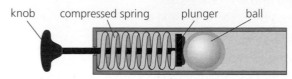

knob   compressed spring   plunger   ball

60 grams. When compressed, there is 20 J of energy stored in the spring. As the spring expands, all its energy is transferred to the ball and the plunger. Find their speeds when the spring is fully expanded.

7 A 100 gram ball is dropped and hits the ground travelling at $4\,\text{m s}^{-1}$.
a) What is the kinetic energy of the ball when it hits the ground?
b) How much potential energy did the ball have when it was released?

8 A cyclist of mass 58 kg starts from rest and free-wheels down a gentle slope with constant acceleration of $0.5\,\text{m s}^{-2}$.(**Hint:** Use $v^2 = u^2 + 2as$)
a) Find the speed of the cyclist after travelling 5 m and 10 m.
b) Find the kinetic energy of the cyclist at each position.
c) How much kinetic energy do you think the cyclist will have after 20 m?

9 A ball of mass 150 grams is dropped from a height of 2 m.
a) By assuming that it has a constant acceleration of $9.8\,\text{m s}^{-2}$, find the speed at which it hits the ground.
b) Find the kinetic energy of the ball when it hits the ground. Hence state the amount of potential energy lost as the ball falls to the ground.
c) State clearly any assumptions that you have made to obtain the final answer to **b)**.

10 A ball of mass 80 grams is dropped from a height of 1 m and rebounds to a height of 80 cm.
a) If the acceleration of the ball is a constant $9.8\,\text{m s}^{-2}$, find the speed at which it hits the ground and hence the kinetic energy on impact.
b) By considering the acceleration of the ball and the rebound height, find the speed at which it leaves the ground and the kinetic energy on rebound.
c) What percentage of the ball's energy was lost while bouncing?
d) Comment on your results.

EXERCISES

12.2 HOMEWORK

1 Find the kinetic energy of each object described below.
a) A child of mass 45 kg running at $5\,\text{m s}^{-1}$.
b) A train of mass 50 tonnes travelling at $10\,\text{m s}^{-1}$.
c) A raindrop of mass 0.5 grams falling at $4.8\,\text{m s}^{-1}$.
d) A motorcycle and rider of combined mass 400 kg travelling at $40\,\text{m s}^{-1}$.

2 The speed of an aeroplane of mass 3000 kg increases from $20\,\text{m s}^{-1}$ to $40\,\text{m s}^{-1}$. Find the gain in kinetic energy.

3 A squash ball of mass 24 grams is travelling at $8\,\text{m s}^{-1}$ when it hits a wall, at right angles to its path.
   a) Find the kinetic energy of the ball when it hits the wall.
   b) Assume that after the bounce the ball has 80% of its original kinetic energy. Find the speed of the ball after the bounce.

4 A catapult is used to launch a stone of mass 50 g at a speed of $6\,\text{m s}^{-1}$.
   a) Find the kinetic energy of the stone when it is launched.
   b) Find the energy that was initially stored in the stretched elastic of the catapult.
   c) At what speed would a 40 gram stone be launched? Explain what assumptions you have made.

5 An air rifle can be used to fire either pellets of mass 2 grams or darts of mass 4 grams. The rifle transfers 16 J of energy to the pellet or dart.
   a) Find the speed at which the pellet is fired.
   b) Find the speed at which the dart is fired.
   c) A new type of dart is launched at a speed of $80\,\text{m s}^{-1}$. What is its mass?

6 A horizontal air track has a vehicle of mass 1 kg which slides smoothly on the track. It is set into motion by a stretched elastic band.
   a) If 5 J of energy are stored in the elastic band, find the speed at which the vehicle will move.
   b) Explain why, in practice, the vehicle does not reach this speed.

7 In an advertisement for a car, the car is shown falling to the ground. Assume the mass of the car is 1000 kg and that it hits the ground moving at $5\,\text{m s}^{-1}$.
   a) Find the kinetic energy of the car when it hits the ground.
   b) How much potential energy did the car have originally? (Assume it was all converted to kinetic energy.)
   c) Comment on why your answer to **b)** is unlikely to be true.

8 A car of mass 1200 kg has an acceleration of $1.2\,\text{m s}^{-2}$, and is at rest.
   a) Find the speed of the car when it has travelled 20 m and 40 m.
   b) Find the kinetic energy of the car at each position.
   c) How much kinetic energy would you expect the car to have when it has travelled 80 m? Verify your answer.

9 A parachutist of mass 70 kg falls 30 m vertically before opening his parachute.
   a) If there were no air resistance find the speed that would be reached by the parachutist, and his kinetic energy.
   b) How much potential energy has the parachutist lost while falling the 30 m?
   c) In fact the parachutist only reaches a speed of $10\,\text{m s}^{-1}$. How much of the potential energy has not been converted to kinetic energy? Explain what has happened to the lost energy.

10 A ball of mass 100 grams hits the ground travelling at $4\,\text{m s}^{-1}$ and rebounds at $3\,\text{m s}^{-1}$. Assume $g = 10\,\text{m s}^{-2}$ in this question.
   a) By assuming that the ball is subject only to the effects of gravity, find the height from which the ball was dropped and the height to which it rebounds.
   b) Find the kinetic energy of the ball immediately before and after the bounce.
   c) Comment on your results.

WORK

The kinetic energy of a moving object has now been used in a range of examples, but how can an object be given kinetic energy? If an object is to gain speed a force must be applied to it. For example a force is required to make a car accelerate and gain kinetic energy. In this section we explore how the gain in kinetic energy is related to the force or forces that are applied.

Spend a few moments thinking about what you understand by the word 'work'. Is there a link between the work done and the kinetic energy of something that has been worked on? For example, consider:

■ pushing a car that is initially at rest.
■ an object falling under gravity.

By pushing the car, you exert a force on it. You certainly feel as if you are doing work and as the car begins to move it gains energy. The work that you have done gives the car its energy.

Now think about a catapult. As the elastic is stretched, work is done and the resulting energy is stored in the elastic. This is then transferred to the missile that is fired. The elastic in turn does work on the missile.

When there is a change in the energy of a system or object, then work has been done to cause this change. Consider as an example the case where the speed of an object increases from u to v. The change in kinetic energy is:

$$\text{change (gain) in KE} = \tfrac{1}{2}mv^2 - \tfrac{1}{2}mu^2$$

From the constant acceleration equation:

$$v^2 = u^2 + 2as$$

it can be seen that:

$$v^2 - u^2 = 2as$$

Returning to the change in kinetic energy gives:

$$\text{change in KE} = \tfrac{1}{2}m\left(v^2 - u^2\right) = \tfrac{1}{2}m \times 2as = mas$$

The resultant force, F, on the object is equal to ma, by Newton's second law; so the change in KE is:

$$\text{change in KE} = mas = Fs$$

The quantity Fs which is the product of the force and distance is the work done by the force and it is equal to the change in KE. This can be expressed as:

$$\text{change in KE} = \text{work done}$$

or:

$$\tfrac{1}{2}mv^2 - \tfrac{1}{2}mu^2 = Fs$$

The equation $v^2 = u^2 + 2as$ is an equation for straight line motion and so this definition of work done will also be restricted to motion in one dimension and as it is a constant acceleration equation, to problems involving constant forces.

Example 12.3

A child exerts a horizontal force of 80 N on a sledge carrying a friend, the combined mass of friend and sledge being 55 kg.
a) Calculate the work done by this force as the sledge moves 10 m.
b) Find the final speed of the sledge if it was initially moving at 0.75 m s⁻¹.
c) What assumption has been made in solving this problem? How does this affect the final speed?

Solution
a) The work done is found from:
work done $= Fs = 80 \times 10 = 800\,\text{J}$
b) To find the speed, use:
work done = change in KE
In this case:
$$800 = \tfrac{1}{2} \times 55v^2 - \tfrac{1}{2} \times 55 \times 0.75^2$$

or:
$$800 = 27.5v^2 - 15.5$$
$$v^2 = \frac{800 + 15.5}{27.5}$$
$$v = 5.45 \text{ m s}^{-1}$$

c) We have assumed that there is no resistance to the motion. There would almost certainly be friction and so the final speed would actually be less than that predicted above. Work has to be done against the friction forces that are present.

Example 12.4

A shot putt of mass 5 kg is held 1.2 m above ground level and released from rest.
a) Find the work done by gravity on the mass as it falls.
b) Find the speed of the mass when it hits the ground.

Solution
a) As the shot putt has a mass of 5 kg, the force of gravity acting is 49 N; so the work done is:
work done $= 49 \times 1.2 = 58.8\,\text{J}$
This is often referred to as the **gravitational potential energy**.
b) To find the speed, use:
work done $= \tfrac{1}{2}mv^2 - \tfrac{1}{2}mu^2$

$$58.8 = \tfrac{1}{2} \times 5v^2 - 0$$
Solving for v gives:
$$v^2 = \frac{58.5}{2.5}$$
$$v = 4.85 \,\text{m s}^{-1}$$

Example 12.5

A filing cabinet of mass 60 kg is being moved across the floor of an office by a single person pushing and exerting a force of 220 N. There is a friction force of 140 N resisting the motion.
a) Find the work done on the filing cabinet by the person as it is moved 2 m.

b) *Find the work done by the friction force.*
c) *Find the overall amount of work done on the filing cabinet.*
d) *Find the speed it reaches.*

Solution
a) *Work done by the person* $= 220 \times 2 = 440\,\text{J}$
b) *Work done to overcome friction* $= -140 \times 2 = -280\,\text{J}$
   Note: *This is negative because this force acts in the opposite direction to the motion. It is said that the* **work done against friction** *is* $280\,\text{J}$.
c) *The overall amount of work done* $= 440 - 280 = 160\,\text{J}$
   This is the work done by the person minus the work done against friction.
d) *Using work done = change in KE gives:*

$$160 = \tfrac{1}{2} \times 60v^2 - \tfrac{1}{2} \times 60 \times 0^2$$

$$160 = 30v^2$$

$$v = \sqrt{\frac{160}{30}} = 2.31 \text{ m s}^{-1}$$

Example 12.6

A crane is lifting a heavy load of mass 1080 kg. The lifting cable is vertical and has a constant tension of 10 700 N.
a) *Find the work done by the tension as the load is raised 5 m.*
b) *Find the work done by gravity.*
c) *Find the overall work done on the load.*
d) *Find the speed reached by the load.*

Solution
a) *The work done by the tension* $= 10\,700 \times 5 = 53\,500\,\text{J}$
b) *The force of gravity on the load is* $10\,584\,\text{N}$, *and so the work done* $= -10\,584 \times 5 = -52\,920\,\text{J}$
   Note: *The negative value means that the force acts in the opposite direction to the motion. We say that the work done* against *gravity is* $52\,920\,\text{J}$.
c) *The overall work done* $= 53\,500 - 52\,920 = 580\,\text{J}$
d) *Using work done = change in KE gives:*

$$580 = \tfrac{1}{2} \times 1080v^2 - \tfrac{1}{2} \times 1080 \times 0^2$$

$$v = \sqrt{\frac{580}{540}} = 1.04 \text{ m s}^{-1}$$

EXERCISES

12.3 CLASSWORK

1 Two men are pushing a car of mass 1400 kg. They each exert forces of 120 N.
   a) Find the work done on the car by the men as it moves 10 m.
   b) Find the speed that the car reaches.

2 A cyclist of mass 70 kg cycles on a bike of mass 12 kg. A constant forward force of 80 N acts on them.
   a) Find the work done as the cyclist moves forward 50 m.
   b) Find the speed of the cyclist after moving this distance.
   c) What factors have you ignored?

3 A ball of mass 70 grams is dropped from a height of 1.4 m into soft mud.
  a) Find the work done by gravity on the ball as it falls the 1.4 m.
  b) Find the speed of the ball when it hits the mud.
  c) The ball penetrates 8 cm into the mud before stopping. Find the average force that the mud exerts on the ball as it comes to rest.

4 Calculate the work that must be done to cause changes in motion as described below.
  a) A car of mass 1200 kg increasing in speed from $10\,\text{m}\,\text{s}^{-1}$ to $15\,\text{m}\,\text{s}^{-1}$.
  b) A ship of mass 7000 tonnes as it increases in speed from $1\,\text{m}\,\text{s}^{-1}$ to $4\,\text{m}\,\text{s}^{-1}$.
  c) A ball of mass 200 grams which changes speed from $2\,\text{m}\,\text{s}^{-1}$ to $5\,\text{m}\,\text{s}^{-1}$ when hit by a bat.

5 In each case below, calculate the work done by the force and the speed reached, assuming the forces act in the direction of motion.
  a) A force of 10 000 N acting on a train of mass 25 000 kg as it travels 50 m, starting at rest.
  b) A fly of mass 3 grams acted on by a force of 0.0001 N as it moves 1.1 m from an initial speed of $0.5\,\text{m}\,\text{s}^{-1}$.
  c) A force of 50 N acting on a sledge of mass 8 kg as a child pulls it from rest for 2 m.

6 A lift has mass 700 kg including its occupants. As the lift begins to move, the tension in the cable is 7010 N.
  a) Find the work done by the tension as the lift rises 1.8 m.
  b) Find the work done against gravity as the lift rises 1.8 m.
  c) Find the gain in kinetic energy of the lift.
  d) What speed does the lift reach?

7 A basketball player throws a ball directly up into the air. While the ball, which has a mass of 2 kg is in contact with his hands, an upward force of 50 N is exerted on the ball.
  a) If the hands remain in contact with the ball as it moves 50 cm, find the work done by this force.
  b) Find the work done against gravity as the ball rises the 50 cm.
  c) Find the gain in kinetic energy of the ball.
  d) At what speed does the ball leave the player's hands?

8 A cyclist on a horizontal road experiences a constant forward force of 80 N while peddling 50 m. A resistance force of 60 N also acts on the cyclist.
  a) Find the work done by the cyclist.
  b) Find the work done against the resistance force.

9 A bungee jumper of mass 72 kg jumps off a bridge and falls 10 m before the elastic rope attached to her legs goes taut.
  a) Find the work done by gravity as the jumper falls the first 10 m and the speed reached at this point.
  b) Before coming to rest the jumper travels a further 8 m. Find the total energy stored in the elastic at this point.

10 Forensic experts working with the police are investigating the scene of a shooting. They find a bullet of mass 30 grams that has penetrated 5 cm into a wooden doorpost. They test the bullet by firing it through a wooden barrier 2 cm thick. If it hits the barrier at $100\,\text{m}\,\text{s}^{-1}$ and leaves at $50\,\text{m}\,\text{s}^{-1}$, estimate the speed at which the bullet hit the doorpost. Criticise your answer.

EXERCISES

1 A child exerts a horizontal force of 30 N on a sledge of mass 8 kg as she pushes it on level ground.
   a) Find the work done by the child as she pushes the sledge 5 m.
   b) Find the speed that the sledge reaches if there are no resistances.
   c) Do you think it is reasonable to assume there is no resistance? Why?

2 A forward force of 8000 N acts on a lorry of mass 4000 kg as it moves forward from rest on a level road.
   a) Find the work done as the lorry moves forward 60 m.
   b) Find the speed of the lorry when it has travelled the 60 m, if there are assumed to be no resistance forces.
   c) If the speed of the lorry is only 8 m s^{-1}, find the work done against the resistance forces.

3 A gymnast of mass 62 kg jumps off a vaulting horse of height 1.2 m onto a rubber mat.
   a) Find the work done by gravity as the gymnast jumps.
   b) What is the speed of the gymnast when she hits the mat?
   c) As the gymnast comes to rest the mat is compressed by 1 cm. Find the average force exerted by the mat as the gymnast is brought to rest. (Note that the gymnast falls a total distance of 1.21 m.)

4 Calculate the work that must be done to cause changes in motion as described below.
   a) A cyclist of mass 73 kg whose speed increases from 5 m s^{-1} to 8 m s^{-1}.
   b) A dinghy of mass 300 kg as its speed increases from 1.5 m s^{-1} to 2.3 m s^{-1}.
   c) A child of mass 54 kg on a roundabout as the speed increases from rest to 3 m s^{-1}.

5 In each case below, calculate the work done by the force and the speed reached, assuming that the force always acts in the direction of motion.
   a) A force of 2400 N acting on a car of mass 1400 kg as it travels 40 m from an initial speed of 5 m s^{-1}.
   b) A train of mass 20 tonnes acted on by a force of 5000 N as it travels 20 m, from an initial speed of 20 m s^{-1}.
   c) A force of 30 N acting on a ball of mass 50 grams while it moves 0.2 m and is in contact with a bat. (Assume the ball is initially at rest.)

6 A crane is lifting a load of mass 750 kg. As the load is lifted the tension on the cable is 7400 N.
   a) Find the work done by the tension as the load is lifted 10 m.
   b) Find the work done against gravity as the load is lifted 10 m.
   c) What is the gain in kinetic energy of the load?
   d) What speed does the load reach?

7 A weightlifter is taking part in a competition. A set of weights of mass 250 kg is to be lifted.
   a) Find the work done against gravity as the weights are lifted 1.2 m.
   b) When the weights have been lifted 1.2 m, they are moving at 0.8 m s^{-1}. Find the total work done by the weightlifter.
   c) The weights are eventually lifted to a maximum height of 2.2 m. Find the work done to achieve this.

8   A car of mass 1080 kg is travelling on a straight horizontal road at a steady speed of 18 m s⁻¹. The car then begins to accelerate, experiencing a forward force of 2000 N. The car is also subject to a resistance forces that are modelled as being of constant magnitude 800 N.
   a) Find the work done by the car as it travels a further 50 m.
   b) Find the work done against the resistance forces.
   c) What is the speed of the car at the end of the 50 m?
   d) Criticise the way in which the resistance forces have been modelled. Suggest how the model could be improved and how this would affect your answer to **c)**.

9   A trampolinist of mass 62 kg is bouncing on a trampoline. She rises 1.2 m above the unstretched trampoline's surface on each bounce.
   a) Find the work done by gravity and her speed when she makes contact with the bed of the trampoline.
   b) As she is brought to rest, before she bounces again, the bed of the trampoline is pushed down 0.5 m. Find the potential energy stored in the trampoline at this point.

10   At a rifle club targets are placed in front of a sand barrier as shown in the diagram. The rifles in use fire bullets of mass 20 grams at speeds of 100 m s⁻¹. An examination of the sand shows that these bullets penetrate the sand to an average depth of 1.2 m.
   a) Find a simple model for the force exerted by the sand on the bullets.
   b) What is the greatest speed at which a bullet can be safely fired at this range?
   c) Comment on the validity of your solution.

WORK IN TWO DIMENSIONS

In the previous section we only looked at forces that act in or directly against the movement of the object. This covers only a small number of the situations that arise in real life. When an athlete runs up a hill gravity acts, but at an angle to the direction of motion. Often, forces act at angles to the direction of motion of an object, rather than in the same direction. There are also forces that do no work. When you stand still a normal reaction acts on you but does not change your kinetic energy. So some forces do not do any work. This section explores forces that act at angles to the motion and forces that do no work.

Exploration 12.2

Forces which do work – and some which don't

This child and her go-cart are being pulled along by a friend. Try to draw a diagram to show all of the forces acting on the go-cart. Which ones actually do the work? Which, if any, do *no* work at all? How could the forces be applied so that they did more work?

Forces doing work

It is easiest to start by thinking of a simple object at rest. Its kinetic energy is not changing and so the forces are not doing any work.

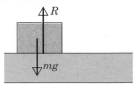

If a force, T, is applied as shown, this will do work, causing the object to gain kinetic energy; but if the surface is horizontal, then forces R and mg do no work. If T is applied horizontally rather than at an angle, then it will do even more work.

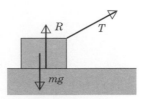

Forces that act at right angles to the direction of motion do no work because they do not cause the kinetic energy of the object to change. When a force acts at an angle to the direction of motion, then only the component in the direction of motion contributes to the work done. We need to be able to calculate this component. If a force of magnitude F acts at an angle θ to the direction of motion, then:

work done = $Fs \cos \theta$

This is the component of the force **in the direction of motion**, $R \cos \theta$ multiplied by s, the distance moved.

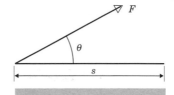

Example 12.7

At a swimming pool there is a slide that can be modelled as an incline of length 5 m at 40° to the horizontal.

a) *Find the work done by gravity as a swimmer of mass 45 kg uses the slide.*

b) *The swimmer was given a push and an initial speed of 1 m s⁻¹ and enters the water moving at 5 m s⁻¹. Find her gain in kinetic energy.*

c) *Calculate the work done against friction.*

Solution

a) *The diagram shows the force of gravity which acts at 50° to the slope. To calculate the work done use $Fs \cos \theta$, with $F = 441$, $s = 5$ and $\theta = 50°$, so:*

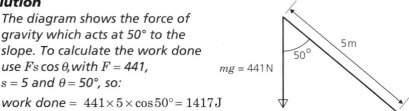

$mg = 441\,\text{N}$

work done = $441 \times 5 \times \cos 50° = 1417\,\text{J}$

b) *The gain in kinetic energy of the swimmer is:*
$$E_k = \tfrac{1}{2}mv^2 - \tfrac{1}{2}mu^2 = \tfrac{1}{2} \times 45 \times 5^2 - \tfrac{1}{2} \times 45 \times 1^2 = 540\,\text{J}$$

c) *The difference between the work done by gravity and the work done against friction will be equal to the change in kinetic energy.*
work done against friction = $1417 - 540 = 877\ \text{J}$

Example 12.8

A button lift is used at a ski-slope. The skier is attached to a cable that makes an angle of 40° with the slope. The skier has mass 72 kg, and travels 50 m up the slope.

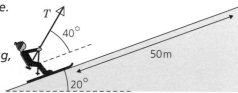

a) *Find the work done against friction (if this is assumed to be a constant force of 70 N) and the work done against gravity.*

b) *If the skier starts at rest and has a speed of 2 m s⁻¹ at the top of the slope, find the work done by the tension force in the rope.*

c) *Find the magnitude of the tension force if it is assumed to be constant.*

d) *At the top of the slope the skier lets go of the lift and moves on a horizontal surface. How far does the skier move before stopping?*

Solution

a) *Work done against friction* $= 70 \times 50 = 3500$ J
Work done against gravity $= 72 \times 9.8 \times 50 \times \cos 70° = 12\,066$ J

b) *The kinetic energy of the skier at the top of the slope is:*
$$E_k = \tfrac{1}{2}mv^2 = \tfrac{1}{2} \times 72 \times 2^2 = 144 \text{ J}$$

The work done by the tension, less the work done against gravity and friction, gives the final kinetic energy of the skier.
Work done by tension $- (3500 + 12\,066) = 144$
Work done by tension $= 144 + 3500 + 12\,066 = 15\,710$ J

c) *The work done by the force T is given by:*
$$T \times 50 \cos 40° = 15\,710$$
$$T = \frac{36\,796}{50 \cos 40°} = 410 \text{ N}$$

EXERCISES

12.4 CLASSWORK

1 In each case find the work done by the force illustrated as the object moves the distance given in the diagram.

a)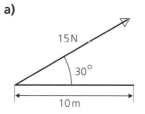
b)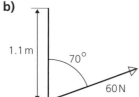
c)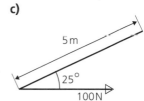
d)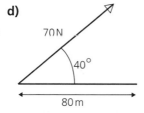

2 As a car of mass 1000 kg drives up a slope at 5° to the horizontal, it is acted on by a forward force of 9000 N that is parallel to the slope. At the bottom of the slope it is travelling at 3 m s^{-1} and it travels 300 m to the top of the slope. Assume there are no resistance forces.
a) Find the work done against gravity.
b) Find the work done by the 9000 N force and hence the change in the kinetic energy of the car.
c) Find the speed of the car at the top of the slope.
d) If there were in fact a resistance force of magnitude 700 N, what would be the speed of the car at the top of the slope?

3 A sledge of mass 5 kg slides on its own down a slope of length 10 m at 10° to the horizontal. It attains a speed of 3 m s^{-1} at the bottom of the slope.
a) Find the work done by gravity.
b) Find the final kinetic energy of the sledge.
c) Find the work done against friction.

4 A 'death slide' is set up which has a length of 30 m and a rope that is assumed to be straight and at 20° to the horizontal. A resistive force that is assumed to be a constant 80 N acts on the pulley. A student of mass 69 kg tries the 'death slide'.
a) Find the work done by gravity and the work done against the resistance force.
b) Find the speed of the student at the bottom of the slide.

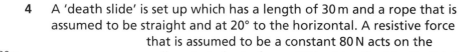

5 A tow truck is towing a broken down car as shown in the diagram. As the truck pulls out of a junction, it travels 80 m increasing in speed from 5 m s^{-1} to 13 m s^{-1}. Assume that the work done against resistance forces is 30% of the work done by the tow rope. The car has mass 950 kg.

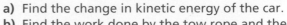

a) Find the change in kinetic energy of the car.
b) Find the work done by the tow rope and the work done against the resistance forces.
c) Find the tension in the tow rope and the magnitude of the resistance forces.
d) What assumption have you made about the road?

6 A cyclist of mass 64 kg free-wheels down a hill on a bicycle of mass 8 kg. The hill can be modelled as a slope at 6° to the horizontal.

a) Find the work done by gravity as the cyclist and cycle travel 50 m.
b) Find the speed reached by the cyclist.
c) In reality, the cyclist's speed is only 5 m s^{-1}. Find the work done against resistance forces.
d) After the 50 m slope, the cyclist free-wheels on a horizontal surface. Estimate how far the cyclist travels before stopping. What assumptions have you made?

7 A tug is attached by a tow rope to a ship of mass 300 tonnes. The tow rope makes an angle of 30° with the horizontal. The speed of the ship increases from 2 m s^{-1} to 3.5 m s^{-1} as the tug pulls the ship 500 m.

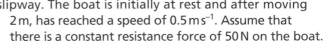

a) Find the gain in kinetic energy of the ship.
b) Express the work done by the tug in terms of T, the tension in the rope.
c) Find the tension in the tow rope.

8 A boat of mass 300 kg is winched up a slipway on a trolley. The slipway is at an angle of 20° to the horizontal and the winching rope is at 10° to the slipway. The boat is initially at rest and after moving 2 m, has reached a speed of 0.5 m s^{-1}. Assume that there is a constant resistance force of 50 N on the boat.

a) Find the gain in kinetic energy for the boat.
b) Find the work done against friction and the work done against gravity.
c) Find the work done by the winch.
d) Find the tension in the winch rope.

9 Three husky dogs are harnessed to a sledge of mass 500 kg as shown in the diagram. Assume that each dog exerts a force of 150 N.

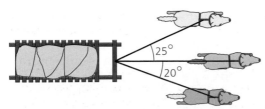

a) Find the work done on the sledge as it moves 100 m.
b) Find the speed of the sledge after 100 m.
c) If the speed is in fact 10% less than your answer to b), find the work done against friction.

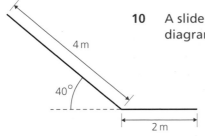

10 A slide at a fairground consists of two sections, as shown in the diagram. A person of mass m kg uses the slide.

a) Explain why the magnitude of the friction force is greater on the horizontal sections. Assume that the coefficient of friction between the slide and the user is 0.4.

b) Find the work done by gravity and the work done against friction on each section.

c) Find the speed of a person when they reach the bottom of the slide.

EXERCISES

12.4 HOMEWORK

1 In each case find the work done as the force shown in the diagram acts and the object moves the distance illustrated.

a) 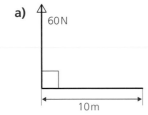 b) 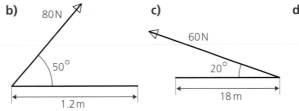 c) d)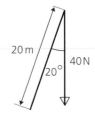

2 Alex, Bobbie and Chris are climbing up a slope and stop for a rest. Alex's mass is 74 kg, Bobbie's mass is 69 kg and Chris's mass is 62 kg.

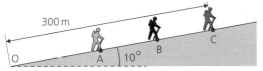

When they stop for a rest they have all done the same amount of work against gravity.

a) Find the work done against gravity by Chris.

b) Find the distances Alex and Bobbie have moved.

3 A slide at a leisure pool is 50 m long and is at a constant 3° to the horizontal. A child of mass 52 kg travels down the slide, reaching a speed of 2.4 m s⁻¹ at the bottom of the slide.

a) Find the final kinetic energy of the child.

b) Find the work done by gravity.

c) Find the work done against the resistance forces.

4 As a car of mass 1110 kg travels 100 m down a hill its speed increases from 20 m s⁻¹ to 22 m s⁻¹. The hill can be modelled as an incline at a constant angle of 4° to the horizontal.

a) Find the gain in kinetic energy of the car.

b) Find the work done by gravity.

c) What is the magnitude of the average resistance forces acting on the car?

d) What will be the speed of the car when it has travelled a total of 200 m down the hill? Describe the assumptions that you make to solve this problem.

5 A gardener pulls a roller of mass 80 kg across a lawn. A resistance force of 60 N acts as the roller is pulled. When the roller has been pulled 6 m it attains a speed of 0.8 m s⁻¹. The roller is to be modelled as a particle.

a) Find the kinetic energy of the roller when it is moving at 0.8 m s⁻¹.

b) Find the work done against the resistance forces acting.

c) What is the magnitude of the force exerted by the gardener on the roller?

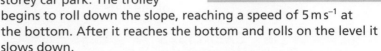

d) What aspect of the motion of the roller has been ignored? Why do you think this may be significant in this case?

6 A loaded supermarket trolley has a mass of 75 kg and is at the top of a slope in a multi-storey car park. The trolley begins to roll down the slope, reaching a speed of 5 m s⁻¹ at the bottom. After it reaches the bottom and rolls on the level it slows down.

a) Find the work done by gravity as the trolley rolls down the slope.

b) Find the work done against any resistance forces.

c) Assume that the resistance forces are constant and determine their magnitude.

d) How far does the trolley travel before it comes to rest on the horizontal car parking area?

7 A car of mass 1050 kg is travelling up a slope at 3° to the horizontal. Over a 100 m stretch its speed drops from 25 m s⁻¹ to 24 m s⁻¹.

a) Find the work done by the car as it travels the 100 m, assuming that there are no resistance forces.

Assume that the car continues to move in the same way.

b) How far will the car travel before it comes to rest?

c) How would your solutions to **a)** and **b)** change if there were a constant resistance force of 400 N?

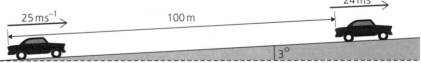

8 The company that manufactures children's toys claim that they have produced a new friction-free material that can be used for the manufacture of children's slides. The material is produced in 5 m lengths.

a) Traditionally slides are positioned at about 45° to the horizontal. Find the speed that a child would reach if a 5 m slide were replaced with the new material.

b) Find the angle, to the horizontal, at which a slide made of the new material should be positioned if a user should reach a speed of 3 m s⁻¹ at the bottom of the slide.

9 A woman is cutting the grass with a lawnmower that hovers. Her lawn is on a slope, as shown in the diagram. The lawnmower begins at rest at the bottom of the slope, and when 5 m up the slope is travelling at 2 m s⁻¹. The mass of the lawnmower is 18 kg.

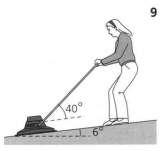

a) Find the work done by the woman if there is a constant resistance force of 30 N parallel to the slope.

b) Find the magnitude of the force exerted on the lawnmower by its handle.

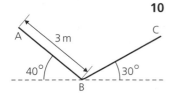

10 At a skateboard park there are two slopes that are to be modelled as shown in the diagram. The skateboarder travels down from A to B reaching a speed of $5\,\mathrm{m\,s^{-1}}$ at B. Assume that skateboarder negotiates the turn at B without losing any energy. Formulate a simple model for the resistance force on the skateboarder and find how far she travels up the slope BC.

GRAVITATIONAL POTENTIAL ENERGY

When any object is positioned at a point above, and then released, it will gain kinetic energy as it falls. The amount of kinetic energy that it gains depends on how far it has to fall. When something is in a position where it can gain kinetic energy, then it is described as having **potential energy** (PE or E_p).

Exploration 12.3

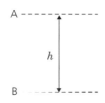

Slopes and speeds

The diagram shows three curves: 1, 2 and 3. A small object is released at level A and allowed to slide to level B. Assume that no work is done against any resistance forces. How will the time of descent and the maximum speed reached compare for each slope? What about an object that is allowed to fall from level A straight to level B?

Conservative systems

Taking two of the above cases as examples, there is little doubt that the object will hit the ground most quickly when dropped rather than being constrained to slide down a curve.

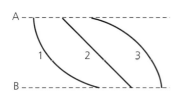

Now consider the ball that falls straight down, through a distance h. Then the work done by gravity is simply mgh, and this will be equal to the final kinetic energy, so:

$$mgh = \tfrac{1}{2}mv^2$$
$$gh = \tfrac{1}{2}v^2$$
$$v = \sqrt{2gh}$$

Now consider the straight slope, numbered 2. We can use trigonometry to calculate the length, s, as:

$$s = \frac{h}{\cos\theta}$$

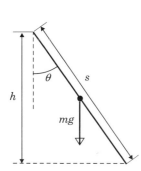

So the work done by gravity will be:

$$mgs\cos\theta = mg \times \frac{h}{\cos\theta} \times \cos\theta = mgh$$

The object that slides down the slope will have the same final kinetic energy, and therefore the same final speed, as the object that fell straight down.

When an object has been raised through a certain height we say that it has **gravitational potential energy**. The amount of energy is simply mgh where h is the distance above some reference point. When an object loses height, this potential energy is converted to kinetic energy.

If, as an object moves, all the potential energy is converted to kinetic energy, then the situation is called a **conservative system**. If some work has to be done against resistance forces, so that not all the potential energy is converted to kinetic energy, this is a **non-conservative system**. In a conservative system, the path taken by an object does not affect the final speed attained.

Example 12.9

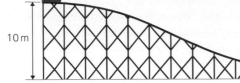

A carriage on a roller coaster ride has mass 150 kg and is at a height of 10 m above the lowest point of the ride.

a) Find the potential energy of the carriage.

b) If it is initially moving at 1.2 m s^{-1}, find the speed it reaches at the lowest point.

Solution

a) The potential energy is given by mgh, so in this case:
$$PE = 150 \times 9.8 \times 10 = 14\,700 \text{ J}$$

b) The final kinetic energy will be the combined total of the initial kinetic energy and the initial potential energy.
$$\text{Final } KE = 108 + 14\,700 = 14\,808 \text{ J}$$
So now the final speed, v, can be found.
$$\tfrac{1}{2}mv^2 = 14\,808$$
$$\tfrac{1}{2} \times 150v^2 = 14\,808$$
$$v^2 = \frac{14\,808}{75}$$
$$v = 14.1 \text{ m s}^{-1}$$

Example 12.10

A bungee jumper, of mass 80 kg falls a distance of 24 m before reaching the lowest point during the jump. How much energy is stored in the stretched 'bungee' at this instant?

Solution

Assuming that there has been no loss of energy all the initial potential energy of the jumper will now be stored in the stretched elastic. Taking the lowest point reached as a reference point gives the initial potential energy:
$$mgh = 80 \times 9.8 \times 24 = 18\,816 \text{ J}$$
So the energy stored in the bungee is 18 816 J.

EXERCISES

12.5 CLASSWORK

1 Find the gravitational potential energy of each mass shown below, relative to the reference level O.

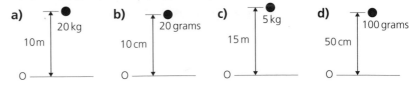

a) 20 kg, 10 m

b) 20 grams, 10 cm

c) 5 kg, 15 m

d) 100 grams, 50 cm

2 Find the speed at which each mass in question **1** would pass the reference level, O, if it is assumed that there is no loss of energy.

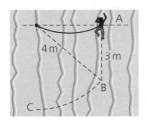

3 A climber at position A slips, falls vertically to B and then swings to C as the safety rope becomes taut. The mass of the climber is 62 kg.
a) Find the potential energy of the climber at A with reference to the point C, the lowest point reached.
b) Find the speed of the climber at point B.
c) Find the speed of the climber at point C.
d) What assumptions have you made?

4 The diagram shows a roller coaster ride with a double loop-the-loop. The diameter of the first loop is 5 m and of the second loop is 4 m. The speed of the carriage which has mass 200 kg is $6\,\mathrm{m\,s^{-1}}$ at C.
a) Find the speed of the carriage at point D.
b) Find the potential energy of the carriage at A, if it can be assumed to be at rest there.
c) Find the height of A above B.

5 A catapult can propel a stone of mass 50 grams vertically upwards to a height of 20 m.
a) Find the energy stored in the stretched elastic of the catapult.
b) Find the speed of the stone when it leaves the catapult.
c) What height would be reached when a 60 gram stone is launched?

6 A parachutist of mass 71 kg jumps from a height of 1000 m and hits the ground moving at $5\,\mathrm{m\,s^{-1}}$.
a) Find the potential energy lost.
b) Find the work done against resistance forces during the jump.

7 A golf ball of mass 40 grams is struck so that it has an initial speed of $20\,\mathrm{m\,s^{-1}}$. If the speed of the ball never drops below $11\,\mathrm{m\,s^{-1}}$, find the maximum amount of potential energy that the ball has during the flight. What is the maximum height reached by the ball?

8 A rocket used at a fireworks display initially has a mass of 300 grams. At the point that all its fuel is used up it has a mass of 200 grams and is moving at $5\,\mathrm{m\,s^{-1}}$. The rocket reaches a maximum height of 50 m.
a) Find the potential energy of the rocket at its highest point.
b) Find the height of the rocket when its fuel is used up.
c) Find the energy given to the rocket by its fuel.

9 A ball of mass 200 grams moves so that the position vector, in metres, at time t seconds is given by:
$$\mathbf{r} = 4t\mathbf{i} + \left(8t - 4.9t^2\right)\mathbf{j}$$
where $\mathbf{i}$ and $\mathbf{j}$ are horizontal and vertical unit vectors respectively.
a) Find an expression for the potential energy of the ball.
b) Find an expression for the kinetic energy of the ball.
c) Is the total energy of the ball constant? If it is, prove the result or else give a counter example.

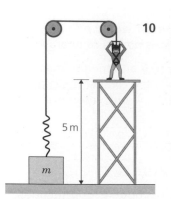

10 A simulator used at a parachuting centre consists of a harness attached to a mass, m, by a rope that passes over two pulleys. The person of mass M jumps from a platform at a height of 5 m above ground level.

a) Find the initial potential energy of the person.

b) After the person has fallen a distance x, the rope becomes taut and the mass, m, begins to rise. Express the speed of the person at this point in terms of x.

c) If the person just comes to rest at ground level, find x, in terms of m and M.

EXERCISES

12.5 HOMEWORK

1 A ball of mass 2 kg is dropped from rest at a height of 10 m.

a) What is the initial gravitational potential energy of the ball?

b) Calculate the speed at which the ball hits the ground.

2 A ball of mass 3 kg initially moves downwards with a speed of $8\,\text{ms}^{-1}$ at a height of 12 m.

a) Find the total initial energy of the ball.

b) Calculate the speed at which the ball hits the ground.

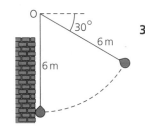

3 A large metal ball of mass 100 kg, attached to the end of a light chain of length 6 m, swings in the vertical plane in order to strike and hence knock over a brick wall. It is released from rest with the chain 30° from the horizontal.

a) Find how much gravitational potential energy is lost as the metal ball swings to its lowest position.

b) Calculate the speed of the ball just before impact with the wall.

4 The diagram shows a roller coaster ride with a single loop the loop. The diameter of the loop, CB is 5 m and the arc AB is a quarter of a circle of radius 10 m. The carriage which has mass 250 kg is released from rest at A.

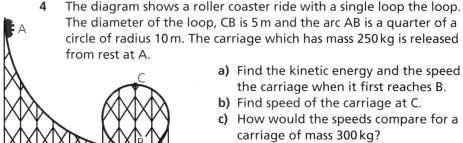

a) Find the kinetic energy and the speed of the carriage when it first reaches B.

b) Find speed of the carriage at C.

c) How would the speeds compare for a carriage of mass 300 kg?

5 A catapult can propel a stone of mass 1 kg vertically upwards to a height of 8 m.

a) Find the energy stored in the stretched elastic of the catapult.

b) Find the speed of the stone when it leaves the catapult.

c) The catapult now propels the same stone horizontally from a height of 1 m, as shown in the diagram. By using energy considerations, find the speed of the stone as it hits the ground.

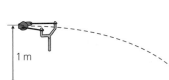

6 It is estimated that a rugby ball of mass 800 grams reached a maximum height of 5 m and was then travelling at $2\,\text{ms}^{-1}$.

a) Find the total energy of the rugby ball at this point.

b) Find the initial kinetic energy and hence the initial speed of the ball.

7 The terminal speed of a skydiver of mass 64 kg is 70 m s⁻¹.
   a) What is the kinetic energy of the skydiver at his terminal speed?
   b) How far does the skydiver have to fall to reach this speed, assuming there is no resistance to his motion?
   c) If in fact the skydiver has to fall 700 m before reaching terminal speed, find the work done against air resistance.

8 Tarzan, who has mass 90 kg, grabs hold of a rope that was initially at an angle of 60° to the vertical. He swings from rest through an angle of 90° and lets go of the rope. The length of the rope is 6 m. Calculate the speed of Tarzan when he lets go of the rope.
   What effect does:
   a) doubling the length of the rope,
   b) Tarzan swinging with Jane (mass 45 kg),
   have on Tarzan's speed when he lets go of the rope?

9 A ball of mass 100 grams moves on a parabolic path so that its kinetic energy varies between 20$\mathbf{j}$ and 50$\mathbf{j}$.
   a) Find the maximum height of the ball, in metres, and its speed at this time.

   Assume that the position vector of the ball, in metres, at time t seconds is given by:
   $$\mathbf{r} = at\,\mathbf{i} + (bt - 4.9t^2)\mathbf{j}$$
   where a and b are constants and $\mathbf{i}$ and $\mathbf{j}$ are horizontal and vertical unit vectors respectively.
   b) Find the values of a and b.

10 A bungee jumper of mass m kg jumps from a bridge of height 100 m.

   a) After the jumper has fallen a distance x metres, the rope becomes taut. Find an expression for the speed of the jumper at this point.
   b) The jumper reaches the ground with zero velocity. Calculate the energy stored in the rope at this point, in terms of m.

POWER

In everyday language, one car may be described as being more powerful than another. Experience suggests that cars that can increase their speed very quickly are more powerful than cars that increase their speed at a slower rate. Very heavy vehicles are also sometimes described as being powerful, not because they can increase their speeds rapidly, but because of the huge mass that may be involved.

Exploration 12.4

The word 'power' is often misused. What do you understand it to mean? Consider the cases below and try to place them in order, the most powerful first.

- A 10 tonne lorry that accelerates from 0 to 27 m s⁻¹ (60 mph) in 20 seconds.
- A 1.2 tonne car that accelerates from 0 to 27 m s⁻¹ (60 mph) in 6 seconds.
- An athlete of mass 65 kg who can accelerate from rest to 12 m s⁻¹ in 2.5 seconds.

Exploration 12.5

Estimating your power

1 You will need a long staircase, the longer the better, a stopwatch, a ruler, bathroom scales and about six fellow mathematicians.
   ■ Find the time it takes for each member of the group to run to the top of the stairs.
   ■ Estimate (or measure) the height of the stairs and hence the work done by each student in running up the stairs.
   ■ Find the average rate of doing work for each student, by dividing the work done by the time taken. This gives you the average power of each student.

2 You could conduct a similar experiment in the school gym using a climbing rope. Are there any differences between the results of this experiment and the staircase experiment? Try to explain.

Power and energy

The more powerful something is, the more quickly it can increase its kinetic energy. Power can be defined as the rate of change of kinetic energy, but it is usual to define power as the rate at which work is done.

Power is the rate at which work is being done, or:

$$\text{power} = \frac{d}{dt}(\text{work done})$$

As for a constant force, the work done is Fs:

$$\text{power} = \frac{d}{dt}(Fs)$$

Differentiating using the product rule gives:

$$\text{power} = F\frac{ds}{dt} + s\frac{dF}{dt}$$

As the force is constant, $\frac{dF}{dt} = 0$ and so:

$$\text{power} = F\frac{ds}{dt} = Fv \quad \left(\text{since } \frac{ds}{dt} = v\right)$$

This expression for power is very useful but is based on the assumption of a constant force. The units of power would be $J\,s^{-1}$ but a special unit, the watt (W), is introduced for power.

$$1 \text{ watt} = 1\,J\,s^{-1}$$

Traditionally the term 'horsepower' has been used as a unit of power. One horsepower is equivalent to 746 watts.

Example 12.11

A motorcycle has a top speed of 45 m s⁻¹ (100 mph) and a maximum power output of 30 kW. Find the resistance force acting on the motorcycle at top speed.

Solution

At top speed, the forward force on the bike, F, is balanced by the resistance force, R, so F = R. Using the power equation: P = Fv gives $30\,000 = F \times 45$

so $F = \dfrac{30\,000}{45} = 667\text{N}$

So the resistance force has magnitude 667 N.

Example 12.12

The resistance force on a car is proportional to the speed squared. The top speed of the car is 50 m s⁻¹ and the maximum power output is 60 kW. Find value of the constant of proportionality for the resistance force.

Solution

At top speed, the forward force, F, has the same magnitude as the resistance force R.

$F = R$

The resistance force is proportional to the speed squared, so:

$R \propto v^2$ or $R = kv^2$

where k is the constant of proportionality. At top speed $F = R = kv^2$.
Using the power equation $P = Fv$ gives:

$60\,000 = kv^2 \times v = kv^3 = k \times 50^3$

$k = \dfrac{60\,000}{50^3} = 0.48$

So the constant of proportionality is 0.48 and the resistance force is modelled by $0.48v^2$.

Example 12.13

A cyclist pedalling flat out on the level can work at a maximum rate of 100 watts. If the resistance force on the cyclist can be modelled as:

$R = (4 + 2v)$

find the top speed of the cyclist.

Solution

At top speed, the forward force, F, produced by the cyclist is equal to the resistance force R. So at top speed $F = (4 + 2v)$.
Using the power equation gives: $P = Fv$

$100 = (4 + 2v)v = 4v + 2v^2 \Rightarrow v^2 + 2v - 50 = 0$

Solving the quadratic equation gives:

$v = \dfrac{-2 \pm \sqrt{4 + 200}}{2} = \dfrac{-2 \pm \sqrt{204}}{2} = 6.14 \text{ or } -8.14$

so the top speed of the cyclist is 6.14 m s⁻¹ to two decimal places.

EXERCISES

12.6 CLASSWORK

1 Find the power required to maintain the motion described below.
   a) A car travelling at 30 m s⁻¹ experiencing a resistance force of 1700 N. What assumption have you made about the motion?
   b) A cyclist travelling at 5 m s⁻¹, on a horizontal road, experiencing a resistance force of 50 N.
   c) A man of mass 69 kg climbing a flight of stairs at a rate of four 20 cm steps per second.

2   A car with a maximum power output of 50 kW has a top speed of 40 m s⁻¹. Find the resistance force on the car at top speed.

3   A cyclist has a power output of 150 watts and experiences a resistance force of 45 N. Find the top speed of the cyclist.

4   The resistance force on a cyclist is assumed to be modelled by $R = \dfrac{v^2}{4}$. The cyclist can reach a maximum speed of 12 m s⁻¹ on the level.
    a) Find the forward force on the cycle at top speed.
    b) Find the maximum power output of the cyclist.
    c) The power output of another cyclist is 20% greater. Find the top speed for this cyclist.

5   A train of mass 150 tonnes can reach a speed of 10 m s⁻¹ while travelling a distance of 400 m, from rest.
    a) Find the acceleration of the train.
    b) Estimate the power output of the train, at 10 m s⁻¹.
    c) In what ways could your answers to a) and b) be criticised?

6   A crane can lift a load of mass 750 kg at speeds of up to 3 m s⁻¹.
    a) Find the maximum power output of the crane.
    b) If the crane is operating at its maximum power output, find the acceleration of the load when it is travelling at 1 m s⁻¹.
    c) Express the acceleration of the mass in terms of its speed.

7   A car has a power output of 70 000 W. It experiences a resistance force of kv and has a top speed of 52 m s⁻¹.
    a) Find the value of k.
    The car is used to tow a caravan. The resistance force on the caravan is $\dfrac{3kv}{2}$.
    b) Find the top speed of the car when towing the caravan.

8   A crane can lift a load of mass 500 kg at speeds of up to 2 m s⁻¹. What is the maximum speed at which it could lift a load of 1.8 tonnes?

9   A cyclist and bicycle have a combined mass of 75 kg and the cyclist is pedalling up a slope at 2° to the horizontal. The speed of the cyclist is a constant 3 m s⁻¹.
    a) Find the component of gravity acting parallel to the slope.
    b) Find the forward force exerted to maintain a constant speed.
    c) Find the power output of the cyclist.
    d) On a level road, the cyclist can reach a top speed of 10 m s⁻¹. Find the resistance force on the cyclist.
    e) Is it reasonable to assume that there are no resistance forces on the cyclist when on the slope?

10   A car has a power output of 50 000 W and a mass of 1000 kg. On a horizontal road, it has a top speed of 50 m s⁻¹.
    a) If the resistance forces on the car are proportional to the speed, i.e. $R = kv$, find the value of k.
    b) A slope is at 5° to the horizontal. Find the component of gravity parallel to the slope.
    c) Find the maximum speed of the car when going up the hill
    d) Find the maximum speed of the car when going down the hill.

EXERCISES

12.6 HOMEWORK

1 Find the power required to maintain the motion described below.
   a) A train that travels at $50\,\text{m s}^{-1}$ against a resistance force of $5000\,\text{N}$.
   b) A roller skater who travels at $4\,\text{m s}^{-1}$ and who experiences a resistance force of $18\,\text{N}$.
   c) A crane that lifts a load of $400\,\text{kg}$ at a speed of $0.8\,\text{m s}^{-1}$.

2 A motorcycle with a top speed of $43\,\text{m s}^{-1}$ on the level has a maximum power output of $22\,\text{kW}$.
   a) Find the resistance force on the motorcycle at top speed.
   b) When the motorcycle is carrying a pillion passenger the resistance force is increased by 5%. What is the top speed when carrying a pillion passenger?

3 As a supermarket trolley is pushed at a constant speed of $2.5\,\text{m s}^{-1}$ a resistance force of $20\,\text{N}$ acts.
   a) Find the power output of the person pushing the trolley.
   b) When the trolley is loaded the resistance force doubles. What happens to the power output of the person pushing?
   c) What assumptions have you made to answer this question?

4 A simple model for the resistance forces experienced by a car is that they are proportional to the speed. A particular car has a maximum power output of $40\,\text{kW}$ and a maximum speed of $32\,\text{m s}^{-1}$.
   a) Find the constant of proportionality for the model described.
   b) An identical car with a larger engine has a maximum power output that is 10% greater.
   Find its maximum speed and compare with the speed of the original car.

5 The resistance force on a cyclist is modelled as a constant force of $90\,\text{N}$. At an instant the cyclist is moving forward on the level at $4\,\text{m s}^{-1}$ and accelerating at $0.3\,\text{m s}^{-2}$. The mass of the bicycle and cyclist is $78\,\text{kg}$.
   a) Find the forward force acting on the cyclist.
   b) What is the power output of the cyclist?

6 A child of mass $40\,\text{kg}$ is running up a slope, inclined at $3°$ to the horizontal, and at a constant speed of $2\,\text{m s}^{-1}$.
   a) Find the component of the force of gravity parallel to the slope.
   b) Find the power output of the child.

7 A crane can lift a load of $600\,\text{kg}$ at a maximum speed of $4\,\text{m s}^{-1}$.
   a) Find the maximum power output of the crane.
   b) If the mass is accelerating at $0.5\,\text{m s}^{-2}$, while the crane is operating at its maximum power output find the speed of the mass.

8 The power output of a car travelling at a constant $20\,\text{m s}^{-1}$ is $15\,\text{kW}$. Two possible models for the resistance forces are that they are proportional to the speed or to the square of the speed. The maximum power output of the car is $60\,\text{kW}$.
   a) Find the constant of proportionality for each model.
   b) Use each model to predict the top speed of the car.
   c) Which model do you think is more realistic?

9 A car with a mass of $1000\,\text{kg}$ can reach a top speed of $42\,\text{m s}^{-1}$ and has a power output of $54\,\text{kW}$.
   a) Find the resistance force on the car at top speed.

b) Assume that the resistance force remains constant at the value you have calculated. Find the maximum speed of the car going up and down a slope inclined at 2° to the horizontal.

c) Is the assumption about the resistance force made in **b)** reasonable?

10 A lorry of mass 20 tonnes has a top speed, on the level, of 30 m s^{-1} and a maximum power output of 100 kW.

a) Assume the resistance forces are proportional to the speed squared and find the constant of proportionality.

b) Find the maximum speed of the lorry going up a slope at 4° to the horizontal.

CONSOLIDATION EXERCISES FOR CHAPTER 12

1 A bullet of mass 6 grams passes horizontally through a fixed, vertical board. After the bullet has travelled 2 cm through the board its speed is reduced from 400 m s^{-1} to 250 m s^{-1}. The board exerts a constant resistive force on the bullet.
Find, to 3 significant figures, the magnitude of this resistive force.

(EDEXCEL Question 2, M2 Specimen Paper)

2 A soldier, of mass 80 kg, swings on a rope of length 80 m. He is to be modelled as a particle that describes a circular arc from A, through B to C. The path is shown in the following diagram.

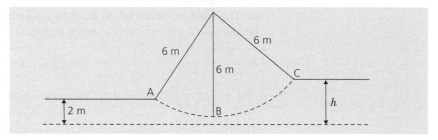

The point A is 2 m higher than B and C is h m higher than B. Initially the soldier moves at 2 m s^{-1} at A and in a direction perpendicular to the rope.

a) Find the kinetic energy and speed of the soldier at B, stating any assumptions that you make.

b) Find h, if the soldier comes to rest at C before swinging back.

c) Explain why the tension does not work in this situation.

(AQA B Question 5, M5 Specimen Paper)

3 A roofer is replacing the slates on a roof inclined at 40° to the horizontal. An old broken slate of mass 0.4 kg, which may be treated as a particle, is placed on the roof and slides from rest. It slides 5 m down the roof and then falls a further vertical distance of 6 m to the ground, as shown in the diagram. While the slate is sliding down the roof the resistance to its motion is a constant 2 N; when the slate reaches the edge of the roof it falls freely and air resistance may be neglected.

a) Calculate the gravitational potential energy lost by the slate in moving from the point of release to the ground. Calculate also the speed with which the slate hits the ground.

A crate of new slates of total mass 12 kg is pulled up from the ground by the roofer, using a light rope. This crate is lifted 6 m vertically from the ground and then slides 5 m up the sloping roof before coming to rest. When the crate is being raised vertically there is negligible resistance to motion. When the crate is sliding up the roof the coefficient of friction between the crate and the roof is 0.6 and the rope is parallel to the roof.

b) It takes the roofer 25 seconds to pull up the crate of slates. Calculate the average power he must develop to achieve this.

c) Show that, if the crate is not secured when the rope is removed, it will slide back down the roof. What would be the least value of the coefficient of friction between the crate and the roof for this not to happen?

(OCR MEI Question 1, M2 Specimen Paper)

4 A straight road is inclined at an angle α to the horizontal, where $\sin\alpha = \frac{1}{20}$. A lorry of mass 4800 kg moves up the road at a constant speed of $12\,\mathrm{m\,s^{-1}}$. The non-gravitational resistance to the motion of the lorry is constant and has magnitude 2000 N.

a) Find, in kW to 3 significant figures, the rate of working of the lorry's engine.

The road becomes horizontal. The lorry's engine continues to work at the same rate and the resistance to motion remains the same. Find:

b) the acceleration of the lorry immediately after the rod becomes horizontal,

c) the maximum speed, in $\mathrm{m\,s^{-1}}$ to 3 significant figures, at which the lorry will go along the horizontal road.

(EDEXCEL Question 5, M2 Specimen Paper)

5 A car, of mass 1200 kg, has a maximum power output of 48 000 W. On a horizontal road the car has a maximum speed of $40\,\mathrm{m\,s^{-1}}$. Assume that the resistance forces acting on the car are proportional to its speed.

a) Find the resistance force acting on the car when it travels at $v\,\mathrm{m\,s^{-1}}$.

b) Find the percentage reduction in the power output of the car if its speed is reduced by 10%.

c) Use your answer to part **b)** to describe one advantage of reducing the speed at which the car is driven.

d) Find the maximum speed of the car, when it is being driven up a slope at 4° to the horizontal.

(AQA B Question 8, M2 Specimen Paper)

6 A car of mass 650 kg is travelling on a straight road which is inclined to the horizontal at 5°. At a certain point P on the road the car's speed is $15\,\mathrm{m\,s^{-1}}$. The point Q is 400 m down the hill from P, and at Q the car's speed is $35\,\mathrm{m\,s^{-1}}$.

a) Assume that the car's engine produces a constant driving force on the car as it moves down the hill from P to Q, and that any resistances to the car's motion may be neglected. By considering the change in energy of the car, or otherwise, calculate the magnitude of the driving force of the car's engine.

b) Assume instead that resistance to the car's motion between P and Q may be represented by a constant force of magnitude 900 N. Given that the acceleration of the car at Q is zero, show that the power of the car's engine at this instant is approximately 12.1 kW. Given that the power of the car's engine is the same when the car is at P as it is when the car is at Q, calculate the car's acceleration at P.

(OCR Question 5, M2 Specimen Paper)

MATHEMATICAL MODELLING ACTIVITY

Problem statement

How much work do you do as you walk?

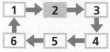

Specify the real problem

Set up a model

Make a list of the key features that you feel are important to consider when solving this problem.

The set of assumptions that have been set out below allow a first model to be formulated.

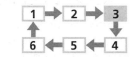

Set up a model

- The mass of the walker is m kg.
- The length of the walker's legs is l m and their pace has length p m.
- The walking takes place on level ground.
- As the person walks their body rises and falls slightly. The work done is simply that required to raise the body at each step.
- The walker's legs do not bend.

Formulate a mathematical problem

Formulate the mathematical problem

The diagram shows the walker at the start and mid-point of a step. Find the height gained during this phase of the step and the work done. Also find the work done as the walker travels 1 km.

Solve the mathematical problem

Solve the mathematical problem

The diagrams show the legs of the walker at the start of the step and the mid-point.

The gain in height is:

$$l - l\cos\alpha$$

Show that:

$$\cos\alpha = \sqrt{1 - \frac{p^2}{4l^2}}$$

Now the gain in height can be expressed as:

$$l - l\cos\alpha = l\left(1 - \sqrt{1 - \frac{p^2}{4l^2}}\right)$$

and the work done per pace as:

$$mgl\left(1 - \sqrt{1 - \frac{p^2}{4l^2}}\right)$$

Show that the work done in travelling 1 km is:

$$\frac{1000\,mgl}{p}\left(1 - \sqrt{1 - \frac{p^2}{4l^2}}\right)$$

Interpretation

Interpret the solution

The result gives the work done as a person walks 1 km. For an adult typical values for the variables are:

$$m = 70\,\text{kg}$$
$$p = 0.8\,\text{m}$$

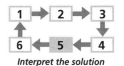

$$l = 0.9\,\text{m}$$

Using this value gives:

$$\text{work done} = \frac{1000 \times 70 \times 9.8 \times 0.9}{0.8} \times \left(1 - \sqrt{1 - \frac{0.8^2}{4 \times 0.9^2}}\right) = 80\,411\,\text{J}$$

Show that this is about the same as the work done when raising a 70 kg mass through 117 m.

Compare with reality

Compare with reality

Conduct the experiment below.
1 Find the power of a student who is climbing a flight of stairs as quickly as possible, assuming that work is only done against gravity.
2 Find the power of the same student who is walking as fast as possible on level ground, using the model above to find the work done.

3 Compare the results and comment.
Also comment on the model and suggest ways in which it could be improved.

POSSIBLE MODELLING TASKS

1 A runner maintains a constant speed while running and so would appear to have no change in kinetic energy and be doing no work. This is clearly not true. By considering the motion of the runner, develop a model that describes the work done by the runner.

2 On some steep hills, you will notice that there are lanes for slow-moving vehicles. Consider the effect of driving uphill on a lorry and recommend a policy for the provision of lorry lanes.

Summary

After working through this chapter you should:

■ be aware of the different types of energy: potential and kinetic

■ be able to calculate kinetic energies using $\frac{1}{2}mv^2$

■ be able to calculate work done using Fs or $Fs\cos\theta$

■ be able to use the result work done = change in kinetic energy

■ be able to calculate gravitational potential energy using mgh

■ be able to use power in the form $P = Fv$

Momentum and collisions

- This chapter builds on the work in the AS book on momentum and collisions.

- Conservation of momentum can be applied in two dimensions.

- The coefficient of restitution can be used to predict what will happen in a collision.

MOMENTUM

Summary of results from the AS book

Impulse $I = Ft$

$$= mv - mu$$

Conservation of momentum $m_A u_A + m_B u_B = m_A V_A + m_B V_B$

Momentum in two dimensions

Example 13.1

*A boat of mass 300 kg is travelling at 2 m s⁻¹ on a bearing of 070°. Express the momentum in terms of the unit vectors **i** and **j** which are east and north respectively.*

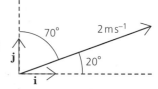

Solution

The diagram shows the velocity of the boat, which can be expressed as:

$$\mathbf{v} = 2\cos 20° \,\mathbf{i} + 2\cos 70° \,\mathbf{j} = 1.88\mathbf{i} + 0.68\mathbf{j}$$

Then the momentum of the boat is given by:

$$m\mathbf{v} = 300(1.88\mathbf{i} + 0.68\mathbf{j}) = 564\mathbf{i} + 204\mathbf{j}$$

IMPULSE AND CHANGE OF MOMENTUM

We shall now consider impulse and change of momentum in two dimensions, using vectors to represent these quantities.

Impulse

When a force acts for a short time, we often refer to its effects as an **impulse**. For a constant force, Newton's second law states that

$\mathbf{F} = m\mathbf{a}$ but as $\mathbf{a} = \dfrac{(\mathbf{v} - \mathbf{u})}{t}$ this can be expressed as:

$$\mathbf{F}t = m\mathbf{v} - m\mathbf{u}$$

This is a vector equation and can be represented as shown in the diagram.

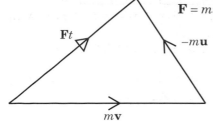

Impulse, **I** is defined as the change in momentum, so:

$$\mathbf{I} = m\mathbf{v} - m\mathbf{u} \text{ and also } \mathbf{I} = \mathbf{F}t$$

Example 13.2

A hockey ball is travelling at $7\,m\,s^{-1}$ when it is hit by a stick. After being hit it is deflected through $60°$ and its speed increases to $9\,m\,s^{-1}$.

a) Explain which aspects of the ball's motion will be ignored if the ball is treated as a particle.

b) Find the impulse on the ball, in terms of suitable perpendicular unit vectors **i** and **j**.

c) If the stick is in contact with the ball for 0.1 seconds, find the average force on the ball. Illustrate this force on a diagram and find its magnitude.

Solution

a) If the ball is to be modelled as a particle its rotation must be ignored.

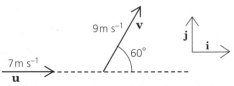

b) The diagram shows the initial and final velocities of the ball. The initial velocity, is clearly:

$$\mathbf{u} = 7\mathbf{i}$$

The final velocity **v** is given by:

$$\mathbf{v} = 9 \cos 60°\mathbf{i} + 9 \cos 30°\mathbf{j} = 4.5\mathbf{i} + \frac{9\sqrt{3}}{2}\mathbf{j}$$

Now the impulse can be calculated.

$$\mathbf{I} = m\mathbf{v} - m\mathbf{u} = 0.2(4.5\mathbf{i} + \frac{9\sqrt{3}}{2}\mathbf{j}) - 0.2 \times 7\mathbf{i}$$

$$= -0.5\mathbf{i} + 1.558\mathbf{j}$$

This is illustrated in the diagram.

c) The average force can now be found using, $\mathbf{I} = \mathbf{F}t$.

$$-0.5\mathbf{i} + 1.558\mathbf{j} = 0.1\mathbf{F} \quad \Rightarrow \mathbf{F} = -5\mathbf{i} + 15.58\mathbf{j}$$

The diagram shows this force which has magnitude given by:

$$F = \sqrt{5^2 + 15.58^2} = 16.4 \text{ N}$$

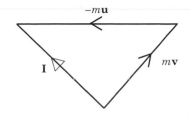

EXERCISES

 13.1 CLASSWORK

1. A skater follows a curved path, moving at a constant speed. What happens to the skater's momentum?

2. Express the momentum of each of the following objects in terms of unit vectors **i** and **j**, that are east and north respectively.
   a) A boat of mass 750 kg travelling at $8\,m\,s^{-1}$ on a bearing of 027°.
   b) An aeroplane of mass 1.5 tonnes travelling at $60\,m\,s^{-1}$ on a bearing of 220°.
   c) A walker of mass 70 kg travelling at $1.1\,m\,s^{-1}$ on a bearing of 110°.

3. Express the momentum of each object below in terms of unit vectors **i** and **j**, that are horizontal and vertically upwards respectively.
   a) A tennis ball of mass 70 grams hit so that it moves at $15\ m\ s^{-1}$ at an angle of 5° below the horizontal.
   b) A shot putt of mass 5 kg launched at $13\ m\ s^{-1}$ at 42° above the horizontal.
   c) A cyclist and cycle of combined mass 80 kg travelling down a slope at 9° to the horizontal with a speed of $8.5\ m\ s^{-1}$.

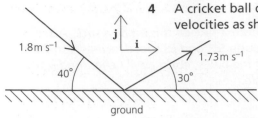

4 A cricket ball of mass 200 grams hits the ground and rebounds with velocities as shown.

a) Express both velocities in terms of the unit vectors **i** and **j**.

b) Find the impulse on the ball.

c) If the average force on the ball during contact is 9 N, find the time of contact.

5 A skateboarder of mass 65 kg is heading towards a wall and tries to take evasive action by pushing on the wall. During the impact the velocity of the skateboard is changed as shown in the diagram.

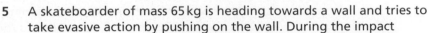

a) Find the impulse on the skateboarder.

b) Draw a diagram to show the impulse, the initial and final momentum of the skateboarder and their relationship.

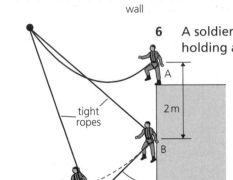

6 A soldier of mass 78 kg, on an assault course, jumps off a ledge at A holding a rope and falls vertical to B, where the rope becomes tight.

At B the direction of the velocity of the soldier changes.

a) Show that the speed of the soldier at B is 6.26 m s^{-1}.

b) Find the impulse on the soldier as he changes direction. Assume that his speed does not change.

c) Draw a diagram to show the impulse and change of momentum of the soldier.

d) Estimate the time taken for the direction of the velocity to change and use this to find the average tension in the rope while the soldier changes direction.

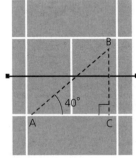

7 A shuttlecock of mass 30 grams travels from A to B. At B it has a speed of 5 m s^{-1} and is travelling at an angle of 20° below the horizontal. After it has been hit it travels towards C with a speed of 6 m s^{-1} and at 30° above the horizontal.

a) Express the velocities of the shuttlecock before and after it is hit in terms of the unit vectors **i** and **j** as shown, and **k** which is vertical.

b) Find the impulse on the shuttlecock.

c) If the time of contact is 0.5 seconds, find the magnitude of the average force on the shuttlecock.

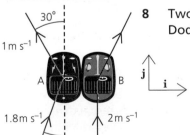

8 Two dodgems at a fair collide giving each other a glancing blow. Dodgem A has mass 320 kg and dodgem B has mass 290 kg. The initial velocities are as shown and A moves with a speed of 1 m s^{-1} after changing direction as shown.

a) Express the initial and final speeds of A in terms of the unit vectors **i** and **j**.

b) Find the impulse on A.

c) Assume that the impulse on B has the same magnitude as the impulse on A, but acts in the opposite direction. Use this to find the final velocity of B.

EXERCISES

13.1 HOMEWORK

1 An athlete claims that her momentum remains constant as she runs round a track. Is this claim justified?

2 Express the momentum of each object described below in terms of unit vectors **i** and **j**, that are east and north respectively.
   a) A dinghy of mass 300 kg travelling at $2.1\,\text{m s}^{-1}$ on a bearing of 070°.
   b) A ship of mass 2000 tonnes travelling at $5\,\text{m s}^{-1}$ on a bearing of 200°.
   c) A competitor of mass 60 kg at an orienteering contest, who runs at $4.3\,\text{m s}^{-1}$ on a bearing of 190°.

3 Express the momentum of each object below in terms of the unit vectors **i** and **j**, that are horizontal and vertical respectively.
   a) A basket ball of mass 900 grams travelling at $5\,\text{m s}^{-1}$ at 40° to the horizontal.
   b) A golf ball of mass 45 grams that is hit so it initially moves at $15\,\text{m s}^{-1}$ at an angle of 50° to the horizontal.
   c) A girl of mass 45 kg running up a ramp at 30° to the horizontal with a speed of $1.8\,\text{m s}^{-1}$.

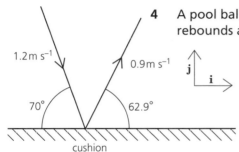

4 A pool ball of mass 120 grams hits the side cushion of a table and rebounds as shown in the diagram.
   a) Express the initial and final velocities of the ball in terms of the unit vectors **i** and **j**.
   b) Find the impulse on the ball.
   c) If the ball is in contact with the cushion for 0.8 s, find the magnitude of the average force on the ball.
   d) Suggest how the force on the ball may vary during the collision.

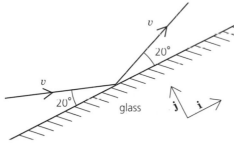

5 A stone of mass 80 grams strikes a glancing blow on a glass window pane as shown in the diagram.
   a) Express the velocities illustrated in terms of **i** and **j**, if $v = 5\,\text{m s}^{-1}$.
   b) Find the impulse on the stone and the impulse on the window.
   c) If the stone had hit the window at right angles to its path and stopped, what would have been the impulse on the window if the speed of the stone was $5\,\text{m s}^{-1}$?
   d) If a glancing blow at 20° as illustrated causes the same impulse as a direct hit, find v.

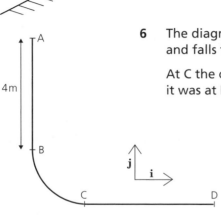

6 The diagram shows a freefall slide. A child of mass 50 kg jumps from A and falls freely to B.

At C the child is travelling horizontally and her speed is 10% less than it was at B.
   a) Assume that $g = 9.8\,\text{m s}^{-2}$ and find the speed of the child at B.
   b) Express the velocities of the child at B and C in terms of **i** and **j**.
   c) Find the impulse on the child between B and C.
   d) If it takes 0.8 s to get from B to C find the average force on the child.

7 A racing car travels at a constant speed of $40\,\text{m s}^{-1}$ around a bend. The direction of motion changes through 20° as shown. The mass of the driver is 66 kg.

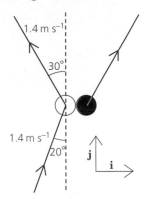

a) Find the impulse upon the driver in terms of the unit vectors **i** and **j**.

b) If the change takes place in three seconds find the magnitude of the average force on the driver and of his average acceleration.

8 The diagram shows a collision between two pool balls, one of which was initially at rest. Assume that the mass of each ball is m.

a) Find the impulse on the moving ball, in terms of m and the unit vectors **i** and **j**.

b) Assume that the stationary ball experiences an impulse of the same magnitude, but opposite direction. Find the velocity of the ball after the collision.

c) At what speed and in what direction does the ball travel after the collision?

COLLISIONS IN TWO DIMENSIONS

Sometimes collisions do take place in one dimension, often where the motion is constrained in some way, as with trucks that run on tracks. However, as the result of a good many collisions, there is motion in two or even three dimensions. When a footballer heads a ball there is motion in three dimensions. When two snooker balls collide there is motion in two dimensions.

Exploration 13.1

Is momentum conserved?

We know momentum is conserved in one dimension, but is momentum conserved in two dimensions? Consider the example below.

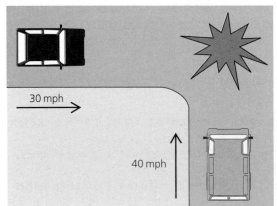

A car travelling at $50\,\text{km h}^{-1}$ (30 mph) hits a van travelling at $65\,\text{km h}^{-1}$ (40 mph). If they are travelling at right angles when the collision takes place, how do you think the two vehicles could move if:

■ they became entangled
■ they bounce apart?

Do you think momentum would be conserved in this situation?

What other collisions would support the suggestion that momentum would be conserved in two dimensions?

Comparing momentum

To investigate whether or not momentum is conserved, we can consider two particles that collide with each other. We can study the velocities of two particles A and B before and after impact and the impulse during impact.

Before impact

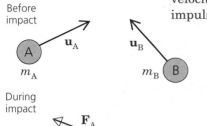

Before the impact A and B have velocities $\mathbf{u}_A$ and $\mathbf{u}_B$ respectively so the total momentum before the collision is $m_A\,\mathbf{u}_A + m_B\,\mathbf{u}_B$.

During impact

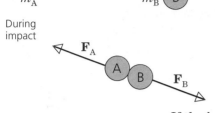

When the balls are in contact they exert forces on each other that are equal in magnitude, but acting in opposite directions. So if $\mathbf{F}_A$ is the force on A and $\mathbf{F}_B$ the force on B, $\mathbf{F}_A = -\mathbf{F}_B$.

If the balls are in contact for t seconds, then:
$$\mathbf{F}_A t = -\mathbf{F}_B\,t$$
or:
$$\mathbf{I}_A = -\mathbf{I}_B$$
So the impulse on A is of equal magnitude, but in the opposite direction to the impulse on B.

After impact

After impact A and B have velocities $\mathbf{v}_A$ and $\mathbf{v}_B$ respectively, so the total momentum after the collision is $m_A\,\mathbf{v}_A + m_B\,\mathbf{v}_B$.

$\mathbf{I}_A$ is the impulse on A and equal to the change in momentum or
$$m_A\,\mathbf{v}_A - m_A\,\mathbf{u}_A.$$
Similarly $\mathbf{I}_B = m_B\,\mathbf{v}_B - m_B\,\mathbf{u}_B$.
As $\mathbf{I}_A = -\mathbf{I}_B$,
this can be expressed as:
$$m_A\,\mathbf{v}_A - m_A\,\mathbf{u}_A = -(m_B\,\mathbf{v}_B - m_B\,\mathbf{u}_B)$$
Bringing the terms with $\mathbf{v}_A$ and $\mathbf{v}_B$ to the left of the equation and those with $\mathbf{u}_A$ and $\mathbf{u}_B$ to the right gives:
$$m_A\,\mathbf{v}_A + m_B\,\mathbf{v}_B = m_A\,\mathbf{u}_A + m_B\,\mathbf{u}_B$$
or:

$$\frac{\text{total momentum}}{\text{after collision}} = \frac{\text{total momentum}}{\text{before collision}}$$

So momentum is still conserved when collisions take place in two or three dimensions, as well as in one dimension.

Example 13.3

The driver of a car of mass 900 kg assumed he had right of way as he came out of a junction. He collided at right angles with a car of mass 1200 kg. In defence the driver claimed that the other car was travelling at a speed far in excess of the 30 mph (13 m s⁻¹) speed limit. The police estimated that immediately after impact the 900 kg car glanced off at 30 m s⁻¹ and at 90° from the original direction of travel and the 1200 kg car glanced off at 12 m s⁻¹ and at 60° from the original direction of travel. Was the first driver right?

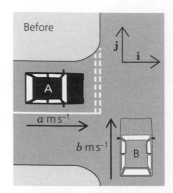

Before

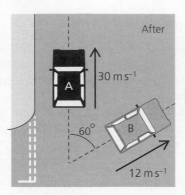

After

Solution

The first diagram shows the velocities of the cars before impact. The vehicles have been labelled A and B.
The initial velocity of A is $\mathbf{u}_A = a\,\mathbf{i}$ and the initial velocity of B is $\mathbf{u}_B = b\,\mathbf{j}$.
The second diagram shows the velocities of the cars after the collision.
The final velocity of car A is $\mathbf{v}_A = 30\mathbf{j}$. The final velocity of B is:
$$\mathbf{v}_A = 12\cos 30°\mathbf{i} + 12\cos 60°\mathbf{j} = 6\sqrt{3}\,\mathbf{i} + 6\mathbf{j}$$

Now the equation for conservation of momentum can be applied.
$$m_A\,\mathbf{v}_A + m_B\,\mathbf{v}_B = m_A\,\mathbf{u}_A + m_B\,\mathbf{u}_B$$
so that:
$$900 \times 30\mathbf{j} + 1200(6\sqrt{3}\,\mathbf{i} + 6\mathbf{j}) = 900a\mathbf{i} + 1200b\mathbf{j}$$

or $27\,000\mathbf{j} + 7200\sqrt{3}\,\mathbf{i} + 7200\mathbf{j} = 900a\mathbf{i} + 1200b\mathbf{j}$
Collecting together the $\mathbf{i}$ *and* $\mathbf{j}$ *components gives:*
$(7200\sqrt{3} - 900a)\mathbf{i} + (27\,000 + 7200 - 1200b)\mathbf{j} = 0$
Consider first the $\mathbf{j}$ *components.*
$34\,200 - 1200b = 0$
$$\Rightarrow b = \frac{34\,200}{1200} = 28.5\ m\ s^{-1}$$

So the car B was travelling well in excess of the $13\,m\,s^{-1}$ or $30\,mph$ speed limit.
Consider also the $\mathbf{i}$ *components.*
$7200\sqrt{3} - 900a = 0$
$$\Rightarrow a = \frac{7200\sqrt{3}}{900} = 13.9\ m\ s^{-1}$$
Car A was also exceeding the speed limit, but only just!

Example 13.4

The white ball travels parallel to the longest side of the table at $10\,ms^{-1}$. The white ball collides with the black ball in such a way that the black ball goes into the right hand pocket and (to the dismay of the player) the white ball goes into the left hand pocket as shown (game lost!). Calculate the speeds of the two balls after impact.

Solution

Assume that the masses of the balls are all equal. In this case the conservation of momentum equation, with B for black and W for white,
$$m_W\,\mathbf{u}_W + m_B\,\mathbf{u}_B = m_W\,\mathbf{v}_W + m_B\,\mathbf{v}_B$$
simplifies to:
$$\mathbf{u}_W + \mathbf{u}_B = \mathbf{v}_W + \mathbf{v}_B$$

Initially $\mathbf{u}_B = 0$ *and* $\mathbf{u}_W = 10\mathbf{j}$

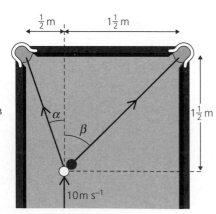

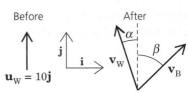

After the collision the balls move as shown in the diagram. First it is necessary to calculate the angles α and β.

$$\tan \alpha = \left(\frac{\frac{1}{2}}{1\frac{1}{2}}\right) = \frac{1}{3} \quad \text{Also} \quad \sin \alpha = \frac{1}{\sqrt{10}} \quad \text{and} \quad \cos \alpha = \frac{3}{\sqrt{10}}$$

Clearly $\beta = 45°$
So the final velocities can now be expressed as vectors.

$$\mathbf{v}_B = v_B \cos 45° \, \mathbf{i} + v_B \cos 45° \, \mathbf{j}$$

and: $\mathbf{v}_W = -v_W \sin \alpha \mathbf{i} + v_W \cos \alpha \mathbf{j}$

Applying the conservation of momentum gives:

$$10\mathbf{j} = (v_B \cos 45° - v_W \sin \alpha)\mathbf{i} + (v_B \cos 45° + v_W \cos \alpha)\mathbf{j}$$

Considering the $\mathbf{i}$ components gives:

$$v_B \cos 45° = v_W \sin \alpha$$

so $v_B = \dfrac{v_W \sin \alpha}{\cos 45°} = \dfrac{\sqrt{2}v_W}{\sqrt{10}} = \dfrac{v_W}{\sqrt{5}}$

Considering the $\mathbf{j}$ components gives:

$$10 = v_B \cos 45° + v_W \cos \alpha$$

or by substituting for v_B:

$$10 = \frac{v_W}{\sqrt{5}} \cos 45° + v_W \cos \alpha$$

and solving for v_W gives:

$$v_W = \frac{10}{\dfrac{\cos 45°}{\sqrt{5}} + \cos \alpha} = 7.91 \, \mathrm{m\,s^{-1}}$$

Now as $v_B = \dfrac{v_W}{\sqrt{5}}$

$$v_B = \frac{v_W}{\sqrt{5}} = 3.54 \, \mathrm{m\,s^{-1}}$$

EXERCISES

13.2 CLASSWORK

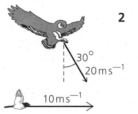

1 Two roller skaters collide and move together after the collision. Their masses are 62 kg and 56 kg and they were moving as shown in the diagram before the collision.
   a) Find the momentum of each skater before the collision, in terms of $\mathbf{i}$ and $\mathbf{j}$.
   b) What is the momentum of the two skaters after the collision?
   c) Find their speed and the direction in which they move after the collision.

2 A small bird of mass 0.4 kg flies horizontally at a speed of $10\,\mathrm{m\,s^{-1}}$. An owl of mass 2 kg swoops down onto the smaller bird with a speed of $20\,\mathrm{m\,s^{-1}}$, travelling at 30° to the vertical.
   a) Find the momentum of each bird just before impact, using suitable unit vectors.
   b) The owl grabs the smaller bird with its claws and they move together. Find their speed just after the impact.
   c) Are there any reasons why momentum should not be conserved in this case? If so, explain why.

3 A goalkeeper of mass 70 kg moves forward to catch a football of mass 2 kg. The goalkeeper moves at 1 m s^{-1} and the football travels at 40 m s^{-1} at an angle of 25° above the horizontal.

   a) Find the total momentum of the ball and the goalkeeper before the collision, in terms of horizontal and vertical unit vectors.

   b) Find the velocity of the goalkeeper after he has caught the ball, in terms of horizontal and vertical unit vectors.

   c) If the goalkeeper keeps hold of the ball, in which direction would he move after catching the ball?

4 Two pucks are placed on an air table, where they hover on a cushion of air. Both pucks have the same mass. One puck is fired at 4 m s^{-1} into the other puck, which is stationary. After the collision the two pucks move as shown in the diagram.

   a) Explain the advantages of using unit vectors as illustrated. Why is this possible in this case?

   b) Find the speed of each puck after the collision.

5 A car of mass 1000 kg that is being chased by a police car hits a stationary vehicle of mass 1200 kg. The motion of the car is shown in the diagram.

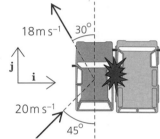

   a) Find the change in the momentum of the moving car.

   b) What is the speed of the stationary car after the collision?

   c) Explain why the car that was stationary does not appear to move very much.

6 A stone of mass 80 grams is fired from a catapult so that it hits a tin can of mass 200 grams. After the collision the can and stone move as shown in the diagram.

   a) Find the total momentum of the can and the stone after the collision, in terms of the unit vectors **i** and **j**.

   b) Find the initial velocity of the stone.

   c) Use a scale drawing to confirm the result obtained above.

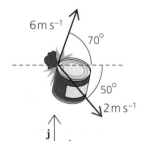

7 A car of mass 3m, and a motorcycle of mass m, are involved in a collision. Initially, they are travelling at right angles, both with speed u. After the collision both travel together with speed v.

   a) Show that the magnitude of the total momentum of both vehicles before the collision is $\sqrt{10}mu$.

   b) Express v in terms of u and find the angle through which each vehicle is deflected.

8 A scientist conducts an experiment to find the mass of a helium atom. A proton of mass 1.67×10^{-27} kg is fired with a velocity of 10^7 m s^{-1} towards a stationary helium atom. The collision leaves the trace shown in a photographic plate. After the collision the speed of the proton is 5×10^6 m s^{-1} and the speed of the helium atom is 2.17×10^6 m s^{-1}.

   a) Find the total momentum of the atom and the proton after the collision in terms of m, the mass of the helium atom, and the unit vectors **i** and **j**.

   b) Use conservation of momentum to find m.

9 A sailor of mass 64 kg jumps off a quay into a rubber dinghy of mass 40 kg. He hits the dinghy travelling at 8 m s^{-1} and at 10° to the horizontal. Assume the dinghy travels horizontally.

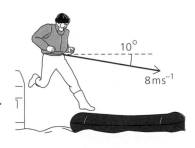

a) Find the vertical impulse on the sailor.

b) If the horizontal component of momentum is conserved, find the speed of the dinghy.

10 A gun of mass 4000 kg fires a shell of mass 100 kg at a speed of 300 m s^{-1} at an angle of 40° above the horizontal. The gun moves backwards horizontally. Describe what happens to the gun, calculating the magnitude of any quantities you use in your description.

EXERCISES

13.2 HOMEWORK

1 A car of mass 1100 kg is travelling at 14 m s^{-1}, as shown in the diagram, when it is hit by a lorry of mass 4 tonnes travelling as shown.

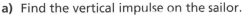

a) Find the momentum of each vehicle before the collision in terms of the unit vectors **i** and **j**.

b) If, after the collision, the two vehicles move together, find their speed and the direction in which they move, just after the collision.

c) What do you expect to happen to the velocity of the vehicles after the collision?

2 A 5000 kg space capsule travelling at 400 m s^{-1} is struck by a lump of debris of mass 200 kg, as shown in the diagram. The debris becomes embedded in the capsule.

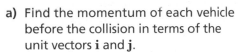

a) Find the momentum of the capsule and the lump of debris before the collision, in terms of the unit vectors **i** and **j**.

b) Find the speed of the capsule after the collision.

c) Find the deflection of the capsule from its original path.

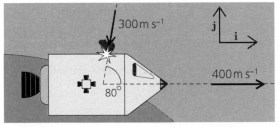

3 A spaceman of mass 66 kg jumps to try and catch a tool. He moves at 2 m s^{-1} as shown in the diagram. The tool has mass 500 grams and moves at 4 m s^{-1}.

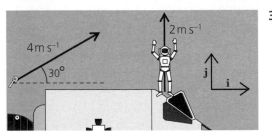

a) Calculate the total momentum of the tool and the spaceman before the collision.

b) Find the speed at which they move and the direction in which they move after the collision.

c) Should the spaceman be worried about the effect of catching the tool?

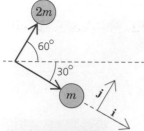

4 An atomic particle of mass m collides with a stationary particle of mass $2m$. After the collision the two particles move in the directions shown. Initially the particle of mass m was travelling along the dotted line at $4 \times 10^6 \, \text{m s}^{-1}$.
  a) Express the initial momentum of the particle of mass m in terms of the vectors **i** and **j**.
  b) Find the speed of each particle after the collision.

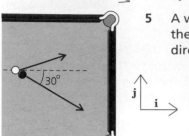

5 A white snooker ball travels straight down a table at $2 \, \text{m s}^{-1}$ parallel to the side and strikes a stationary red ball, which then moves in the direction shown at $1.5 \, \text{m s}^{-1}$.
  a) Find the total momentum of the two balls before the collision, in terms of the unit vectors **i** and **j** and the mass, m, of each ball.
  b) Find the direction in which the white ball travels after the collision.
  c) State any assumptions that you have made.

6 The diagram show how two snooker balls, of mass m, move after a collision. Assume that the masses of the balls are equal and that one was initially at rest.
  a) Find the total momentum of the two balls after the collision.
  b) Find the velocity of the moving ball before the collision.
  c) Sketch a diagram that could be used to find the velocity by scale drawing.

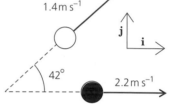

7 Two atomic particles A and B collide and join together. Both particles were initially moving at right angles. A has mass m and initial speed u, while B has mass $3m$ and initial speed $2u$.
  a) Find the magnitude of the total momentum before the collision.
  b) Find the speed of the two combined particles after the collision.
  c) Find the deflection of each particle.

8 Two air pucks that hover on a glass surface have masses M and m. The puck of mass M is fired and hits the puck of mass m which was stationary. After the collision the pucks move as shown in the diagram.
  a) Find the total momentum of the two pucks after the collision.
  b) Find M in terms of m.
  c) Find v.

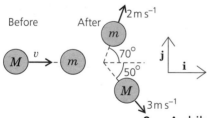

9 A child of mass $40 \, \text{kg}$ jumps from a wall onto a stationary skateboard of mass $5 \, \text{kg}$. The child travels at $5 \, \text{m s}^{-1}$, at $20°$ to the horizontal, before impact.
  a) If the skateboard begins to move horizontally, find the magnitude of the vertical impulse on the child.
  b) If the horizontal component of momentum is conserved, find the speed of the child and the skateboard.

10 A trolley of mass $80 \, \text{kg}$ is freewheeling at a constant speed of $4 \, \text{m s}^{-1}$. A heavy sack of mass $30 \, \text{kg}$ is dropped onto the trolley, so that it is moving at right angles to the trolley when it impacts. What happens to the motion of the trolley?

THE COEFFICIENT OF RESTITUTION

Exploration 13.2

Comparing heights of bounce

If you drop different types of balls onto the floor and let them bounce, they will rebound to different heights. Why is there this difference, and what do you think causes it?

Materials that bounce

What happens depends on the material from which the ball is made and the surface onto which it is dropped. Soft, spongy materials will not bounce well. To demonstrate how the nature of a ball affects its bounce, take a table tennis ball and make a small hole in it. First observe how it bounces. Then push some elastic bands in through the hole and see how this affects the bounce. Try to produce a ball that does not bounce. Then push in more elastic bands and observe what happens to the bounce.

Exploration 13.3

Bouncing balls

- Collect several different sports balls (for example, football, basketball, tennis ball, squash ball, cricket ball, etc.).
- Drop each ball, in turn (from a variety of heights), onto the floor and record how high each rebounds. What happens?
- Calculate the speed at which the ball hits the ground and the speed at which it rebounds in each case. (**Note**: $v = \sqrt{2gh}$.) What is the ratio of impact to rebound speeds?
- Next, find a floor with a different covering and repeat the above experiment. What happens this time?

Your results should indicate that the rebound height is dependent on the two materials involved in the collision, and the height from which the balls are released.

Newton's experimental law

Newton proposed an experimental law that describes how the impact and rebound velocities are related. He stated that:

$$v = -eu$$

where v is the rebound velocity, u the impact velocity and e is a constant called the **coefficient of restitution**. The constant e depends on the type of ball and the surface it bounces on.

If $e = 1$ the collision is said to be **perfectly elastic**.
If $0 < e < 1$ the collision is said to be **elastic**.
If $e = 0$ the collision is said to be **inelastic**.

Example 13.5

A ball is dropped from a height of 1.5 m, onto the floor where it bounces. The coefficient of restitution is 0.6.
a) Find the velocity of the ball on impact.
b) Find the velocity of the ball on rebound.
c) Find the height to which the ball bounces.

Solution
Note first that the downward direction is defined as positive.
a) As the ball is subject to a constant acceleration of 9.8 m s^{-2}, the constant acceleration formula:

$$v^2 = u^2 + 2as$$

can be applied. In this case $u = 0$, $a = 9.8$ and $s = 1.5$, so:
$$v^2 = 0^2 + 2 \times 9.8 \times 1.5 = 29.4$$
and $v = 5.42\,\text{m s}^{-1}$

b) The rebound velocity can be found using:
$$v = -eu$$
In this case $e = 0.6$ and $u = 5.42$, so:
$$v = -0.6 \times 5.42 = -3.252\,\text{m s}^{-1}$$

c) The constant acceleration formula:
$$v^2 = u^2 + 2as$$
can be used to find the rebound height. Here $u = -3.252$, $v = 0$ and $a = 9.8$, so:
$$0^2 = (-3.252)^2 + 2 \times 9.8s$$

$$s = \frac{-(-3.252)^2}{2 \times 9.8} = -0.54\text{m}$$

So the ball rebounds to a height of 54 cm. The answer for s is negative as the ball has moved upwards.

Example 13.6

Show that if a ball is dropped from a height H and rebounds to a height h, then the coefficient of restitution is:
$$e = \sqrt{\frac{h}{H}}$$

Solution
If the ball is allowed to fall from a height H, under gravity the equation:
$$v^2 = u^2 + 2as$$
can be applied with $u = 0$ and $s = H$ to give:
$$v^2 = 2gH$$
so the impact velocity is $\sqrt{2gH}$.

Similarly the rebound velocity is $-\sqrt{2gh}$.

Using $v = -eu$ gives:
$$-\sqrt{2gh} = -e\sqrt{2gH} \quad \Rightarrow \quad \sqrt{h} = e\sqrt{H} \text{ so } e = \sqrt{\frac{h}{H}}$$

Exploration 13.4

Momentum and restitution

When a collision takes place involving two superballs, momentum is conserved. Is momentum conserved when two spongy balls collide? Does conservation of momentum depend on the value of e?

Momentum for any collision

Before   After

The law of conservation of momentum *does* hold for any collision provided no external forces act. If two balls of the same mass are travelling towards each other at the same speed, then the total momentum before collision is zero. If the collision brings them both to rest, then the total momentum after the collision is also zero. This extreme case illustrates conservation of momentum taking place, but more information is needed about what happens in a collision. This is where the coefficient of restitution is important.

Before   After

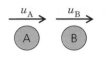

Consider two balls A and B moving, with velocities u_A and u_B respectively, along a straight line. As they collide the velocity of impact is $u_A - u_B$. After the collision, the velocity of separation will be $v_A - v_B$.

Newton's experimental law applies in this situation, with $u = u_A - u_B$ and $v = v_A - v_B$ to give:

$$v = -eu$$

or:

$$v_A - v_B = -e(u_A - u_B)$$

This result can be used in conjunction with conservation of momentum to predict what will happen after a collision.

Example 13.7

Two identical superballs are moving as shown in the diagram. The coefficient of restitution between the two balls is 0.8. Find what happens to each ball after the collision.

Solution

First define the positive direction to the right, so the initial velocities are $u_A = 10$ and $u_B = 6$, with v_A and v_B as the final velocities. As the balls have the same mass the conservation of momentum equation:

$$m_A u_A + m_A u_B = m_A v_A + m_A v_B$$

reduces to:

$$u_A + u_B = v_A + v_B$$

and substituting for u_A and u_B gives:

$$10 + 6 = v_A + v_B$$

so $v_A + v_B = 16$ *(1)*

Using the experimental law:

$$v_A - v_B = -e(u_A - u_B)$$

gives:

$$v_A + v_B = -0.8(10 - 8)$$

so $v_A + v_B = -1.6$ *(2)*

Adding equations (1) and (2) gives:

$2v_A = 12.8$ *so* $v_A = 6.4\,\mathrm{m\,s^{-1}}$

Substituting this into equation (1) gives:

$6.4 + v_B = 16$ *so* $v_B = 9.6\,\mathrm{m\,s^{-1}}$

So in the collision A loses speed and B gains speed.

Example 13.8

When a footballer heads a football, it can be modelled as a collision between two spheres. Assume that the head and the ball are travelling towards each other along a straight line as shown in the diagram, and that the coefficient of restitution is 0.3.

a) Find the velocity of the ball after the collision.

b) If the contact time is 0.005 s find the force acting on the head and its acceleration.

c) What factor has been ignored and do you think that this is reasonable in this situation?

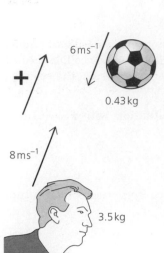

Solution

The diagram shows the positive direction, the initial velocities and the masses of the two spheres.

a) *Using the conservation of momentum:*

$$m_H u_H + m_B u_B = m_H v_H + m_B v_B$$

gives:

$$3.5 \times 8 + 0.43 \times (-6) = 3.5 v_H + 0.43 v_B$$

or:

$$3.5 v_H + 0.43 v_B = 25.42 \qquad (1)$$

Using the experimental law:

$$v_H - v_B = -e(u_H - u_B)$$

gives:

$$v_H - v_B = -0.3(8 - (-6)) = -4.2 \qquad (2)$$

Multiplying equation (2) by 0.43 gives:

$$0.43 v_H - 0.43 v_B = -1.806 \qquad (3)$$

Now adding equations (1) and (3) gives:

$$3.93 v_H = 23.614$$

so $v_H = 6.01\,m\,s^{-1}$

Substituting this into equation (2) gives:

$$6.01 - v_B = -4.2$$

so $v_B = 10.21\,m\,s^{-1}$

b) *The force on the players head can be found using:*

$$Ft = mv - mu$$

in this case:

$$F \times 0.005 = 3.5 \times 6.01 - 3.5 \times 8$$

so that $F = -1393\,N$

If the force is assumed to be constant, then the acceleration can be found using:

$$F = ma$$

$$-1393 = 3.5a$$

so that $a = -398\,m\,s^{-2}$

While this figure is very large it should be noted that it is only experienced for a very short period of time. Boxers can experience accelerations of up to about $900\,m\,s^{-2}$.

c) *The effects of gravity have been ignored, but this is justifiable as the time of the collision is so short the effects of gravity would be negligible.*

EXERCISES

13.3 CLASSWORK

1   In each situation below find the unknown quantity.

a) $u = 4\,m\,s^{-1}$

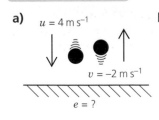

$v = -2\,m\,s^{-1}$

$e = ?$

b) $u = 10\,m\,s^{-1}$

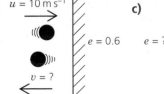

$e = 0.6$

$v = ?$

c) $u = -4\,m\,s^{-1}$

$e = ?$

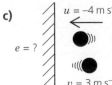

$v = 3\,m\,s^{-1}$

d) $u = ?$

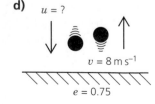

$v = 8\,m\,s^{-1}$

$e = 0.75$

2 A ball is dropped from a height of 2m and rebounds to a height of 1.2m.
a) Find the velocity of the ball when it hits the ground.
b) Find the velocity of the ball when it leaves the ground.
c) What is the coefficient of restitution between the ball and the ground?

3 In each situation below find the unknown quantity, when a ball bounces on the ground.

a)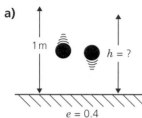
$e = 0.4$

b)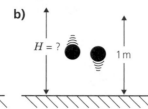
$e = 0.6$

c)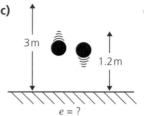
$e = ?$

d)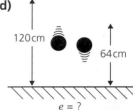
$e = ?$

4 Two identical balls are moving directly towards each other at $10\,\text{ms}^{-1}$. Find the velocities of the two balls after the collision if:
a) $e = 0.95$, **b)** $e = 0.1$.

5 A ball of mass 3kg is moving at $8\,\text{ms}^{-1}$ when it strikes a ball of mass 5kg which is moving in the same direction at $3\,\text{ms}^{-1}$. The coefficient of restitution between the two balls is 0.4.
a) Find the velocities of the two balls after the impact.
b) What important factor has been ignored?

6 The diagram shows a simplified Newton's Cradle. The ball A is moving horizontally at $4\,\text{ms}^{-1}$ when it strikes ball B, which was at rest. After the collision ball B moves at $3.95\,\text{ms}^{-1}$.
a) Use conservation of momentum to find out what happens to ball A after the collision.
b) Find the coefficient of restitution between the balls.

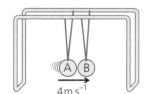

7 An object, travelling at speed v, strikes a stationary object of the same mass, that is at rest. What happens to the velocity of each object if:
a) $e = 1$, **b)** $e = 0.5$, **c)** $e - 0$?

8 Three balls A, B and C are moving horizontally with the speeds shown in the diagram. The coefficient of restitution between the balls is 0.5.
a) The first collision that takes place is between A and B. Find the velocities of these two balls after the collision.
b) The next collision is between B and C. Find the velocities of these two balls after this collision.
c) What collision takes place next?

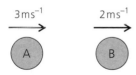

9 Three identical spheres A, B and C lie with their centres on a straight line. Initially A moves with speed u towards B and C, which are at rest. The coefficient of restitution between the spheres is e.
a) Find the velocities of A and B after the first collision, in terms of e.
b) Find the velocities of B and C after the second collision, in terms of e.

10 A ball is dropped from a height h onto a horizontal floor. The coefficient of restitution between the ball and the floor is e. If the ball is allowed to bounce continually until it comes to rest, find the total distance travelled by the ball.

EXERCISES

13.3 HOMEWORK

1 Find the unknown quantity in each situation described below, where a ball bounces against another surface.

a)

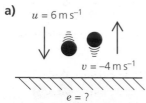

$u = 6\,\mathrm{m\,s^{-1}}$
$v = -4\,\mathrm{m\,s^{-1}}$
$e = ?$

b)

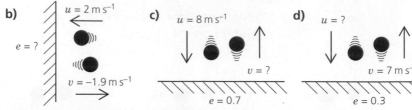

$u = 2\,\mathrm{m\,s^{-1}}$
$e = ?$
$v = -1.9\,\mathrm{m\,s^{-1}}$

c)

$u = 8\,\mathrm{m\,s^{-1}}$
$v = ?$
$e = 0.7$

d)

$u = ?$
$v = 7\,\mathrm{m\,s^{-1}}$
$e = 0.3$

2 A ball is dropped from a height of 5 m. The coefficient of restitution between the ball and the ground is 0.4.
a) Find the velocity of the ball when it hits the ground.
b) Find the rebound velocity of the ball.
c) To what height does the ball rebound?

3 For each situation illustrated below, where a ball is allowed to bounce on the ground, find the unknown quantity.

a)

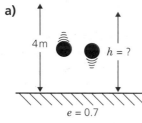

4 m $h = ?$
$e = 0.7$

b)

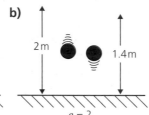

2 m   1.4 m
$e = ?$

c)

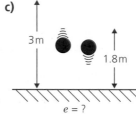

3 m   1.8 m
$e = ?$

d)

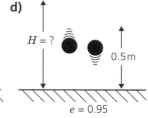

$H = ?$ 0.5 m
$e = 0.95$

4 Two identical balls are moving in the same direction, one at $5\,\mathrm{m\,s^{-1}}$ and the other at $10\,\mathrm{m\,s^{-1}}$. Find the velocities of the balls after a collision if:
a) $e = 0.8$,   **b)** $e = 0.4$.

5 Two balls are moving towards each other as shown in the diagram. The coefficient of restitution between the two balls is 0.2. Find the velocity of each ball after the collision.

 $4\,\mathrm{m\,s^{-1}}$ $3\,\mathrm{m\,s^{-1}}$
2 kg   1 kg

6 An object travelling at $2\,\mathrm{m\,s^{-1}}$ and with a mass of 1 kg strikes a stationary object of mass 2 kg. What happens after the collision if:
a) $e = 1$,   **b)** $e = 0.2$?

7 A car of mass 1000 kg travelling at $18\,\mathrm{m\,s^{-1}}$ drives into a stationary car of mass 900 kg. The speed of the moving car is halved during the collision.
a) Use conservation of momentum to find what happens to the other car.
b) Find the coefficient of restitution between the two cars.

8 Three identical spheres are travelling along a straight line with the speeds shown. The coefficient of restitution between each sphere is 0.4.

$4\,\mathrm{m\,s^{-1}}$ $2\,\mathrm{m\,s^{-1}}$ $2\,\mathrm{m\,s^{-1}}$
A   B   C

a) Find the speeds of A and B after they collide.
b) Find the speeds of B and C after they collide.
c) Are there any further collisions? If so which spheres are involved in the next collision?

9 Three identical spheres are moving as shown in the diagram. The coefficient of restitution is 0.4.

$2u$

A

u

B

C

a) If A and B collide first, what are their velocities after the collision?

b) Next, B hits C which is stationary. What are the velocities of B and C after the collision?

c) Do any further collisions take place? Find the final velocities of each sphere.

10 A sphere of mass m, travelling at speed V, hits another sphere of the same mass that is travelling in the same direction, with speed v. The coefficient of restitution between the two spheres is e.

a) Find the velocity of each sphere after the collision.

b) Show that the magnitude of the impulse on each sphere is:

$$\tfrac{1}{2}m(1+e)(V-v)$$

OBLIQUE COLLISIONS

In the last section we considered direct impacts between particles and a surface.

In an oblique impact with a smooth surface, the impulse will be perpendicular to the surface, because the surface is smooth. As a result of this, the component of velocity parallel to the surface will be unchanged and the coefficient of restitution can be applied to the components of the velocity perpendicular to the surface, as for a direct impact.

Example 13.9

A particle, travelling at 4 ms⁻¹ in the direction shown in the diagram, hits a smooth, stationary surface. The diagram also shows the direction in which it moves after the collision.

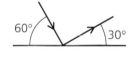

Find the speed of the particle after the collision and the coefficient of restitution between the surface and the particle.

Solution

Let v be the speed of the particle after the collision. The component of the velocity parallel to the surface will be unchanged by the collision, so:

$$4\cos 60° = v\cos 30°$$

$$2 = v\frac{\sqrt{3}}{2}$$

$$v = \frac{4}{\sqrt{3}} = 2.31\,\mathrm{m\,s^{-1}}$$

The component perpendicular to the wall after the collision will be e times the component perpendicular to the wall before the collision.

$$e \times 4\cos 30° = v\cos 60°$$

$$e \times 2\sqrt{3} = \frac{2}{\sqrt{3}}$$

$$e = \frac{1}{3}$$

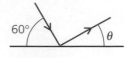

EXERCISE

13.4 CLASSWORK

1   A particle travelling at $10\,\text{m}\,\text{s}^{-1}$ in the direction shown in the diagram, hits a smooth, stationary surface. The diagram also shows the direction in which it moves after the collision.

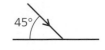

   a) Find the speed of the particle after the collision and θ, if the coefficient of restitution between the surface and the particle is 0.2.
   b) Also calculate the impulse on the particle if its mass is $0.9\,\text{kg}$.

2   A particle, travelling at $7\,\text{m}\,\text{s}^{-1}$, hits a smooth plane at 45°, as shown in the diagram.
   Find the coefficient of restitution between the particle and the plane if:
   a) it rebounds at the same speed,
   b) it rebounds at $6\,\text{m}\,\text{s}^{-1}$.

3   A ball, of mass 300 grams, hits a stationary surface directly, travelling at $7.5\,\text{m}\,\text{s}^{-1}$, and rebounds at $5\,\text{m}\,\text{s}^{-1}$.
   a) How would the ball rebound if it hit the surface at the same speed, but travelling at an angle of 80° to the surface?
   b) Calculate the magnitude of the impulse on the ball in each case.

4   When a ball hits a horizontal stationary plane for the first time it is travelling at $8\,\text{m}\,\text{s}^{-1}$ and travelling so that the angle between the plane and its velocity is 60°. The coefficient of restitution between the plane and the ball is 0.8.
   a) Find the speed and direction of the ball when it leaves the plane.
   The ball then moves as a projectile until it hits the plane for the second time.
   b) Find the speed of the ball after the second bounce.

EXERCISE

13.4 HOMEWORK

1   A particle, of mass $4\,\text{kg}$, travelling at $8\,\text{m}\,\text{s}^{-1}$ in the direction shown in the diagram, hits a smooth stationary surface. The diagram also shows the direction in which it moves after the collision.

   a) Find the speed of the particle after the collision and the coefficient of restitution between the surface and the particle.
   b) Calculate the magnitude of the impulse on the particle.

2   A particle, travelling at $5\,\text{m}\,\text{s}^{-1}$, hits a smooth stationary surface and leaves travelling at $v\,\text{m}\,\text{s}^{-1}$. The diagram shows the directions in which the particle moves before and after the collision.
   Find v and θ if the coefficient of restitution between the surface and the particle is:
   a) 0.25   b) 0.5.

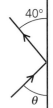

3   A ball, of mass 250 grams, travelling at $4\,\text{m}\,\text{s}^{-1}$, hits a wall at an angle of 45° to the wall. The coefficient of restitution between the ball and the wall is 0.6.
   a) What should you assume to calculate the rebound velocity of the ball?
   b) Calculate the speed of the ball after the impact.
   c) Calculate the magnitude of the impulse on the ball.

4 A projectile is launched from ground level with an initial speed of 20 m s^{-1}, and at an angle of 45° above the horizontal. The coefficient of restitution between the ball and the ground is 0.5. Find the speed of the ball immediately after its second bounce.

IMPULSE AND VARIABLE FORCES

The relationship $Ft = mv - mu$ can be useful, but in many cases we must take into account the fact the forces acting during the period of time are *not* constant. When a ball is squashed as it bounces the reaction force between the ball and the ground increases to a maximum and then decreases as the ball begins to rise. In this section we explore how to deal with the variable forces which are encountered much more often, in reality, than the constant forces that we have considered so far.

Exploration 13.5   *Forces acting on a ball*

■ When a ball bounces on the ground or is hit by a bat or racquet, a force acts on the ball. How does this force change during the time of contact? Sketch possible graphs of force against time.
■ Now consider the resultant force on the ball, i.e. including gravity. How does the resultant force change during the bounce? Try sketching graphs of this.

Variable reaction forces

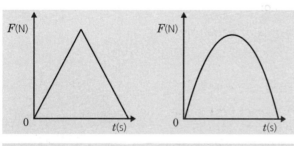

A reaction force begins to act as soon as the ball makes contact with the ground. The way in which the force increases as the ball is deformed or squashed depends on the type of ball and the material from which it is made. The force may be quite complex. Some simple models for the behaviour of this force are shown in the graphs.

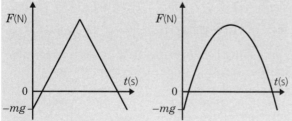

The resultant force on the ball is the resultant of the reaction force R and the force of gravity mg. As they act in opposite directions the resultant is $R - mg$, taking the upward direction as positive. The graph shows the resultant force corresponding to each model illustrated above.

Note that as the ball is squashed the resultant force remains negative, or downward, until the reaction becomes greater than the force of gravity.

Example 13.10

A ball of mass 250 grams bounces on the ground, hitting the ground at $5\,ms^{-1}$ and rebounding at $4\,ms^{-1}$. It is in contact with the ground for $0.25\,s$.

a) Find the impulse on the ball.

b) Assume that the ground exerts a constant force on the ball during contact. Sketch a graph of force against time and find the area under the curve.

c) Assume that the force on the ball varies as shown in the graph. Find the area under the graph and compare with the impulse on the ball.

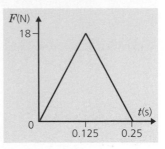

Solution

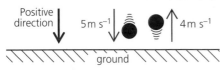

a) Defining down as positive, gives $u = 5$ and $v = -4$ with $m = 0.25$.

Using: $I = mv - mu$

gives: $I = 0.25 \times 5 - 0.25 \times (-4) = 2.25\,\text{N}\,s$

b) For a constant force $I = Ft$, so with $t = 0.25$ and $I = 2.25$ this gives:

$2.25 = 0.25\,F$

$\Rightarrow F = \dfrac{2.25}{0.25} = 9\,\text{N}$

The graphs shows a sketch of F against t during the collision. The shaded area is:

$9 \times 0.25 = 2.25$

c) The area under the graph can be found easily as the area of a triangle is $\frac{1}{2} \times base \times height$

So here:

$area = \frac{1}{2} \times 0.25 \times 18 = 2.25$

The area here is the same as the area under the graph in b), which is the same as the impulse on the ball.

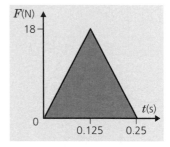

Area under a force–time graph

There seems to be a relationship between the area under a force–time graph and impulse. Consider the area under the graph shown.

This area is given by:

$$\int_{t_1}^{t_2} F(t)\,dt$$

Using Newton's second law this can be expressed as:

$$\int_{t_1}^{t_2} F(t)\,dt = m\int_{t_1}^{t_2} a(t)\,dt$$

where m is assumed to be constant.

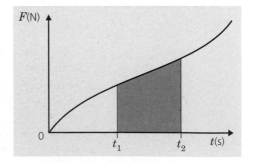

Integrating the acceleration gives the velocity, so:

$$m\int_{t_1}^{t_2} a(t)\,dt = m\big[v(t)\big]_{t_1}^{t_2} = m\big(v(t_2) - v(t_1)\big)$$

If the velocity at $t = t_1$ is u and at $t = t_2$ is v, then:

$$m\big(v(t_2) - v(t_1)\big) = mv - mu$$

So combining these steps gives:

$$\int_{t_1}^{t_2} F(t)\,dt = mv - mu$$

or $I = \int_{t_1}^{t_2} F(t)\,dt$

This result allows the impulse to be found when a variable force acts. When the force is constant it reduces to $Ft = I$.

Example 13.11

When a train hits a buffer it is brought to rest in 0.8 seconds. The mass of the train is 10 tonnes and the force exerted by the buffer is modelled by:

$$F(t) = 6400t^2 - 10\,000t^4$$

a) Find the impulse on the train.
b) Find the initial speed of the train.

Solution

a) The impulse is given by:

$$I = \int_0^{0.8} \big(6400t^2 - 10\,000t^4\big)\,dt$$

$$= \left[\frac{6400t^3}{3} - \frac{10\,000t^5}{5} \right]_0^{0.8}$$

$$= \frac{6400}{3} \times 0.8^3 - 2000 \times 0.8^5 = 437 \text{ N s}$$

b) As the train stops $v = 0$, so using:

$$I = mv - mu$$

and noting that $I = -437$ since the force opposes the motion of the train gives:

$$-437 = -10\,000u$$

$$u = \frac{437}{10\,000} = 0.044 \text{ m s}^{-1}$$

EXERCISES

13.5 CLASSWORK

1 A squash ball of mass 24 grams is travelling horizontally at $6\,\text{m s}^{-1}$ when it hits a wall and rebounds at a speed of $4.5\,\text{m s}^{-1}$.

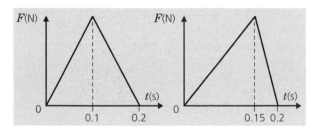

a) Find the magnitude of the impulse on the ball.

b) If the force on the ball increases and decreases as shown in the first graph, find the magnitude of the maximum force on the ball.

c) If the force varies as shown in the second graph, find the magnitude of the maximum force on the ball.

2 A parachutist of mass 80 kg is travelling at 70 m s⁻¹ with a failed parachute when he enters a dense forest. The trees exert a force as shown in the diagram for a period of three seconds.

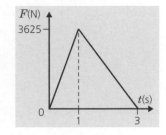

a) Find the impulse on the parachutist.
b) Find his speed after three seconds when he hits the ground.

3 When a squash ball of mass 24 grams bounces on a wall the force exerted on the ball can be modelled by:

$$F(t) = 10 \sin 20\pi t \text{ for } 0 \le t \le 0.05 \text{ s}$$

a) Find the impulse on the ball during the 0.05 seconds that the ball is in contact with the wall.
b) If the ball rebounds at 6 m s⁻¹, find the speed of impact with the wall.
c) An alternative model for $F(t)$ is: $F(t) = 750t - 15\,000t^2$
What speed of impact does this model give?

4 A skateboarder of mass 50 kg collides with a bush, which brings her to rest after two seconds. The force exerted by the bush on the skateboarder can be modelled by: $F(t) = 1000t - 500t^2$
a) Find the impulse on the skateboarder.
b) Find the initial speed of the skateboarder.
c) An alternative model for the force on the skateboarder is:

$$F(t) = A \sin \omega t$$

Find the values of A and ω if the skateboarder is still stopped after two seconds, has the same initial speed and the force becomes zero when the skateboarder stops.

5 When a superball of mass 170 grams bounces off a vertical wall, at right angles to the surface, with an impact speed of 5 m s⁻¹, it experiences a force that can be modelled as: $F(t) = 25 \sin 15\pi t$
a) Sketch a graph of $F(t)$ and state the range of values of t for which you think the model is valid. How long is the ball in contact with the wall?
b) Find the impulse on the ball and the speed at which it leaves the wall.
c) The same ball is dropped onto the ground at the same speed. Assume that the ground exerts the same force on the ball as the wall. Find the resultant force on the ball.
d) Find the speed at which the ball rebounds.

EXERCISES

13.5 HOMEWORK

1 A ball of mass 120 grams hits the ground travelling at 6 m s⁻¹ and rebounds at 4 m s⁻¹ in the opposite direction.
a) Find the magnitude of the impulse on the ball.
b) The graph shows a model for how the force on the ball could vary with time. Find the impulse on the ball in terms of T, the time for which the ball is in contact with the ground.

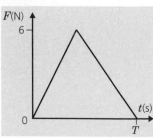

c) Find T.
d) Comment on the shape of the graph, suggest an alternative model for the force.

2 A diver of mass 64 kg enters the water travelling vertically. The graph shows a possible model for the resultant force on the diver as he is brought to rest in 0.8 s.
  a) Find the value of P, if the diver enters the water at $5 \, \text{ms}^{-1}$.
  b) An alternative model is:
    $$F(t) = 400 - 625t^2$$

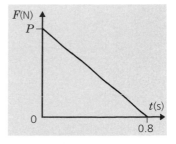

Show that $F(0) = \frac{1}{2}P$ and $F(0.8) = 0$. Find the speed at which the diver would have entered the water if this model is used.

3 As a light aeroplane of mass 1500 kg travels down a runway the resultant force on the plane can be modelled as:
  $$F(t) = 5000 - \frac{50}{9}t^2$$
  The aeroplane takes off when $t = 30 \, \text{s}$.
  a) Find the impulse on the plane between $t = 0$ and $t = 30$.
  b) Find the speed of the plane when it takes off.

4 When a ball bounces against a vertical wall, the force that the wall exerts on the ball can be modelled by: $F(t) = A \sin 10 \pi t$
  a) Find when $F(t)$ is zero and explain why the ball is in contact with the wall for 0.1 s.
  b) Find the impulse on the ball during the bounce in terms of A.
  c) If a ball of mass 50 grams hits the wall at $6 \, \text{ms}^{-1}$ and rebounds at $5 \, \text{ms}^{-1}$ find the value of A.
  d) When the ball bounces against the ground the model for the resultant force, is:
    $$F(t) = A \sin 10\pi t - mg$$

Assume $g = 10 \, \text{ms}^{-2}$ and find the speed at which a ball would rebound if it hits the ground at $6 \, \text{ms}^{-1}$.

5 When a ball of mass 100 grams bounces off a vertical wall, the wall exerts a force given by:
  $$F(t) = 120t - 400t^2$$
  a) The ball hits the wall when $t = 0$. Find when the force is zero and state when the ball leaves the wall.
  b) If the ball hits the wall at $10 \, \text{ms}^{-1}$ find the speed at which it bounces back off the wall.
  c) If the ball were to bounce off a horizontal surface, with the same speed of impact, what would happen to the speed at which it rebounds?

CONSOLIDATION EXERCISES FOR CHAPTER 13

1 The vectors **i** and **j** are perpendicular unit vectors in a horizontal plane. A ball of mass 0.5 kg is moving with velocity $-20\mathbf{i} \, \text{m s}^{-1}$ when it is struck by a bat. The bat gives the ball an impulse of $(15\mathbf{i} + 10\mathbf{j})$ Ns. Find, to 3 significant figures, the speed of the ball immediately after it has been struck.

(EDEXCEL Question 1, M2 Specimen Paper)

2 Two spacecraft, A and B, with masses m and M respectively, are moving along the same straight line during an attempt to link up. There is a direct collision which occurs when the two spacecraft are approaching each other with speed u, as shown in the diagram. The spacecraft fail to link up and after the collision each moves in the opposite direction to its original motion. Spacecraft A now has a speed of $\frac{1}{2}u$.

a) Draw diagrams indicating the velocities of A and B before and after the collision.

Show that after the collision the speed, v, of B is $u\left(\dfrac{3m}{2M} - 1\right)$ and explain why $\dfrac{m}{M} > \dfrac{2}{3}$.

b) The coefficient of restitution between the spacecraft in the collision is e. Use the fact that $e \le 1$ to show that

$$v \le \frac{3u}{2} \text{ and hence } \frac{m}{M} \le \frac{5}{3}.$$

The rocket motor of spacecraft B is now fired so that its direction of motion is reversed. It catches up spacecraft A and links up with it. You may assume that there is a negligible loss of mass from spacecraft B when its rocket motor is used.

c) If the combined spacecraft has a speed of $\frac{3}{4}u$, calculate the impulse given to B by its rocket motor in terms of m and M.

(OCR Question 2, M2 Specimen Paper)

3 A particle A of mass m is moving with speed $3u$ on a smooth horizontal table when it collides directly with a particle B of mass $2m$ which is moving in the opposite direction with speed u. The direction of motion of A is reversed by the collision. The coefficient of restitution between A and B is e.

a) Show that the speed of B immediately after the collision is $\frac{1}{2}(1 + 4e)u$.

b) Show that $e > \frac{1}{8}$.

Subsequently B hits a wall fixed at right angles to the line of motion of A and B. The coefficient of restitution between B and the wall is $\frac{1}{2}$. After B rebounds from the wall, there is a further collision between A and B.

c) Show that $e < \frac{1}{4}$.

(EDEXCEL Question 8, M2 Specimen paper)

MATHEMATICAL MODELLING ACTIVITY

Problem statement

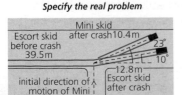

Specify the real problem

A Mini and its occupants of total mass 760 kg pulled out of a side road into the path of an Escort of mass 1040 kg including its passengers. The diagram shows the skid marks measured by the police at the scene.

Advise the police who to prosecute bearing in mind that the Mini did not give way and the speed limit was 30 mph.

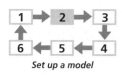

Set up a model

Set up a model

Key to this problem is the need to estimate the coefficient of friction between the cars and the road.

A possible assumption is that this is 0.8.

Comment on this assumption, obtaining your own data if possible. Also list any other assumptions that you consider should be made.

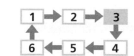

Formulate the mathematical problem

Formulate a problem

a) Find the speeds of both vehicles just after the collision.
b) Find the speeds of both vehicles just before the collision.
c) Find the speed of the Escort when it began to skid.

Mathematical solution

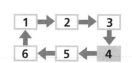

Solve the mathematical problem

a) Explain why both vehicles will have an acceleration of $-7.84\,\text{m s}^{-2}$ while skidding.
The speed of the mini just after the collision can be found using
$v^2 = u^2 + 2as$, with $v = 0$, $a = -7.84$ and $s = 10.4$.
$0^2 = u^2 + 2 \times (-7.84) \times 10.4$
$u = 12.8\,\text{m s}^{-1}$
Show that the speed of the Escort just after the collision is $14.2\,\text{m s}^{-1}$.

b) The velocities of the vehicles can be expressed as vectors, as summarised in this table.

	Before	After
Mini	$u\mathbf{j}$	$11.8\mathbf{i} + 5.0\mathbf{j}$
Escort	$w\mathbf{i}$	$14.0\mathbf{i} + 2.5\mathbf{j}$

Define the unit vectors and variables that have been used in the table.
Applying conservation of momentum gives:
$1040 \times w\mathbf{i} + 760 \times u\mathbf{j} = 1040(14.0\mathbf{i} + 2.5\mathbf{j}) + 760(11.8\mathbf{i} + 5.0\mathbf{j})$
Show that $w = 22.6\,\text{m s}^{-1}$ and find u.

c) The initial speed of the Escort can now be found using $v^2 = u^2 + 2as$, with $v = 22.6$, $a = -7.84$ and $s = 39.5$.
$22.6^2 = u^2 + 2 \times (-7.84) \times 39.5$
$u = 33.6\,\text{m s}^{-1}$

Interpretation

Interpret the solution

Converting the speed of $33.6\,\text{m s}^{-1}$ to mph gives:

$$33.6\,\text{m s}^{-1} = \frac{33.6 \times 3600}{1609} = 75\,\text{mph}$$

The Escort driver was clearly travelling at an excessive speed for a 30 mph speed limit.

Compare with reality

Compare with reality

It is difficult to compare this problem with reality. However, you could compare the total distance travelled by the Escort with the stopping distances given in the *Highway Code*.

Refining the model

Investigate how using different values for the coefficient of friction would effect the final solution to the problem.

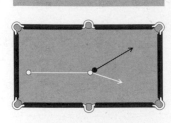

POSSIBLE MODELLING TASKS

1 A snooker ball is stationary on a table, and is hit by a ball that moves parallel to the side of the table. The balls make contact on a line of symmetry of the table. Investigate which ball reaches the side of the table first.

2 By considering the path of a ball hit by a bat or racquet, try to find the impulse on the ball when it is hit.

Summary

After working through this chapter you should:

■ be aware that momentum is a vector $m\mathbf{v}$

■ know that the change in momentum is equal to the impulse:
$$\mathbf{I} = m\mathbf{v} - m\mathbf{u}$$
and that for a constant force:
$$\mathbf{I} = \mathbf{F}t = m\mathbf{v} - m\mathbf{u}$$

■ know that the impulse of a variable force is:
$$\mathbf{I} = \int F\,\mathrm{d}t$$

■ know that momentum is conserved in any collision:
$$m_A\mathbf{v}_A + m_B\mathbf{v}_B = m_A\mathbf{u}_A + m_B\mathbf{u}_B$$

■ know Newton's experimental law of restitution in the forms:
$$v = -eu$$
and: $v_A - v_B = -e(u_A - u_B)$

■ Know that in an oblique impact with a smooth surface:
  ▪ the impulse will be perpendicular to the surface,
  ▪ the component of velocity parallel to the surface will be unchanged,
  ▪ the coefficient of restitution can be applied to the components of the velocity perpendicular to the surface as for a direct impact.

MECHANICS

14

Moments and equilibrium

- *Moments can be taken when the forces act in any direction.*

- *This can be used to determine the forces acting in any static situation.*

MOMENTS

Resolving to find moments

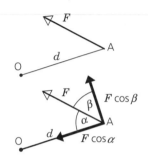

When a force acts in a perpendicular direction, at the distances specified, it is easy to find its moment. But what happens when a force acts as shown in the next diagram? It can be awkward to find the perpendicular distance in a situation like this.

To solve problems like this, we need to split the force, F, into two components, one **parallel** to the line OA and the other **perpendicular** to OA. The moment of the component $F\cos\alpha$ is zero because it is along the line through O. The moment of the component $F\cos\beta$ is simply $Fd\cos\beta$.

Example 14.1

The diagram shows a lever OA.
A force of 100 N acts on the lever as shown.
a) Find the component of the force perpendicular to OA.
b) Find the moment of the force acting.
c) Explain why the moment is negative.

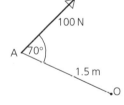

Solution
a) The component of the force perpendicular OA is: $100\cos 20° - 94\,\text{N}$
b) The moment of the force about O is then: $-1.5 \times 94 = -141\,\text{N}$
c) The moment is negative because the force would cause a clockwise rotation.

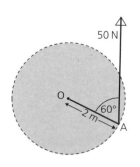

Example 14.2

A force is applied to a playground roundabout as shown in the diagram.
a) Show that the component of the force perpendicular to OA is 43.3 N.
b) Find the moment of the force about O.
c) Describe how a greater moment could be obtained with the same force.

Solution
a) The component of the force perpendicular to the radius is OA is given by: $50\cos 30° = 43.3\,\text{N}$
b) Moment about O $= 2 \times 43.3 = 86.6\,\text{Nm}$
c) If the force is applied along a tangent, the component of the force perpendicular to OA is 50 N, which gives a moment of 100 Nm.

285

EXERCISES

14.1 CLASSWORK

1 Find the moment of each force about the point O.

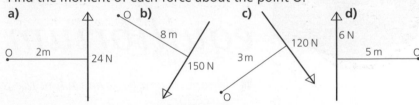

a) b) c) d)

2 A man tries to operate a lever by exerting a force of 50 N as shown in the diagram.

a) Show that the component of the force perpendicular to OA is 38.3 N.
b) Find the moment of the force about O.
c) If a moment of 70 Nm would just turn the lever, is it possible for the man to move the lever with the 50 N force?

3 For each of these diagrams, find the moment of each force about the point O.

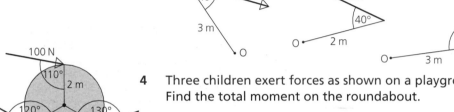

a) b) c) d)

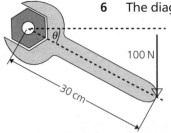

4 Three children exert forces as shown on a playground roundabout. Find the total moment on the roundabout.

5 Find the distance OA if the magnitude of the moment of each force illustrated below is 30 Nm.

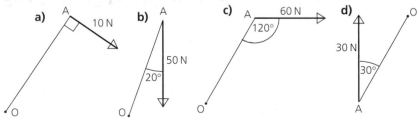

a) b) c) d)

6 The diagram shows a spanner of length 30 cm being used to undo a nut.

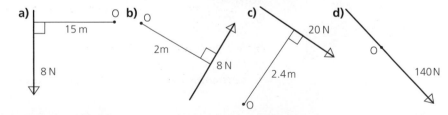

A constant vertical force of 100 N acts as shown. Find θ if the moment of this force is:
a) 15 Nm, b) 10 Nm.

EXERCISES

14.1 HOMEWORK

1 Find the moment of each force about the point O, stating if your answer is a clockwise or anticlockwise moment.

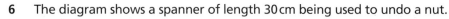

a) b) c) d)

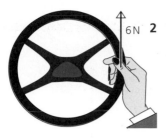

2 A driver steers a car by pushing upward on the steering wheel of radius 20 cm with a force of 6 N.
  a) If the driver's hand is in the position shown in the diagram, calculate the moment about the centre of the wheel.
  b) As the wheel turns does the moment remain constant? Give reasons for your answer.

3 For each diagram, find the moment of the given force about the point O.

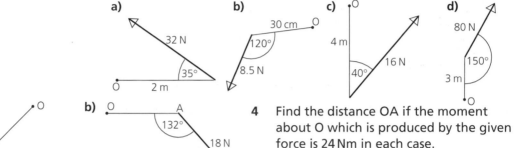

a)

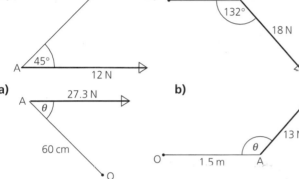

4 Find the distance OA if the moment about O which is produced by the given force is 24 Nm in each case.

5 Find the angle θ if the moment about O which is produced by the given force is 9 Nm in each case.

Explain why there are two possible values for θ in each of the above.

MOMENTS AND EQUILIBRIUM

For equilibrium a rigid body must satisfy both of the following conditions.
■ The resultant force must be zero.
■ The total moment about any point must be zero.
These two conditions are used in the following worked examples.

Example 14.3

A ladder of length 5 m rests with one end on rough horizontal ground and the other against a smooth vertical wall.

If the angle between the ladder and the horizontal is 60°, find the minimum value of coefficient of friction between the ladder and the ground.

Solution
The diagram shows the forces acting on the ladder.

For the resultant force to be zero we must have

$F = S$ and $R = mg$.

Taking moments about the bottom end of the ladder gives:

$mg \times 2.5 \cos 60° = S \times 5 \sin 60°$

$S = \dfrac{mg}{2 \tan 60°} = \dfrac{mg}{2\sqrt{3}}$

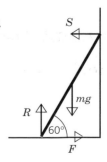

Also we then have:

$$F = \frac{mg}{2\sqrt{3}}$$

As the ladder remains at rest the friction inequality $F \leq \mu R$ can be used with values above.

$$F \leq \mu R$$

$$\frac{mg}{2\sqrt{3}} \leq \mu mg$$

$$\mu \geq \frac{1}{2\sqrt{3}}$$

Example 14.4

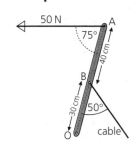

A climber of mass 60 kg has his feet resting against a vertical wall and a rope attached to him to support him. Assume that the force of gravity acts at the same point that the rope is attached. Find the magnitude of the forces acting on the climber.

Solution

The forces acting on the climber are shown in the diagram.
The component of mg perpendicular to OA is:
$60g \cos 10° = 588 \cos 10° = 579 \, N$
Taking moments about O gives:
$T \times 1 - 579 \times 1 = 0$
and rearranging gives:
$T = 579 \, N$
Now the resultant force on the climber is:
$(R - T \cos 80°)\mathbf{i} + (F + T \cos 10° - 588)\mathbf{j}$
As the forces are in equilibrium:
$R - T \cos 80° = 0$
$\Rightarrow \quad R = 579 \cos 80° = 100 \, N$
and $F + T \cos 10° - 588 = 0$
$\Rightarrow \quad F = 588 - 579 \cos 10° = 18 \, N$

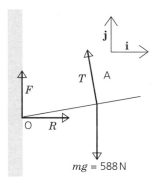

Example 14.5

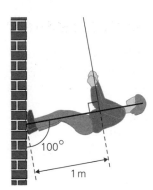

The lever shown is at rest and is pivoted at O and a force of 50 N is applied at A. A cable is attached to the lever at B.
a) *By taking moments about O, find the tension in the cable.*
b) *Find the magnitude of the force exerted on the lever by the pivot at O.*

Solution

a) *The component of the 50 N force*
perpendicular to OA is $50 \cos 15° = 48.3 \, N$
and the moment of this force about O is:
$0.7 \times 48.3 = 33.8 \, Nm$
The component of T perpendicular to OA is:
$T \cos 40° = 0.766 T$
and the moment of T about O is then:
$-0.3 \times 0.766 T = 0.230 T$
As the lever is in equilibrium the total moment must be zero, so:
$33.8 - 0.230 T = 0$
$$T = \frac{33.8}{0.230} = 147 \, N$$

b) *The force exerted by the pivot on the lever can be found since the resultant force must be zero. The two other forces can be expressed in terms of* **i** *and* **j** *as* $-50\mathbf{i}$ *and* $147\cos 55°\mathbf{i} - 147\cos 35°\mathbf{j}$.
If the reaction force exerted by the pivot is $a\mathbf{i} + b\mathbf{j}$, *then the resultant is:*
$(147\cos 55° - 50 + a)\mathbf{i} + (b - 147\cos 35°)\mathbf{j}$
So for equilibrium:
$147\cos 55° - 50 + a = 0$
$a = 50 - 147\cos 55° = -35\,\text{N}$
and: $b - 147\cos 35° = 0$
$b = 147\cos 35° = 120\,\text{N}$
So the force is $-35\mathbf{i} + 120\mathbf{j}$, *which has a magnitude:*
$\sqrt{35^2 + 120^2} = 125\,\text{N}$

EXERCISES

14.2 CLASSWORK

1 A ladder of length 4 m rests in equilibrium with one end on rough horizontal ground and the other against a smooth vertical wall. The mass of the ladder is 12 kg. The ladder is at an angle of 45° to the horizontal.
  a) Find the magnitude of the friction force that acts on the base of the ladder.
  b) Find the minimum value for the coefficient of friction between the ladder and the ground.

2 A beam, of mass 50 kg and length 3 m, is pivoted at a distance of 1 m from one end. A load of mass 200 kg hangs from one end of the beam and a rope is attached to the other end, as shown in the diagram.

  a) Find the tension in the rope if $\theta = 130°$.
  b) What would happen to the tension in the rope if θ increased?

3 The diagram shows a light lever that is free to move in a vertical plane and pivoted at O. Two forces that lie in the plane in which the lever is free to move are also shown in the diagram. The length of the lever is 1.2 m and AB = 0.4 m.

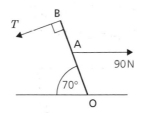

  a) Find T.
  b) Find the magnitude of the reaction force on the lever at O.

4 The diagram shows a light beam and a rope.

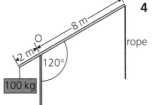

  a) If the beam makes the angle shown with the vertical, find the tension in the rope when the system is at rest, by taking moments about O.
  b) If the rope becomes perpendicular to the beam, what is the tension in the rope?

5 The diagram shows a simple crane, which is supporting a load of mass 55 kg.

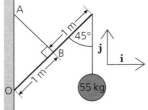

  a) Find the tension in each cable.
  b) Find the force exerted on the rod by the pivot at O, and the tension in the cable AB in terms of the unit vectors **i** and **j**.

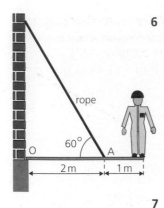

6   A plank has length 3 m and mass 20 kg. One end rests on a narrow ledge at O and a rope is fixed to the point A as shown. A man of mass 75 kg starts at the far end of the plank. Assume the plank remains at rest, but is on the point of slipping.
  a) Draw a diagram to show the forces acting on the plank.
  b) By taking moments about the point A, where the rope is attached, find the friction force acting on the end of the plank.
  c) By taking moments about O, find the tension in the rope.
  d) Find the reaction force exerted by the wall on the end of the plank.
  e) Find the coefficient of friction between the wall and the plank. Is this value realistic?

7   A builder places a plank of length 4 m and mass 20 kg so that it rests on the back of a lorry, as shown in the diagram. Assume that there is no friction between the plank and the lorry.

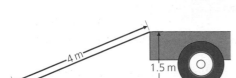

  a) By taking moments about the lower end of the plank find the force the lorry exerts on the plank.
  b) Find the normal reaction force and the friction force acting at the bottom of the plank.
  c) Find the minimum value of the coefficient of friction between the plank and the ground.

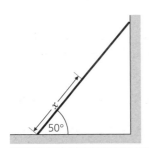

8   A ladder of length 2 m and mass 10 kg rests against a smooth wall. A firewoman of mass 60 kg climbs the ladder. The coefficient of friction between the ground and the ladder is 0.45.
  a) Find the reaction and friction forces on the bottom of the ladder, when the firewoman is in the position shown.
  b) When the firewoman climbs along the ladder it begins to slip. How far up the ladder can she get before it begins to slip?

EXERCISES

14.2 HOMEWORK

1   A steel rod has mass 8 kg and length 50 cm. The rod leans against a wall so that the angle between the rod and the horizontal is 80°. Assume that the rod is uniform and that the wall is smooth and the ground is rough.
  a) Draw a diagram to show the forces acting on the rod.
  b) Find the magnitude of each of these forces.

2   A uniform rod of length 2 m has mass 45 kg. It is freely pivoted at O and held in equilibrium by a horizontal rope attached to it at A. In this position the angle between the rod and the vertical is 25°.
  a) Find the tension in the rope.
  b) Find the magnitude of the force exerted on the rod at O.

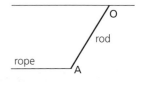

3   A uniform rod of length 80 cm has mass 4 kg. At each end the rod rests on supports as shown in the diagram. The support at A is rough and the support at B is smooth. The rod is in equilibrium and at an angle of 10° to the horizontal.
  a) Find the magnitude of each force that acts on the rod.
  b) If the rod is on the point of slipping, find the coefficient of friction between the rod and the support at A.

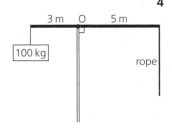

4 The diagram shows a beam of mass 20 kg with a mass of 100 kg attached to one end and a rope attached to the other end.
a) By taking moments, find the tension on the rope.
b) Find the reaction at O.
The same beam is then allowed to tilt at 30° to the horizontal, and the rope is held so that it forms a right angle with the beam.
c) By taking moments about O find the tension in the rope.
d) Find the magnitude and direction of the reaction at O.

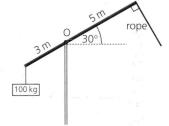

5 A man of mass 70 kg stands on a uniform platform of mass 30 kg and width 1.5 m. The platform is smoothly hinged to the wall at A and is kept horizontal by two parallel ropes attached to the two outer corners of the platform, inclined at 60° to the horizontal.
a) Draw a diagram showing all the forces acting on the platform (represent the reaction at the hinge as a horizontal and a vertical component).
b) By taking moments about A, find the tension in each rope.
c) Find the horizontal and vertical components of the reaction force at A.

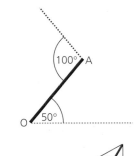

6 A uniform hatch door of a yacht, of mass 15 kg, is held open at 50° to the horizontal by a rope as shown. The door is hinged at O, and OA is 1.5 m.
a) Find the tension in the rope.
b) Find the vertical and horizontal components of the reaction force at the hinge.
c) Find the magnitude and direction of the reaction force at the hinge.

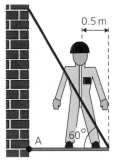

7 Some children construct a simple crane to support a load of 20 kg as shown in the diagram. The rope is fixed to a peg in the ground at A and the rod rests on the ground at B.
a) By taking moments about B, find the tension in the rope.
b) Find the magnitude of the force in the rod.
c) If the bottom of the rod is about to slip, find the value of the coefficient of friction, μ.

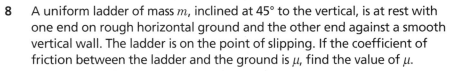

8 A uniform ladder of mass m, inclined at 45° to the vertical, is at rest with one end on rough horizontal ground and the other end against a smooth vertical wall. The ladder is on the point of slipping. If the coefficient of friction between the ladder and the ground is μ, find the value of μ.

FRAMEWORKS AROUND US

The photograph shows part of a framework in a roof structure. This type of design is very common and gives much more strength than a single beam or girder. It is important for designers to be able to predict the forces that will act in each **member** of such a framework. In this chapter we develop an approach that allows the forces to be estimated subject to some simple, but important assumptions.

Exploration 14.1

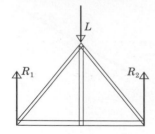

A simple framework

The diagram shows a simple framework that might be found in the roof of an older house or other building. Assume that the framework supports a load, L, at the top and itself is supported by the forces R_1 and R_2.

- What are the magnitudes of R_1 and R_2?
- Consider one member of the framework, describe the forces acting on it.

Give examples of frameworks that you have seen.

Modelling a framework

There may be many factors to consider at the joints of a framework, for example when rods are welded together or fixed by a number of bolts or nails as shown in the diagram.

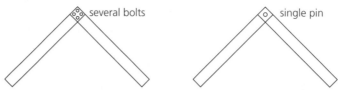

The force of gravity on each member may also complicate the situation. A first model of the forces acting in a framework is based on the following two assumptions.

- The members of a framework are light rods and their mass is assumed to be zero.
- All the joints are smooth pin-joints. This means that all the members at any joint are fixed by a pin, about which they can freely pivot. Imagine two strips of card with holes punched in them, joined by a simple clip.

Example 14.6

The diagram shows a roof truss. The roof exerts three forces on the truss as illustrated.

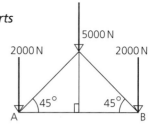

By modelling the truss as a light pin-jointed framework find:
a) the external forces acting on the truss at the supports A and B,
b) the force in each member.
   Comment on the design of the truss.

Solution

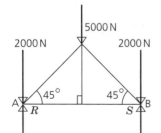

a) First consider the truss as a single object. The diagram shows the external forces acting on the truss. As all these forces must be in equilibrium $R + S = 9000$
   Due to the symmetry of the truss:
   $R = S \Rightarrow R = S = 4500$ N
b) To find the forces in each member, start by considering the point A. Assume that all the rods are in tension and so they exert forces that act toward their centres. The diagram shows the forces at A.

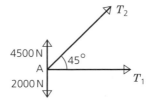

The resultant force at A must be zero. Considering the vertical components of the forces gives:

$4500 - 2000 + T_2 \cos 45° = 0$

$\Rightarrow \quad T_2 = \dfrac{2000 - 4500}{\cos 45°} = -3536\text{N}$

The negative sign indicates that the rod is not in tension but **compression** and so exerts a thrust of 3536 N.

Now consider the horizontal component of the forces, which gives:

$T_2 \cos 45° + T_1 = 0$

$\Rightarrow \quad -3536 \cos 45° + T_1 = 0$

$T_1 = 3536 \cos 45° = 2500$ N

As this is positive this member is in tension.

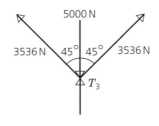

Now consider the peak of the truss. The diagram shows the forces acting at this point. Note that due to the symmetry of the truss the force in the other sloping member will also be 3536 N. As there is only one unknown force here, only the vertical components need be considered to give:

$2 \times 3536 \cos 45° + T_3 - 5000 = 0$

$\Rightarrow \quad T_3 = 5000 - 2 \times 3536 \cos 45° = 0$

As there is no force in the vertical member it appears to serve no useful purpose in the truss.

Example 14.7

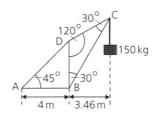

The diagram shows a simple crane that is supporting a load of 150 kg.

a) Find the external forces that act on the crane where it is fixed to the ground at A and B.

b) Find the force in each member, stating whether it is in tension or compression.

c) Which member is most likely to fracture during a lift?

Solution

a) Considering the framework as a single body and taking moments about A gives: $4R = 7.46 \times 1470$

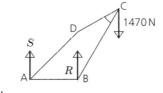

$\Rightarrow \quad R = \dfrac{7.46 \times 1470}{4} = 2742$

Also by considering the resultant force:

$R + S = 1470$

$\Rightarrow \quad 2742 + S = 1470$

$S = 1470 - 2742 = -1272$ N

So an upward force of 2742 N acts at B and a downward force of 1272 N acts at A.

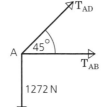

b) Begin by considering the point A. The diagram shows the forces acting.

All the rods have been assumed to be in tension and T_{AB} denotes the tension in the rod AB, etc. All the forces at each joint must be in equilibrium.

Considering the vertical components of the forces gives:

$T_{AD} \cos 45° - 1272 = 0$

$\Rightarrow \quad T_{AD} = \dfrac{1272}{\cos 45°} = 1799\text{N}$

The rod AD is in tension as T_{AD} is positive. Considering the horizontal components gives:

$T_{AD} \cos 45° + T_{AB} = 0$
$\Rightarrow 1799 \cos 45° + T_{AB} = 0$
$T_{AB} = -1779 \cos 45° = -1272 \text{ N}$

The rod AB is in compression as T_{AB} is negative.
Now consider the forces at B, which are shown on the diagram. Considering the horizontal components of the forces gives:
$T_{BC} \cos 60° + 1272 = 0$

$$\Rightarrow T_{BC} = -\frac{1272}{\cos 60°} = -2544 \text{N}$$

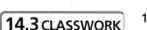

As T_{BC} is negative the rod BC is in compression.
Now considering the vertical components gives:

$T_{BD} + T_{BC} \cos 30° + R = 0$
$\Rightarrow T_{BD} - 2544 \cos 30° + 2742 = 0$
$T_{BD} = 2544 \cos 30° - 2742 = -539 \text{ N}$

As T_{BD} is negative, there is a thrust in BD.
Now consider the point D. The diagram shows the forces acting at D. Considering the horizontal components of the forces gives:
$T_{DC} \cos 30° - 1799 \cos 45° = 0$

$$T_{DC} = \frac{1799 \cos 45°}{\cos 30°} = 1469 \text{ N}$$

As T_{DC} is positive it is in tension.
The diagram summarises the forces present in the framework.

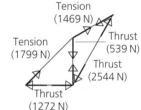

c) The member BC has to exert the greatest force and so is the member that is most likely to fracture.

EXERCISES

14.3 CLASSWORK

1 The diagram shows a light pin-jointed framework, with three external forces acting as shown.
a) Which rods do you think will be in tension?
b) Calculate the length BD.
c) Take moments about A to find S.
d) Find R.
e) Consider the forces acting at A and find the tension or thrust in AB and AC.
f) What forces act in BC?
g) Compare your answers in **e)** and **f)** with your predictions in **a)**.

2 The diagram shows a simple framework, with three external forces acting as shown.
a) By taking moments about A find the magnitude of R.
b) By considering the resultant force on the framework find S.
c) Consider the forces acting at A to find the force in AC and then the force in AB.
d) Find the force in BC.
e) For each member of the framework, state whether it is in tension or compression.

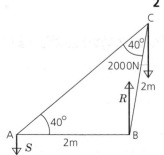

3 Three scaffolding poles joined at A, B and C form a framework that is used to support a wall that is in danger of collapsing.

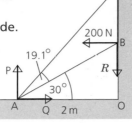

200 N

a) Explain why P and R have the same magnitude.
b) State the magnitude of the force Q.
c) Show that OB = BC and that $P = 348$ N.
d) Find the force in each pole, stating if it is in tension or compression.
e) What assumption have you made about the poles?

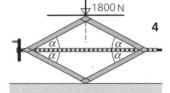

4 The diagram shows a car jack which supports a load of 1800 N.
a) Which components of the jack would you expect to exert tensions and which thrusts?
b) Confirm your predictions by finding the force in each component when $\alpha = 30°$.

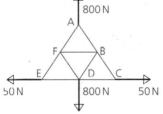

5 The diagram shows a design for a simple crane that supports a load of 5000 N at C.

By making suitable assumptions and giving your answers correct to two significant figure, find:
a) the vertical forces that act at A and B,
b) the force in each member, stating whether this force is a tension or a thrust.

6 The diagram shows a light pin-jointed framework, made up of equilateral triangles.
a) Find the magnitude of the forces R and S.
b) Describe how the symmetry of the framework can help you to find the forces in each rod.
c) Find the force in each rod.

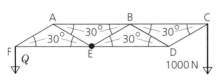

7 For the framework shown find the force in each member and state whether it is in tension or compression. All the triangles of the framework are equilateral.

8 The diagram shows a framework that is part of a crane.

The framework is pivoted at E and a force Q acts at F. By making suitable assumptions, find the external forces on the framework and the force in each member.

EXERCISES

14.3 HOMEWORK

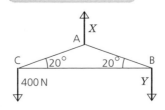

1 The diagram shows a simple light pin-jointed framework, with three external forces acting as shown.
a) By taking moments about the point B, find the magnitude of the force X.
b) Find Y by considering the resultant force on the framework.
c) By considering the forces at C, find the force in CA and then the force in CB. Which rod is in tension and which is in compression?
d) What is the force in AB?

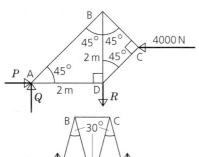

2 The diagram shows a framework with three external forces acting on it.

a) What assumptions can be made to allow you to estimate the forces in each rod?

b) If the force Q has magnitude 500 N, find P and R.

c) Find the force in each member of the framework and state if it is in tension or compression.

3 The diagram shows part of a linkage used to connect a trailer to a tractor. The tractor exerts a 5000 N force at C and the linkage is connected to the trailer at A and B, where forces of magnitude P act.

a) Find P.

b) Find the force in each member if they are assumed to be light and pin-jointed. Also state whether the members are in tension or compression.

c) Comment on the design of the linkage.

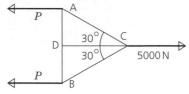

4 The diagram shows a simple crane that is attached to the ground at A and B and supports a load of 6000 N at C as shown.

a) Which members do you think will be in tension and which in compression?

b) Find the forces acting at A and B.

c) By modelling the crane as a light pin-jointed framework, find the force in each member and compare with your predictions made in a).

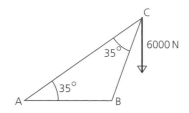

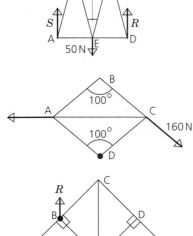

5 The diagram shows the design of a new type of railway buffer. A train exerts a force of 4000 N on the buffer. Forces P, Q and R act to maintain equilibrium.

a) Find the magnitude of the forces P, Q and R.

b) Find the force in each member of the buffer by modelling it as a light pin-jointed framework.

6 The diagram shows a pin-jointed framework that consists of three isosceles triangles.

Find the force in each rod. Clearly illustrate your results on a diagram that indicates whether forces are tensions or thrusts.

7 The diagram shows a light pin-jointed framework that is freely pivoted on a hinge at D. A cable attached at C exerts a force of 160 N as shown. Another force acts at A in the direction shown. The framework remains in equilibrium. Find the magnitude of the force acting at A, the force in each member and the horizontal and vertical components of the forces acting on the framework at D.

8 The diagram shows a light pin-jointed structure that is acted on by forces P, Q and R.

a) Explain why $P = 3Q$, and state R in terms of P.

b) If P is 90 N find the force in each rod.

c) Use a diagram to illustrate the forces in each rod, showing if they are in tension or compression.

CONSOLIDATION EXERCISES FOR CHAPTER 14

1 A uniform ladder, of mass m and length $2a$, has one end on rough horizontal ground. The other end rests against a smooth vertical wall. A man of mass $3m$ stands at the top of the ladder and the ladder is in equilibrium. The coefficient of friction between the ladder and the ground is $\frac{1}{4}$, and the ladder makes an angle α with the vertical, as shown in the diagram. The ladder is in a vertical plane perpendicular to the wall.

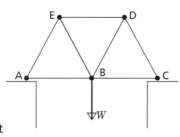

Show that $\tan \alpha \le \dfrac{2}{7}$.

(EDEXCEL Question 4, M2 Specimen Paper)

2 The diagram shows a framework ABCDE which is formed from seven light, pin-jointed rods and rests on two smooth supports at A and C, with AC horizontal. The framework supports a weight W acting at the point B. Given that the triangles ABE, BCD and BDE are all equilateral, find, in terms of W, the exact value of the thrust in the rod DE.

(AQA A Question 2, M3 Specimen Paper)

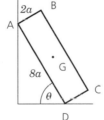

3 A uniform rectangular box of weight W stands on a horizontal floor and leans against a vertical wall. The diagram shows the vertical cross-section ABCD containing the centre of mass G of the box. AD makes an angle θ with the horizontal, and the lengths of AB and AD are $2a$ and $8a$ receptively.

a) by splitting the weight into components parallel and perpendicular to AD, or otherwise, show that the anticlockwise moment of the weight about the point D is $Wa(4\cos \theta - \sin \theta)$.

b) The contact at A between the box and the wall is smooth. Find, in terms of W and θ, the magnitude of the force acting on the box at A.

c) The contact at D between the box and the ground is rough, with coefficient of friction μ. Given that the box is about to slip, show that $\tan \theta = \dfrac{4}{8\mu + 1}$.

(OCR A Question 6, M2 Specimen Paper)

MATHEMATICAL MODELLING ACTIVITY

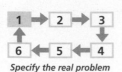

Specify the real problem

Problem statement

The diagram shows a design of temporary road signs. A mass is placed at A to stop the sign blowing over in high winds. How should the mass relate to the size of the sign?

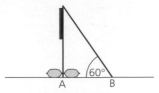

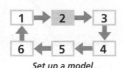

Set up a model

Set up a model

Make a list of the important features that you feel should be included in a solution to this problem. The assumptions set out below allow a first attempt to be made to solve the problem.

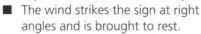

- The wind strikes the sign at right angles and is brought to rest.
- The maximum wind speed is $30\,\text{m}\,\text{s}^{-1}$.
- The density of air is $1.29\,\text{kg}\,\text{m}^{-3}$.
- The effect of the wind can be considered as a single force acting at the centre of the sign.
- The mass of the frame supporting the sign is negligible.
- The sign has width a, height b and its base is h m above the ground.

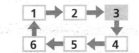

Formulate the mathematical problem

Formulate a mathematical problem

Find the force exerted on the sign by the wind.
Find the moment of this force about B.
Find the mass that must be placed at A if the sign is to remain at rest.

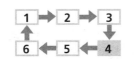

Solve the mathematical problem

Mathematical solution

First, find the force exerted by the wind. The volume of air hitting the sign each second is: $V = 30ab\,\text{m}^3$
The mass of this air is found by multiplying the volume by its density to give:
$\text{M} = 30ab \times 1.29 = 38.7ab\,\text{kg}$

The momentum of this air is: $P = 38.7ab \times 30 = 1161ab\,\text{N}\,\text{s}$
In order to stop this air moving the sign exerts an impulse of $1161ab\,\text{N}\,\text{s}$ each second. Using $I = Ft$ with $t = 1$ gives a force of $1161ab\,\text{N}$.

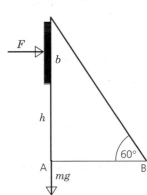

Show that the moment of this force about B has magnitude $1161ab\left(h + \tfrac{1}{2}b\right)$
and that the moment of the force of gravity on the mass at A has magnitude

$$\frac{mg(h + b)}{\tan 60°}$$

Verify that: $m = \dfrac{1161ab\left(h + \tfrac{1}{2}b\right)\tan 60°}{g(h + b)}$

Interpret the solution

Interpretation

Now the required mass can be calculated for any rectangular sign. As an example assume a sign has $a = b = 2\,\text{m}$ and $h = 1.5\,\text{m}$. Then:

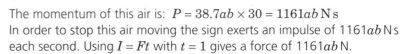

$$m = \frac{1161 \times 2 \times 2(1.5 + 1)\tan 60°}{9.8(1.5 + 2)} = 586\,\text{kg}$$

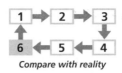

Compare with reality

Compare with reality

Often temporary road side signs are weighted with sand bags. Estimate the mass of a sand bag and comment on how this compares with the solution obtained above. (The density of sand is $2000 \, \text{kg} \, \text{m}^{-3}$.)

Refinement of the model

Clearly the sign could also blow over if the wind was in the opposite direction. Suggest how this could be prevented.

POSSIBLE MODELLING TASKS

1 Is it possible to design a road barrier that stays up when it is up and down when it is down? Investigate designs that might have this property.
2 Consider the ramp that is used for loading vehicles into a ferry. Investigate how the tension in the cables changes as the ramp is lifted.
3 An empty tipper lorry raises its back. Investigate how the forces on the back of the lorry vary as it is tipped. Consider also the forces acting on the lorry.
4 If a ladder is placed at a low angle against a wall, as shown, it will almost certainly slip. Investigate to see if there is a minimum safe angle that you could recommend to those who use ladders regularly.

Summary

After working through this chapter you should:

■ be able to calculate the magnitude of the moment of a force using
   a) the magnitude force multiplied by the perpendicular distance, Fd
   b) the magnitude of the component of the force perpendicular to the defined distance, multiplied by the distance

■ know that a positive moment indicates an anticlockwise turning effect and a negative moment a clockwise turning effect

■ know that for equilibrium both the resultant force and the total moment must be zero

■ know that a couple consists of two forces of which the resultant force is zero, but the combined moment is not zero.

■ be able to model a framework as a system of light rods that are smoothly pin-jointed

■ be able to find external force on a framework by considering it as a whole

■ be able to find the forces in individual members by considering the forces at each joint to be in equilibrium.

15

Centre of mass

■ *The force of gravity on a body can be assumed to act at a point known as the centre of mass.*

■ *The centre of mass of a moving object will follow the path that would be taken by a particle of the same mass.*

GRAVITY ACTING ON A BODY

In many of the situations that have been discussed so far in this book the force of gravity has been assumed to act at the centre of an object. If the object is to be modelled as a particle then this is very reasonable. In other cases it is reasonable to assume that the force of gravity acts at the centre of the object, for example a plank or a metal rod. But in yet other cases it is difficult to know where to consider the force of gravity to be acting, for example a tennis racquet, a model or toy bird (as shown in the diagram) or even a human body. In this chapter we explore this issue and meet the term **centre of mass**, which is used to describe the point in an object where the force of gravity can be assumed to act.

Exploration 15.1

Centre of mass of a rocking bird

Consider the rocking bird toy, shown in the diagram above. Assume that the only two forces acting on the bird are the force of **gravity** downwards and an upward **normal** reaction.

■ Consider the forces on the bird when it is at rest. What information does this give you about the position of the centre of mass?

■ If the centre of mass were above the level of the shelf, what would happen when the bird rocked?

■ Explain why the centre of mass *must* be below the level of the shelf.

Forces in equilibrium

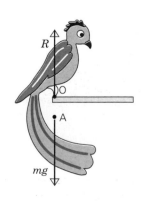

When the bird is at rest, both the resultant force and the total moment of the forces acting must be zero. For this condition to be satisfied the normal reaction and the force of gravity must act along the same straight line. As the normal reaction must act on the pin, the force of gravity must act along a vertical line through the pin.

The diagram shows one possible position for the force of gravity to act. If it were to act as shown, the centre of mass would be at the point A. You can see that the centre of mass may not actually be on the bird itself.

So the centre of mass must lie on the line shown, but whereabouts on this line? If the centre of mass is above the level of the shelf, the forces will act as shown when the top of the bird is pushed to the left.

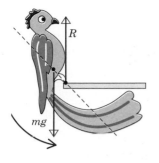

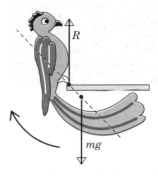

The effect of these forces would be to cause the bird to continue to turn anticlockwise until it falls off the shelf.

If the centre of mass is below the level of the shelf, then the forces would act as shown and produce a clockwise turning effect, so that the bird turns back towards its equilibrium position.

Exploration 15.2

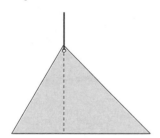

The centre of mass of a triangle

The aim of this activity is to find a general result that can be used to find the position of the centre of mass of any triangle.

- ■ Cut out a triangle from a piece of stiff card. Make a hole in one corner and hang the triangle from a length of string. When the triangle is at rest draw a line that is an extension of the string, as shown in the diagram. (It may help to use a length of string and a mass to form a plumb line.)
- ■ Why must the centre of mass of the triangle lie on the line that you have drawn?
- ■ Suspend the card from each of the other two corners. By drawing vertical lines, find the position of the centre of mass.
- ■ Repeat for some different triangles. Try to find a general rule to find the centre of mass of any triangle. (**Hint:** Measure the **height** of the triangle and the distance of the centre of mass from the **base**.)

The position of the centre of mass

The centre of mass of a triangle is always at a distance $\frac{1}{3}$ of its height from its base. For the triangle ABC shown the height is h and so the centre of mass is a distance $\frac{1}{3}h$ from the base BC, so it lies on the line EF.

The process can be repeated, using each side as the base to find the position of the centre of mass.

In this diagram, if AB is taken as the base, the height is 9 cm and so the centre of mass is 3 cm from AB. If BC is taken as the base the height is 15 cm and so the centre of mass is 5 cm from BC. This allows the centre of mass to be pin-pointed, as shown in the diagram.

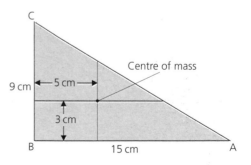

Systems of particles

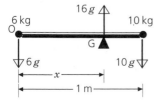

Imagine a light rod with masses fixed at each end. Somewhere along the length of that rod there is a point where the rod would balance as shown in the diagram. This point where the rod balances is its centre of mass.

An upward force of $16g$ N must act at G. Assuming that the centre of mass is at distance x from O, and taking moments about O gives:
$$16gx = 6g \times 0 + 10g \times 1$$

This simplifies to $16x = 10 \Rightarrow x = \frac{5}{8} = 0.625$ m

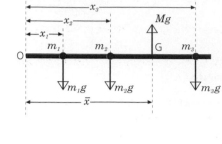

This approach can be extended to give a general formula for the centre of mass.

The rod shown has masses $m_1, m_2, \ldots$ at distances $x_1, x_2, \ldots$ from O. If gravity acts then the forces shown act on each mass and they are balanced by an upward force at G of magnitude:
$$m_1g + m_2g + \ldots = Mg$$

acting at the centre of mass, where M is the total mass. If the distance of the centre of mass from O is $\bar{x}$, then taking moments about O gives $Mg\bar{x} = m_1gx_1 + m_2gx_2 + \ldots$

which simplifies to $M\bar{x} = m_1x_1 + m_2x_2 + \ldots$

$$\Rightarrow \quad \bar{x} = \frac{1}{M}\sum_{i=1}^{n} m_i x_i$$

We shall use this result in the following examples.

Example 15.1

Four masses are attached to a rod as shown. Find the centre of mass of the system.

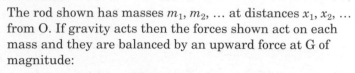

Solution

By measuring distances from the left-hand end of the rod, and using the result $\bar{x} = \dfrac{1}{M}\displaystyle\sum_{i=1}^{n} m_i x_i$ gives:

$$\bar{x} = \frac{1}{20}\left(5 \times 0 + 3 \times 0.2 + 2 \times 0.6 + 10 \times 0.9\right) = \frac{1}{20} \times \left(0.6 + 1.2 + 9\right) = \frac{10.8}{20} = 0.54 \text{ m}$$

So the centre of mass is 0.54 m from the left-hand end of the rod.

Frameworks

The diagram shows a light square framework with masses fixed to each corner.

It is possible to attach a string to a point on the side OA so that the square hangs vertically. The centre of mass then lies on the dotted line shown at a distance $\bar{x}$ from OC.
The value of $\bar{x}$ can
be found by using the general formula:

$$\bar{x} = \frac{1}{M}\sum_{i=1}^{n} m_i x_i$$

where x_i is the distance of each particle from OA.

The framework could be hung from OC as shown, with the centre of mass at the point of intersection of the two dotted lines. If the distance of each mass from OC is y_i then:

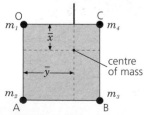

$$\bar{y} = \frac{1}{M}\sum_{i=1}^{n} m_i y_i$$

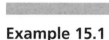

If unit vectors are introduced, so that each particle has its position given by $\mathbf{r}_i = x_i\mathbf{i} + y_i\mathbf{j}$ then the position of the centre of mass is:

$$\bar{\mathbf{r}} = \bar{x}\mathbf{i} + \bar{y}\mathbf{j} = \left(\frac{1}{M}\sum_{i=1}^{n} m_i x_i\right)\mathbf{i} + \left(\frac{1}{M}\sum_{i=1}^{n} m_i y_i\right)\mathbf{j}$$

Example 15.2

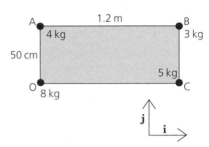

The diagram shows a light rectangular framework with masses fixed at each corner.

a) Find the centre of mass of the system in terms of the unit vectors $\mathbf{i}$ and $\mathbf{j}$.

b) If the framework is suspended from A, find the angle the side OA makes with the vertical.

Solution

a) First note the position vector of each mass:

$$\begin{aligned} \mathbf{r}_O &= 0\mathbf{i} + 0\mathbf{j} & m_O &= 8 \\ \mathbf{r}_A &= 0\mathbf{i} + 0.5\mathbf{j} & m_A &= 4 \\ \mathbf{r}_B &= 1.2\mathbf{i} + 0.5\mathbf{j} & m_B &= 3 \\ \mathbf{r}_C &= 1.2\mathbf{i} + 0\mathbf{j} & m_C &= 5 \end{aligned}$$

Using the result: $\bar{\mathbf{r}} = \left(\dfrac{1}{M}\sum_{i=1}^{n} m_i x_i\right)\mathbf{i} + \left(\dfrac{1}{M}\sum_{i=1}^{n} m_i y_i\right)\mathbf{j}$

and noting that $M = 20$ gives:

$$\mathbf{r} = \tfrac{1}{20}(8 \times 0 + 4 \times 0 + 3 \times 1.2 + 5 \times 1.2)\mathbf{i}$$
$$+ \tfrac{1}{20}(8 \times 0 + 4 \times 0.5 + 3 \times 0.5 + 5 \times 0)\mathbf{j}$$
$$= \tfrac{9.6}{20}\mathbf{i} + \tfrac{3.5}{20}\mathbf{j} = 0.48\mathbf{i} + 0.175\mathbf{j}$$

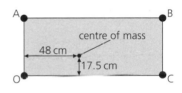

So the position of the centre of mass is as shown in the diagram on the left.

b) When the framework is suspended from A it will hang so that the centre of mass is directly below A as shown in the diagram to the right.

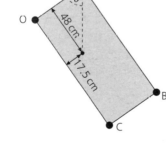

We need to find the angle marked θ. Using trigonometry gives:

$$\tan\theta = \frac{48}{50 - 17.5} = 1.477 \Rightarrow \theta = 56°$$

Example 15.3

The diagram shows a light triangular plate with bolts of mass 100 grams fixed at two corners. Find the mass of the third bolt if the centre of mass is on the dotted line, then find the position vector of the centre of mass.

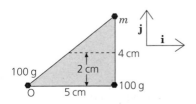

Solution

Taking O as the origin and using the unit vectors $\mathbf{i}$ and $\mathbf{j}$ as defined in the diagram, the centre of mass has position vector $\bar{\mathbf{r}} = \bar{x}\mathbf{i} + 0.02\mathbf{j}$

Now using $\bar{y} = \dfrac{1}{M}\displaystyle\sum_{i=1}^{n} m_i y_i$ *gives:*

$$0.02 = \frac{1}{0.2+m} \times 0.04m$$

$$0.004 + 0.02m = 0.04m$$

$$0.004 = 0.02m$$

$$m = 0.2 \text{ kg}$$

So the mass is 0.2 kg or 200 grams.
The value of $\bar{x}$ can now be calculated using:

$$\bar{x} = \frac{1}{M}\sum_{i=1}^{n} m_i x_i = \frac{1}{0.4}\left(0.1 \times 0 + 0.1 \times 0.05 + 0.2 \times 0.05\right) = \frac{0.015}{0.4} = 0.0375$$

So the position vector of the centre of mass is $\bar{\mathbf{r}} = 0.0375\mathbf{i} + 0.02\,\mathbf{j}$.

EXERCISES

15.1 CLASSWORK

1   Light rectangular frameworks, as in the diagram, have masses fixed at each corner. Find the position of the centre of mass, for each example below, in terms of the unit vectors **i** and **j** with reference to the corner marked O.

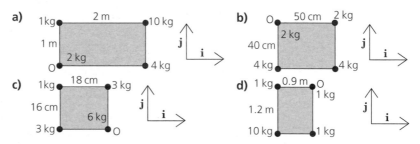

2   The diagram shows a light cross-shaped frame that is free to rotate about its centre, O. Four masses are fixed to the framework as shown, each 30 cm from O.
   a) Find the position of the centre of mass when the framework is in the position shown.
   b) Describe the path of the centre of mass when the framework rotates.

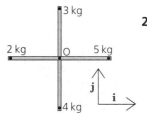

3   A light disc has three masses fixed to it as shown in the diagram. The mass A is 50 grams, B is 100 grams and C is 80 grams.
   a) Find the distance of the centre of mass from O.
   b) If a 100 gram mass is attached to the disc at O, what happens to the centre of mass?

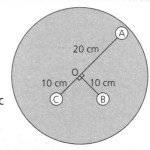

4   The diagram shows a light rod to which two masses have been attached.

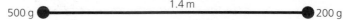

500 g ———— 1.4 m ———— 200 g

   a) Find the position of the centre of mass of the rod and masses.
   b) The 500 gram mass is replaced by a 300 gram mass. What mass must be attached to the other end if the centre of mass is to remain in the same place?

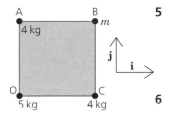

A B *m*
4 kg
j **i**
O C
5 kg 4 kg

5 The diagram shows four masses attached to a light square frame, of side 40 cm.
  a) Find the position of the centre of mass of the frame in terms of m, **i** and **j**.
  b) Find m if the centre of mass is to be at a distance of 20 cm from O.

6 A roundabout in a children's playground has radius 1.6 m. Three children sit as shown in the diagram.

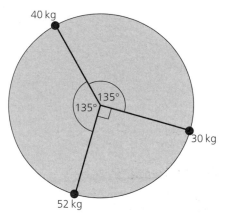

  a) Find the distance of the centre of mass from the centre, assuming that the mass of the roundabout is zero.
  b) Describe how the position of the centre of mass would change if the mass of the roundabout were to be considered.
  c) Suggest how the mass of the roundabout could be considered in this problem.
  d) If the roundabout is represented as a point of mass 200 kg at its centre, find the distance from the centre of the circle of the centre of mass of the roundabout and the children.

7 A man of mass 68 kg climbs a ladder of mass 20 kg and of length 8 m. Model the man as a point of mass and the ladder as a light rod with a point mass at its centre.
  a) Find the highest and lowest distances of the centre of mass from the bottom of the ladder, while the man is on the ladder.
  b) Find the distance of the man from the bottom of the ladder when the centre of mass is $\frac{1}{4}$ of the way up the ladder.

8 A light triangular frame has masses attached to it as shown in the diagram.

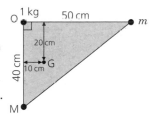

  a) Find M and m, if the centre of mass is at G in the position shown.
  b) Is it possible for the centre of mass to lie on the hypotenuse of the triangle? Explain why.

EXERCISES

1 For each of the following light frameworks, find the position of the centre of mass in terms of the unit vectors **i** and **j** with reference to the corner marked O.

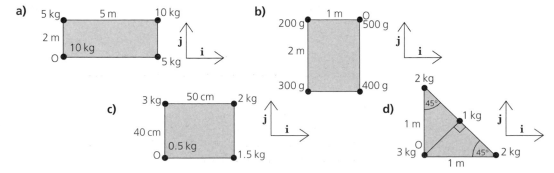

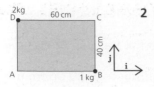

2 A light sheet of metal ABCD has masses attached to it as shown in the diagram.
   a) Find the position of the centre of mass relative to A.
   b) The sheet is suspended from A. What angle does the side AB make with the vertical?

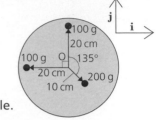

3 A disc of mass 100 grams has three masses fixed to it as shown.
   a) Find the distance of the centre of mass from O.
   b) Find the distance of the centre of mass from O if the mass of the disc is negligible.

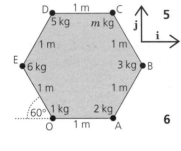

4 The diagram shows a light, L-shaped rod to which two masses have been attached.
   a) Find the position of the centre of mass of the rod and masses.
   b) The 3 kg mass is replaced by a 2 kg mass. What mass should be attached to the other end of the rod if the centre of mass is to stay in the same place?

5 Six masses are attached to a light regular hexagonal plate, as shown in the diagram.
   a) Find the position of the centre of mass of the plate and the masses, in terms of m, $\mathbf{i}$ and $\mathbf{j}$ relative to O.
   b) Find m if the position of the centre of mass is $0.4\mathbf{i} + \alpha\mathbf{j}$.
   c) For this value of m, find the value of α.

6 A roundabout in a children's playground has radius 2 m. Four children sit on the roundabout as shown in the diagram.
   a) Find the distance of the centre of mass from the centre of the roundabout, assuming that the mass of the roundabout is zero.
   b) Describe how the position of the centre of mass would change if the mass of the roundabout were to be considered.
   c) Is it reasonable to assume that the mass of the roundabout is zero in this case?

7 In order to find the mass of a plank AB of length 4 m, a builder attaches a 10 kg mass to the end, A, of the plank. The plank balances when it is horizontal and resting on a metal bar that is 1 m from A. Find the mass of the plank.

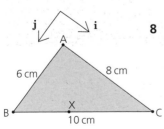

8 A light triangular frame can have masses attached to each of its vertices. The frame is shown in the diagram.
   a) What must be the mass at A if the centre of mass is to be at X?
   b) If the masses at each of vertices A, B and C are m, find the centre of mass of the framework, relative to the corner A.

CENTRES OF MASS FOR COMPOSITE BODIES

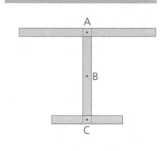

In reality very few things actually consist of systems of particles, but many can be **modelled** as systems of particles, so we can find their centre of mass. For example a table that consists of a top, a base and a pole can be modelled as three particles as shown in the diagram. Thus a composite body can be treated as a collection of particles which can then be considered individually.

The centre of mass can be found by considering particles at A, B and C. The particle at A has the same mass as the table top. The particle at B has the same mass as the pole and the particle at C has the same mass as the base. We assume that each particle is placed at the centre of mass of the component of the body that it represents.

Example 15.4

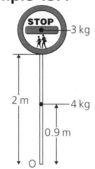

A 'lollipop stick' used by a person on a school crossing is made up of a pole of mass 4 kg and length 1.8 m, and a disc of mass 3 kg and radius 0.2 m. Find the height from the base of the stick to the centre of mass of the lollipop stick.

Solution
Assume that there is no overlap of the pole at the disc. The diagram shows the two components and their centres of mass. If the distance of the centre of mass from O is $\bar{x}$, then:

$$\bar{x} = \frac{2 \times 3 + 0.9 \times 4}{3 + 4} = 1.37 \text{ m}$$

Example 15.5

A parasol has three components and these can be modelled as a circular disc of mass 3 kg, fixed to a pole of mass 2 kg and length 2 m and inclined at 60° to the horizontal. The pole is fixed to a base of mass 12 kg. Find the position of the centre of mass of the complete parasol.

Solution
*The diagram shows the parasol's three components, the origin O at the centre of the base and the unit vectors **i** and **j**, and three particles at A, B and C that can be used to represent each component.*

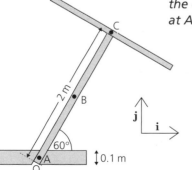

The table gives the mass of each component and the position of its centre of mass.

	Mass (kg)	Position
A	12	$0.05\mathbf{j}$
B	2	$\cos 60°\mathbf{i} + \cos 30°\mathbf{j}$
C	3	$2\cos 60°\mathbf{i} + 2\cos 30°\mathbf{j}$

So the position of the centre of mass, $\bar{\mathbf{r}}$, is given by:

$$\bar{\mathbf{r}} = \frac{12 \times 0.05\mathbf{j} + 2 \times (\cos 60°\mathbf{i} + \cos 30°\mathbf{j}) + 3(2\cos 60°\mathbf{i} + 2\cos 30°\mathbf{j})}{12 + 2 + 3}$$

$$= \frac{4\mathbf{i} + 7.53\mathbf{j}}{17} = 0.235\mathbf{i} + 0.443\mathbf{j}$$

Example 15.6

The diagram shows a hoist used for lifting engines out of cars. It is made from three metal bars with masses and lengths as shown. Assume that the width of the bars is negligible and find the position of the centre of mass relative to O in terms of the unit vectors **i** and **j**.

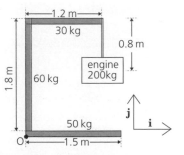

Solution

The table below gives the mass of each component and its centre of mass.

	Mass (kg)	Position of centre of mass
Bottom bar	50	0.75**i**
Upright bar	60	0.9**j**
Top bar	30	0.6**i** + 1.8**j**
Engine	200	1.2**i** + 1.0**j**

The position of the centre of mass, $\bar{\mathbf{r}}$, is then given by:

$$\bar{\mathbf{r}} = \frac{50 \times 0.75\mathbf{i} + 60 \times 0.9\mathbf{j} + 30(0.6\mathbf{i} + 1.8\mathbf{j}) + 200(1.2\mathbf{i} + 1.0\mathbf{j})}{50 + 60 + 30 + 200}$$

$$= \frac{295.5\mathbf{i} + 308\mathbf{j}}{340} = 0.87\mathbf{i} + 0.91\mathbf{j}$$

EXERCISES

15.2 CLASSWORK

1 A wheel has mass 0.7 kg and radius 25 cm. A 50 gram mass is attached to the edge of the wheel. How far does the centre of mass move from the centre of the wheel when the mass is added?

2 The diagram on the left shows a coat stand. The base is made of two sections, the lower one with a mass of 5 kg and the upper one with a mass of 2 kg. The mass of the upright is 4 kg. Find the height of the centre of mass of the coat stand.

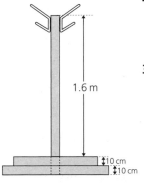

3 The diagrams on the right show a book modelled as two hinged sections, each of mass 200 grams, as it is being closed.
a) Find the position of the centre of mass relative to O for each case illustrated.
b) Draw a diagram to show how the position of the centre of mass changes as the book closes.

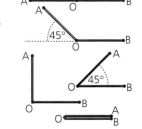

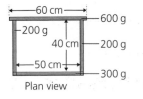

Plan view

4 The diagram on the left shows a wooden drawer. Assuming the mass of the base is negligible, find the position of the centre of mass of the drawer.

5 A children's slide is made up of a metal ladder, of length 1.2 m and mass 8 kg, and a reinforced plastic slide of length 1.8 m and mass 6 kg. The two sections are joined as shown in the diagram.

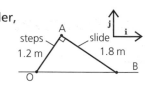

Find the position of the centre of mass of the slide if:
a) no one is using the slide,
b) a child of mass 20 kg sits at A.
State clearly any assumptions that you make.

6 The diagram shows the cross-section of a table made up of four sections with dimensions and masses shown in the diagram.

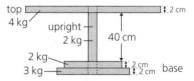

top 4 kg, upright 2 kg, 40 cm, 2 cm, 2 kg, 3 kg, 2 cm, 2 cm base

a) Find the height of the centre of mass.
b) A jug of water of mass 3 kg is paced on the table 30 cm from its centre. Model the jug as a particle. Find the new height of the centre of mass and its distance from the centre of the table.

7 The diagrams show the highest and lowest positions of a person doing press-ups. The person is modelled as a straight rod of length 1.5 m and mass 60 kg (labelled A), a sphere of mass 6 kg and radius 12 cm (labelled B) and a rod of mass 6 kg that varies in length between 20 and 45 cm (labelled C).

highest position, A, B, C, O
lowest position, A, B, C, O, **j**, **i**

a) Find the position of the centre of mass in each position.
b) Find the height gained by the centre of mass.
c) Find the work done during the lifting stage of each press up.
d) Comment on the assumptions that the arms can be modelled as straight rods that are perpendicular to the ground.

8 The diagram shows a design for a stand used in a city centre. Baskets are hung from A and a hook is fixed to the stands at B so they can be lifted by a small crane.

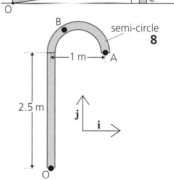

B, semi-circle, 1 m, A, 2.5 m, **j**, **i**, O

a) Find the distance of the centre of mass of the stand from a vertical line through O. Assume the stands are made from uniform tubes.
b) The local council wish to be able to remove and replace the stand easily so that the long straight section hangs vertically when the stands are lifted by a rope attached to the hook at B. Find the position of B relative to O in terms of **i** and **j**.

9 A steel plate has a square hole of side 3 cm cut in it.

B, 18 cm, C, 10 cm, 3 cm, 3 cm, 3 cm, A, 4 cm, D

a) If the mass of the original plate was 3.6 kg, find the mass lost when the hole was drilled.
b) The centre of mass is at a distance x from AB. By taking moments about AB show that the equation $1620 = 171x + 126$ holds and find the distance of the centre of mass from AB.
c) Find the distance of the centre of mass from AD.
d) The plate is suspended from the corner A by a rope. Find the angle between AB and the rope.

10 A drinks can of radius r and height H of mass 50 grams contains 250 grams of drink when full.
a) Find an expression for the position of the centre of mass of the can and drink, when the height of the drink is h.
b) Find the lowest possible position for the centre of mass.

EXERCISES

15.2 HOMEWORK

1 A wheel has mass 1.1 kg and radius 50 cm. A 100 gram mass is attached to one edge of the wheel and a 250 gram mass is attached diagonally opposite the first mass, at the edge of the wheel. Find the distance of the centre of mass from the centre of the wheel.

15 Centre of mass

2 A lamp can be modelled as a sphere of mass 100 grams, a metal base of mass 2 kg and a vertical rod of mass 500 grams. Find the height of the centre of mass of the lamp if the dimensions are as shown in the diagram.

3 The diagram on the right shows a simple model of a crane.
   a) Find the centre of mass relative to the point O, if the angle θ is:
   i) 80° **ii)** 45° **iii)** 15°.
   b) Draw a diagram to show how the position of the centre of mass changes as the jib of the crane is raised or lowered.

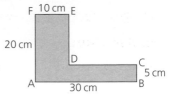

4 **a)** Find the position of the centre of mass relative to A of the uniform lamina shown in the diagram.
   b) The lamina is suspended from the point A. Find the angle that the side AB makes with the vertical.

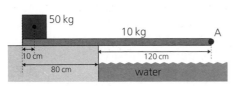

5 A makeshift diving board is made by fixing a concrete mass to the end of a plank, as shown in the diagram.
   a) Find the distance of the centre of mass from A.
   b) What is the largest vertical force that could be exerted on the diving board at A, if it does not tip?

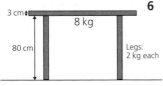

6 The diagram shows a side view of a table that has four legs and a top.
   a) Find the height of the centre of mass of the table.
   b) A small uniform box of mass 4 kg is placed on the table. Find the new height of the centre of mass of the table if the height of the box is: **i)** negligible, **ii)** 20 cm.

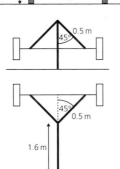

7 The diagrams show the highest and lowest positions of a weightlifter lifting a set of weights. The weightlifter is modelled as a straight rod of length 1.6 m and mass 80 kg. Assume the weightlifter's arms are light rods of length 0.5 m. The bar is assumed to be light and the masses at each end are 100 kg each. The diagrams show two positions of the weightlifter and weights.
   a) Find the height of the centre of mass for each position.
   b) Find the height gained by the centre of mass as it is lifted from the lower to the higher position.
   c) Find the work done during the lifting stage.

8 A circular metal plate has a radius of 20 cm. A hole of radius 10 cm is drilled in it as shown in the diagram. Find the angle that the diagonal AB makes with the vertical when the plate is suspended from A.

9 A tank has a mass of 1 kg and contains 9 kg of water. The tank is tipped until the water is level with side AE. Find the position of the centre of mass when the tank is in this position.

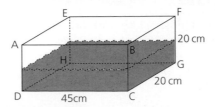
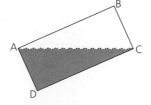

10 A cylindrical tank of mass 4 kg, radius 40 cm and height 1.2 m is slowly filled with water at a rate of 250 cm^3 every second. The mass of 1000 cm^3 of water is 1 kg. Find the height of the centre of mass at time t seconds and sketch a graph to show how the height of the centre of mass varies with time.

SLIDING OR TOPPLING

A force can have different effects on an object depending on where and how it is applied. Applying a horizontal force to the top of a cereal packet may cause it to topple over, while applying the same force at the base may cause the packet to slide. In this section we explore the ideas of sliding and toppling and try to predict which will happen in a given situation.

Exploration 15.3

Practical activity

■ A force is applied to a table as shown in the diagram. What could happen? What is most likely to happen? Try it out and see. You could experiment with tables of different dimensions, if they are available, or place them on different surfaces.

■ What difference does it make if the force is applied at an angle, as shown in the diagrams?

■ What difference does it make if a heavy object is placed on the table, or if someone sits on it? Try out an experiment with the heavy object in a variety of positions.

On the point of sliding or toppling

Exploration 15.3 showed that objects can either slide or topple. To decide if an object will slide or topple we need to examine two cases, when the object is *on the point of* sliding and when it is *on the point of* toppling.

■ When an object is on the point of sliding, the magnitude of friction force is equal to μR.

■ When the object is about to topple, the reaction force acts at the corner about which the object would topple.

This is illustrated in the following examples.

Example 15.7

A box of mass 5 kg has the dimensions shown in the diagram. The coefficient of friction between the box and the floor is 0.5. A horizontal force of magnitude Q is applied to the box as shown.
a) Find Q if the box is on the point of sliding.
b) Find Q if the box is about to topple.
c) Does the box slide or topple?

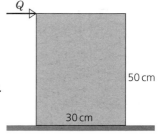

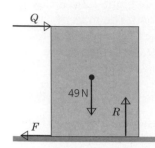

Solution

The diagram on the left shows the forces acting on the box.

a) *If the box is about to slide then:*

$$Q = F = \mu R$$

As the vertical forces must be in equilibrium $R = 49$ N and so:

$$Q = \mu R = 0.5 \times 49 = 24.5 \text{ N}$$

b) *If the box is about to topple then R must act at the corner shown and the total moment of the other forces will be zero, so taking moments about this corner gives:*

$$0.15 \times 49 - 0.5Q = 0 \implies Q = \frac{0.15 \times 49}{0.5} = 14.7$$

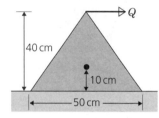

c) *A force of 24.5 N is required for the box to slide, but only 14.7 N for the box to topple. So the box will topple before it slides.*

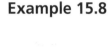

Example 15.8

A force of magnitude Q is applied horizontally to the top of a cone of mass 1 kg. The centre of mass of the cone is 10 cm from the base.

a) *Find Q when the cone is on the point of toppling.*

b) *Find Q when the cone is on the point of sliding, in terms of μ the coefficient of friction.*

c) *What can be deduced about μ if the cone slides before it topples?*

Solution

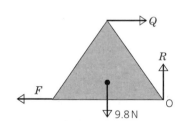

a) *When the cone is on the point of toppling the forces will act as shown in the diagram, and the total moment about O will be zero. So taking moment about O gives:*

$$9.8 \times 0.25 - 0.40 \times Q = 0$$

$$\implies Q = \frac{9.8 \times 0.25}{0.40} = 6.125 \text{N}$$

b) *If the cone is on the point of sliding $Q = F = \mu R$*

As the vertical forces are in equilibrium:

$$R = 9.8 \text{ N} \implies Q = 9.8\mu$$

c) *If the cone slides before it topples, then the force for sliding must be less than the force for toppling.*

$$9.8\mu < 6.125 \implies \mu < \frac{6.125}{9.8} = 0.625$$

Sliding and toppling on slopes

When an object is placed on a slope, it may remain at rest. Alternatively, it could slide down the slope or topple over. We now explore the ideas of sliding and toppling on slopes.

Exploration 15.4

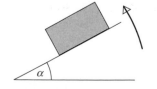

Practical activity

A box is placed on a board and one end of the board is lifted. What could happen to the box?

If the box slides down the slope, what is the relationship between the angle, α, and the coefficient of friction between the box and the board?

If the box topples, what is the relationship between the angle, α, and the dimensions of the box?

The angle of friction

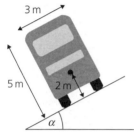

If the box is on the point of sliding down the slope, then the angle between the slope and the horizontal will be the **angle of friction**. $\tan \alpha = \mu$

If the box is *on the point of toppling*, the centre of mass of the box will be directly above the corner about which it will topple. So for a uniform box as illustrated:

$$\tan \alpha = \frac{a}{b}$$

Example 15.9

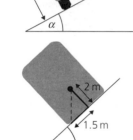

A bus has dimensions as shown and its centre of mass is 2 m above the road. It is placed on a test ramp and tilted at an angle α to the horizontal.
a) At what angle would the bus topple?
b) At what angle would the bus slide on the ramp if the coefficient of friction between its tyres and the ramp is 0.8?
c) Does the bus slide or topple first?

Solution
a) The bus topples when the centre of mass is above the bottom corner as shown. In this position:

$$\tan \alpha = \frac{1.5}{2} \Rightarrow \alpha = 36.9°$$

b) The bus slides, at the angle of friction, when $\tan \alpha = \mu$. So in this case $\tan \alpha = 0.8 \Rightarrow \alpha = 38.7°$.
c) As the angle for toppling is less than the angle for sliding, the bus will topple.

EXERCISES

15.3 CLASSWORK

1 The diagram shows a crate of mass 50 kg. A horizontal force of magnitude P acts at the top of the crate as shown. The coefficient of friction between the crate and the ground is 0.6.

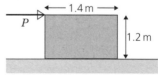

a) What is P when the box is about to slide?
b) What is P when the box is about to topple?
c) Does the box slide or topple?

2 The diagram shows a force of magnitude Q that is applied as shown to a cylinder of mass 100 kg. The coefficient of friction between the cylinder and the ground is 0.707.

a) Show that $Q = 693$ N when the cylinder is about to slide.
b) Find Q when the cylinder is about to topple.
c) Explain why the cylinder topples before it slides.
d) For what range of values of μ would the cylinder slide before it topples?

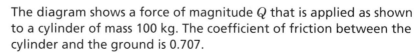

3 In each example below find the values of α at which the box shown would topple or slide and state which happens in each case.

a)

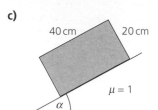

b)

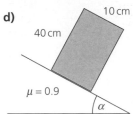

c)

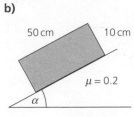

d)

4 At a school fete there is a stall where cans of cola have to be knocked over by competitors. Two students suggest two different strategies. One suggests filling the empty can completely with sand. The other suggests filling the can one-third full with sand. Assume the mass of the can is negligible in this problem.

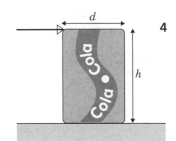

 a) Show that for the full can to topple a horizontal force of $\dfrac{mgd}{2h}$ must be applied at the top of the can, as shown in the diagram.
 b) What force must be applied for the one-third full can to topple?
 c) Show that the full can will slide before it topples if $\mu < \dfrac{d}{2h}$.
 d) Find a similar result for the can that is one-third full.
 e) Comment on your results, recommend how far to fill a can and state any important features of the problem that have been overlooked.

5 The diagram shows a car parked on a steep slope. The centre of mass is at A. If the angle α were increased would the car slide or topple first and at what angle? Assume the coefficient of friction between the tyres and the surface is 0.8.

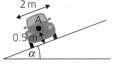

6 The diagram shows a pencil with hexagonal cross-section of side length a. The coefficient of friction between the hexagon and the slope is μ.

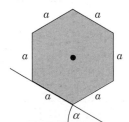

 a) Find the angle α if the pencil is on the point of rolling down the slope.
 b) Find an inequality involving μ if the pencil rolls before it slides.
 c) Repeat (a) and (b) for a pencil with a regular octagonal cross-section.

7 A force of magnitude F is applied to the top of a triangular lamina. The mass of the lamina is m and the coefficient of friction is μ. Find F in terms of m and g if the triangle topples, and the condition that μ must satisfy.

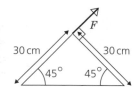

EXERCISES

15.3 HOMEWORK

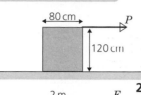

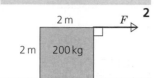

1 A horizontal force of magnitude P acts at the top of a box of mass 40 kg as shown in the diagram. The coefficient of friction between the box and the ground is 0.7.
a) What is P when the box is about to slide?
b) What is P when the box is about to topple?
c) Does the box slide or topple first?

2 A force of magnitude F acts as shown on a crate of mass 200 kg. The coefficient of friction between the crate and the ground is 0.6.
a) Show that when $F = 980$ N the crate is about to topple.
b) Find F if the crate is about to slide.
c) Does the crate slide or topple first?

3 In each case below, what happens to the box illustrated as the angle α is increased?

a)
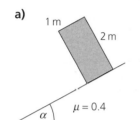

b)
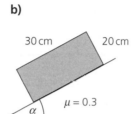

c)
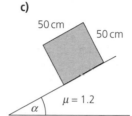

d)
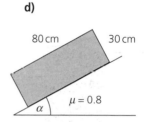

4 The diagram shows two forces that are applied to a crate of mass 4 kg. The coefficient of friction between the crate and the horizontal surface is 0.4.
a) Find P if the box is about to slide.
b) Find P if the box is about to topple.
c) What happens to the box?
d) Would your answer to **c)** change if the 10 N force were removed?

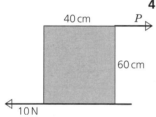

5 At a factory, boxes are placed on a slope at 40° to the horizontal and allowed to slide down ready to be loaded onto lorries. The coefficient of friction between the boxes and the slope is 0.2.
a) Explain why the boxes can slide down the slope.
b) If the base of a box is of length a and the height of the box is b, find the value of b, in terms of a, for which the box is about to topple.

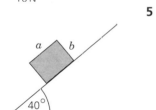

6 A force of magnitude P is applied as shown to the lamina, of mass m, illustrated. The coefficient of friction between the lamina and the ground is μ. Find P if the lamina topples, and the condition for μ if it topples before it slides.

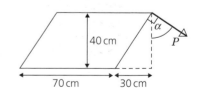

7 The diagram shows a lamina of mass m. The force of magnitude P is shown and the coefficient of friction between the lamina and the surface is μ. Find a condition for μ if the lamina slides before it topples.

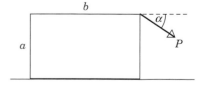

FINDING THE POSITION OF THE CENTRE OF MASS BY INTEGRATION

In many cases the position of the centre of mass of a body can be found by modelling it as if it were made up of simpler shapes and using the approach for composite bodies. In many other cases, though, this is impossible. For example, where is the centre of mass of a semi-circular plate? In this section we shall develop an approach that can be used for objects that have some symmetry. First we shall consider the plate shown in the diagram.

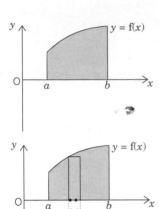

Assume that the plate is made from a material which has uniform density, giving it a mass of ρ per unit area, so that its mass is simply ρ multiplied by its area. Then the mass of the plate is given by:

$$m = \rho\int_a^b y\,\mathrm{d}x$$

Now imagine that the shape is split into a number of strips of width δx. One is shown in the diagram.

The mass of each strip is $\rho y\,\delta x$, and its distance from the y-axis is simply x. If the whole shape were split into similar strips then the distance of the centre of mass from the y-axis would be given by:

$$\bar{x} = \frac{\sum(2\rho y\,\delta x)x}{m}$$

If the width of the strips, δx, is allowed to tend to zero, then the expression for $\bar{x}$ becomes: $\bar{x} = \dfrac{\displaystyle\int_a^b \rho y x\,\mathrm{d}x}{m}$

and using the result obtained for m this gives: $\bar{x} = \dfrac{\displaystyle\int_a^b \rho y x\,\mathrm{d}x}{\displaystyle\int_a^b \rho y\,\mathrm{d}x} = \dfrac{\displaystyle\int_a^b y x\,\mathrm{d}x}{\displaystyle\int_a^b y\,\mathrm{d}x}$

Similarly the distance of the centre of mass from the x-axis is $\frac{1}{2}y$ for each strip. Then if the shape were made of these strips we should have:

$$\bar{y} = \frac{\sum\left(\rho\dfrac{y}{2}\delta x\right)y}{m}$$

Again if δx tends to zero, this expression becomes:

$$\bar{y} = \frac{\displaystyle\int_a^b \tfrac{1}{2}\rho y^2\,\mathrm{d}x}{m} = \frac{\displaystyle\int_a^b \tfrac{1}{2}\rho y^2\,\mathrm{d}x}{\displaystyle\int_a^b \rho y\,\mathrm{d}x} = \frac{\displaystyle\int_a^b \tfrac{1}{2}y^2\,\mathrm{d}x}{\displaystyle\int_a^b y\,\mathrm{d}x}$$

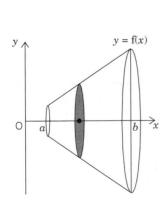

A similar approach can be taken to a solid formed by rotating a region about the x-axis.

The diagram shows how, when working with solid shapes, we must consider discs instead of the strips we used for flat plates or laminas. If the density of the material is ρ then the mass of each disc is $\pi\rho y^2\delta x$.

The mass of the solid is given by: $m = \displaystyle\int_a^b \rho\pi y^2\,\mathrm{d}x$

and the centre of mass is given by: $\bar{x} = \dfrac{\displaystyle\int_a^b \rho\pi y^2 x\,\mathrm{d}x}{\displaystyle\int_a^b \rho\pi y^2\,\mathrm{d}x} = \dfrac{\displaystyle\int_a^b y^2 x\,\mathrm{d}x}{\displaystyle\int_a^b y^2\,\mathrm{d}x}$

Example 15.10

A lamina is bounded by the curve $y = x^2$, the lines $x = 1$, $x = 4$ and $y = 0$. Find the coordinates of the centre of mass of the lamina.

Solution

First find the area of the lamina.

$$A = \int_1^4 x^2 dx = \left[\frac{x^3}{3}\right]_1^4 = \frac{64}{3} - \frac{1}{3} = 21$$

Now find the x-coordinate of the centre of mass.

$$\overline{x} = \frac{\int_1^4 x^3 dx}{21} = \frac{\left[\frac{x^4}{4}\right]_1^4}{21} = \frac{64 - \frac{1}{4}}{21} = \frac{85}{28} = 3.036 \quad \text{to 3 decimal places}$$

Now find the y-coordinate of the centre of mass.

$$\overline{y} = \frac{\int_1^4 \frac{1}{2} x^4 dx}{21} = \frac{\left[\frac{x^5}{10}\right]_1^4}{21} = \frac{102.4 - 0.1}{21} = \frac{341}{70} = 4.871 \quad \text{to 3 decimal places}$$

Example 15.11

Show that the distance of the centre of mass of an isosceles triangles of height h is $\frac{2}{3}h$ from its top.

Solution

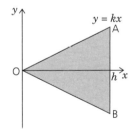

The diagram shows an isosceles triangle.
The sloping sides of the triangle are straight lines, so the line OA will be given by $f(x) = kx$. Now the centre of mass can be found.

$$\overline{x} = \frac{\int_0^h 2xy\,dx}{\int_0^h 2y\,dx} = \frac{\int_0^h 2kx^2\,dx}{\int_0^h 2kx\,dx} = \frac{\left[\frac{2}{3}kx^3\right]_0^h}{\left[kx^2\right]_0^h} = \frac{\frac{2}{3}kh^3}{kh^2} = \frac{2}{3}h$$

So the centre of mass is at a distance $\frac{2}{3}h$ from the top of the triangle.

Centre of mass of a solid truncated cone

Example 15.12

The diagram shows a truncated cone of height 5 cm. Find the distance of the centre of mass from O.

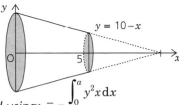

Solution

The centre of mass can be found using: $\overline{x} = \dfrac{\int_0^a y^2 x\,dx}{\int_0^a y^2\,dx}$

In this case $y = 10 - x$ and $a = 5$ which gives:

$$\overline{x} = \frac{\int_0^5 (10-x)^2 x\,dx}{\int_0^5 (10-x)^2\,dx} = \frac{\int_0^5 \left(100x - 20x^2 + x^3\right)dx}{\int_0^5 \left(100 - 20x + x^2\right)dx} = \frac{\left[50x^2 - \frac{20}{3}x^3 + \frac{1}{4}x^4\right]_0^5}{\left[100x - 10x^2 + \frac{1}{3}x^3\right]_0^5}$$

$$= \frac{50 \times 5^2 - \frac{20}{3} \times 5^3 + \frac{1}{4} \times 5^4}{100 \times 5 - 10 \times 5^2 + \frac{1}{3} \times 5^3} = \frac{6875}{12} \times \frac{3}{875} = \frac{55}{28} = 1.96$$

So the centre of mass is 1.96 cm from the base.

Centre of mass of a hemisphere

Example 15.13

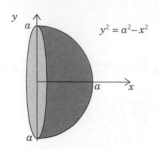

Find the position of the centre of mass of a solid hemisphere of radius a.

Solution

The diagram shows the hemisphere.
The equation of the circle of radius a is $x^2 + y^2 = a^2$ or $y^2 = a^2 - x^2$.
The mass of the hemisphere can be calculated without integration as:
$$m = \rho \times \tfrac{1}{2} \times \tfrac{4}{3}\pi a^3 = \tfrac{2}{3}\rho\pi a^2$$
The centre of mass can now be found using:

$$\bar{x} = \frac{\int_0^a \pi\rho y^2 x\,dx}{m} = \frac{\int_0^a \pi\rho(a^2 - x^2)x\,dx}{\tfrac{2}{3}\pi\rho a^3} = \frac{3}{2a^3}\int_0^a (xa^2 - x^3)\,dx$$

$$= \frac{3}{2a^3}\left[\frac{a^2 x^2}{2} - \frac{x^4}{4}\right]_0^a = \frac{3}{2a^3}\left(\frac{a^4}{2} - \frac{a^4}{4}\right) = \frac{3}{2a^3}\times\frac{a^4}{4} = \frac{3a}{8}$$

So the centre of mass is at a distance $\tfrac{3}{8}a$ from the base of the hemisphere.

Centre of mass of a conical shell

Example 15.14

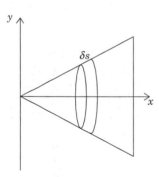

A conical shell is formed by rotating the line with equation $y = \tfrac{1}{2}x$, for $0 \le x \le 6$ through 360° around the x-axis. Find the distance of the centre of mass from the y-axis.

Solution

The diagram shows a cross-section of the cone.
We imagine that the shell is made up of hoops,
like the one shown in the diagram, where δs is the width of the hoop as measured along the slope. We have to relate this to δx.

Consider this diagram.
$$(\delta s)^2 = (\delta x)^2 + (\delta y)^2$$

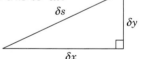

But since $y = \tfrac{1}{2}x$, we have $\delta y = \tfrac{1}{2}\delta x$, which then gives:

$$(\delta s)^2 = (\delta x)^2 + \left(\tfrac{1}{2}\delta x\right)^2$$
$$= \tfrac{5}{4}(\delta x)^2$$
$$\delta s = \frac{\sqrt{5}}{2}\delta x$$

Now consider the mass of each hoop. This will be $\rho \times 2\pi y \times \delta s = \rho\pi\sqrt{5}\,y\,\delta x$.

Hence the total mass of the shell will be given by:

$$m = \int_0^6 \rho\pi\sqrt{5}\,\frac{x}{2}\,dx$$
$$= \rho\pi\sqrt{5}\left[\frac{x^2}{4}\right]_0^6$$
$$= \rho\pi 9\sqrt{5}$$

The moment of each hoop about the y-axis will be
$\rho \times 2\pi y \times \delta s \times x = \rho\pi\sqrt{5}xy\,\delta x$.

Hence the centre of mass will be given by:

$$\bar{x} = \frac{\displaystyle\int_0^6 \rho\pi\sqrt{5}\,\frac{x^2}{2}\,dx}{\rho\pi 9\sqrt{5}} = \frac{\left[\dfrac{x^3}{6}\right]_0^6}{9} = \frac{36}{9} = 4$$

EXERCISES

15.4 CLASSWORK

1   Find the centre of mass of the trapezium shown in the diagram.

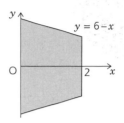

2   A region is bounded by the curves $y = x^2$, $y = 0$ and $x = 1$. A sheet of material has the same shape as this region. Find the position of the centre of mass of the shape.

3   A steel plate is in the shape of a trapezium as shown in the diagram. Find the position of the centre of mass of the plate.

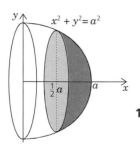

4   A lamina has the same shape as a region bounded by the curves $y = \sqrt{x}$, $y = 0$ and $x = 4$. Find the position of the centre of mass of this shape.

5   a) Show that the centre of mass of a semicircular lamina of radius a is at a distance $\frac{4a}{3\pi}$ from the straight edge.
    b) Find the centre of mass of the lamina shown in the diagram.

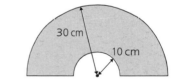

6   The diagram shows a solid cone that has been split to form a smaller cone and a solid known as a frustum.
    a) Find the distance of the centre of mass of the smaller cone from O.
    b) Show that the centre of mass of the frustum is $\frac{11}{56}h$ from the base of the frustrum.

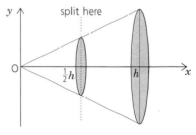

7   A solid object is formed by rotating the area under the curve $y = x^2$ around the x-axis. Find the position of the centre of mass of the solid if the curve is rotated for values of x:
    a) between 0 and 2,   b) between 1 and 2,   c) between 0 and a.

8   A component for a pulley is formed by the solid enclosed when the curve $y = x^2 - 2x + 2$ and lines $x = 0$ and $x = 2$ are rotated about the x-axis to give the outline of the solid. Find the distance of the centre of mass from its base.

9   The diagram shows a hemisphere that has been cut into two parts. By integrating between the limits $\frac{1}{2}a$ and a find the centre of mass of the smaller part of the hemisphere.

10 A conical shell is formed by rotating the line $y = 2x$ for $0 \le x \le 12$ through 360° around the x-axis. Find the coordinates of the centre of mass of the shell.

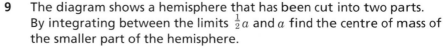

EXERCISES

15.4 HOMEWORK

1 Find the distance from O of the centre of mass of the trapezium shown in the diagram.

2 A region is bounded by curves $y = x^3$, $y = 0$ and the line $x = 1$. A sheet of material has the same shape as the region. Find the position of the centre of mass of the sheet of material.

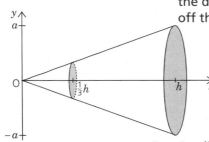

3 A steel plate is in the shape of a trapezium as shown in the diagram. Find the position of the centre of mass of the plate.

4 A lamina has the same shape as a region bounded by the curves $y = x + x^2$, $y = 0$, $x = 0$ and $x = 2$.
a) Give the position vector of the centre of mass from the origin.
b) A similar shape is bounded by $y = x + x^2$, $y = 0$, $x = 0$ and $x = 4$. Find the coordinates of its centre of mass.

5 Find the centre of mass of the lamina shaded in the diagram. The lamina was formed by cutting off the top half of a semi-circle.

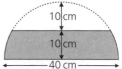

6 The diagram shows a cone that is to be split into two parts.
a) Show that the centre of mass of the cone is $\frac{3}{4}h$ from O.
b) Find the distance of the centre of mass of the smaller cone from O.
c) Find the distance of the centre of mass of the frustum from its base.

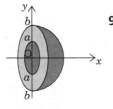

7 A solid object is found by rotating the area under the curve $y = \frac{1}{x}$ around the x-axis between the lines $x = a$ and $x = b$.

a) Show that the distance of the centre of mass from O is $\dfrac{ab\ln\frac{b}{a}}{a - b}$

b) Find the distance of the centre of mass from the line $x = a$.

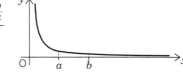

8 A flange is formed by rotating the curve $y = 10 + x^6$ about the x-axis between the lines $x = 0$ and $x = 1.5$. Find the distance of the centre of mass from the end of the flange with the smallest diameter.

9 a) A hollow hemisphere is formed as shown in the diagram. Show that the centre of mass is at a distance $\bar{x}$ from O, where $\bar{x} = \dfrac{3\left(b^4 - a^4\right)}{8\left(b^3 - a^3\right)}$.

b) Find the position of the centre of mass of a hemispherical shell of outer radius 10 cm and thickness 2 mm.

10 The line $y = x + 1$ for $0 \le x \le 4$ is rotated through 360° around the x-axis, to form a hollow shell. Find the coordinates of the centre of mass of the shell.

CONSOLIDATION EXERCISES FOR CHAPTER 15

1 A lollipop stick of a children's crossing patrol warden can be modelled by a uniform rod AB together with a uniform circular disc attached to the rod at B. The diameter BC of the disc is in the same straight line as AB, as shown in the diagram. The rod is of length 1.4 m and weight 20 N and the disc is of diameter 0.4 m and weight 10 N.

Show that the centre of mass of the lollipop stick is at a distance of one metre from A.

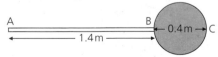

(AQA A Question 1, M2 Specimen Paper)

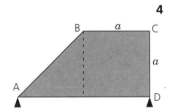

2 The diagram shows a uniform lamina.
The lamina is suspended from the corner A. Find the angle between the side AB and the vertical, when the lamina is at rest.

(AQA B Question 2 M1 Specimen Paper)

3 A uniform plane lamina ABCDE is formed by joining a uniform square ABDE with a uniform triangular lamina BCD, of the same material, along the side BD, as shown in the diagram. The lengths AB, BC and CD are 18 cm, 15 cm and 15 cm receptively.
a) Find the distance of the centre of mass of the lamina from AE.
The lamina is freely suspended from B and hangs in equilibrium.
b) Find, in degrees to one decimal place, the angle which BD makes with the vertical.

(EDEXCEL Question 7, M2 Specimen Paper)

4 A uniform lamina ABCD has the shape of a square of side a adjoining a right-angled isosceles triangle whose equal sides are also of length a. The weight of the lamina is W. The lamina rests, in a vertical plane, on smooth supports at A and D, with AD horizontal (see diagram).
a) Show that the centre of mass of the lamina is at a horizontal distance of $\frac{11}{9}a$ from A.
b) Find, in terms of W, the magnitudes of the forces on the supports at A and D.

(OCR A Question 3, Specimen Paper)

MATHEMATICAL MODELLING ACTIVITY

Problem statement

Athletes in events such as the pole vault and high jump often adopt positions so that their centre of mass is as far below their bodies as possible as they go over the bar. How far below their body is it reasonable to assume that their centre of mass can be?

Specify the real problem

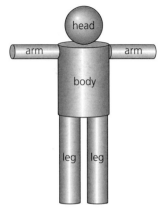

Set up a model

The solution to this problem will be based on a model of a human body as five cylinders and a sphere. The sphere represents the head and the body, the arms and legs are all modelled as cylinders.

Set up a model

The table below gives some data that suggest how the mass of the body is divided among these five components and the approximate dimensions of each component.

Component	Mass (%)	Length (m)	Radius (m)
Body	52	0.65	0.18
Arms	5	0.75	0.04
Legs	15	0.95	0.09
Head	8	–	0.10

In addition it will be assumed that the body joints are completely flexible.

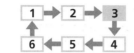

Formulate the mathematical problem

Formulate a mathematical problem

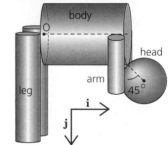

Assume that the athlete can take up the position shown in the diagram.
Find the position of the centre of mass of the athlete with reference to O and in terms of **i** and **j**.

Mathematical solution

As the body is made up of several components, each can be considered as if it were a particle located at its centre of mass. The table below gives the mass of each component and the position of its centre of mass.

	Mass	Position of centre of mass
Body	$0.52m$	$0.325\mathbf{i}$
Arms (both)	$0.10m$	$0.63\mathbf{i} + 0.375\mathbf{j}$
Legs (both)	$0.30m$	$-0.045\mathbf{i} + 0.475\mathbf{j}$
Head	$0.08m$	$0.721\mathbf{i} + 0.251\mathbf{j}$

The position of the centre of mass can now be found.

$$\bar{\mathbf{r}} = \frac{0.52m \times 0.325\mathbf{i} + 0.1m(0.63\mathbf{i} + 0.375\mathbf{j}) + 0.3m(-0.045\mathbf{i} + 0.475\mathbf{j}) + 0.08m(0.721\mathbf{i} + 0.251\mathbf{j})}{m}$$

$$= 0.276\mathbf{i} + 0.200\mathbf{j}$$

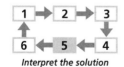

Interpret the solution

Interpretation

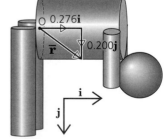

The diagram shows the position of the centre of mass.

Note that it has just moved below the body of the athlete. The advantage gained is quite considerable compared to an athlete who crosses the bar in a horizontal position, as the athlete can clear a bar 20 cm higher. It is interesting to note that the centre of mass may pass under the bar, while the athlete goes over it.

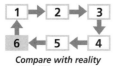

Compare with reality

Compare with reality

The position that the athlete is assumed to have adopted is rather extreme. In fact it is probably unobtainable in real life. It may also be difficult for an athlete who adopts this position to get their arms and legs over the bar.

Refining the model

By examining photographs, try to establish the type of positions that athletes use in events like the high jump. Assume a more realistic position for an athlete and explore how this affects the position of their centre of mass.

POSSIBLE MODELLING TASKS

1   A road barrier should *stay* down when it is down and up when it is up. Design a barrier that is made from metal tubes of mass 10 kg per metre and a single mass, so that when the barrier is down the centre of mass is to the right of the pivot, and when the barrier is up the centre of mass is to the left of the pivot.

2   Not all objects have uniform density or uniform mass per unit area. You can create such objects by cutting a shape from a piece of card and sticking smaller pieces of card to it. Create or find such an object. Find its centre of mass and confirm your prediction experimentally.

3   Investigate how the centre of mass of the human form moves during participation in various sports. You could use the data given in the mathematical modelling activity.

4   Find the centre of mass of an object, for example a tennis racquet. Mark this point clearly on the racquet. Then throw the object so that it spins and rides its motion. Replay in slow motion or a frame at a time. Describe the path of the centre of mass.

Summary

After working through this chapter you should be able to:

■ find the centre of mass of a system of particles using:

$$\bar{\mathbf{r}} = \bar{x}\,\mathbf{i} + \bar{y}\,\mathbf{j} = \left(\frac{1}{M}\sum_{i=1}^{n} m_i x_i\right)\mathbf{i} + \left(\frac{1}{M}\sum_{i=1}^{n} m_i y_i\right)\mathbf{j} = \frac{\sum m_i \mathbf{r}_i}{\sum m_i}$$

■ find the centre of mass of a composite body by modelling it as a system of particles

■ describe the conditions when this will happen.

MECHANICS 16

Circular motion

■ *There are many examples of circular motion that can be modelled in a simple way.*

■ *In this chapter we explore the specific requirements that the forces on an object must satisfy if it is to move in a circle.*

CIRCULAR PATHS

Exploration 16.1

These objects follow circular paths.
■ a conker on a string,
■ a car navigating a sharp icy corner,
■ a fairground 'chair-o-plane' ride.

There are many questions we could ask about motions of this type.
■ What happens as a fairground ride slows down?
■ What happens if a car hits black ice?
■ What happens if the conker string breaks?

Discuss the following questions for each example.
■ What forces are acting on the object?
■ How would you describe circular motion?
■ What makes objects move in circles?
■ What specific problems might you meet in each case?

Horizontal circular motion

These are examples of **horizontal circular motion** in which each object moves in a horizontal plane. In this chapter we shall explore motion of this type, in which the object moves with constant speed. However, although the speed is constant, since the direction of the object keeps changing its direction of motion the velocity is not constant. Consequently the object is accelerating so that there is a net force acting on it.

Your own experience of the three examples may have led you to say that:
■ as the fairground ride slows down, the radius of the rider's motion decreases,
■ if the car hits black ice the car will tend to skid,
■ if the conker string breaks the conker will fly off initially along the tangent to the circular path.

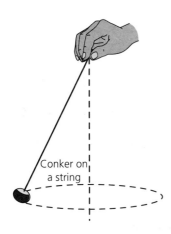

Conker on a string

Consider the motion of the conker in more detail. There are two forces acting on the conker – the force of **gravity** and the **tension** in the conker string.

The features of the motion that we would want to describe might be:
■ the speed of the conker,
■ the angle that the string makes with the vertical,
■ how large the tension in the string needs to be to maintain the motion.

Clearly these features are likely to be related. In this chapter, we shall be investigating problems associated with the size of these features and relationships between them. One important point to observe from each of the three examples of circular motion is that to maintain circular motion there needs to be a force towards the centre of the circle. If we cut the conker string, circular motion is no longer possible and the conker becomes a projectile moving freely under gravity.

Exploration 16.2

Practical activity – Penny on a turntable

This practical activity uses equipment from the Unilab Mechanics Kit.

1   Set up the apparatus as shown in the photograph. Place a penny on the disc and gradually increase the motor speed. Describe what happens.
2   Describe the path of the penny when it is not slipping. Explain why the penny does not have a constant velocity.
3   Explain why the penny is accelerating.
4   What forces act on the penny while it is moving in a circle? Draw diagrams to show these forces.
5   Which will slip first, a penny near the centre or a penny near the edge of the disc? Place three pennies on the disc, as shown, and gradually increase the motor speed.
6   Will a heavy coin slip at the same motor speed as a lighter coin? Try out a simple experiment a few times to see if you get consistent results.
7   Place a coin close to the edge of the disc. How does it move when it leaves the disc?

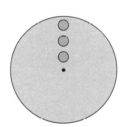

Results

This physical situation is modelled fully in Example 12.7, when you can compare your answers with the mathematical solution.

CALCULATOR ACTIVITY

Exploration 16.3

Firstly scale your axes using the range settings:

$$x_{\min} = -6; \quad x_{\max} = 6$$
$$y_{\min} = -4; \quad y_{\max} = 4$$
$$T_{\min} = 0; \quad T_{\max} = 2\pi; \quad \text{Step/Ptch} = 0.1$$

1   With your calculator in parametric plotting mode and radian
   mode, plot the path of an object that moves with position
   vector $\mathbf{r} = \cos t\,\mathbf{i} + \sin t\,\mathbf{j}$.
   Describe the path that is produced.

2   Now try these.
   a) $\mathbf{r} = 2\cos t\,\mathbf{i} + 2\sin t\,\mathbf{j}$
   b) $\mathbf{r} = 4\cos t\,\mathbf{i} + 4\sin t\,\mathbf{j}$

3   Clear your screen. Now plot the path of an object that moves with
   position vector $\mathbf{r} = \cos(2t)\,\mathbf{i} + \sin(2t)\,\mathbf{j}$.
   What differences do you notice when compared with $\mathbf{r} = \cos t\,\mathbf{i} + \sin t\,\mathbf{j}$?

Results

In each case the position vector is in the form $\mathbf{r} = r\cos(\omega t)\mathbf{i} + r\sin(\omega t)\mathbf{j}$
and the path of the object is a circle. The greater the value of r the
larger is the radius of the circle and the greater the value of ω the
more quickly the circle is completed. These features will be important
as we model motion in a circle with constant speed.

Position vector and angular speed

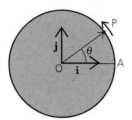

Consider an object that moves with constant speed around a circular
path with centre O and radius r. If the object starts at point A, then
suppose that after t seconds the position vector **OP** will have turned
through an angle θ. So at time t the position vector of the object will be:
   $\mathbf{r} = r\cos\theta\,\mathbf{i} + r\sin\theta\,\mathbf{j}$.
As time increases so θ increases. The rate of increase of θ is called the
angular speed and is usually denoted by the Greek letter omega, ω.
If the speed of the object is constant then ω is also constant.

Hence $\dfrac{\mathrm{d}\theta}{\mathrm{d}t} = \omega$ and integrating this we find $\theta = \omega t$.

In this integration we have set the constant of integration to zero
assuming that $t = 0$ when the object is at the point A.
We can now write the position vector of an object moving in a circle
with constant speed as a function of time t. This gives:
   $\mathbf{r} = r\cos(\omega t)\,\mathbf{i} + r\sin(\omega t)\,\mathbf{j}$
for appropriate perpendicular unit vectors $\mathbf{i}$ and $\mathbf{j}$.

In circular motion, angles are measured in radians, so the angular
speed ω is usually measured in radians per second (rad s^{-1}). Sometimes
the angular speed may be measured in other units, for example in
revolutions per minute (rpm).

Example 16.1

*The small hand of a clock completes one revolution every 12 hours
and the big hand one revolution every hour. Find the angular speed
of each hand in rad s^{-1} and rpm.*

Solution

*The small hand completes one revolution or 2π radians in 12 hours.
or 43 200 s. So the angular speed in radians per second is:*

$$\omega = \frac{2\pi}{43\,200} = 1.45 \times 10^{-4}\,\mathrm{rad\,s^{-1}}$$

The big hand completes one revolution or 2π radians in 1 hour, or 3600 seconds. So the angular speed in radians per second is:

$$\omega = \frac{2\pi}{3600} = 1.75 \times 10^{-3} \; rad\,s^{-1}$$

To express this in revolutions per minute the small hand completes one revolution in $12 \times 60 = 720$ minutes so we have:

$$\omega = \frac{1}{720} = 1.39 \times 10^{-3} \, \text{rpm}$$

and for the big hand

$$\omega = \frac{1}{60} = 1.67 \times 10^{-2} \, \text{rpm}$$

Example 16.2

The flywheel in a motorcycle engine is rotating at 5000 rpm. Find its angular speed in $rad\,s^{-1}$.

Solution
The flywheel completes 5000 revolutions in one minute or 60 seconds. So it turns through $2\pi \times 5000 = 10\,000\pi$ radians in 60 seconds.

So the angular speed is given by $\omega = \dfrac{10000\pi}{60} = 524 \, \text{rad s}^{-1}$

Velocity and angular velocity

The **speed** of a car travelling round a roundabout is shown on the car's speedometer but its **velocity** is a **vector** with **direction**.

When specifying the velocity of an object moving with a circular path, we need to identify its direction as well as its magnitude. We will show that for circular motion at constant speed, at any instant the direction of the velocity is along the tangent to the circular path. For **angular velocity** the magnitude is the angular speed, discussed above, but its direction is a bit more tricky. In fact it is defined to be perpendicular to the plane of the motion, although the explanation for this will have to wait. For the moment it is convenient to take the angular velocity as positive for an anticlockwise rotation and negative for a clockwise rotation.

In order to obtain the velocity vector for an object moving round a circle, it is simply necessary to differentiate the position vector with respect to time. Starting with

$$\mathbf{r} = r\cos(\omega t)\mathbf{i} + r\sin(\omega t)\mathbf{j}$$

and differentiating gives

$$\mathbf{v} = -r\omega\sin(\omega t)\mathbf{i} + r\omega\cos(\omega t)\mathbf{j}$$

The magnitude of this vector is the actual speed of the object describing circular motion.

$$v = |\mathbf{v}| = \sqrt{(-r\omega \sin(\omega t))^2 + (r\omega \cos(\omega t))^2}$$

$$= \sqrt{r^2\omega^2 \sin^2(\omega t) + r^2\omega^2 \cos^2(\omega t)}$$

$$= \sqrt{r^2\omega^2 \left(\sin^2(\omega t) + \cos^2(\omega t)\right)}$$

$$= \sqrt{r^2\omega^2} \quad \left(\text{since } \sin^2(\omega t) + \cos^2(\omega t) = 1\right)$$

$$= r\omega$$

So the speed of the object is given by the product of the radius and the angular speed. It is sometimes useful to express this in the form

$$\omega = \frac{v}{r}$$

The velocity vector can be expressed as $\mathbf{v} = -v\sin(\omega t)\,\mathbf{i} + v\cos(\omega t)\,\mathbf{j}$.

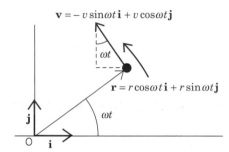

At each instant of time, the velocity vector of an object in circular motion is at right angles to its position vector. This is illustrated in the diagram.

The position vector points outwards along a radius from the centre of motion. This is called the **radial direction**. The velocity vector points at right angles to this radial direction and this is called the **transverse direction**. Notice that the transverse direction is that of ωt increasing in an anticlockwise sense.

Example 16.3

A fairground roundabout takes three seconds to complete one revolution. Rachel and Ben sit on seats that are 5 m and 3 m from the centre of rotation respectively.

For each child find:
a) their position vector and velocity vector,
b) their speed.

Solution

First we need to find the angular speed. The ride completes one revolution or 2π radians in three seconds so

$$\omega = \frac{2\pi}{3} \text{ rad s}^{-1}$$

a) Choosing unit vectors $\mathbf{i}$ and $\mathbf{j}$ in the horizontal plane, the position vectors will be given in the form:

$$\mathbf{r} = r\cos(\omega t)\,\mathbf{i} + r\sin(\omega t)\,\mathbf{j}$$

So for Ben:

$$\mathbf{r} = 3\cos\left(\frac{2\pi t}{3}\right)\mathbf{i} + 3\sin\left(\frac{2\pi t}{3}\right)\mathbf{j}$$

and differentiating gives:

$$\mathbf{v} = -2\pi\sin\left(\frac{2\pi t}{3}\right)\mathbf{i} + 2\pi\cos\left(\frac{2\pi t}{3}\right)\mathbf{j}$$

For Rachel:

$$\mathbf{r} = 5\cos\left(\frac{2\pi t}{3}\right)\mathbf{i} + 5\sin\left(\frac{2\pi t}{3}\right)\mathbf{j}$$

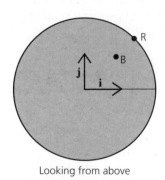

Looking from above

and differentiating gives:

$$\mathbf{v} = -\frac{10}{3}\pi\sin\left(\frac{2\pi t}{3}\right)\mathbf{i} + \frac{10}{3}\pi\cos\left(\frac{2\pi t}{3}\right)\mathbf{j}$$

b) *Their speeds are given by $v = r\omega$, so for Ben:*

$$v = 3\times\frac{2\pi}{3} = 2\pi = 6.28\,\text{m s}^{-1}$$

and for Rachel:

$$v = 5\times\frac{2\pi}{3} = \frac{10\pi}{3} = 10.47\,\text{m s}^{-1}$$

Example 16.4

A motorcyclist describes part of a circle as she goes round a roundabout. The radius of the circle is 20 m and the speed of the motorcyclist is 30 mph. Find the angular speed (in rad s⁻¹).

Solution
Converting 30 mph to m s⁻¹ gives

$$v = \frac{30\times 1609}{3600} = 13.4\,\text{m s}^{-1}.$$

The angular speed ω can be obtained using

$$\omega = \frac{v}{r} = \frac{13.4}{20} = 0.67\,\text{rad s}^{-1}.$$

EXERCISES

16.1 CLASSWORK

1 The Earth rotates about its axis once every 24 hours.
 a) What is the angular speed of the Earth about its axis?
 b) The radius of the Earth is 6.4×10^6 m. What is the speed of a person on the surface of the Earth at the equator?

2 A car is moving at $10\,\text{m s}^{-1}$ and has wheels of radius 25 cm.
 a) How long does it take for the wheel to complete one revolution?
 b) What is the angular speed of the wheel?

3 Complete the table below.

Object	Angular speed (rad s⁻¹)	Time for one revolution	Revolutions per minute
Engine flywheel			500
Record			45
Fairground ride	π/3		
Planet		20 hours	

4 A car with wheels of diameter 50 cm tows a trailer that has wheels of diameter 40 cm. Find the angular speed of both wheels when the car and trailer are travelling at $20\,\text{m s}^{-1}$.

5 An object moves with position vector, $\mathbf{r}$ metres, at time t seconds:

$$\mathbf{r} = 4\cos(3t)\mathbf{i} + 4\sin(3t)\mathbf{j}$$

 a) What is the speed of the object?
 b) What is the angular speed of the object?
 c) How long would it take to complete one revolution?
 d) How many revolutions would it complete in one minute?

6 A chain passes over a circular sprocket of radius 10 cm. If the chain is moving at 0.8 m s^{-1}, find the angular speed of the sprocket.

7 Emma gets into a big wheel at the fairground and sits on a seat that is at its lowest point. The wheel has radius 5 m and takes 10 seconds to complete one revolution. Using unit vectors that are horizontal and vertical, find position and velocity vectors for Emma at time t seconds after the ride starts if:
a) the origin is at the centre of the wheel,
b) the origin is at the lowest point of the ride.

8 The moon completes one orbit around the Earth every 28 days. Assume that the moon describes a circular path of radius 3.84×10^8 m. Calculate the speed at which the moon is moving.

9 A satellite is in geostationary orbit, which means it always stays above the same point on the Earth's surface. It is at a height of 4.24×10^7 m above the centre of the Earth, and it always stays above the same point on the equator. Find the speed of this satellite.

10 A spin drier rotates at 1100 rpm and has a drum of radius of 22 cm. Find the speed of the clothes in the drier.

EXERCISES

16.1 HOMEWORK

1 A fairground ride rotates once every five seconds.
a) What is the angular speed of the ride?
b) If the radius of the ride is 5 m, what is the speed of a person at the edge of the ride?

2 A bicycle has wheels of radius 40 cm. The bicycle is moving at 5 m s^{-1}.
a) Find the circumference of the wheel in metres.
b) How long does it take for the wheel to complete one revolution?
c) Find the angular speed of the wheel.

3 For each situation below, convert the angular speed from rpm to rad s^{-1} and find the time for one revolution.
a) A motorcycle engine's flywheel rotating at 5000 rpm.
b) A record rotating at 33 rpm.
c) The PTO shaft of a tractor rotating at 200 rpm.
d) A clockwork mobile that it is rotating at 10 rpm.

4 An object moves so that its position, **r** metres, at time t seconds is given by:

$$\mathbf{r} = 3\cos(2t)\mathbf{i} + 3\sin(2t)\mathbf{j}$$

where **i** and **j** are perpendicular unit vectors.
a) Find an expression for the velocity of the object at time t.
b) What is the speed of the object?
c) How long does it take for the object to complete one revolution?

5 A drive belt is moving at 20 m s^{-1} as it passes over a pulley, of radius 0.15 m.
a) Assume that the belt does not slip on the pulley and find the angular speed of the pulley in rad s^{-1}.
b) Convert the angular speed to rpm.

6 A car is moving at $20\,\text{m s}^{-1}$. The wheels of the car have radius 25 cm. A small mass is attached to the wheel 15 cm from the centre.

a) Find the angular speed of the wheel.

b) What is the speed of the mass?

7 The large hand of a clock is 0.14 m long, and the small hand is 0.08 m long. Using a suitable origin and unit vectors **i** and **j**:

a) find an expression for the position vectors of the tip of each hand,

b) find the velocity of the tip of each hand.

8 A car of mass 950 kg moves on a roundabout so that its position in metres at time t seconds is given by:

$$\mathbf{r} = 50\cos\left(\frac{\pi}{10}t\right)\mathbf{i} + 50\sin\left(\frac{\pi}{10}t\right)\mathbf{j}$$

where **i** and **j** are perpendicular unit vectors.

a) Find the velocity of the car at time t.

b) Show that the kinetic energy of the car is constant, and find its value.

9 A particle is constrained to move in a circle by a length of string so that its position vector in metres at time t seconds is:

$$\mathbf{r} = 0.2\cos(20t)\mathbf{i} + 0.2\sin(20t)\mathbf{j}$$

a) Find the velocity of the particle at time t.

b) When $t = 3$ the string breaks, find the velocity of the particle at this time.

c) Find the position of the particle when $t = 5$, stating any assumptions you make.

10 A child sits on the edge of a roundabout of radius 2.5 m holding a ball.

a) Find the speed of the ball if the roundabout rotates once every two seconds.

b) Sketch the path of the ball if the child lets go of it. Assuming that the ball is 1.5 m above ground level when released, how long does it take to reach the ground?

c) If the child throws the ball horizontally towards the centre of the roundabout at $3\,\text{m s}^{-1}$, find its actual velocity. Sketch the path of the ball as viewed from above.

THE ACCELERATION VECTOR

The acceleration vector is one of the most important vectors in mechanics because it acts in the same direction as the resultant force acting on the object. If you know the acceleration you can find the force and vice-versa. We have seen above that although the speed of circular motion might be constant the velocity is changing because the direction of motion is continually changing. Where there is a change of velocity an object has an acceleration, but how are its magnitude and direction related to radius r and angular speed ω?

To get some insight into the answer, consider the motion of a conker on a string moving in a horizontal circle with constant speed. We can identify two forces acting on the conker: the **tension** force along the string and the force of **gravity**. The vertical component of the tension will balance the force of gravity ($T\cos\theta = mg$) and the horizontal component of the tension ($T\sin\theta$) is the resultant force.

This points towards the centre of the circle, so we might deduce that the acceleration vector also points towards the centre of the circle (using Newton's second law).

The magnitude is perhaps more difficult to deduce. Intuitively, we could argue that as the conker is swung harder the radius of the circle and the angular speed of the conker both increase so that the angle θ increases. Then mathematically we can say that as the angle θ increases the tension increases (since $T\cos\theta = mg$) and so the acceleration will increase.

So from this physical situation we can suggest that for circular motion with constant speed, the acceleration vector:

- points inwards along the radius
- has magnitude which increases when r and ω increase.

Now we shall see if we can confirm these results using calculus. The acceleration vector can be obtained by differentiating the velocity vector with respect to time.
Starting with:

$$\mathbf{v} = -r\omega \sin(\omega t)\mathbf{i} + r\omega \cos(\omega t)\mathbf{j}$$

and differentiating gives:

$$\begin{aligned} \mathbf{a} &= -r\omega^2 \cos(\omega t)\mathbf{i} - r\omega^2 \sin(\omega t)\mathbf{j} \\ &= -\omega^2 \big(r\cos(\omega t)\mathbf{i} + r\sin(\omega t)\mathbf{j}\big) \\ &= -\omega^2 \mathbf{r} \end{aligned}$$

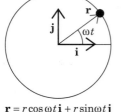

$\mathbf{r} = r\cos\omega t\,\mathbf{i} + r\sin\omega t\,\mathbf{j}$
$\mathbf{v} = -r\omega\sin\omega t\,\mathbf{i} + r\omega\cos\omega t\,\mathbf{j}$

The acceleration vector is related to the position vector. The negative sign indicates that the acceleration vector is directed towards the centre of the circle. The magnitude of the acceleration is $r\omega^2$ where r is the radius of the circle. This confirms the experimental evidence for the conker on a string.

It is sometimes useful to be able to express the acceleration of an object describing a circle in terms of its speed rather than its angular speed. Substituting for $\omega = \dfrac{v}{r}$ in $a = r\omega^2$ we get:

$$a = \frac{v^2}{r}$$

We now have the main results needed to model any circular motion with constant speed. These results are summarised in the following figures.

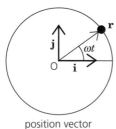

position vector
$\mathbf{r} = -r\cos\omega t\,\mathbf{i} + r\sin\omega t\,\mathbf{j}$

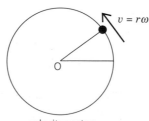

velocity vector
$\mathbf{v} = -v\sin\omega t\,\mathbf{i} + v\cos\omega t\,\mathbf{j}$

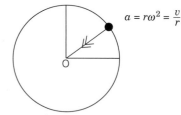

acceleration vector
$\mathbf{a} = -a\cos\omega t\,\mathbf{i} - a\sin\omega t\,\mathbf{j}$

Newton's second law tells us that the resultant force required for any motion acts in the same direction as the acceleration. Hence the resultant force required for circular motion at constant speed to be sustained acts *towards* the centre of the circle. This may be intuitively obvious for the chairoplanes ride and the conker on a string. For the car going round the roundabout the frictional force directed towards the centre of the circle is essential to maintain the circular path.

Example 16.5

A car of mass 1100 kg is travelling at 12 m s⁻¹ round a roundabout of radius 50 m. Find the acceleration of the car and the force needed to keep the car moving in a circle.

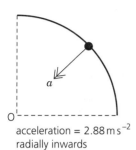

acceleration = 2.88 m s⁻² radially inwards

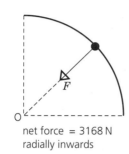

net force = 3168 N radially inwards

Solution

The magnitude of the acceleration is given by:

$$a = \frac{v^2}{r} = \frac{12^2}{50} = 2.88 \text{m s}^{-2}$$

As the car is describing the circle at constant speed, the acceleration must act towards the centre of the circle. The resultant force must also have the same direction, towards the centre of the circle. The magnitude of this resultant force is given by
$$F = ma = 1100 \times 2.88 = 3168 \text{N}.$$
This force is supplied by friction.

Example 16.6

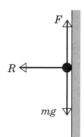

A fairground ride – 'wall of death' – consists of a cylindrical drum that rotates. Riders stand inside the drum and lean against the drum wall. When the drum rotates the floor is lowered, but the riders appear to stick to the sides of the drum, i.e. they do not slide down the wall. The radius of the drum is 3 m and the coefficient of friction between the riders and the drum is 0.7. Find the minimum speed at which the drum must rotate if the riders are to stay in position as the floor drops.

Solution

Modelling the rider as a particle and identifying the forces acting on the rider gives the diagram shown. Gravity acts downwards, friction acts upwards (opposing the tendency of the rider to slide down) and a normal reaction acts towards the centre of the drum.
The friction force must balance the force of the gravity so:
$$F = mg \qquad\qquad (1)$$
The normal reaction must provide an acceleration of $r\omega^2$ toward the centre so that:
$$R = mr\omega^2 = 3m\omega^2 \qquad\qquad (2)$$
As the coefficient of friction is 0.7, in the limiting case when the rider is about to slide:
$$F = \mu R = 0.7R \qquad\qquad (3)$$
Using equations (1) and (3) gives:
$$0.7R = mg \ \Rightarrow \ R = \frac{mg}{0.7}$$
Now substituting into equation (2) gives:
$$\frac{mg}{0.7} = 3m\omega^2 \Rightarrow \omega^2 = \frac{g}{2.1}$$

$$\omega = \sqrt{\frac{g}{21}} = 2.16 \text{ rad s}^{-1}$$

Example 16.7

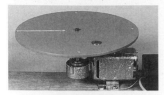

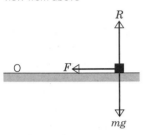

view from above

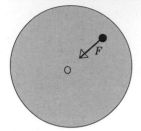

view from side

Penny on a turntable

This example models the practical activity of Exploration 16.2. The photograph shows a horizontal flat disc which rotates about an axis through its centre. A penny is placed on the disc and the disc rotates so that the penny remains at rest relative to the disc. Investigate the motion of the penny as the angular speed of the disc and the initial position of the penny changes.

Solution

While the penny is at rest relative to the disc it describes a horizontal circle with constant speed, the same speed as the disc. The penny is accelerating because its direction of motion is changing. The figure shows the forces on the penny which is modelled as a particle.

*There are three forces acting on the penny: the force of **gravity**, the **normal reaction** and **friction** towards the centre. Remember that it is essential that the friction is towards the centre because the acceleration is towards the centre.*

The vertical forces are in balance so that $R = mg$

Applying Newton's second law to the particle gives $F = mr\omega^2$.

If the coefficient of friction is denoted by μ then $F \le \mu R$. Substituting for R and F gives $mr\omega^2 \le \mu R = \mu mg$

Dividing by m we get $r\omega^2 \le \mu g$.

For a given angular speed ω, the penny must be within a circle of radius $\frac{\mu g}{\omega^2}$; if the penny is placed on the disc outside this circle, it cannot remain at rest as the disc rotates. The motion of the penny relative to the disc is a complicated path as the photograph below shows. (The mathematical description of this motion is beyond the scope of this book.) Similarly, for a given initial position of the penny on the disc, the angular speed must be less than $\sqrt{\frac{\mu g}{r}}$ for the penny to remain at rest relative to the disc.

As the angular speed ω increases, the friction force F increases until limiting friction is reached. Beyond this critical value of ω, the friction is no longer sufficient to maintain the relative rest between the penny and disc so that the penny slides, following the path shown in the photograph.

An important thing to notice about the solution is that it is independent of the mass of the penny. According to the theory, heavy masses will behave in the same way as light masses. However, once the penny begins to slide the mass does become important in the subsequent motion.

Look back at Exploration 16.2 and compare your answers with the mathematical description in this example.

Banked tracks

In a cycle velodrome, the track is banked so that the outside of the circuit is higher than the inside. This feature is also found on bends on some roads and on railway tracks. The photograph shows an example of banking.

The banking is intended to reduce the tendency for the vehicle to slide outwards as it travels round the circular path at high speeds. The next example shows how to model problems involving banked tracks.

Example 16.8

A cyclist is describing part of a circle of radius 30 m at a constant speed on a track banked at an angle of 30° to the horizontal. Find the speed of the cyclist for a model in which friction is assumed to be negligible.

Solution

Assume that the cyclist is a particle and neglect friction forces. In the plane perpendicular to the motion there are two forces: the force of gravity and the normal reaction.

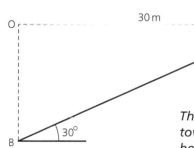

The particle is moving with constant speed in a circular path with centre O. (Note that the centre of the circle is in a horizontal plane not at the bottom of the track B.) The force of gravity must be balanced by the vertical component of R, so:

$$mg = R\cos 30° \qquad (1)$$

The horizontal component of R must provide the acceleration towards the centre of the circle, otherwise circular motion would not be possible, so:

$$m\frac{v^2}{30} = R\cos 60° \qquad (2)$$

Eliminating R from equations (1) and (2) gives:

$$m\frac{v^2}{30} = \left(\frac{mg}{\cos 30°}\right)\cos 60°$$

Solving for v^2:

$$v^2 = \frac{30 \times g \times \cos 60°}{\cos 30°}$$

and then $v = 13.0\,\mathrm{m\,s^{-1}}$.

Without the banking, circular motion would not be possible, because without friction there would be no force towards the centre of the circle to provide the acceleration.

EXERCISES

16.2 CLASSWORK

The following data are used in some of these exercises.
The radius of the Earth is 6.37×10^6 m and the mass of the Earth is 5.98×10^{24} kg. **Gravitational constant, G** = 6.67×10^{-11} N m^2 kg^{-2}
A geostationary orbit is one where the orbiting object remains above the same point on the Earth.

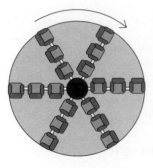

1 Calculate the acceleration experienced in each situation described below.
   a) A car travelling at a constant $12\,\text{m}\,\text{s}^{-1}$ on a bend of radius $80\,\text{m}$.
   b) A child on a roundabout of radius $2\,\text{m}$ in a park, that rotates at $1\,\text{rad}\,\text{s}^{-1}$.
   c) A fairground big wheel, with radius $5\,\text{m}$, that completes one revolution every $10\,\text{seconds}$.

2 Where should you sit on the fairground ride shown if you want to experience the greatest acceleration? Explain why.

3 A car of mass $1200\,\text{kg}$ is trying to negotiate a roundabout of radius $50\,\text{m}$. The coefficient of friction between the tyres and the road is 0.9.
   a) Draw a diagram showing the forces acting on the car in the plane perpendicular to the direction of motion of the car.
   b) Find the magnitude of the maximum friction force that can act on the car.
   c) Calculate the maximum magnitude of the acceleration of the car.
   d) Calculate the maximum speed that the car can travel round the roundabout.
   e) Would a lighter car be able to get round the roundabout at a speed of $25\,\text{m}\,\text{s}^{-1}$?

4 A satellite is to be placed in a circular orbit around the Earth.
   a) Draw a diagram to show the forces acting on the satellite while it is in orbit.
   b) The satellite is to orbit the Earth at a height of $450\,000\,\text{m}$ above the Earth's surface. Find the magnitude of the acceleration of the satellite. (**Hint:** At this distance from the Earth you will need to use Newton's law of universal gravitation.)
   c) Find the angular speed of the satellite required for this orbit.
   d) How long does it take for the satellite to orbit the Earth once?

5 An aeroplane of mass $20\,000\,\text{kg}$ is flying with constant velocity in a circular path of radius $500\,\text{m}$ while waiting to land. Assume that the lift force on the aeroplane is perpendicular to the aeroplane.
   a) Draw a diagram to show the forces acting on the aeroplane if it is banked at an angle of $15°$ to the horizontal.
   b) By considering the vertical components of the forces acting, calculate the magnitude of the lift force.
   c) Use your result from **b)** to find the resultant force on the aeroplane, and hence its acceleration.
   d) Find the speed of the aeroplane.
   e) The air traffic controllers want to instruct a lighter aeroplane to circle in an identical way. What speed should they specify?

6 **a)** Modelling the Earth as a sphere rotating about an axis through its centre, calculate the angular speed of the Earth in $\text{rad}\,\text{s}^{-1}$. Hence deduce the angular speed of a satellite in geostationary orbit.
   b) Find an expression for the resultant force on a satellite in a geostationary orbit above the equator in terms of its mass, m, and the radius, r, of the orbit.
   c) Find an expression for the magnitude of the gravitational force acting on the satellite in terms of G, m and M, the mass of the Earth.
   d) Use your answers to **b)** and **c)** to find the radius of the geostationary orbit.

7 A crate is placed on the back of a lorry but not secured in any way. The coefficient of friction between the crate and the back of the lorry is 0.6.
a) A bend has a radius of 20 m and the speed of the lorry is 15 m s^{-1}. Does the crate slip?
b) What is the maximum speed that the lorry can travel round the bend, if the crate is not to slip?

8 A cycle track is circular and banked at 30° to the horizontal, with a radius of 60 m.
a) In a first model, ignoring the friction force, find the maximum speed of the cyclist.
b) If the coefficient of friction between the tyres and the track is 0.7, find the maximum speed of the cyclist on the track if friction is included.

9 a) Draw a diagram to show the forces acting on a person standing on the surface of the Earth.
b) Calculate the acceleration of the person due to the rotation of the Earth.
c) Use your answer to calculate the difference between the normal reaction and the force of gravity on a person of mass m.
d) Is it reasonable to ignore the effects of the Earth's rotation when considering objects at rest on the surface of the Earth?

10 On the spin cycle, the drum of a washing machine rotates at 1100 rpm about a horizontal axis so that clothes in the drum move in a vertical circle with constant speed.
a) Draw diagrams to show the forces acting on an item of clothing, modelled as a particle of mass M, at the top and bottom of the drum.
b) Find the acceleration of the clothes in the drum, which has radius 45 cm.
c) Express the magnitude of the normal reaction in terms of M, at the top and bottom of the drum.

11 A motorcyclist performs a loop the loop stunt by riding inside a cylinder, which has a horizontal axis of symmetry and a radius of 4 m. The rider ensures that the motorbike maintains a constant speed at all times.
a) Describe what happens to the normal reaction force on the motorcycle as it completes the loop.
b) Explain why at the slowest safe speed the normal reaction can drop to zero at the top of the cylinder.
c) Calculate the slowest safe speed for the motorcycle.

EXERCISES

16.2 HOMEWORK

The following data are used in some of these exercises.
The radius of the Earth is 6.37×10^6 m and the mass of the Earth is 5.98×10^{24} kg.
A geostationary orbit is one where the orbiting object remains above the same point on the Earth.

1 Calculate the acceleration experienced in each situation described below.
a) A particle in a centrifuge that describes a circle of radius 8 cm, and rotates at 400 rpm.
b) An aeroplane travelling at 200 m s^{-1} in an arc of a circle of radius 500 m.
c) A jet-ski travelling at 5 m s^{-1} in a circle of radius 20 m.

2 Find the magnitude of the force required for each object to move as described.

a) A car of mass 1000 kg, travelling at 10 m s⁻¹ on a roundabout of radius 60 m.

b) A children's roundabout in a playground that rotates at 3 rad s⁻¹ (The child has mass 40 kg and sits 1.2 m from the centre of the roundabout.)

c) A satellite of mass 300 kg in a circular orbit of radius 7×10^8 m, which completes one revolution every 8 hours.

3 A shirt in a spin drier that rotates about a vertical axis can be modelled as a particle. The drum of the drier rotates at 1000 rpm and has radius 30 cm.

a) Find the acceleration of the shirt.

b) If the shirt has a mass of 1 kg when wet, find the reaction force exerted by the drum.

4 A particle moves so that its position vector is

$$\mathbf{r} = 6\cos(2\pi t)\mathbf{i} + 6\sin(2\pi t)\mathbf{j}$$

where $\mathbf{i}$ and $\mathbf{j}$ are perpendicular unit vectors.

a) Find the acceleration vector.

b) Find the magnitude of the acceleration.

5 A child of mass 42 kg is sitting on the edge of a roundabout of radius 1.4 m in a playground.

a) Find the normal reaction force acting on the child.

b) Find the angular speed of the roundabout when the child would slip off, if the coefficient of friction between the child and the roundabout is 0.6.

c) How would your answer change for a heavier or lighter child?

d) Do you think that there is likely to be an accident, while the roundabout is in normal use?

6 A car of mass 1200 kg travels on a road banked at 5° to the horizontal. Assume that there is no friction present.

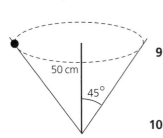

a) Find the normal reaction force on the car.

b) Find the speed of the car if it describes a circle of 80 m.

c) Comment on how helpful it would be to have a 5° banked road, as part of an approach to a motorway.

7 The coefficient of friction between the tyres of a racing motorcycle and the surface of the race track is 1.0. Find the greatest speed at which a bend of radius 150 m can be taken.

8 A fairground ride has seats 4 m from the centre of rotation. The ride completes one revolution every five seconds. It is to be replaced by a new ride with seats at 5 m from the centre of rotation. How should the time for one complete revolution be altered so that riders experience the same acceleration as on the old ride?

9 A marble of mass 20 grams describes a circle inside the cone illustrated. The centre of the circle is 50 cm above the bottom of the cone.

a) Find the speed of marble and the size of the normal reaction force.

b) What role, if any, does friction have in this situation?

10 To be most effective the clothes in a tumble drier should not always stick to the side of the drier. A designer considers that ideally the clothes should fall away at the position shown in the diagram. Calculate the rate of rotation for a drum of radius 40 cm.

THE CONICAL PENDULUM

Conker on
a string

The chairoplanes theme park ride and the conker on the string shown
in the figure are both examples of **conical pendulums**. Such a system
consists of an object, attached to a fixed point by an inextensible
string, made to rotate in a horizontal circle. We begin this section with
a practical activity to explore the properties of a conical pendulum.

Exploration 16.4

Practical activity

*For this practical activity you will need the conical pendulum
components from the Unilab Mechanics Kit.*

1   *Set up the apparatus as shown in the photograph. You may find it helpful
    to use a slide projector or an OHP to shine a bright light on the apparatus,
    so that it casts a shadow onto a wall or screen.*

2   *What forces act on the object at the end of the string while it is
    rotating? Illustrate these forces on a diagram.*
    *Without further experimentation, answer the following questions
    about the motion of the object.*

3   *What happens when the angular speed of the system is increased?
    Is there a maximum angle that can be obtained between the string
    and the post?*

4   *What happens if you change the length of the string?*

5   *What happens if you change the mass at the end of the string?*
    Now check your answers by carrying out simple experiments.

6   *Describe what happens to the velocity and acceleration of the mass as
    it rotates.*
    *Before modelling the conical pendulum, here are two examples which
    will give some insight as to how to proceed in the general case.*

Example 16.9

*A child of mass 40 kg swings on the end of a rope of length 4 m,
describing a horizontal circle of radius 1.5 m. Find the angular speed
of the child and the tension in the rope.*

Solution

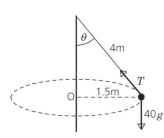

*Modelling the child as a particle, the diagram below shows the
circular motion with centre O and the forces acting.*
*The vertical component of the tension must balance the force of
gravity, so using $g = 9.8\,\mathrm{m\,s^{-2}}$ gives:*

$$T\cos\theta = 40 \times 9.8 = 392 \qquad (1)$$

*As the child describes a circle, the acceleration is $r\omega^2$ towards the
centre of the circle. The horizontal component of the tension provides
this acceleration, so:*

$$T\sin\theta = 40 \times 1.5\omega^2 \qquad (2)$$

Eliminating T from equations (1) and (2) gives:

$$\frac{392}{\cos\theta} \times \sin\theta = 60\omega^2$$

so:

$$\omega^2 = \frac{392}{60}\tan\theta \qquad (3)$$

From the diagram and using simple trigonometry:

$$\tan\theta = \frac{1.5}{\sqrt{4^2 - 1.5^2}}$$

Now the value for ω is found by substituting for $\tan\theta$ in equation (3).

$$\omega^2 = \frac{392}{60} \times \frac{1.5}{\sqrt{4^2 - 1.5^2}}$$

$$\omega = 1.63 \text{ rad s}^{-1}$$

So the angular speed is 1.63 rad s^{-1}. The tension is found using equation (1).

$$T\cos\theta = 392$$

and $\cos\theta = \dfrac{\sqrt{4^2 - 1.5^2}}{4}$

Solving for T:

$$T = \frac{392}{\cos\theta} = 392 \times \frac{4}{\sqrt{4^2 - 1.5^2}} = 423 \text{ N}$$

Example 16.10

A toy aeroplane is suspended from a ceiling by a piece of string of length 50 cm. When the aeroplane is wound up it describes a horizontal circle and the string makes an angle of 30° to the vertical. Find the speed of the aeroplane.

Solution

The forces acting on the aeroplane, modelled as a particle, are the tension and the force of gravity.

The vertical component of the tension must balance the force of gravity, so:

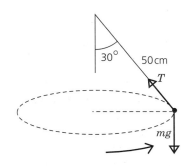

$$T\cos 30° = mg \qquad\qquad (1)$$

The aeroplane must have an acceleration of $\dfrac{v^2}{r}$ towards the centre of the circle, and the horizontal component of the tension must cause this acceleration, so Newton's second law gives:

$$T\sin 30° = \frac{mv^2}{r} \qquad\qquad (2)$$

Dividing equation (1) by equation (2) eliminates T to give:

$$\tan 30° = \frac{v^2}{rg}$$

Solving for v^2 gives:

$$v^2 = rg\tan 30°$$

The radius of the circle is given by:

$r = 0.5\sin 30° = 0.25\,m$

Now v can be found.

$$v^2 = rg\tan 30° = 0.25 \times 9.8 \times \tan 30°$$

$$v = 1.19\,m\,s^{-1}$$

Angles and speed

These two examples show us how to proceed for the general conical pendulum with an object of mass m, attached to an inextensible string of length l, describing circular horizontal motion with constant speed. Suppose that the radius of the circular motion is r and the angle of the string to the vertical is θ. The figure shows the object modelled as a

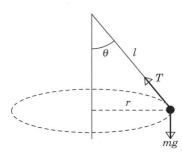

particle, and the forces which are acting. These are the tension in the string and the force of gravity.

The vertical component of the tangent balances the force of gravity so

$$T\cos\theta = mg \qquad (1)$$

For circular motion to be possible, there must be a force towards the centre of the circle O. This force is the horizontal component of the tension. Applying Newton's second law gives:

$$T\sin\theta = mr\omega^2$$

where ω is the constant angular speed.

From the figure:

$$r = l\sin\theta$$

giving

$$T\sin\theta = ml\omega^2\sin\theta$$

and dividing both sides by $\sin\theta$ gives:

$$T = ml\omega^2$$

Substituting for T from equation (1) gives:

$$\frac{mg}{\cos\theta} = ml\omega^2$$

and solving for $\cos\theta$ gives:

$$\cos\theta = \frac{g}{l\omega^2}$$

This is a general formula relating the angle between the conical pendulum and the vertical to the length of the string and the angular speed. From this result we can make three mathematical deductions:

- the motion of the object is independent of its mass,
- as the length l increases, $\cos\theta$ decreases and so the angle θ increases,
- as the angular speed ω increases, $\cos\theta$ decreases and so the angle θ increases.

The consequences of these results are important in many fairground rides which can be modelled by the conical pendulum. For example, on a chairoplanes ride, the rider will travel at the same angle to the vertical, whatever their mass. This is rather fortunate! Imagine two adjacent seats, one containing a heavyweight boxer and the other containing a light ballet dancer. If the motion depended on the mass of the rider it could be unfortunate for the ballet dancer on the inside!

EXERCISES

16.3 CLASSWORK

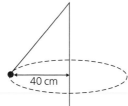

1 A conker on the end of a length of string is set in horizontal motion with a speed of $4\,\mathrm{m\,s^{-1}}$, so that it describes a circle.
  a) Draw a diagram to show the forces acting on the conker.
  b) Write down two equations by considering first the vertical component of the tension and secondly the horizontal component of the tension and the acceleration of the conker.
  c) Eliminate the tension from the two equations above and find the angle that the string makes with the vertical.

2 A child of mass $50\,\mathrm{kg}$ swings on the end of a rope of length $6\,\mathrm{m}$ and describes a horizontal circle of radius $2\,\mathrm{m}$.
  a) Find the tension in the rope.
  b) Find the angular speed of the child and the time taken to complete one circle.
  c) What assumptions have been made about the rope?

d) Two children, of masses 40 kg and 45 kg, swing together on the rope in the same way. What happens to the tension and the time to complete one circle?

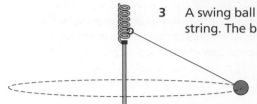

3 A swing ball game consists of a ball of mass 100 grams attached to a string. The ball is hit so that it moves at 2 m s⁻¹, in a circle of radius 1.2 m.
    a) Find the angular speed of the ball.
    b) Find the angle that the string makes with the vertical post.
    c) Find the tension of the string.

4 At a School Fayre a ball on the end of a piece of string has to be swung to hit a skittle. The diagram shows the set up, and the position of the skittle.
Find the speed at which the ball should be thrown if it is to hit the skittle.

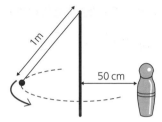

5 An object of mass 2 kg rests on a rough horizontal table with coefficient of friction 0.5. It is attached to another object of mass 0.8 kg by a light inelastic string which passes through a small hole in a table. This object describes a horizontal circle with constant speed 2 m s⁻¹ and the object on the table is on the point of slipping.
    a) Draw a diagram showing the forces acting on each object.
    b) Find the tension in the string.
    c) Calculate the radius of the circle and the length of the string below the table.

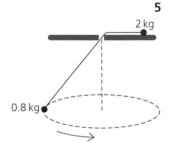

6 The diagram shows an object attached by two strings. The object has mass 200 grams and completes three revolutions per second.
    a) Find the acceleration of the object.
    b) Find the tension in each string.

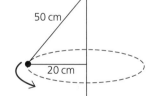

7 The mechanism shown in the diagram is designed to regulate the flow of steam from a boiler, to control the speed of an engine. It is called an 'engine governor'. It consists of four light rods together with two metal spheres A and B. The rods AD and BD are smoothly jointed to a smooth vertical spindle at D. A small ring is smoothly jointed to AC and BC at C and can slide on the spindle below D. When a valve is open the ring rests on a smooth horizontal ledge fixed to the spindle. The system rotates with the engine drive shaft about the axis CD.

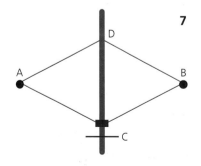

As the angular speed increases so the ring slides up the spindle, controlling the flow of steam from the boiler and the pressure needed to drive the engine.
    a) What assumptions do you think would be appropriate when modelling this system?
    b) Draw a diagram to show the forces on one sphere.
    c) For a particular system, spheres of mass 250 grams are used on arms of length 15 cm. The mass of the ring is 100 grams. At the optimum operating speed the governors rotate at 120 rpm. What angle do the arms make with the vertical?
    d) What rate of rotation is needed before the system can be effective if the radius of each sphere is 2.4 cm?
    e) What would happen if you assume the mass of the ring is zero?

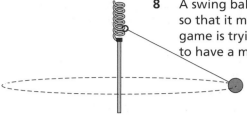

8 A swing ball game consists of a ball attached to a string. The ball is hit so that it moves in a horizontal circle. The designer of a swingball game is trying to decide how strong the string needs to be. The ball is to have a mass of 120 grams and the string has a length of 1.2 m.

  a) Estimate the greatest speed at which a swing ball is likely to move and then determine the greatest tension that the string must be able to withstand.

  b) Find a general expression for tension, T, in terms of the speed of the ball, v, and its mass, m.

EXERCISES

16.3 HOMEWORK

1 A conical pendulum consists of a string of length 1.2 m and an object of mass 3 kg. The string makes an angle of 20° to the vertical as the object describes a circle.

  a) Find the radius of the circle.

  b) Use the vertical components of the force to find the tension in the string.

  c) Find the angular speed of the object, by considering the horizontal components of the forces acting on it.

2 A heavy ball, of mass 200 kg, that is used for demolition work, is set into motion so that it moves in a horizontal circle at a constant speed. The cable supporting the ball is 6 m long and makes an angle of 5° with the vertical.

  a) Find the tension in the cable, by considering the vertical components of the forces acting.

  b) Find the speed of the ball.

3 Two children play a game, using conkers on the ends of strings of length 40 cm. They take turns to swing the conker round in a circle and try to get their hand as close as possible to the surface of a table. One child's hand is 12 cm above the table. Find the speed of the conker.

4 Find the speed of each particle and the tension in each string shown below.

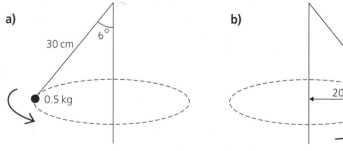

a)   30 cm   6°   0.5 kg

b)   50 cm   20 cm   1 kg

5 The diagram shows a length of string that has been passed through a hole in a table. Masses are attached to the ends of each string as shown in the diagram.

The mass on the table top is on the point of slipping.

  a) Draw two diagrams to show the forces acting on each mass.

  b) Find the tension in the string.

  c) Find the acceleration of the lower mass.

  d) What is the coefficient of friction between the 100 gram mass and the surface?

  e) Is the value that you have obtained reasonable?

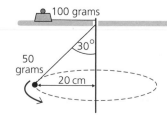

100 grams
50 grams
30°
20 cm

6 A conical pendulum consists of a string of length l, and a mass, m. The string makes an angle α with the vertical. The mass moves with speed v.
  a) Find an expression for the tension, T, in the string in terms of m, v, l and α.
  b) Find an expression for $\tan\alpha$ in terms of g, v and r.

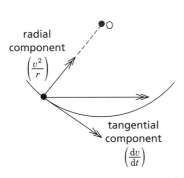

7 A mass, M, is at rest on the outer surface of a smooth cone. It is attached by a length of string to another mass, m, which describes a circle of radius r.
  a) Find the tension in the string.
  b) Find the angular speed of the moving mass in terms of g, r, m and M.
  c) Express M in terms of m.
  d) If the centre of the circle is 50 cm below the vertex of the cone find ω.

8 An object, of mass 2 kg, is attached by two ropes to a spindle that rotates at a constant angular speed of 10 rad s^{-1}. Find the tension in each string, given that the object describes a circle of radius 1 m.

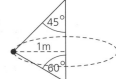

MOTION IN A VERTICAL CIRCLE WITH VARIABLE SPEED

The idea of circular motion at constant speed can be extended to vertical circular motion, where the speed varies as the object travels round a circle. For example, a pendulum describes part of a circle and its speed varies as it moves round. The acceleration will now have two components. One acts towards the centre with magnitude $\frac{v^2}{r}$ which corresponds to the acceleration for the constant speed case. The second component is along the tangent and has magnitude $\frac{dv}{dt}$, the rate of change of the speed.

The diagram shows the two components of acceleration for a simple pendulum.

radial component $\left(\frac{v^2}{r}\right)$

tangential component $\left(\frac{dv}{dt}\right)$

Example 16.11

A loop-the-loop track has a loop of radius 20 cm.

a) *Find the speed of the car at the top of the loop if it is just to loop the loop.*
b) *Find the height of release needed to reach this speed.*

Solution
a) *If the car loops the loop it will remain in contact with the track and so the normal reaction force R will always act. In the case of the car that just loops the loop the reaction force will be zero at the top of the loop, i.e. $R = 0$.*

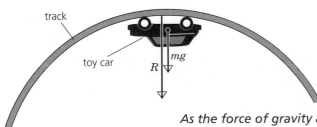

track

toy car

As the force of gravity acts straight down the resultant force is simply mg towards the centre of the circle. The car must have an acceleration of $\dfrac{v^2}{r}$ towards the centre, so applying Newton's second law gives:

$$mg = m\frac{v^2}{r}$$

or

$$v^2 = rg = 0.2 \times 9.8 = 1.96$$

and so $v = 1.4\,\mathrm{m\,s^{-1}}$.

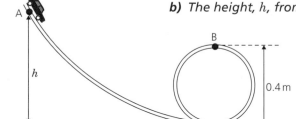

b) The height, h, from which to release the car can be determined by conservation of energy.

PE of car at A = PE of car at B + KE of car at B

$$mgh = mg \times 0.4 + \tfrac{1}{2}m \times 1.4^2$$

$$9.8h = 3.92 + 0.98$$

$$h = \frac{4.9}{9.8} = 0.5\text{ m}$$

Example 16.12

A particle, P, of mass 4 kg is attached to the end of a light string. The string has length 0.8 m. The other end of the string is fixed at O. The particle is released with the string horizontal.

a) Find an expression for the speed of the particle when the string makes an angle θ with the vertical, as shown in the diagram.
b) Find an expression for the tension in the string in terms of g and θ.
c) Find the maximum tension in the string.

Solution

a) The speed is found using conservation of energy.
The potential energy lost is $4 \times g \times 0.8\cos\theta = 3.2g\cos\theta$.
As this will be equal to the kinetic energy, we have:

$$\frac{1}{2} \times 4v^2 = 3.2g\cos\theta$$

$$v^2 = 1.6g\cos\theta$$

$$v = \sqrt{1.6g\cos\theta}$$

b) The diagram shows the forces acting on the particle.
Resolving parallel to the string gives the resultant force towards the centre as $T - mg\cos\theta$.
Then using Newton's second law gives:

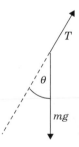

$$\frac{4v^2}{0.8} = T - 4g\cos\theta$$

$$T = \frac{4v^2}{0.8} + 4g\cos\theta$$

The expression for v can now be substituted to eliminate v from this expression.

$$T = \frac{4 \times 1.6g\cos\theta}{0.8} + 4g\cos\theta$$

$$= 12g\cos\theta$$

c) *As the maximum value of* $\cos\theta$ *is 1, when* $\theta = 0°$, *the maximum tension will be:*

$$T_{max} = 12 \times 9.8 \times 1$$
$$= 117.6\,\text{N}$$

EXERCISES

16.4 CLASSWORK

1 A sphere of mass 10 kg is attached to one end of a light string, of length 2 m. The other end of the string is fixed at O. The sphere is held below O, with the string taut and at an angle of 60° to the vertical. The sphere is then released.
   a) Find the maximum speed of the sphere.
   b) Find the maximum tension in the string.
   c) Find the tension in the string when the sphere is moving at 1 m s⁻¹.

2 A particle, of mass 5 kg, hangs in equilibrium on the end of a light string of length 0.5 m. The particle is struck so that it initially has a horizontal velocity of v m s⁻¹.
   a) Find v if the particle just completes a circle.
   b) Using the value of v from part **a)**, find the tension in the string when:
   i) the string is horizontal,
   ii) the string has rotated through an angle of 30° from its initial position,
   iii) the string has rotated through an angle of 120° from its initial position.

3 A particle, P, of mass m kg is attached to the end of a light string. The string has length l metres.
   The other end of the string is fixed at O. The particle is released with the string horizontal.
   a) Find an expression for the speed of the particle when the string makes an angle θ with the vertical.
   b) Find an expression for the tension in the string in terms of m, l, g and θ.

4 A gymnast is swinging in vertical circles about a horizontal bar. Model the gymnast as a particle of mass 50 kg at a distance of 0.95 m from the bar. The gymnast just completes the circle. Find the speed of the gymnast at the bottom of the circle and the tension in her arms at this position.

5 A new type of slide has been introduced at an amusement park. It consists of a smooth hemisphere. Children climb up inside and slide off it as shown. Safety experts recommend that to be safe the children should always remain in contact with the slide.
   a) Use conservation of energy to show that the speed of a child is given by:

   $$v = \sqrt{2gr(1-\cos\theta)}$$

   where r is the radius (in metres) of the hemisphere and θ is the angle between the child and the upward vertical through C.
   b) Explain what happens to the forces on a child if they lose contact with the slide.
   c) Find the value of θ when the children will leave the slide.
   d) Recommend a revised design for the slide that would be considered safe.

EXERCISES

16.4 HOMEWORK

1 A particle is attached to one end of a light string of length 80 cm. The other end of the string is fixed at O. The particle is set into motion directly below O with the string taut. Initially the velocity of the particle is v m s^{-1} horizontally.

Does the particle move in a circular path around O if:

a) $v = 4$ m s^{-1}

b) $v = 6$ m s^{-1}

c) $v = 8$ m s^{-1}?

2 A particle, of mass m, is placed on the top of an inverted hemisphere, with centre O and radius a. It is released from rest and slides on the surface to the point P, as shown in the diagram.

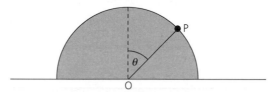

a) Find the speed of the particle in the position shown.

b) Find an expression for the magnitude of the reaction force that the hemisphere exerts on the particle.

c) If the particle leaves the surface of the sphere in the position shown, find θ.

3 A particle lies inside a hollow sphere of radius 40 cm and centre O. The particle is set into motion at A, which is the lowest point inside the sphere. The initial horizontal velocity of the particle is u m s^{-1}. The particle leaves contact with the surface of the sphere at the point B, where the angle AOB is 120°. Find u.

4 A particle of mass m is attached to a fixed point O by a string of length L. It is initially held, with the string taut, at the same horizontal level as O and then released from rest.

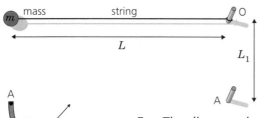

When the particle is vertically below O the string catches on a peg A (at a distance L_1 below O). The particle subsequently moves on a circular path centred on A. Show that complete revolutions about A are not possible unless $L_1 > \frac{3}{5}L$.

5 The diagram shows a design of a slide for a children's adventure park. The children should always remain in contact with the slide. The children begin at rest at A. Assume there is no friction on the slide.

a) Find the speed of a child at B.

b) Find the maximum value of θ if the child is not to lose contact with the slide.

CONSOLIDATION EXERCISES FOR CHAPTER 16

1 A motorcyclist drives her motorcycle at a constant speed of 27 km h^{-1} on a circular path of radius 15 metres around a roundabout.
a) i) Express 27 km h^{-1} in metres per second.
 ii) Calculate the magnitude of the acceleration of the motorcycle.
b) The total mass of the motorcycle and the rider is 400 kg. The magnitude of the friction force between the motorcycle and the road cannot exceed 2940 N without skidding taking place. Find the greatest speed, in metres per second, at which the motorcyclist can drive her motorcycle around this roundabout without skidding.

(AQA A Question 2, M2 Specimen Paper)

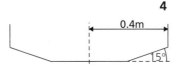

2 A car moves round a bend in a road which is banked at an angle α to the horizontal, as shown in the diagram. The car is modelled as a particle moving in a horizontal circle of radius 100 m. When the car moves at a constant speed of 14 ms^{-1}, there is no sideways frictional force on the car. Find, in degrees to one decimal place, the value of α.

(EDEXCEL Question 1, M3 Specimen Paper)

3 An aeroplane of mass m kg describes a horizontal circle of radius r m at a constant speed of v ms^{-1}.
a) Find the magnitude of the resultant force on the aeroplane if $m = 2000$, $v = 50$ and $r = 500$.
b) A lift force of magnitude L N acts on the aeroplane. This force lies in the vertical plane that contains the aeroplane and the centre of the circle and acts at an angle α to the vertical when the aeroplane is flying in a circle at a constant speed. Find L and α in terms of v, r and g.
c) Describe how L and α would change if the radius of the circle were reduced, but the speed of the aeroplane remained unchanged.

(AQA B Question 7, M2 Specimen Paper)

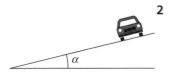

4 The top diagram shows the cross-section of a hollow container. The base of the container is circular, and is horizontal. The sloping part of the side makes an angle of 15° with the horizontal, and the vertical part of the side forms a circular cylinder of radius 0.4 m. A small steel ball of mass 0.1 kg moves in a horizontal circle inside the container, in contact with the vertical and sloping parts of the side at A and B respectively, as shown in the lower diagram.
It is assumed that all contacts are smooth and that the radius of the ball is negligible compared to 0.4 m.
a) Given that the ball is moving with constant speed 3 ms^{-1}, find the magnitudes of the contact forces acting on the ball at A and at B.
b) Calculate the least speed that the ball can have while remaining in contact with the vertical part of the side of the container.

(OCR 6 Question 6, M2 Specimen Paper)

5 The diagram shows a conical pendulum in which a light rod CD of length l rotates with constant speed ω about a vertical pole fixed at A. The rod CD is smoothly hinged at C and carries a mass m at D. The angle between CD and the downward vertical has the constant value β.

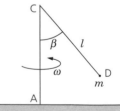

a) Draw a diagram showing all the forces acting on the mass m.

b) Write down the equations of motion for m in the vertical direction and the direction of the horizontal radius.

If $l > \dfrac{g}{\omega^2}$, deduce that $\cos\beta = \dfrac{g}{\omega^2 l}$.

The pendulum is now modified by attaching a rod BC of length a to the top of the vertical pole, as shown in this diagram. The light rod CD is smoothly hinged at C but the rigid rod BC is attached to the pole at B and is constrained to move in a horizontal plane. When the system rotates about the vertical pole AB with the same constant speed ω, the points A, B, C and D are always coplanar and the angle between CD and the downward vertical has the constant value θ.

c) By writing down the equation of motion for m in this case, show that $a = l\tan\theta(\cos\beta - \cos\theta)$.

d) Using the same value of ω, explain, by examining the behaviour of $\cos\theta$ and $\tan\theta$ as θ varies, how an angle of inclination of the rod CD greater than θ can be achieved by using a rod BC with a length greater than a.

(OCR, MEI Question 2, M3 Specimen Paper)

MATHEMATICAL MODELLING ACTIVITY

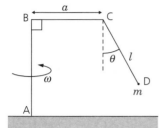

Specify the real problem

Problem statement

Many people, when they first see a chairoplanes ride at a theme park or fun fair, are amazed that the angle of inclination of the support chain for each chair appears to be independent of the size of the passenger – child or adult – or even whether the chair is occupied at all. Develop a model which could be used to explain this phenomenon. Use it to predict how a passenger's ride will be affected by other design features of the ride.

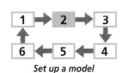

Set up a model

Set up a model

The first stage in setting up a model is to identify the important features:
- the length of the chains,
- the angular speed of rotation,
- the mass of a passenger.

Are there any other important factors that you feel should be included?

Having considered these features, we can list a set of assumptions:
- the chairoplane can be modelled as a conical pendulum,
- the mass of each chair is negligible,
- the chains are all of length l (m),
- the angular speed of rotation is constant at ω (rad s^{-1}),
- the path of each passenger of mass m (kg) is a horizontal circle when the chairoplane is rotating with constant angular speed,
- the support chains are all attached at the same point, vertically above the centre of rotation of the passengers,
- air resistance effects can be ignored.

These assumptions allow a simple first model to be formulated.

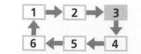

Formulate the mathematical problem

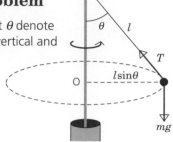

Formulate a mathematical problem

Consider one of the passengers of mass m. Let θ denote the inclination of her chain to the downward vertical and T be the tension in the chain.

Explain why the radial component of acceleration is $l\omega^2\sin\theta$ directed towards the centre of the circular path.

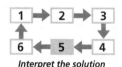

Solve the mathematical problem

Mathematical solution

Now applying Newton's second law of motion radially gives:

$$mw^2 l\sin\theta = T\sin\theta \qquad (1)$$

Furthermore, since the path of the passenger is assumed to be a horizontal circle then the net vertical force must be zero and so:

$$mg = T\cos\theta \qquad (2)$$

and from equation (1):

$$T = ml\omega^2 \qquad (3)$$

then from (2):

$$\cos\theta = \frac{g}{l\omega^2} \qquad (4)$$

Interpretation

Equation (4) is independent of m which means that the angle of inclination of each chain does not depend on the mass of the passenger or even on whether the chair is occupied at all. This agrees with the observed behaviour. *What else does equation (4) tell us? Devise a simple experiment to confirm your conclusions.*

Equation (3) shows that the tension in each chain is increased if the mass of the passenger is increased and/or the chain is lengthened and/or the angular speed is increased. Equation (4) shows that the angular inclination would be greater in an amusement park on the Moon for the same values of l and ω.

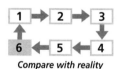

Compare with reality

Compare with reality

The fact that the angle of inclination of the chains does not depend on the attached mass is confirmed by our observations. The major criticism of the model developed so far relates to the point of attachment of the support chains. In fact they are not all attached to the same point on the axis of rotation but are attached to points on the circumference of a circular disc with its centre on the axis of rotation, as shown in the diagram.

Refining the model

Develop a revised model, based upon the above criticism, and solve the resulting revised problem to show that the angle of inclination θ now satisfies the equation:

$$R\cot\theta + l\cos\theta = \frac{g}{\omega^2} \qquad (5)$$

where R is the radius of the circular disc.

Interpretation of the refined model

a) The absence of the mass, m, from equation (5) means that the angle θ remains independent of the mass of the passenger, in agreement with our observations.

b) While solution of equation (5) will give a more realistic solution to the problem than that of equation (4), it is evident that equation (5) is considerably more complicated. It is not possible to obtain an analytical solution. Instead we could adopt a graphical approach.

Use a graphics package or graphics calculator to plot graphs of ω against θ for a range of different values of R (e.g. $R = 1.0, 1.5, 2.0, 2.5\,\text{m}$) and $l = 2\,\text{m}$.

Is it possible for the chains to become parallel to the ground? Explain your answer. How do the radius of the disc and the speed of rotation affect the angle of inclination?

POSSIBLE MODELLING TASKS

1   How fast should the drum of a tumble drier rotate?
2   When 'preparing' the bride and groom's car at weddings, a favourite trick is to place small stones inside the hub caps. What happens when the car is driven away?
3   A pendulum fixed inside a car can be used to estimate the radius of curvature of bends when the car is driven round them at constant speed. Use this experiment to estimate the radius of a bend.
4   A car negotiating a bend on a banked road can slide in two ways: if the speed of the car is too slow it could tend to slide inwards down the road; however, if it is too fast the car could tend to slide outwards. Investigate the motion of cars on banked racing tracks.

Summary

After working through this chapter you should:

■   be able to identify and model circular motion with constant speed
■   know that for circular motion with constant angular speed ω and radius r that the velocity has magnitude $v = r\omega$ and is directed in the transverse direction and the acceleration has magnitude $a = \dfrac{v^2}{r} = r\omega^2$ and is directed radially inwards towards the centre
■   know that for circular motion with constant speed, the required force is directed radially inwards towards the centre
■   be able to apply the principles of circular motion to the conical pendulum
■   know that when objects follow circular paths with variable speed they experience one component of acceleration towards the centre of the circle and another along a tangent to the circle
■   know that the radial component of the acceleration has magnitude $\dfrac{v^2}{r}$
■   know that the tangential component of the acceleration has magnitude $\dfrac{\mathrm{d}v}{\mathrm{d}t}$

MECHANICS
17

Further energy topics

■ *In Chapter 12 we covered the basic concepts of energy, work and power. In this chapter we extend the ideas developed for constant forces to variable forces.*

■ *A definition of work done is introduced for use with vectors. This involves a new concept called the **scalar product**.*

HOOKE'S LAW : A MODEL FOR THE TENSIONS IN SPRINGS

Springs and elastic strings exert forces that vary as they are stretched (or compressed, in the case of springs). A model to describe how the tension or compression varies was formulated by Hooke. The following exploration, which is a practical activity, explores this model.

Exploration 17.1

Forces in springs

■ Set up the apparatus as shown in the diagram.
■ What forces act on the mass on the end of the spring?
■ The upward force exerted by the spring on the mass is the tension in the spring. When the mass is at rest, this force is balanced by the force of gravity on the mass. Record the unstretched length of the spring. Add a small mass to the end of the spring and record how much it stretches. Repeat this process, recording the tension force and the extension of the spring in a table as shown in the example below. (Do not include the sample results shown.)

Mass (g)	Tension (N)	Extension (m)
50	0.49	0.02

■ Plot a graph of tension against extension, by drawing a line of best fit through your points. Comment on your results. It is reasonable to assume that there is a linear relationship. The gradient of the line is known as the **stiffness** of the spring.

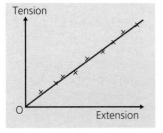

■ Join two identical springs together, to make a spring of twice the length, and repeat the experiment. How does the stiffness of the spring compare with that of the original?

Tension in springs

A spring that is stretched exerts a tension force, the magnitude of this force is ke, where k is the **spring stiffness** and e is the **extension** of the spring. The result is known as **Hooke's law**.

For springs of different lengths the spring stiffness is given by:

$$k = \frac{\lambda}{l}$$

where λ is the **modulus of elasticity** and l is the natural (or unstretched) length of the spring.

A compressed spring exerts a thrust force of ke, where e is the **compression**.

Elastic strings are similar to springs, but cannot exert thrust forces.

Example 17.1

A spring, of natural length 8 cm, stretches 4 cm when a 200 gram mass is attached to it and the whole system hangs vertically. Find:
a) the tension in the spring,
b) the stiffness of the spring,
c) the modulus of elasticity.

T

$mg = 1.96\,\text{N}$

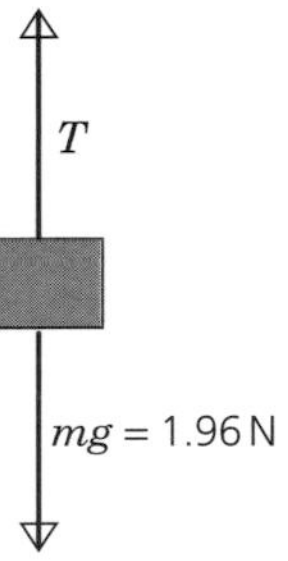

Solution
a) The diagram shows the forces acting on the mass. When it is at rest the upward tension balances the downward force of gravity. As the mass is 0.2 kg the force of gravity is 1.96 N and so the tension is also 1.96 N.

b) Hooke's law states that:
$T = ke$
Here T = 1.96 N and e = 0.04 m, giving:
$1.96 = k \times 0.04$
or:
$$k = \frac{1.96}{0.04} = 49\ \text{N}\,\text{m}^{-1}$$

c) The stiffness and the modulus of elasticity are related by:
$$k - \frac{\lambda}{l}$$
Here k = 49 and l = 0.08, so that substituting gives:
$$49 = \frac{\lambda}{0.08}$$
or
$\lambda = 49 \times 0.08 = 3.92\,\text{N}$
***Note**: While k has units $\text{N}\,\text{m}^{-1}$ the units of λ are N.*

Example 17.2

A 50 cm length of elastic extends 10 cm when a force of 10 N is applied to it.
a) Find the modulus of elasticity of the elastic.
b) If a force is to double a length of the same type of elastic, what force must be applied?

Solution
a) Using Hooke's law in the form:
$$T = \frac{\lambda}{l}e$$
with T = 10, l = 0.5 and e = 0.1 gives:
$$10 = \frac{\lambda}{0.5} \times 0.1$$

Solving for λ gives:

$$\lambda = \frac{10 \times 0.5}{0.1} = 50\,\text{N}$$

b) *If the elastic is to double in length then the extension will be equal to the natural length l, which in this case is 0.5 m. Using Hooke's law gives:*

$$T = \frac{50}{0.5} \times 0.5 = 50\,\text{N}$$

In fact the tension required to double the length of any spring or elastic string is equal to λ, the modulus of elasticity.

EXERCISES

17.1 CLASSWORK

1   When a 2 kg mass is hung from a spring the length of the spring increases from 20 cm to 32 cm.
   a) Find the stiffness of the spring.
   b) What is the modulus of elasticity?
   c) What would be the extension of a similar spring of natural length 10 cm supporting the same mass?

2   The pointer on a simple spring balance used by an angler moves 4.5 cm when it supports a fish of mass 800 grams.
   a) Find the stiffness of the spring.
   b) Find the extension for a 1.2 kg fish.

3   The spring in a set of bathroom scales is connected to the platform by a series of levers, so that the thrust in the spring is $\frac{1}{5}$ of the normal reaction acting on the platform. If the spring is compressed by 3 cm for a person of mass 60 kg, find:
   a) the stiffness of the spring,
   b) the compression for an 18 kg child.

4   A clock is controlled by a 40 gram mass that vibrates on the end of a spring.
   a) When the clock stops the mass remains at rest and the spring has an extension of 3 cm. Find the spring stiffness.
   b) The mass moves up and down 2 cm from its central position. What range of values does the tension in the spring cover as it moves up and down?

5   A spring has a natural length of 5 cm. When it supports a 100 gram mass it stretches to 7 cm.
   a) Determine the value of λ, the modulus of elasticity.
   b) How far would a similar spring of length 8 cm stretch when supporting the 100 gram mass?
   c) How far would a similar spring of length 3 cm stretch when supporting a 200 gram mass?

EXERCISES

1 When a mass of 3 kg is hung from an elastic thread of natural length 20 cm it increases in length to 25 cm.
   a) Find the stiffness of the thread.
   b) What is its modulus of elasticity?
   c) What would be the extension of a thread of the same material but of natural length 15 cm supporting the same mass?

2 The pointer on a set of scales moves 3 cm along a straight scale, when it supports a bag of rice of mass 1 kg.
   a) Find the stiffness of the spring.
   b) Find the mass of a bag of rice which causes a movement of 2 cm.

3 The mass of a car is determined by parking the car on a weigh-bridge platform. The spring in the weigh-bridge is connected to the platform by a set of levers so that the thrust in the spring is $\frac{1}{300}$ of the normal reaction acting on the platform. If the spring is compressed by 15 cm for a car of mass 1.5 tonnes find:
   a) the stiffness of the spring,
   b) the compression for a motorcycle of mass 240 kg.

4 A particle of mass 100 grams oscillates vertically on the end of a spring. When hanging in equilibrium the spring is extended by 5 cm.
   a) Find the stiffness of the spring.
   b) If the oscillatory motion has an amplitude of 3 cm, what are the greatest and least tensions in the spring?

5 A spring has a natural length of 8 cm. When it supports a 200 gram mass it stretches to a length of 10 cm.
   a) Determine the value of λ, the modulus of elasticity.
   b) How far would a similar spring of length 10 cm stretch when supporting the 200 gram mass?
   c) How far would a similar spring of length 4 cm stretch when supporting a 400 gram mass?

THE WORK DONE BY A VARIABLE FORCE

The work done by a constant force has been established as *Fs* or *Fs* cos θ, but this cannot be applied, for example, to a spring because the applied force must vary as the tension on the spring varies. There are many other situations where it is useful to be able to calculate the work done by a variable force. For example as a space capsule containing astronauts returns to Earth the gravitational attraction increases as it gets closer to the Earth.

Exploration 17.2

Forces on a bouncing ball

Consider a bouncing ball. How is the deformation of the ball linked to the force that is exerted on the ball? Try to illustrate your response with a graph.

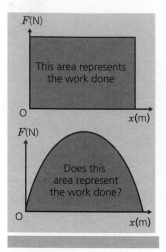

This area represents the work done

Does this area represent the work done?

Work done

So far, our results indicate that the greater the deformation, the greater the force. Here is a situation where the force acting depends on the deformation or the distance moved by the ball while in contact with the surface. In reality there are many other situations where force varies with distance. In this section we set out to find the work done by a variable force.

The work done by a constant force is Fd. This can be represented by the area under the graph as shown. Can the work done by a variable force be represented in the same way?

Example 17.3

Show that

$$\int_a^b F \, \mathrm{d}x = \tfrac{1}{2} m v^2 - \tfrac{1}{2} m u^2$$

where u is the speed when $x = a$ and v is the speed when $x = b$ and hence deduce that the work done by a variable force is $\int F \, \mathrm{d}x$.

Solution

First note that Newton's second law can be expressed in the form:

$$F(x) = m \frac{\mathrm{d}v}{\mathrm{d}t}$$

where the force is assumed to be a function of x.
Now using the chain rule:

$$\frac{\mathrm{d}v}{\mathrm{d}t} = \frac{\mathrm{d}v}{\mathrm{d}x} \times \frac{\mathrm{d}x}{\mathrm{d}t}$$

we can say that $F(x) = m \dfrac{\mathrm{d}x}{\mathrm{d}t} \times \dfrac{\mathrm{d}v}{\mathrm{d}x}$

or $F(x) = m v \dfrac{\mathrm{d}v}{\mathrm{d}x}$

Using the method of separation of variables gives:

$$\int_a^b F(x)\mathrm{d}x = m \int_u^v v \, \mathrm{d}v$$

where u is the speed when $x = a$ and v the speed when $x = b$.

Integrating the right hand side gives:

$$\int_a^b F(x)\mathrm{d}x = m \left[\frac{v^2}{2} \right]_u^v = \tfrac{1}{2} m v^2 - \tfrac{1}{2} m u^2$$

Now the right-hand side is the change in kinetic energy which is equal to the work done, so the work done by a variable force must be given by:

$$\int_a^b F(x)\mathrm{d}x$$

Example 17.4

As a car of mass 1.05 tonnes moves, the resultant force on it can be modelled as:

$$F(x) = 2000 - \frac{x^2}{5}$$

a) Find the work done as the car travels 100 m.
b) Find the speed at the end of the distance.

Solution

a) Work done $= \int_0^{100} 2000 - \frac{x^2}{5}\,dx = \left[2000x - \frac{x^3}{15} \right]_0^{100}$

$$= 2000 \times 100 - \frac{100^3}{15} = 133\,333 \text{ J}$$

b) Using work done = change in KE gives:

$133\,333 = \frac{1}{2} \times 1050 \times v^2 - \frac{1}{2} \times 1050 \times 0^2$

so that $v^2 = 254$
and $v = 15.9 \text{ m s}^{-1}$

EXERCISES

17.2 CLASSWORK

1 As a car moves it experiences a resultant force modelled by:
$$F(x) = 2000 - 5x$$
a) Find the work done as the car moves 400 m.
b) If the car has mass 1000 kg and was initially at rest, find the speed reached by the car.

2 A chain of length 3 m and mass 60 kg is resting on the floor. A light rope that passes over a pulley is attached to the chain and used to raise the chain off the floor.
a) Show that the mass of the chain lifted off the floor is $20x$, when x is the length of the chain that has been lifted.
b) Find the work that must be done to lift the whole chain.

3 The graph shows how the forward force on a train of total mass 30 tonnes varies as it leaves a station.
a) Find the work done in the first 300 m.
b) Find the speed at the end of the first 300 m.

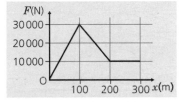

4 A builder is hoisting a leaky drum of water to the top of a scaffold. The mass of the drum is 20 kg and it initially contains 30 litres of water. (1 litre of water has a mass of 1 kg.) Assume that the water leaks out at a constant rate and that only 10 litres remain at the top of the scaffold, 5 m above the ground.
a) If the drum is raised at a constant speed show that its mass at height x is modelled by $m = 50 - 4x$.
b) Find the work done by the builder.

5 Forensic scientists assume that when a bullet enters a certain type of timber the retarding force is $100x^2$ kN, where x is the distance penetrated, in m. A bullet of mass 30 grams penetrates 8 cm into the timber.
a) Find the work done to stop the bullet moving.
b) Find the speed of the bullet when it enters the timber.

6 A space capsule of mass 500 kg is moving at a speed of 10 m s^{-1} when 1000 km above the surface of the Earth.
a) Find the work done by gravity on the space capsule as it returns to Earth, by using Newton's universal law of gravitation. (The radius of the Earth is 6.4×10^6 m and its mass is 5.98×10^{24} kg).
b) Find the speed of the capsule at the surface of the Earth.
c) Assume the capsule experiences a constant resistance force. The speed reached is in fact 30% less than that predicted in **b)**. Find the magnitude of the resistance force.

EXERCISES

17.2 HOMEWORK

1   A body of mass 50 kg is pulled along a straight line AB on a smooth horizontal surface by a force

$$F(x) = 2 - \frac{x}{100}$$

where x m represents the distance moved from A.
a) Find the work done as the body moves from A to B if AB = 5 m.
b) If the body was initially at rest, find the speed it has attained when it reaches B.

2   Construction sites often require the excavation of large holes for the foundations of buildings. One such hole has a rectangular cross section 2 m × 3 m and a depth of 25 m. The average density of the material removed from the hole is 900 kg m^{-3}. Determine the work done against gravity in excavating the hole, assuming that the material removed is spread thinly over the ground.

3   The graph shows how the force on a car of mass 1 tonne varies as it leaves a set of traffic lights.
a) Find the work done in the first 150 m.
b) Determine the speed of the car after 150 m.

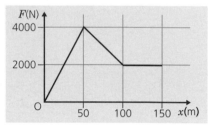

4   A bucket of mass 2 kg which is initially empty is being lowered 10 m from P to the ground while it is being filled with water at a constant rate. It is full when it reaches the ground and contains 18 litres of water. (1 litre of water has a mass of 1 kg.)

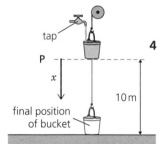

a) If the bucket is lowered at a constant speed show that its mass at a distance x below P is modelled by $m = 2 + 1.8x$.
b) Determine the work done in lowering the bucket to the ground.

5   Many car racing circuits have sand traps provided on corners so that if a car spins off the track if can be brought to rest quickly by the sand without causing injury to the driver or too much damage to the car. A racing car of mass 500 kg enters such a sand trap at a speed of 50 m s^{-1} and is brought to rest in a distance of 75 m. Assume the car travels along a straight line.
a) Determine the work done in bringing the car to rest.
b) Assuming that the resistive force provided by the sand is modelled as $F = kx^2$ determine the value of the constant k.

6   A meteoroid of mass 200 kg initially at rest a large distance from the sun falls towards the Sun under the influence of gravity.
a) Determine the work done in falling to the surface of the Sun assuming that 'a large distance from the Sun' is represented mathematically as an infinite distance.
b) Determine the velocity with which the meteoroid hits the Sun. You may assume that the mass of the Sun is 1.99×10^{30} kg and the radius of the Sun 6.96×10^8 m.

ELASTIC POTENTIAL ENERGY

A stretched or compressed spring has the ability to make an object move, gaining speed as it does move. Thus a stretched or compressed spring has the potential to create kinetic energy. The amount of energy that a spring can create as it is allowed to expand or contract is known as the **elastic potential energy** (EPE).

Exploration 17.3

Work in stretching a spring

- How much work do you need to do to stretch a spring?
- Do you need to do the same amount of work to increase the length from 5 cm to 10 cm as to increase it from 10 cm to 15 cm?
- Does it get harder to stretch a spring, the longer it gets?

The work done in stretching a spring

The work done in stretching a spring is $\frac{1}{2}ke^2$. This result can be derived theoretically by considering the work done when a spring is stretched.
The work done by a variable force is given by $\int F(x)\mathrm{d}x$.

If we assume that $F(x)$, the force applied to stretch the string, is kx, where x is the extension of the spring, then if x increases from 0 to e, we obtain:

$$\text{work done} = \int_0^e kx\,\mathrm{d}x = \left[\tfrac{1}{2}kx^2\right]_0^e = \tfrac{1}{2}ke^2$$

so the elastic potential energy stored in the spring is $\frac{1}{2}ke^2$.

As the tension in the spring can also be expressed as:

$$T = \frac{\lambda}{l}x$$

the elastic potential energy can also be expressed as: $\dfrac{\lambda e^2}{2l}$

Example 17.5

A ball of mass 100 grams is placed in a tube on top of a spring of natural length 10 cm and modulus of elasticity 16 N. The spring is compressed by 2 cm.
a) Find the work done to compress the spring.
b) Find the kinetic energy of the ball when it leaves contact with the spring.
c) Find the height reached by the ball above its point of release.

Solution
a) Using the result for the work done as $\dfrac{\lambda e^2}{2l}$ gives:

$$\text{work done} = \tfrac{1}{2} \times \frac{16}{0.1} \times 0.02^2 = 0.032 \text{ J}$$

b) When the spring is released, the energy given to the ball is the same as the work that was done in compressing the spring, namely 0.032 J.

c) At the highest point reached by the ball, its potential energy is equal to its initial elastic potential energy, so:
$$mgh = 0.032$$
$$0.1 \times 9.8 \times h = 0.032$$
$$h = 0.33 \text{ m}$$
So the ball rises to a height of 33 cm.

Example 17.6

A spring of natural length 8 cm and modulus of elasticity 8 N is used to project a ball of mass 50 grams in a pin-ball machine. The spring is compressed 20 cm and released to set the ball into motion. Find the speed of the ball when it loses contact with the spring if:
a) the table is horizontal,
b) the table is at 10° to the horizontal.

Assume all the energy from the spring is transferred to the ball.

Solution
When the spring is compressed, it has elastic potential energy. This is given by:

$$EPE = \frac{\lambda e^2}{2l} = \frac{1}{2}\frac{8}{0.08} \times 0.2^2 = 2\text{ J}$$

a) When the ball leaves the spring, all this energy is converted to the kinetic energy of the ball, so:

$$2 = \frac{1}{2}mv^2$$
$$v^2 = 80$$
$$v = 8.94\text{ m s}^{-1}$$

b) On the sloping table, the ball gains gravitational potential energy as well as kinetic energy, so:

$$2 = \frac{1}{2}mv^2 + mgh$$

The gain in height of the ball is:

$$h = 20\sin 10° = 3.5\text{cm}$$

20 cm   10° $h = 20\sin 10°$

So considering the energy gives:

$$2 = \frac{1}{2} \times 0.05v^2 + 0.05 \times 9.8 \times 0.035$$
$$2 = 0.025v^2 + 0.017$$
$$v^2 = \frac{2 - 0.017}{0.025} = 79.32$$
$$v = 8.92\text{ m s}^{-1}$$

So the ball is only marginally slower on the sloping table.

EXERCISES

17.3 CLASSWORK

1 A pop-up toy frog of mass 30 grams jumps up in the air when the spring suddenly expands. It jumps up 30 cm.
   a) Find the potential energy of the frog when it reaches a height of 30 cm.
   b) Find the elastic potential energy stored in the spring when it is compressed.
   c) If the spring was compressed by 1 cm before the frog jumped, find the stiffness of the spring.

2 A train of mass 30 tonnes is travelling at 0.05 m s⁻¹ when it hits a buffer containing a spring. The buffer brings the train to rest. Assume that the train runs on horizontal tracks.
   a) Calculate the initial kinetic energy of the train.
   b) What is the elastic potential energy stored in the spring, when the train stops?
   c) If the stiffness of the spring is 2000 N m⁻¹, calculate how far it was compressed.
   d) Explain why your answer to b) is likely to be incorrect.

3 A spring of stiffness $60\,N\,m^{-1}$ is used to launch a ball of mass 50 grams up a sloping table, as shown in the diagram on the next page. The spring is compressed 5 cm and released to fire the ball.
   a) Find the elastic potential energy stored in the spring when it is compressed.
   b) Assuming that all this energy is transferred to the ball, find its speed when it loses contact with the spring.
   c) How far does the ball travel up the table?
   d) Criticise the assumption made in part **b)**.

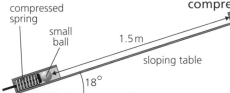

compressed spring
small ball
1.5 m
sloping table
18°

4 A child's toy consists of three plastic acrobats that are fired into the air by a compressed spring. The mass of each acrobat is 100 grams.
   a) When used properly, each acrobat rises 20 cm. Find the elastic potential energy stored in the spring.
   b) A child replaces the acrobats with a small object of mass 50 grams. Find the maximum speed of the object and the height it reaches.

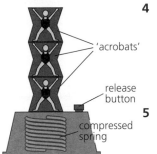

'acrobats'
release button
compressed spring

5 a) The elastic potential energy of a spring is 100 J. Find the modulus of elasticity of the spring if its natural length has been doubled to 0.4 m.
   b) If the natural length of the spring were decreased by 75%, what extension would be required to give an EPE of 100 J?

6 When a person stands on a set of bathroom scales they are depressed vertically through a distance 0.5 cm.
   a) Find the loss in potential energy for a person of mass 62 kg.
   b) If the spring inside the scales moves 2 cm, find its stiffness.

EXERCISES

17.3 HOMEWORK

1 The spring of a vehicle suspension system has a stiffness of $4\times10^4\,N\,m^{-1}$. How much work is done in compressing this spring from its natural length of 0.3 m to 0.25 m?

2 A toy gun shoots pellets horizontally by means of a compressed spring. To load the gun the pellet is placed against the horizontal spring which is then compressed and released. Determine the speed of the pellet when the spring reaches its natural length, if the mass of the pellet is 5 g, the stiffness of the spring is $200\,N\,m^{-1}$ and the spring compression when fully loaded is 5 cm.

3 A spring of stiffness $k\,N\,m^{-1}$ is used to launch a ball of mass m kg horizontally. If the spring is initially compressed a distance x m determine the velocity of the ball when it loses contact with the spring.
   a) If the ball is changed for another one of double the mass would the release velocity of this new ball be different and if so what would be its value?
   b) Would changing the spring for one of half the original stiffness have any effect on the release velocity of the original ball? If so, what?
   c) Suppose the stiffness of the spring and the mass of the ball are each doubled. What can you say about the release velocity this time?

4   A particle of mass 2 kg is attached to the origin by a spring of stiffness 40 N m^{-1}. The particle is released from rest when the extension of the spring is 0.2 m. What is the velocity of the particle when the spring attains its natural length?

5   A particle of mass 1 kg moves on a smooth horizontal surface and is attached to a fixed point O by a spring of stiffness 2 N m^{-1}. Initially the particle has an extension of 0.5 m and a velocity of –2 m s^{-1}.

   a) What is the particle's maximum speed during the motion?

   b) At what position is the particle momentarily at rest?

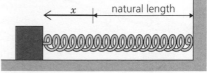

6   A block of mass 1 kg moves on a horizontal track and is accelerated by a compressed spring. While in contact with the spring the block moves on a smooth surface but when the spring attains its natural length the surface becomes rough (with a coefficient of friction of 0.2).

The spring stiffness is 100 N m^{-1}. Determine the initial compression of the spring if the block travels a distance 0.5 m on the rough surface before coming to rest.

SCALAR PRODUCTS AND ENERGY

A scalar product of two vectors **r** and **s**, written as **r.s**, gives a scalar quantity, hence its name. The scalar product has some useful applications in energy.

The scalar product is defined as:

r.s = $rs \cos \theta$

where r and s are the magnitudes of the vectors and θ is the angle between them.

For two column vectors $\mathbf{r} = \begin{pmatrix} a \\ b \end{pmatrix}$ and $\mathbf{s} = \begin{pmatrix} c \\ d \end{pmatrix}$, the scalar product is very simple to calculate.

$$\mathbf{r.s} = \begin{pmatrix} a \\ b \end{pmatrix}\begin{pmatrix} c \\ d \end{pmatrix} = ac + bd$$

There are three applications of the scalar product that we shall consider in this section.

■ For a constant force **F** applied as a particle's displacement is changed by **r**, the work done is given by **F.r**

■ For a variable force **F** that acts on a particle moving with velocity **v** the work done by the force is $\int \mathbf{F.v} \mathrm{d}t$

■ For a constant force **F** that acts on an object with velocity **v** the power is **F.v**

Example 17.7

As the force $\begin{pmatrix} 9 \\ 5 \end{pmatrix}$N acts on a particle, of mass 0.5 kg, it moves from the point with position vector $\begin{pmatrix} 6 \\ 7 \end{pmatrix}$m to the point with position vector $\begin{pmatrix} 20 \\ 40 \end{pmatrix}$m. The particle starts at rest.

a) Find the work done.
b) Find the final speed of the particle.

Solution

a) First find the displacement of the particle.

$$\mathbf{r} = \begin{pmatrix} 20 \\ 40 \end{pmatrix} - \begin{pmatrix} 6 \\ 7 \end{pmatrix} = \begin{pmatrix} 14 \\ 33 \end{pmatrix}$$

Now use the scalar product to find the work done.

$$\mathbf{F.r} = \begin{pmatrix} 9 \\ 5 \end{pmatrix}.\begin{pmatrix} 14 \\ 33 \end{pmatrix} = 9 \times 14 + 5 \times 33 = 291 \text{ J}$$

b) Using work done = change in kinetic energy, gives:

$$291 = \frac{1}{2} \times 0.5 v^2$$

$$v = \sqrt{1164} = 34.1 \text{ m s}^{-1}$$

Example 17.8

A particle moves with velocity $\begin{pmatrix} 4 \\ 3 \end{pmatrix}$m s^{-1} when acted on by a force $\begin{pmatrix} 6 \\ 2 \end{pmatrix}$N. Calculate the power.

Solution

Power = $\mathbf{F.v}$ = $\begin{pmatrix} 6 \\ 2 \end{pmatrix}.\begin{pmatrix} 4 \\ 3 \end{pmatrix}$ = 24 + 6 = 30 W

Example 17.9

A particle of mass 5 kg, moves so that at time t seconds its velocity is $\begin{pmatrix} t^2 \\ t^3 \end{pmatrix}$m s^{-1}. Find the work done by the force acting on the particle during the first 5 seconds of its motion.

Solution

First differentiate the velocity to obtain the acceleration.

$$\mathbf{a} = \begin{pmatrix} 2t \\ 3t^2 \end{pmatrix}$$

Now multiply by the mass to give the resultant force.

$$\mathbf{F} = \begin{pmatrix} 10t \\ 15t^2 \end{pmatrix}$$

Then find $\mathbf{F.v}$ and integrate to obtain the work done.

$$\mathbf{F.v} = \begin{pmatrix} 10t \\ 15t^2 \end{pmatrix}.\begin{pmatrix} t^2 \\ t^3 \end{pmatrix} = 10t^3 + 15t^5$$

Work done = $\int_0^5 \left(10t^3 + 15t^5\right) dt = \left[\frac{5}{2}t^4 + \frac{5}{2}t^6\right]_0^5 = 40\,625 \text{ J}$

EXERCISES

1 As the force $\begin{pmatrix} 90 \\ 50 \end{pmatrix}$N acts on a particle, of mass 40 kg, it moves from the point with position vector $\begin{pmatrix} 5 \\ 12 \end{pmatrix}$m to the point with position vector $\begin{pmatrix} x \\ y \end{pmatrix}$m. The particle has an initial velocity of $5\,\text{m s}^{-1}$.

Find the final speed of the particle, if:
a) $x = 30$ and $y = 40$ **b)** $x = 8$ and $y = 14$.

2 A particle is initially at rest at the origin. A force $\begin{pmatrix} 6 \\ 2 \end{pmatrix}$N acts on the particle, until it is moving at a speed of $10\,\text{m s}^{-1}$ and has position vector $\begin{pmatrix} 12 \\ y \end{pmatrix}$. The particle has mass 4 kg. Find y.

3 A particle of mass 20 kg moves so that at time t seconds its velocity is $\begin{pmatrix} 2t \\ 3 - t^2 \end{pmatrix}\text{m s}^{-1}$. Find the work done by the force in the first 3 seconds of the particle's motion.

4 The position of a particle at time t seconds is $\begin{pmatrix} 3t + t^2 \\ t^4 \end{pmatrix}\text{m s}^{-1}$. The mass of the particle is 3 kg.

  a) Find the work done between $t = 0$ and $t = 3$.
  b) State the initial speed of the particle.
  c) Find the final speed of the particle.

5 A particle moves with velocity $\begin{pmatrix} v \\ 2v \end{pmatrix}\text{m s}^{-1}$. A force $\begin{pmatrix} 12 \\ 15 \end{pmatrix}$N acts on the particle. The power is calculated as 210 W. Find v.

6 The velocity of a particle at time t is $\begin{pmatrix} \alpha t^2 \\ t^2 \end{pmatrix}\text{m s}^{-1}$. The particle has mass 4 kg. The work done by the force acting on the particle between $t = 2$ and $t = 4$ is 1440 J. Find the possible values of α.

EXERCISES

1 As the force $\begin{pmatrix} X \\ Y \end{pmatrix}$N acts on a particle of mass 6 kg it moves from the point with position vector $\begin{pmatrix} 5 \\ 12 \end{pmatrix}$m to the point with position vector $\begin{pmatrix} 10 \\ 20 \end{pmatrix}$m. The particle has an initial velocity of $5\,\text{m s}^{-1}$.

Find the final speed of the particle, if:
a) $X = 10$ and $Y = 4$ **b)** $X = 2$ and $Y = 1$.

2 As a particle moves from the point with position vector $\begin{pmatrix} 4 \\ -9 \end{pmatrix}$m to the point with position vector $\begin{pmatrix} -2 \\ -21 \end{pmatrix}$m, it is acted on by a force $\begin{pmatrix} X \\ Y \end{pmatrix}$N.

The mass of the particle is 10 kg. The speed of the particle decreases from $5\,\text{m s}^{-1}$ to $2\,\text{m s}^{-1}$.

  a) Find a relationship between X and Y.
  b) Find X if $Y = 40$.
  c) Find Y if $X = 2$.

3 A particle has mass 8 kg. The velocity of a particle at time t seconds is $\begin{pmatrix} 3 + t^2 \\ t^4 \end{pmatrix}\text{m s}^{-1}$.

  a) Find the work done between $t = 0$ and $t = 4$.

b) State the initial speed of the particle.

c) Find the final speed of the particle.

4 As a force $\begin{pmatrix} 2 \\ 1 \end{pmatrix}$N acts on a particle its velocity changes from $\begin{pmatrix} 3 \\ 4 \end{pmatrix}$ to $\begin{pmatrix} 7 \\ 6 \end{pmatrix}$ m s^{-1}. Calculate the increase in the power.

5 The position vector of a particle at time t seconds is $\begin{pmatrix} t^3 + 3t \\ 9t^2 - t \end{pmatrix}$N.

The mass of the particle is 4 kg. Find the kinetic energy of the particle after 6 seconds.

6 The velocity of a particle is $\begin{pmatrix} 4 \\ t^2 - \alpha \end{pmatrix}$ m s^{-1}. The mass of the particle is 10 kg.

a) Find α if the kinetic energy of the particle has increased by 40 J after 2 seconds.

b) Find the final speed of the particle.

CONSOLIDATION EXERCISES FOR CHAPTER 17

1 A body of mass 5 kg moves in the x–y plane and passes through the points A and B.

a) At the point A the body has velocity $(3\mathbf{i} + 7\mathbf{j})$ m s^{-1}.
Find its kinetic energy at this point.

b) The position vectors of A and B are $(\mathbf{i} + \mathbf{j})$ and $(5\mathbf{i} + 4\mathbf{j})$ respectively, where the unit of length is the metre.
During its motion, a constant resultant force $(\lambda\mathbf{i} + 2\mathbf{j})$ N acts on the body. Given that the kinetic energy of the body as it passes through B is 175 J, find the value of λ.

(AQA A Question 3, M2 specimen paper)

2 A man of mass 75 kg is attached to one end of a light elastic rope of natural length 12 m. The other end of the rope is attached to a point on the edge of a horizontal ledge 19 m above the ground. The man steps off the ledge and falls vertically under gravity. The man is modelled as a particle falling from rest. He is brought to instantaneous rest by the rope when he is 1 m above the ground.

Find:

a) the modulus of elasticity of the rope,

b) the speed of the man when he is 2 m above the ground, giving your answer in m s^{-1} to 3 significant figures.

(EDEXCEL Question 4, M3 specimen paper)

3  The diagram shows an amateur climber on a rock face. For safety, the climber is attached at the waist, close to her centre of mass, to one end of a rope, the other end of which is attached to the rock face at a point P. The rope is of natural length 10 metres and obeys Hooke's law with spring constant 2940 N m^{-1}. The climber is of mass 60 kg. At the moment when her centre of mass is 7.5 metres vertically below P, she slips and falls.

Take $g = 9.8\,\mathrm{m\,s^{-2}}$.

a) Find the speed of the climber at the moment when the rope just becomes taut.

b) The climber falls until she is brought momentarily to rest by the rope. The extension of the rope is then x metres.

   i) Show that $5x^2 - 2x - 5 = 0$.

   ii) find the value of x, giving your answer correct to two significant figures.

(AQA A Question 4, M2 specimen paper)

Summary

After working through this chapter you should:

- know and be able to use Hooke's law in the form:
$$T = ke \text{ or } T = \frac{\lambda e}{l}$$

- know that the work done by a variable force is:
$$\int F\,\mathrm{d}x$$

- know that the elastic potential energy in a spring is:
$$\tfrac{1}{2}ke^2 \quad \text{or} \quad \frac{\lambda e^2}{2l}$$

- know that the work done can be found using the scalar product **F.r**

Differential equations in mechanics

- *Some resistance forces depend on the speed of an object. When they occur, they often lead to differential equations that cannot be solved by direct integration.*

- *In this chapter we use the method of separation of variables to solve these differential equations.*

FORMING EQUATIONS

When solving dynamics problems we almost always need to apply Newton's second law to produce an expression for the acceleration of the object under consideration. If this expression is a function of time, t, then the acceleration can be equated to $\frac{d^2 x}{dt^2}$ (rate of change of displacement or distance per second per second) or $\frac{dv}{dx}$ (rate of change of velocity per second) and then integrated. However if the acceleration is a function of x or v, we have to use the method of **separation of variables**.

If the acceleration is a function of x it is useful to use an alternative expression for $\frac{dv}{dt}$, that involves dx not dt. This is obtained using the chain rule:

$$\frac{dv}{dt} = \frac{dx}{dt} \times \frac{dv}{dx} = v \frac{dv}{dx}$$

Example 18.1

A swimmer of mass 60 kg pushes off the side of a swimming pool and moves with an initial speed of 4 m s⁻¹ under the water. There is a resistance force of $120v$ acting on the swimmer as she moves through the water. How far does the swimmer move before she comes to a halt?

Solution

The resultant force on the swimmer is simply $-120v$, so the acceleration is $-2v$. Using $\frac{dv}{dt}$ for the acceleration gives:

$$\frac{dv}{dt} = -2v$$

Separating the variables and integrating gives:

$$\frac{1}{v}\frac{dv}{dt} = -2 \quad \Rightarrow \quad \int \frac{1}{v}\,dv = \int -2\,dt \quad \Rightarrow \quad \ln v = -2t + c$$

Making v the subject of the expression gives:

$$v = e^{-2t+c} \Rightarrow v = A\,e^{-2t}$$

where $A = e^c$. The value of A can now be determined using the initial conditions $v = 4$ when $t = 0$. This gives:

$$4 = Ae^0 \quad A = 4 \quad \Rightarrow \quad v = 4e^{-2t}$$

Now assume that $v = 0$ when $t = \infty$.
The distance that the swimmer travels can now be found by integrating. This distance is given by:

$$\int_0^\infty 4e^{-2t}\,dt = \left[-2e^{-2t}\right]_0^\infty = \left(-2e^{-2\infty}\right) - \left(-2e^0\right) = 0 + 2 = 2$$

The distance is 2 m.

Example 18.2

The terminal speed of a parachutist is estimated to be 5 m s⁻¹.
Assume the air resistance is proportional to the mass and speed of the parachutist, and that the parachutist is moving at 20 m s⁻¹ when the parachute opens and becomes effective.
a) Formulate a simple model for the air resistance on the parachutist.
b) Find an expression for the speed of the parachutist.

Solution

a) The air resistance is given by: $R = mkv$
where k is an unknown constant.
When the parachutist is at terminal speed the **resultant** force on the parachutist is zero.
So $mg = mkv$
since $v = 5$ this gives $k = \dfrac{g}{5}$

So the resistance force, R, can be modelled as: $R = \dfrac{mgv}{5}$

b) With the downward direction defined as positive, the resultant force on the parachutist is:

$$mg - R = mg - \frac{mgv}{5} = mg\left(1 - \frac{v}{5}\right)$$

Applying Newton's second law with $a = \dfrac{dv}{dt}$ gives:

$$m\frac{dv}{dt} = mg\left(1 - \frac{v}{5}\right) \Rightarrow \frac{dv}{dt} = g\left(1 - \frac{v}{5}\right)$$

Now this can be integrated using the method of separation of variables.

$$\frac{1}{1 - \tfrac{1}{5}v}\frac{dv}{dt} = g \;\Rightarrow\; \int \frac{1}{1 - \tfrac{1}{5}v}\,dv = \int g\,dt \;\Rightarrow\; -5\ln\left(1 - \tfrac{1}{5}v\right) = gt + c$$

This can be rearranged to make v the subject.

$$\ln\left(1 - \tfrac{1}{5}v\right) = -\tfrac{1}{5}(gt + c)$$
$$1 - \tfrac{1}{5}v = e^{-\frac{1}{5}(gt+c)}$$
$$\tfrac{1}{5}v = 1 - e^{-\frac{1}{5}(gt+c)}$$
$$v = 5\left(1 - e^{-\frac{1}{5}(gt+c)}\right)$$
$$= 5\left(1 - Ae^{\frac{-gt}{5}}\right)$$

where $A = e^{-\frac{c}{5}}$. Now the value of A can be determined using the initial conditions, $v = 20$ when $t = 0$. Substituting these values gives:

$$20 = 5\left(1 - Ae^0\right)$$
$$4 = 1 - A \Rightarrow A = -3$$

So the expression for v becomes: $v = 5\left(1 + 3e^{-\frac{gt}{5}}\right)$

Example 18.3

A bungee jumper of mass 75 kg jumps and reaches a speed of 15 m s⁻¹ when the rope becomes taut. The stiffness of the rope is 100 N m⁻¹. Assume g = 10 m s⁻².

a) *Find an expression for the speed of the jumper in terms of the distance fallen after the rope becomes taut.*
b) *Find the maximum speed of the jumper.*
c) *Find the maximum extension of the rope.*
d) *Sketch a graph of v against the extension of the rope as the jumper descends.*

Solution

a) *The diagram shows the forces acting and the downward direction defined as positive.*
The resultant force is:
$$mg - kx = 750 - 100x$$
where x is the extension of the rope after it becomes taut.

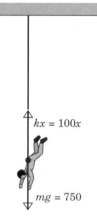

So the acceleration is described by: $a = 10 - \dfrac{4x}{3}$

As the acceleration depends on x it is appropriate to use $v\dfrac{\mathrm{d}v}{\mathrm{d}x}$ *for the acceleration, so:*
$$v\frac{\mathrm{d}v}{\mathrm{d}x} = 10 - \frac{4x}{3}$$
Integrating gives:
$$\int v\,\mathrm{d}v = \int\left(10 - \frac{4x}{3}\right)\mathrm{d}x$$
$$\frac{v^2}{2} = 10x - \frac{4x^2}{6} + c$$
$$v^2 = 20x - \frac{4x^2}{3} + 2c$$

The initial conditions, x = 0 and v = 15 can be used to find the value of the constant c.
$$225 = 2c \ \Rightarrow \ c = 112.5$$
so $v^2 = 20x - \tfrac{4}{3}x^2 + 225$

b) *The speed is a maximum when* $\dfrac{\mathrm{d}v}{\mathrm{d}x} = 0$. *However, when v is maximum, v^2 will also be a maximum, so we can find when*
$\dfrac{\mathrm{d}(v^2)}{\mathrm{d}x} = 0$. *This is easier to deal with.*

Differentiating the expression for v^2 gives:
$$\frac{\mathrm{d}(v^2)}{\mathrm{d}x} = 20 - \tfrac{8}{3}x$$

So for the maximum speed:
$$20 - \tfrac{8}{3}x = 0 \Rightarrow x = \tfrac{60}{8} = 7.5 \text{ m}$$

Substituting into the expression for v^2 gives:
$$v^2 = 20 \times 7.5 - \frac{4 \times 7.5^2}{3} + 225 = 300 \text{ and } v = 17.3\,\mathrm{m\,s^{-1}}$$

c) *At the lowest point v = 0, so* $0 = 20x - \tfrac{4}{3}x^2 + 225$

Solving this quadratic equation gives:

$$x = \frac{-20 \pm \sqrt{20^2 - 4 \times \left(-\frac{4}{3}\right) \times 225}}{2 \times \left(-\frac{4}{3}\right)} = \frac{-20 \pm \sqrt{1600}}{-\frac{8}{3}} = 22.5 \text{ or } -7.5$$

d) *The sketch should include the following three points:*
   i) *an initial speed of 15 ms^{-1} when $x = 0$,*
   ii) *a maximum speed of 17.3 ms^{-1} when $x = 7.5$ m,*
  iii) *a speed of 0 when $x = 22.5$ m.*

These are illustrated in the graph.

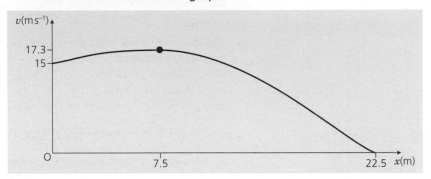

EXERCISES

18.1 CLASSWORK

1 As a cyclist free-wheels he experiences a resistive force of magnitude $40v$. Assume that the combined mass of the cycle and cyclist is 80 kg.
   a) Find an expression for $\frac{dv}{dt}$, that models the motion of the cyclist freewheeling on a horizontal surface.
   b) If the initial velocity of the cyclist is 10 m s^{-1} find an expression for the speed of the cyclist at time t.
   c) Find an expression for the distance travelled from the initial position in terms of t. Use this to show that the cyclist travels a distance of 20 m before stopping.

2 A skydiver in free-fall has a terminal speed of 60 m s^{-1}. Assume that the air resistance is proportional to the speed of the skydiver.
   a) Show that $\dfrac{dv}{dt} = g\left(1 - \dfrac{v}{60}\right)$.
   b) Find an expression for v, if the skydiver is initially at rest.
   c) How long does it take for the skydiver to reach a speed equal to half of his terminal speed?

3 The acceleration of a parachutist can be modelled by the expression:
$$a = g\left(1 - \frac{v}{4}\right)$$
   a) What is the terminal speed of the parachutist?
       The parachutist was moving at 10 m s^{-1} when the parachute opened.
   b) Find an expression for v in terms of t.
   c) Find an expression for x in terms of t.
   d) Use these results to find the speed and the distance travelled by the parachutist after ten seconds.

4 A particle of mass 1 kg is attached to a fixed point by a length of elastic cord of stiffness 5 N m^{-1}, and natural length 1 m. The particle has an initial speed of 20 m s^{-1} and moves on a smooth horizontal surface. The particle is initially at the point where the elastic is attached. What is the maximum displacement of the particle?

5 The forces acting on an unpowered probe of mass m that is propelled from a submarine at a speed of 20 m s^{-1} are in equilibrium vertically, but include a horizontal resistance force of magnitude mkv^2.
a) Find expressions for v in terms of t and in terms of x.
b) After ten seconds the speed of the probe has dropped to 5 m s^{-1}. Find k and the distance travelled by the probe at this time.

6 Two identical balls of mass m are allowed to fall from rest. They are subject to a resistance force kmv, where k is a constsnt. The first ball is released when $t = 0$ and the second is released when $t = T$. Find expressions for the distance fallen by each ball and describe what happens to the distance between them.

EXERCISES

18.1 HOMEWORK

1 A car with a power output of 40 kW has a top speed of 50 m s^{-1}.
a) Find a simple model for the resistance forces in the car by assuming that they are proportional to its speed.
b) The car, which has mass 800 kg, is travelling at 20 m s^{-1} when the driver allows it to free-wheel until it comes to rest. Find the distance that the car travels before it stops.

2 A boat with maximum power output of 30 kW can reach a top speed of 10 m s^{-1}. The mass of the boat is 1200 kg.
a) What can be deduced about the resultant force on the boat when it is travelling at its top speed?
b) By assuming the resistance forces on the boat are proportional to its speed find a simple model for the resistance force.
c) By assuming that the forward force on the boat is a constant and always takes its maximum value show that: $\dfrac{dv}{dt} = \dfrac{10 - v}{4}$
d) Find an expression for v in terms of t, if $v = 0$ when $t = 0$.
e) How long would it take the boat to reach a speed of 5 m s^{-1}?

3 A ship of mass m is subject to a resistance force of magnitude kv^2.
a) Suggest the factors on which k might depend.
b) The ship's motors stop, so that it is only acted upon by the resistance force. Show that when the ship has travelled a distance $\dfrac{m}{k} \ln 2$ its initial speed has been halved.

4 A particle, of mass 100 grams, is attached to a 1m length of elastic of stiffness 20 N m^{-1}. The particle is projected with an initial speed of 10 m s^{-1} from the point where the other end of the elastic is fixed on a smooth table.
a) Find the maximum displacement of the particle.
b) State two factors that would in reality affect the motion of the particle. Revise the differential equation that you used to solve this problem, clearly defining any variables that you introduce.

5   A cycle and cyclist of total mass 75 kg experience a forward force of
     magnitude $\dfrac{150}{v}$ and a resistance force of magnitude $75kv$.
     a) Find an expression for the acceleration of the cyclist and use it to
        obtain an expression for v^2, in terms of k and t if the cyclist starts
        at rest.
     b) The maximum speed of the cyclist is 12 m s^{-1}. Use this to find the
        value of k.

6   A torpedo, of mass m, is fired horizontally at 50 m s^{-1} from a
     stationary submarine. It continues to move horizontally and after
     three seconds hits a target at a speed of 20 m s^{-1}. Assume that the
     torpedo is subject to a resisting force of magnitude mkv^3, where v is
     the speed of the torpedo and k a constant.
     By considering $\frac{dv}{dt}$ and $\frac{dv}{dx}$ find the distance of the target from
     the submarine.

CONSOLIDATION EXERCISES FOR CHAPTER 18

1   A particle P of mass 0.5 kg moves away from the origin O along the
     positive x-axis under the action of a force, directed towards O, of
     magnitude $\dfrac{2}{x^2}$ N, where OP = x metres. When $x = 1$, the speed of P is
     3 m s^{-1}. Find the distance of P from O when its speed has been reduced
     to 1.5 m s^{-1}.

(EDEXCEL Question 3, Specimen Paper M2)

2   The motion of a cyclist on a horizontal surface is to be modelled
     based on the following assumptions:
     i) the cycle and cyclist are to be modelled as a single particle of mass
        m kg,
     ii) a constant forward force of magnitude F N acts on the particle,
     iii) a resistance force of magnitude kv N acts on the particle when it
        is travelling at a speed of v m s^{-1}.
     a) Show that at time t seconds, the speed v of the cyclist is given by:
     $$v = \frac{F - A\mathrm{e}^{-\frac{kt}{m}}}{k}$$
        where A is a constant.
     b) The cyclist starts at rest and moves at a speed of 6 m s^{-1} after
        5 seconds. The maximum speed that the cyclist can attain is 8 m s^{-1}.
        Show that:
     $$v = 8\left(1 - \mathrm{e}^{-\frac{t\ln 4}{5}}\right).$$

(AQA B Question 8, Specimen Paper M2)

Summary

After you have worked through the chapter you should be able to:

■ use the different forms of acceleration: $\dfrac{d^2 x}{d t^2}, \dfrac{dv}{dt}$ and $v\dfrac{dv}{dx}$

■ set up differential equations to describe real situations

■ solve problems using separation of variables.

Simple harmonic motion

■ *Simple harmonic motion is the motion performed by objects such as pendulums and springs.*

■ *Simple harmonic motion can be used to model the motion of many vibrating or oscillating systems.*

■ *In this chapter we assume that there are no resistance forces in the models and systems we consider.*

SPRINGS AND SIMPLE HARMONIC MOTION (SHM)

There are many situations in which springs are involved in vibrating systems. One of the most familiar is probably the use of springs in the suspension systems of motor vehicles. Bungee jumpers also experience vibration, although they are attached to an elastic rope rather than a spring! In both of these examples the vibrations **decay** very quickly, and it is important that they do. In this chapter ideal systems where the vibrations do not decay will be considered and this first section deals specifically with vibrating spring systems.

Example 19.1

An object of mass m is suspended from a spring of natural length l and modulus of elasticity λ. Find an expression for the acceleration of the mass if it is allowed to oscillate freely, in terms of x, its displacement from its equilibrium position.

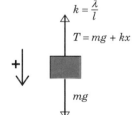

Solution
When in its equilibrium position the tension in the spring is mg. When the mass is moved a distance x from the equilibrium position the tension increases by $\dfrac{\lambda x}{l}$, so the tension is $mg + \dfrac{\lambda x}{l}$.

The resultant force is:
$$mg - T = mg - \left(mg + \frac{\lambda x}{l}\right) = -\frac{\lambda x}{l}$$

Applying Newton's second law allows us to find the acceleration, $\dfrac{\mathrm{d}^2 x}{\mathrm{d}t^2}$.

$$m\frac{\mathrm{d}^2 x}{\mathrm{d}t^2} = -\frac{\lambda x}{l} \implies \frac{\mathrm{d}^2 x}{\mathrm{d}t^2} = -\frac{\lambda x}{ml}$$

The SHM equation

The acceleration of a mass–spring system is given by:

$$\frac{\mathrm{d}^2 x}{\mathrm{d}t^2} = -\frac{\lambda x}{ml}$$

An equation like this cannot be solved by direct integration, because the right-hand side is in terms of x. The following examples show that the solution of this equation is the form:

$$x = A\cos(\omega t + \alpha)$$

When the acceleration of an object and its position are of the form given above then the motion is described as **simple harmonic motion** or SHM.

Example 19.2

The acceleration of an oscillating mass–spring system is given by:

$$\frac{d^2x}{dt^2} = -9x$$

a) *Show that if the displacement of the mass is $x = A\cos 3t$, this satisfies the equation above.*

b) *If the amplitude of the oscillations is 0.06 state the value of A.*

c) *Sketch the graph of displacement against time, indicating on the graph the period. Also describe how the motion begins if the downward direction is positive.*

Solution

a) *If $x = A\cos 3t$*

then $\dfrac{dx}{dt} = -3A\sin 3t$

and $\dfrac{d^2x}{dt^2} = -9A\cos 3t = -9x$

since $x = A\cos 3t$

So $x = A\cos 3t$ satisfies the initial differential equation.

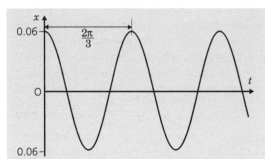

b) *As the amplitude of the oscillations is 0.06 the value of A must be 0.06.*

c) *The graph is shown.*

Note that the one complete oscillation is completed when:

$$3t = 2$$

or $t = \dfrac{2\pi}{3}$

So the period of the oscillation is $\dfrac{2\pi}{3}$.

Initially the mass is displaced in the positive direction and released. As the position direction has been defined as downward, this means that the mass was pulled down and released.

Example 19.3

Show that:

$$x = A\cos(\omega t + \alpha)$$

is a solution of the differential equation:

$$\frac{d^2x}{dt^2} = -\frac{\lambda x}{ml}$$

that arises from a vibrating mass–spring system, and find ω in terms of m, l and λ. Find the period of the oscillations.

Solution

Starting with $x = A\cos(\omega t + \alpha)$ and differentiating gives:

$$\frac{dx}{dt} = -A\omega\sin(\omega t + \alpha)$$

and:

$$\frac{d^2x}{dt^2} = -A\omega^2\cos(\omega t + \alpha)$$

As $x = A\cos(\omega t + \alpha)$ this is equivalent to:

$$\frac{d^2x}{dt^2} = -\omega^2 x$$

This will satisfy the differential equation:

$$\frac{\mathrm{d}^2x}{\mathrm{d}t^2} = -\omega^2 x$$

if $\omega^2 = \dfrac{\lambda}{ml}$

One oscillation will be completed when:

$$\omega t = 2\pi \quad \text{or} \quad t = \frac{2\pi}{\omega}$$

So the period will be $\dfrac{2\pi}{\omega}$

Note: For a spring mass system the period is $2\pi\sqrt{\dfrac{ml}{\lambda}}$.

Example 19.4

A clock is regulated by a 10 gram mass hanging on a spring of natural length 10 cm and modulus of elasticity 100 N.

a) Find an expression for the acceleration, $\dfrac{\mathrm{d}^2x}{\mathrm{d}t^2}$, of the mass, where x is the displacement from the equilibrium position.

b) Find an expression for x, if the mass is set in motion by being pulled down 1.5 cm and released.

c) State the period of the oscillations that take place.

Solution

a) The diagram shows the forces acting on the mass. If the displacement is measured from the equilibrium position, then the resultant force will be:

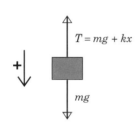

$$mg - T = mg - \left(mg + \frac{\lambda x}{l}\right) = -\frac{\lambda x}{l}$$

Using Newton's second law gives:

$$m\frac{\mathrm{d}^2x}{\mathrm{d}t^2} = -\frac{\lambda x}{l}$$

Substituting for m, l and λ gives:

$$0.01\frac{\mathrm{d}^2x}{\mathrm{d}t^2} = -10x$$

or $\dfrac{\mathrm{d}^2x}{\mathrm{d}t^2} = -1000x$

b) The displacement x will be of the form:

$x = A\cos(\omega t + \alpha)$

where $\omega^2 = 1000$ or $\omega = 31.6$. As the mass is initially displaced 1.5 cm or 0.015 m, the amplitude A will be 0.015, giving:

$x = 0.015\cos(31.6t + \alpha)$

When $t = 0$, $x = 0.015$, giving:

$0.0015 = 0.015\cos\alpha$

so $\alpha = 0$ and

$x = 0.015\cos 31.6t$

c) One oscillation will be completed when:

$31.6t = 2\pi$

or $t = \dfrac{2\pi}{31.6} = 0.205$ seconds

EXERCISES

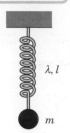

1 For each mass–spring system shown below, find an expression for $\frac{d^2x}{dt^2}$ the acceleration of the mass in terms of x its displacement from the equilibrium position.
a) $\lambda = 60$ $\quad l = 0.04\,\text{m}$ $\quad m = 4\,\text{kg}$
b) $\lambda = 20\,\text{N}$ $\quad l = 0.2\,\text{m}$ $\quad m = 2\,\text{kg}$

2 Show that each differential equation below is satisfied by the expression, $x = A\cos(\omega t + \alpha)$ and find the value of ω:
a) $\frac{d^2x}{dt^2} = -4x$ $\qquad$ **b)** $\frac{d^2x}{dt^2} = -100x$

3 Find the period for each mass–spring system defined below, if a single mass is suspended from a spring with the characteristics given.
a) $m = 100\,\text{grams}$, $\quad \lambda = 4\,\text{N}$, $\quad l = 0.2\,\text{m}$
b) $m = 200\,\text{grams}$, $\quad \lambda = 50\,\text{N}$, $\quad l = 0.1\,\text{m}$

In which cases do you think it would be feasible to carry out an experiment to determine the period by observing the number of oscillations in a given time interval?

4 Two springs with natural length 0.2 m and modules of elasticity 8 N are attached to a 0.5 kg mass as shown in the diagram. It is pulled 3 cm to the right and released.

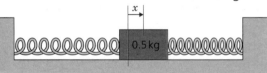

a) Find the acceleration of the mass, in terms of x, its displacement to the right of its equilibrium position.
b) Find the period of the oscillations.
c) Find an expression for x.
d) If the mass were initially moved to the left instead of the right, now give an expression for x.

5 Two identical springs and masses are arranged as shown. How will the period of oscillation of the systems compare?

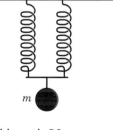

6 A clock manufacturer uses a spring of natural length 20 cm and modulus of elasticity 2 N and a mass of 50 grams, to regulate a clock.

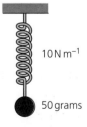

a) Find the period of oscillation.
A clock is taken to the moon, where $g = 1.6\,\text{ms}^{-2}$.
b) Find the resultant force on the mass and hence its acceleration.
c) Find the period of the oscillations when the clock is on the moon.
d) What difference is there between the oscillations of two identical clocks, one on Earth and the other on the moon?

7 The mass–spring system shown is at rest in its equilibrium position. The mass is set into motion by being given an initial upward velocity of $2\,\text{ms}^{-1}$.

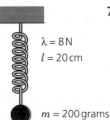

a) Show that the displacement of the mass from its equilibrium position is given by:
$$x = A\cos(\omega t + \alpha)$$
and find the value of ω.

b) Use the fact that when $t = 0$, $x = 0$, to find the value of α.
c) Find an expression for the velocity of the mass and hence find the value of A.

EXERCISES

19.1 HOMEWORK

1 For each mass–spring system below, find an expression for $\dfrac{d^2x}{dt^2}$, the mass in terms acceleration of the of x its displacement from the equilibrium position.

a) $\lambda = 40\,\text{N}$ $l = 0.5\,\text{m}$ $m = 2\,\text{kg}$
b) $\lambda = 30\,\text{N}$ $l = 60\,\text{cm}$ $m = 5\,\text{kg}$

2 The diagram shows an object of mass 0.2 kg and two springs of length 0.3 m and modulus of elasticity 12 N.

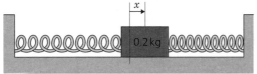

a) Find the resultant force on the mass in terms of x, the displacement of the mass from its equilibrium position.
b) Hence find the acceleration of the mass in terms of x.

3 Show that each differential equation below is satisfied by the expression $x = A\cos(\omega t + \alpha)$ and find the value of ω.

a) $\dfrac{d^2x}{dt^2} = -25x$ **b)** $\dfrac{d^2x}{dt^2} = -81x$

4 Find the period for each mass–spring system below, if a single mass is suspended from a spring with the characteristics given.
a) $m = 200\,\text{grams}$, $\lambda = 5\,\text{N}$, $l = 0.4\,\text{m}$
b) $m = 1\,\text{kg}$, $\lambda = 40\,\text{N}$, $l = 0.8\,\text{m}$

5 Two springs with length 0.9 m and modulus of elasticity 54 N are attached to a 0.4 kg mass as shown in the diagram. It is pulled 5 cm to the right and released.

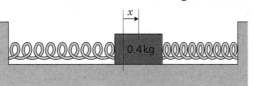

a) Find the acceleration of the mass, in terms of x its displacement to the right of its equilibrium position.
b) Find the period of the oscillations.
c) Find an expression for x.
d) If the mass were initially moved to the left instead of the right, how would your answer change?

6 A baby-bouncer is required to oscillate with a period of two seconds. Assume that the average mass of a baby is 12 kg and make a recommendation on length and modulus of elasticity of the elastic to be used in the bouncer.

7 Two identical springs are attached to identical masses. One is pulled down 3 cm and the other is pulled down 4 cm from their equilibrium positions and released.
a) How would the amplitude and the period of motion for each system compare?
b) If the springs have natural length 50 cm and modulus of elasticity 20 N and the mass is 100 grams, find the period.

AN ENERGY APPROACH TO SHM

As we have seen, applying Newton's second law leads to a detailed description of the motion of a spring system describing simple harmonic motion. Often, though, problems can be solved using a simpler approach based on energy considerations. We start by considering the transfer of potential and kinetic energy as the system vibrates.

Exploration 19.1

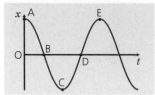

The graph shows displacement from the equilibrium position, plotted against time, for a mass that is oscillating on the end of a spring. At each point indicated consider how much potential and kinetic energy the mass has and what happens to this energy.

Energy considerations

At some positions the gravitational potential energy of the mass is at its lowest value and the kinetic energy is zero. This is a situation where much of the energy of the system is stored in the spring. Energy stored in an elastic string or spring is known as **elastic potential energy**.

We have studied elastic potential energy earlier. The work done in stretching a spring of natural length l and modulus of elasticity λ a distance e from its natural length, where $T(x)$ is the tension in the spring, is:

$$\int_0^e T(x)\mathrm{d}x = \int_0^e \frac{\lambda}{l}x\mathrm{d}x = \left[\frac{1}{2}\frac{\lambda}{l}x^2\right]_0^e = \frac{\lambda e^2}{2l}$$

so the elastic potential energy, stored in the spring, is:

$$\frac{\lambda e^2}{2l}$$

Example 19.5

The diagram shows a spring of natural length l and modulus of elasticity λ, attached to a mass m.

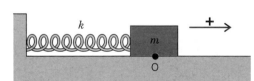

The mass is pulled a distance a to the right and released. Show that velocity of the mass can be modelled by:

$$v = \omega\sqrt{a^2 - x^2}$$

where x is the extension of the spring and a is the maximum displacement. What important assumption has to be made about the system?

Solution

When the mass is pulled a distance a to the right the elastic potential energy (EPE) will be:

$$EPE = \frac{\lambda e^2}{2l} = \frac{\lambda a^2}{2l}$$

This is the total energy of the system. As the mass moves this will converted into kinetic energy (KE) and back to elastic potential energy. At any time the kinetic energy is $\frac{1}{2}mv^2$ and the elastic potential energy is $\frac{\lambda x^2}{2l}$ so by conservation of energy:

$$\text{total energy} = KE + EPE \quad \Rightarrow \quad \frac{\lambda a^2}{2l} = \frac{1}{2}mv^2 + \frac{\lambda x^2}{2l}$$

Rearranging for v gives:

$$\lambda a^2 = mlv^2 + \lambda x^2$$
$$mlv^2 = \lambda\left(a^2 - x^2\right)$$
$$v^2 = \frac{\lambda}{ml}\left(a^2 - x^2\right)$$

In this case $w^2 = \dfrac{\lambda}{ml}$*, so the equation becomes:*
$$v^2 = \omega^2\,(a^2 - x^2)$$
or $v = \omega\sqrt{a^2 - x^2}$

It is important to realise that this result is only true if no energy is lost from the system, for example by doing work against air resistance.

The result demonstrated above holds true for all cases of simple harmonic motion.

Example 19.6

A 2 kg mass suspended on a spring of natural length 0.4 m and modulus of elasticity 80 N is at rest in its equilibrium position. The mass is struck so that it leaves the equilibrium position moving upwards at 0.4 m s^{-1}.
a) Find the period of the motion.
b) Find the amplitude.

Solution
a) The period for simple harmonic motion, as described by the mass,
is $T = \dfrac{2\pi}{\omega}$*, and for the mass–spring system* $\omega^2 = \dfrac{\lambda}{ml}$ *. So in this case:*

$$w^2 = \frac{80}{2 \times 0.4} = 100$$
$$w = 10$$

So the period is:
$$T = \frac{2\pi}{\omega} = \frac{2\pi}{10} = \frac{\pi}{5} = 0.63 \text{ seconds.}$$

b) The amplitude can be found using:
$$v = \omega\sqrt{a^2 - x^2}$$

Initially $v = 0.4$ *and* $x = 0$*, so using* $\omega = 10$*, gives:*
$$0.4 = 10\sqrt{a^2 - 0}$$
$$a = \frac{0.4}{10} = 0.04\,\text{m}$$

Example 19.7

A thin steel rod is displaced and released. Assume that the tip of the rod describes simple harmonic motion with period 0.01 seconds. If the tip of the rod moves between extremities 0.4 m apart find the maximum speed of the tip of the rod.

Solution

Fist the value of must be found. Since the period is $\frac{2\pi}{\omega}$, this gives:

$$0.01 = \frac{2\pi}{\omega}$$

so

$$\omega = \frac{2\pi}{0.1} = 200\pi$$

Now using

$$v = \omega\sqrt{a^2 - x^2}$$

and noting that $a = 0.2$ and $x = 0$ when the tip has its maximum speed gives:

$$v = 200\pi\sqrt{0.2^2 - 0} = 40\pi = 126 \text{ m s}^{-1}$$

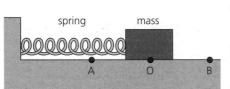

0.4 m

EXERCISES

19.2 CLASSWORK

1   A spring has natural length 30 cm and modulus of elasticity 15 N and one end is attached to a 100 gram mass, which is free to move on a smooth horizontal plane. The other end of spring is fixed as shown in the diagram.

    a) Find the energy stored in the spring when it is moved to B, 5 cm from O, the position of the mass when the spring is at its natural length.

    b) State the KE of the mass as it passes through O, and hence find the speed of the mass at this point.

    c) Repeat **a)** and **b)** for an initial displacement of 10 cm.

spring   mass

A   O   B

2   A mass–spring system performs simple harmonic motion with amplitude 5 cm and period 2 seconds. Find the maximum speed attained by the mass.

3   A bottle bobbing up and down in a tank of water oscillates with simple harmonic motion. The amplitude of the motion is 6 cm and the period is 1.2 seconds. Find the maximum speed reached by the bottle.

4   The manufacturer of an electric saw claims that the saw completes two cycles per second and that the blade reaches a maximum speed of 0.75 m s^{-1}. Find the amplitude of the motion.

5   The motion of the needle of a sewing machine can be modelled as simple harmonic motion. The top of the needle moves between points 1.2 cm above and 0.6 cm below the flat surface of the sewing machine. The needle reaches a maximum speed of 5 cm s^{-1}.

    a) What is the amplitude of the motion?

    b) What is the speed of the needle when it pierces the material resting on the flat surface?

    c) An improved model reduces the period of the motion by 10%. What happens to the speed of the needle when it enters the cloth?

6   An object describes simple harmonic motion. When 1 cm from the centre of its oscillations it moves at 2 m s^{-1} and when 2 cm from its centre it moves at 0.5 m s^{-1}.

    a) Find the amplitude and period of the motion.

    b) Find the period of the motion.

EXERCISES

1   When a mass is suspended from a spring it oscillates with simple harmonic motion. If the amplitude is 9 cm and the period is 0.36 seconds, find the maximum speed attained by the mass.

2   The end of a metal beam is oscillating with simple harmonic motion. The amplitude of the motion is 1.5 cm and the period is 0.3 seconds. Find the maximum speed reached by the end of the beam.

3   A machine-operated punch forces a metal probe to move up and down with simple harmonic motion.
    a) If the probe completes 450 oscillations every minute, find ω.
    b) The probe moves between two points which are 15 cm apart. Find the maximum speed of the probe.
    c) Find the speed of the probe when it is 2.5 cm from its lowest position.

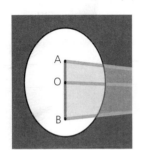

4   Part of a light show for a rock concert involves a laser. It is used to project a spot of light onto a circular screen. The spot of light is made to move up and down with simple harmonic motion through the centre of the screen between the two points A and B. A is 2.4 metres above O and B is 4 m below O. The spot reaches a maximum speed of $4\,\mathrm{m\,s^{-1}}$.
    a) What is the amplitude of the motion?
    b) What is the speed of the spot as it passes through O?
    c) The period is then changed, increasing it by 20%. What effect does this have on the speed of the spot as it passes through the point O?

5   An object is moving with simple harmonic motion about an equilibrium position O. When 3 cm from O it moves at $4\,\mathrm{m\,s^{-1}}$ and when 6 cm from O it moves at $1\,\mathrm{m\,s^{-1}}$. Find the amplitude and the period of the motion.

6   The suspension system in a car allows a wheel to oscillate vertically with simple harmonic motion. The designers have been instructed to ensure that at a displacement of 8 cm from the equilibrium position the vertical speed of the wheel is one-quarter of the maximum speed. If the maximum vertical speed is $2\,\mathrm{m\,s^{-1}}$, find:
    a) the amplitude of the motion,
    b) the period of the motion.

CONSOLIDATION EXERCISES FOR CHAPTER 19

1   A particle moves with simple harmonic motion between the two points A and B, which are 10 cm apart. The particle is moving at a speed of $2\,\mathrm{m\,s^{-1}}$, when it is 2 cm from A.
    a) Find the time that it takes the particle to move from A to B.
    b) Find the maximum speed of the particle

    (AQA B Question 3, M2 Specimen Paper)

2   A particle P of mass m is attached to one end of a light elastic string of natural length a and modulus of elasticity $6\,mg$. The other end of the string is attached to a fixed point O. Wen the particle hangs in equilibrium with the string vertical, the extension of the string is e.
    a) Find e.
    The particle is now pulled down a vertical distance $\frac{1}{3}a$ below its equilibrium position and released from rest. At time t after being released, during the time when the string remains taut, the extension

of the string is $e + x$. By forming a differential equation for the motion of P while the string remains taut:

b) show that during this time P moves with simple harmonic motion

of period $2\pi\sqrt{\dfrac{a}{6g}}$

c) Show that, while the string remains taut, the greatest speed of P is $\frac{1}{3}\sqrt{(6ga)}$

d) Find t when the string becomes slack for the first time.

(EDEXCEL *Question 7, M3 Specimen Paper*)

Summary

After working through this chapter you should:

■ be aware that if:
$$\frac{\mathrm{d}^2x}{\mathrm{d}t^2} = -\omega^2 x$$
then simple harmonic motion will take place with:
$$x = A\cos(\omega t + \alpha)$$

■ know that the period of oscillation for a mass spring system is:
$$2\pi\sqrt{\frac{m}{k}} \text{ or } 2\pi\sqrt{\frac{ml}{\lambda}}$$

■ know that the velocity of an object describing simple harmonic motion can be found using:
$$v = \omega\sqrt{a^2 - x^2}$$

Discrete probability distributions

In this chapter:

■ *we discover how the concepts of probability and the associated results may be used to model real-world situations,*

■ *we meet probability distributions as models for real random variables: geometric, binomial and Bernoulli,*

■ *we explore the process of mathematical modelling,*

■ *we discover how a calculator may be used to explore properties of random variables.*

MOST LIKELY EVENT – MODE

In many board games, players have to throw a six or roll a double to start. If the player fails, the forfeit is to wait for a turn before trying again. Imagine you are taking part in such a game. You have to roll a double (any double) using a pair of ordinary dice to start playing.

What is the probability that you will start playing on your first attempt?

The pair of dice can land in any one of 36 equally likely ways. Of these, exactly six result in a double. Hence:

$$P(\text{double}) = \frac{6}{36} = \frac{1}{6}$$

This is the chance that the dice will land showing a double on the first attempt. Not every player succeeds in getting started on their first attempt. What is the most likely number of attempts that a player will need to roll the dice to start the game? Is it twice, three times, six times, twelve times, ...? Before we provide a definitive answer, try this.

Suppose the rule to start the game is different. Instead of throwing a double with a pair of dice, you need to flip a head with a coin. Have a go at flipping a coin until you get a head. How many times did you need to flip the coin, was it once, twice, three times, ...?

What is the probability of obtaining a head on the first flip?
A coin may be assumed to be symmetric with only two possible outcomes, hence:
$P(H) = \frac{1}{2}$

What is the probability of not getting a head until the second flip? third flip? ... If we do not get a head until the second flip then the outcome must have been tail then head. The probability of this outcome is:

$$P(TH) = \frac{1}{2} \times \frac{1}{2} = \frac{1}{4}$$

Similarly, the probability of not getting a head until the third flip is:
$$P(TTH) = \tfrac{1}{2} \times \tfrac{1}{2} \times \tfrac{1}{2} = \tfrac{1}{8} \text{ etc.}$$
What is the most likely number of flips needed to get a head?

The answer is 1, because the probability of getting a head in one go is $\tfrac{1}{2}$ and the probability of taking any other number of attempts must be less than $\tfrac{1}{2}$.

Suppose, now, that the rules are again different. This time you must roll a tetrahedral die and get a 3 (the vertices of the die are numbered 1, 2, 3, 4).

What is the probability of getting the first 3 on:
■   the first roll.
■   the second roll,
■   the third roll?
It is reasonable to assume that the die is symmetrical and then:

$$P(3) = \tfrac{1}{4}$$

Hence, the probability of a 3 on the first attempt is $\tfrac{1}{4}$. If it takes two rolls to get the first 3 the outcome must have been 'not 3' then '3'. Hence:

$$P(\text{needing 2 rolls}) = P(\text{'not 3' and then '3'})$$
$$= P(\text{not 3}) \times P(3) = \tfrac{3}{4} \times \tfrac{1}{4}$$

which is, less than $\tfrac{1}{4}$, the probability of a 3 on the first attempt.

$$P(\text{needing three rolls}) = \tfrac{3}{4} \times \tfrac{3}{4} \times \tfrac{1}{4}$$

which is less than P(needing two rolls).

What is the most likely number of rolls needed to get a 3? The answer is 1. 'One roll' has the largest probability $\tfrac{1}{4}$, since all subsequent probabilities are $\tfrac{3}{4}$ of the preceding probability. So, a player is more likely to start the game on their first attempt than any other attempt.

Is this also true when the rule is 'throw a double to start'?

The probability of throwing a double on the first attempt is $\tfrac{1}{6}$. If it takes two throws to get started, it means that the first throw was not a double and the second was a double. The probability of this combined outcome can be written:

$$P\left(\overline{D} \text{ and } D\right) = P\left(\overline{D}\right) \times P(D) = \tfrac{5}{6} \times \tfrac{1}{6}$$

which is $\tfrac{5}{6}$ of the probability of getting started on the first attempt. So a player is less likely to need two attempts than just one attempt.

What is the probability of taking exactly:
a) three,   **b)** four,   **c)** n,
attempts to get a double?

a) Taking three attempts means that the first two did not result in a double and that the third did:
$$P\left(\overline{D}\,\overline{D}\,D\right) = P\left(\overline{D}\right) \times P\left(\overline{D}\right) \times P(D) = \tfrac{5}{6} \times \tfrac{5}{6} \times \tfrac{1}{6} = \left(\tfrac{5}{6}\right)^2 \times \tfrac{1}{6}$$

which is $\tfrac{5}{6}$ of the probability of getting started on the second attempt.

b) $P(\overline{D}\,\overline{D}\,\overline{D}\,D) = P(\overline{D}) \times P(\overline{D}) \times P(\overline{D}) \times P(D) = \frac{5}{6} \times \left(\frac{5}{6} \times \frac{5}{6} \times \frac{1}{6}\right) = \left(\frac{5}{6}\right)^3 \times \frac{1}{6}$

which is $\frac{5}{6}$ of the previous probability.

c) P(exactly n attempts)

$$= \underbrace{P(\overline{D}) \times P(\overline{D}) \times \ \cdots \ \times P(\overline{D})}_{(n-1)} \times P(D) = \left(\frac{5}{6}\right)^{n-1} \times \frac{1}{6}$$

The probabilities are getting smaller by a factor of $\frac{5}{6}$ each time. The conclusion is that the largest probability is associated with getting started on the first attempt.

CALCULATOR ACTIVITY

Exploration 20.1

Flipping two coins

How might a calculator be used to simulate the outcome of flipping two coins? Suppose that the rules of a game require a player to get two 'heads' when two coins are flipped. Use a calculator to simulate 60 players successfully attempting to get started. Record the number of flips each player takes. What is the **modal** number of attempts? Compare the number of players who are successful on their first, second, third, ... attempts.

Probability distribution

So far, we have introduced a way of modelling the likelihood of any given number of attempts at getting started. A player might get started on the first attempt, or it might take two, three, four, ... attempts.

No. of attempts	Probability
1	$\frac{1}{6}$
2	$\frac{5}{6} \times \frac{1}{6}$
3	$\left(\frac{5}{6}\right)^2 \times \frac{1}{6}$
4	$\left(\frac{5}{6}\right)^3 \times \frac{1}{6}$
n	$\left(\frac{5}{6}\right)^{n-1} \times \frac{1}{6}$

The table shows the number of possible attempts together with their probabilities when the probability of a successful outcome is $\frac{1}{6}$. It represents a **probability distribution** which aims to model the occurrence of a particular **random variable**. The random variable, R, is the number of attempts required to get started. The probability distribution can be summarised with the following probability function:

$$P(R = n) = \left(\frac{5}{6}\right)^{n-1} \times \frac{1}{6} \qquad n = 1, 2, 3, \ldots$$

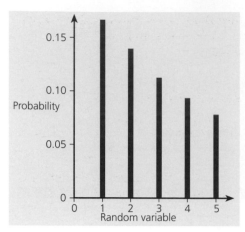

A graphical display of the distribution is shown in the diagram.

A probability distribution has the following features:

a)   all possibilities must be identified,

b)   all associated probabilities must lie between 0 and 1,

c)   the total of all the probabilities must be 1.

Are these features met in the probability distribution here?

a)   *All possibilities* – a player could get started on their first go, or it could take two attempts, or three, or ..., or thirty-three, ... It could take any positive whole number of attempts. So, the random variable, R, could be any positive whole number.

b)   *Lie between 0 and 1* – the largest probability is $\frac{1}{6}$. The next largest is $\frac{5}{6} \times \frac{1}{6}$, then $\frac{5}{6}$ of this, etc. All probabilities are a positive fraction of $\frac{1}{6}$. So, the probabilities lie between 0 and 1.

c)   *The total, T, of the probabilities is:*

$$T = \tfrac{1}{6} + \tfrac{5}{6} \times \tfrac{1}{6} + \left(\tfrac{5}{6}\right)^2 \times \tfrac{1}{6} + \left(\tfrac{5}{6}\right)^3 \times \tfrac{1}{6} + \ldots$$

It is far from obvious what this comes to. One simple approach to evaluating T is firstly to find $\frac{5}{6}T$.

$$\tfrac{5}{6}T = \tfrac{5}{6}\left\{\tfrac{1}{6} + \tfrac{5}{6} \times \tfrac{1}{6} + \left(\tfrac{5}{6}\right)^2 \times \tfrac{1}{6} + \left(\tfrac{5}{6}\right)^3 \times \tfrac{1}{6} + \ldots\right\} = \tfrac{5}{6} \times \tfrac{1}{6} + \left(\tfrac{5}{6}\right)^2 \times \tfrac{1}{6} + \left(\tfrac{5}{6}\right)^3 \times \tfrac{1}{6} + \ldots$$

Now find the difference between T and $\frac{5}{6}T$.

$$T - \tfrac{5}{6}T = \left\{\tfrac{1}{6} + \tfrac{5}{6} \times \tfrac{1}{6} + \left(\tfrac{5}{6}\right)^2 \times \tfrac{1}{6} + \left(\tfrac{5}{6}\right)^3 \times \tfrac{1}{6} + \ldots\right\} - \left(\tfrac{5}{6} \times \tfrac{1}{6} + \left(\tfrac{5}{6}\right)^2 \times \tfrac{1}{6} + \left(\tfrac{5}{6}\right)^3 \times \tfrac{1}{6} + \ldots\right) = \tfrac{1}{6}$$

Since the two expressions are almost identical, but, treated as an algebraic expression: $T - \frac{5}{6}T = \frac{1}{6}T$.

thus $\frac{1}{6}T$ and $\frac{1}{6}$ represent the same value: $\frac{1}{6}T = \frac{1}{6} \Rightarrow T = 1$.

This means that the total of all the probabilities is 1, as required for a probability distribution.

Exploration 20.2

Two heads

Develop a probability distribution to model the number of times you need to flip a pair of coins to get two heads. State your probability function, and show that the three features required are present in your model. Ensure you give a graphical presentation of your distribution.

Geometric distribution

The probability distributions considered in this chapter are examples of the **geometric probability distribution**. A simple notation often used for this distribution would be:

$$\text{Geo}\left(\tfrac{1}{6}\right)$$

in the case of the 'double' on the pair of dice. In general terms: $\text{Geo}(p)$ is used where p is the probability of succeeding at the first attempt.

A geometric sequence is one in which there is a constant ratio between successive terms. Examples of geometric sequences are:

3, 6, 12, 24, 48, 96, 192, 384, ... and

$$\frac{1}{4}, \frac{3}{16}, \frac{9}{64}, \frac{27}{256}, \frac{81}{1024}, \frac{243}{4096}$$

In the first sequence, the constant ratio is 2 and in the second sequence, it is $\frac{3}{4}$.

The general geometric sequence is often written:

$$a, ar, ar^2, ar^3, ar^4, ar^5, ...$$

The sum of all the terms in the sequence is $\frac{a}{1-r}$, where a is the first term, and r the ratio (provided the magnitude of r is less than 1).

Exploration 20.3

The probability distribution

■ Consider again, the probability distribution, $\text{Geo}\left(\frac{1}{6}\right)$.
   The possible values of the random variable, x, associated with this distribution and the relevant probabilities can be written:

x	1	2	3	4	5	6	...
$P(x)$	$\frac{1}{6}$	$\frac{1}{6}\left(\frac{5}{6}\right)$	$\frac{1}{6}\left(\frac{5}{6}\right)^2$	$\frac{1}{6}\left(\frac{5}{6}\right)^3$	$\frac{1}{6}\left(\frac{5}{6}\right)^4$	$\frac{1}{6}\left(\frac{5}{6}\right)^5$	...

   Identify the first term and the constant ratio of the sequence of probabilities. Hence, find the sum of all the probabilities.
■ Now repeat the process for:

   a) $\text{Geo}\left(\frac{3}{4}\right)$ **b)** $\text{Geo}\left(\frac{2}{3}\right)$ **c)** $\text{Geo}(0.8)$.

Example 20.1

Potatoes being prepared for packing are carried in a single file along a conveyor belt. The potatoes are visually inspected for blemishes. Those which are blemished are rejected. The inspector, having just rejected a potato, counts the number of potatoes he inspects until he next rejects another one.

If the proportion of blemished potatoes is five per cent calculate:
a) the probability that the inspector counts exactly five potatoes,
b) the probability that the inspector counts at least five potatoes.

Solution
a) Let B represent a potato which is blemished, and S a potato which is sound. Then the combined outcome sought is:

1st	2nd	3rd	4th	5th potato
S	S	S	S	B

If we assume that the quality of one potato is independent of the quality of any other potato, the probability of this combined event can be found from the multiplication law as:

$$P(SSSSB) = P(S) \times P(S) \times P(S) \times P(S) \times P(B)$$
$$= 0.95 \times 0.95 \times 0.95 \times 0.95 \times 0.05$$
$$= (0.95)^4 \times 0.05$$
$$P(\text{exactly } 5) = 0.0407$$

b) *There are at least three different ways in which we might approach the solution of this part.*

i) *A fairly direct approach can be found using the formula for the sum of all the terms of a geometric sequence. If the number of potatoes counted is at least 5, then it could be exactly 5, exactly 6, exactly 7, exactly ... . The probability could be calculated from:*

$$P(\text{at least } 5) = P(5 \text{ or } 6 \text{ or } 7 \text{ or } ...)$$
$$= P(5) + P(6) + P(7) + ...$$
$$= 0.95^4 \times 0.05 + 0.95^5 \times 0.05 + 0.95^6 \times 0.05 + ...$$

Notice, this is a geometric sequence with the first term equal to $0.95^4 \times 0.05$ and the common ratio equal to 0.95. Hence, using $\dfrac{a}{(1-r)}$, its sum is:

$$\frac{0.95^4 \times 0.05}{(1-0.95)} = \frac{0.95^4 \times 0.05}{0.05} = 0.95^4$$

$$P(\text{at least } 5) \approx 0.8145$$

ii) *An alternative approach is to consider the complementary event to 'at least 5', which is 'fewer than 5', i.e.*

$$P(\text{at least } 5) = 1 - P(\text{fewer than } 5)$$
$$= 1 - \{P(1) + P(2) + P(3) + P(4)\}$$
$$= 1 - \{0.05 + 0.95 \times 0.05 + 0.95^2 \times 0.05 + 0.95^3 \times 0.05\}$$
$$= 1 - \{0.05 + 0.0475 + 0.045\,125 + 0.042\,868\,...\}$$
$$= 1 - 0.185\,49\,...$$
$$P(\text{at least } 5) \approx 0.8145$$

iii) *A third, and perhaps the most direct approach, considers the implications of the count being at least five. This means that the first four potatoes were all sound.*

$$P(\text{at least } 5) = P(\text{first four sound})$$
$$= P(SSSS) = P(S) \times P(S) \times P(S) \times P(S) = (0.95)^4$$
$$P(\text{at least } 5) \approx 0.8145$$

Example 20.2

A tetrahedral die, with vertices numbered 1, 2, 3 and 4, is rolled repeatedly until a 3 is scored. What is the probability that the first 3 is scored in fewer than eight rolls?

Solution

Again, there are several different approaches which we could adopt to solve this problem. Let T denote the event that the outcome of rolling the die is 3, and N describe the event that the outcome is not a 3.

a) *For the first 3 to appear in fewer than eight rolls, one of the following must take place:*

T or NT or NNT or NNNT or NNNNT or NNNNNT or NNNNNNT

So, the probability required is:

P(T or NT or NNT or ... or NNNNNNT)

$= P(T) + P(NT) + P(NNT) + ... + P(NNNNNNT)$

$= \frac{1}{4} + \frac{3}{4} \times \frac{1}{4} + \left(\frac{3}{4}\right)^2 \times \frac{1}{4} + ... + \left(\frac{3}{4}\right)^6 \times \frac{1}{4}$

This can be found, perhaps using a calculator, to be approximately 0.8665.

b) *There is a formula for summing n terms of a geometric sequence:*

$$S_n = a + ar + ar^2 + \ldots + ar^{n-1} = \frac{a(1-r^n)}{1-r}$$

In this case, $n = 7$, $a = \frac{1}{4}$, $r = \frac{3}{4}$ hence:

$$P(\text{fewer than 8}) = S_7 = \frac{\frac{1}{4}\left(1-\left(\frac{3}{4}\right)^7\right)}{1-\frac{3}{4}} \approx 0.8665$$

c) *A fairly direct solution can be found by considering the complementary event. In this case the complement of 'fewer than 8' is '8 or more'. Thus:*
P(fewer than 8) = 1 − P(at least 8) = 1 − P(none of the first 7)

$$= 1 - \left(\frac{3}{4}\right)^7 \approx 0.8665$$

EXERCISES

20.1 CLASSWORK

1 A game requires a player to roll a six with a cubical die before the player may start the game.
   a) What is the most likely number of rolls of the die the player needs to get started?
   b) What is the probability that a player will need exactly four rolls?
   c) What is the probability that a player will need at least four rolls?

2 A random variable may be modelled by the distribution Geo(0.6). Calculate the probability:
   a) P(variable = 1) **b)** P(variable = 2) **c)** P(variable = 3)
   d) P(variable = 4) **e)** P(variable > 4).
   Illustrate the occurrence of the variable using a probability line graph.

3 A pack of cards is shuffled and the top card is turned over. The process is repeated until a heart is turned up.
   a) What is the probability that this occurs after exactly one shuffle?
   b) What is the probability that it takes fewer than four shuffles?
   c) What is the probability that it takes at least four shuffles?

4 A car salesman knows that 15 per cent of the cars he sells are red.
   a) What is the probability of his next five sales not being red?
   b) What is the probability of selling at least one red car in the next five sales?
   c) What is the probability of him having to make at least five sales before he sells a red car?

5 Calculate the probability of having to roll a cubical die fewer than ten times before the first six appears.

6 How many times does a cubical die need to be rolled for the probability of getting at least one 6 to be greater than 0.995?

EXERCISES

20.1 HOMEWORK

1 In a game there is a stage where a player could land in 'jail'. The player must throw a double with an ordinary pair of cubical dice to get out of jail.

a) What is the probability that a player will get out of jail on the first attempt?
b) What is the probability that a player will take exactly three attempts to get out of jail?
c) What is the probability that a player will not get out of jail in three attempts?
d) What is the most likely number of attempts a player will make to get out of jail?

2   A random variable follows the geometric distribution Geo($\frac{1}{4}$).
   a) Calculate the probability that the random variable:
      i) is exactly one,
      ii) is exactly two,
      iii) is exactly three,
      iv) is more than three.
   b) Write down the modal value of the variable.
   c) Illustrate the occurrence of the variable using a probability line graph.
   d) Calculate the probability that the variable:
      i)   is at least four,   ii)   is at least ten.

3   A student is conducting a survey of road traffic. One part of the survey involves the country of manufacture of road vehicles. A simple classification is used: home or foreign. The student has to record the country of manufacture of each vehicle passing her. The proportion of foreign vehicles is 65 per cent.
   a) What is the probability that the first two vehicles are foreign?
   b) What is the probability that there is no foreign vehicle in the first four that pass her?
   c) What is the probability that she records at least six vehicles before the first foreign vehicle?
   d) What is the probability she records more than ten vehicles before the first home-manufactured vehicle?

4   A tetrahedral die is rolled.
   a) What is the probability of not getting a 4 in five rolls of the die?
   b) What is the probability of getting at least one 4 in five rolls of the die?
   c) What is the probability of having to roll the die at least five times to get the first 4?

5   What is the probability that a coin needs to be flipped fewer than six times before the first head occurs?

6   How many times does a coin need to be flipped for the probability of not getting a head to be less than 0.0001?

MEAN

We have considered the geometric probability distribution, Geo(p), for a variety of values of the probability p. For instance, in the first section of this chapter, the value of p was $\frac{1}{6}$; in Exploration 20.1, p was $\frac{1}{4}$, etc. In every case, the modal value of the random variable was 1. Is this also true for the mean value of the random variable? Let's find out.

Consider the distribution used to model the number of flips of a coin to get a head. This is Geo($\frac{1}{2}$). Suppose we conduct an experiment where we flip a coin repeatedly and record the outcome: H, T; on each occasion.

The results are likely to be rather like those in the diagram.

How many flips did it take to get the first head? How many more flips were needed to get the next head? ... the next one? ... the next?

The diagram indicates that the first flip resulted in a head, so it took one flip. The next head appeared on the third flip after that, so four flips were needed. The next occurred one flip later. The next ... it is not possible to tell from the diagram.

However, suppose we had recorded the results of, say, 200 flips. Why is it reasonable to expect 100 of these to be heads?

The probability of a head is assumed to be $\frac{1}{2}$. We should expect half of the outcomes to be heads and half of 200 is 100! Let us now think about the situation where a half of the outcomes are heads – i.e. where, on average, every other outcome is a head. What is the average number of flips before the next head?

Since, on average, the outcomes alternate between tails and heads, the number of flips is two. The discussion so far leads to the following suggestion regarding the mean for Geo($\frac{1}{2}$):

mean of Geo($\frac{1}{2}$) = 2

CALCULATOR ACTIVITY

Exploration 20.4

Using expected value

It should be possible to verify this result using 'expected value':
mean of $X = E(X) = \sum x P(X = x)$
In Geo($\frac{1}{2}$), x can be any positive integer i.e. 1, 2, 3, 4, ... and the probability associated with the value is $(\frac{1}{2})^x$.
The following table presents part of the probability distribution.

x	$P(X = x)$	$x\,P(X = x)$
1	$\frac{1}{2}$	$1 \times \frac{1}{2}$
2	$(\frac{1}{2})2$	$2 \times (\frac{1}{2})^2$
3	$(\frac{1}{2})3$	$3 \times (\frac{1}{2})^3$
4	$(\frac{1}{2})4$	$4 \times (\frac{1}{2})^4$
$\mathbb{N}$	$\mathbb{N}$	$\mathbb{N}$

Clearly, the number of possible flips of the coin needed to get a head could be extremely large and it could be quite tedious keying in the calculations needed to evaluate the mean, i.e:
$1 \times \frac{1}{2} + 2 \times (\frac{1}{2})^2 + 3 \times (\frac{1}{2})^3 + ...$

If you have a programmable calculator you could use a program based on the following flowchart where N represents the number of terms in

the series $\displaystyle\sum_{r=1}^{N} r \times \left(\frac{1}{2}\right)^r$ and M is the mean.

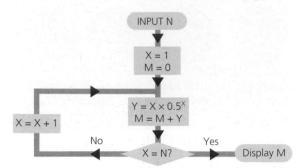

Note: M will always be slightly less than the true expected value since N cannot be infinite.

Try for $N = 10, 20, 30$; what do you think the expected value is?

If your calculator does not have the facility to run programs, you could input the values of X and $P(X = x)$ in its statistics mode and find the mean in that way.

Interpreting the results

The work in this section has led us to conclude that the mean number of flips required to get a head is two. This suggests that the mean value of a random variable which follows the geometric distribution, $\text{Geo}(\frac{1}{2})$, is two. What is the mean value of a random variable which follows the geometric distribution $\text{Geo}(\frac{1}{6})$?

Earlier, we decided that $\text{Geo}(\frac{1}{6})$ could be used to model the number of rolls of two dice required to get started in a board game. Imagine the scene at the annual convention for players of such a board game. There are hundreds, perhaps a thousand or more, players. Each player has to roll a double with a pair of ordinary dice. Suppose at some stage in this convention there have been 600 rolls of the dice, how many of these rolls could we expect to have resulted in a double? Since a double occurs one roll in every six, on average, it would be reasonable to expect that 100 of the 600 would result in a double. This suggests that the average number of rolls to get a double would be six, i.e. mean of $\text{Geo}(\frac{1}{6}) = 6$

CALCULATOR ACTIVITY

Exploration 20.5

Testing the assertion

It ought to be possible to test the assertion just made about the mean of $\text{Geo}(\frac{1}{6})$. How might the program you have written for $\text{Geo}(\frac{1}{2})$ be adapted for $\text{Geo}(\frac{1}{6})$? The following flowchart is one possible solution.

Try using your calculator to find the mean of $\text{Geo}(\frac{1}{6})$; you may need to set N to 30, 40, 50, 60 or more.

It is quite possible to adapt the program to cope with any value of p and then to find the mean of $\text{Geo}(p)$. An additional input will be required which is the value of p. Then the program will need to evaluate the complementary probability, $1 - p$, which is often labelled q. This flowchart presents one way of carrying this out.

INPUT N

X = 1
M = 0

X = X + 1

$Y = X \times \frac{1}{6} \times \frac{5}{6}^{(X-1)}$
M = M + Y

No

Yes

X = N?

Display M

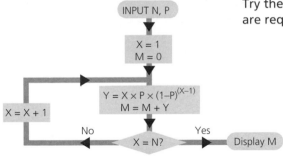

Try the following values for p and N (larger values of N are required the smaller p is).

p	N (at least)
$\frac{1}{2}$	20
$\frac{1}{6}$	75
0.8	10
0.75	15
0.6	20
$\frac{1}{3}$	30
$\frac{1}{4}$	40

The results you obtain could be displayed in a table like this.

Value of p	Mean of Geo(p)
$\frac{1}{2}$	2
$\frac{1}{6}$	6
0.8	$1\frac{1}{4}$
0.75	$1\frac{1}{3}$
0.6	$1\frac{2}{3}$
$\frac{1}{3}$	3
$\frac{1}{4}$	4

What do you think the relationship between the value of the probability, p, and the mean of the geometric distribution is?

$$\textbf{Mean of Geo}(p) = \frac{1}{p}$$

Variance

The definition of the variance of the probability distribution involving expectation:

$$\text{Var}(X) = \text{E}(X^2) - \text{mean}^2$$

where $\text{E}(X^2) = \sum x^2 \times \text{P}(X = x)$

Exploration 20.6

Mean and variance

Use this expression to explore the relationship between the mean and the variance of the geometric probability distribution Geo(p).

As an example, consider Geo(0.8), with mean $\dfrac{1}{0.8} = 1\frac{1}{4}$.

x	$\text{P}(X = x)$
1	0.8
2	0.8 0.2
3	0.8 0.2^2
4	0.8 0.2^3
$\vdots$	$\vdots$

The expected value of the square, $E(X^2)$ is:

$$E\left(X^2\right) = \sum_{x=1}^{\infty} x^2 \times 0.8 \times 0.2 + 3^2 \times 0.8 \times 0.2^2 + 4^2 \times 0.8 \times 0.2^3 + \dots \approx 1.875$$

(using a calculator to sum the first 15 terms).

Then the variance can be found as:

$$\mathrm{Var}(X) = E\left(X^2\right) - (\text{mean})^2$$
$$= 1.875 - \left(1\tfrac{1}{4}\right)^2$$
$$= \tfrac{5}{16}$$

Then, for Geo$(\tfrac{4}{5})$, the mean is $1\tfrac{1}{4}$ and the variance is $\tfrac{5}{16}$.

Try to find the variance for other geometric distributions. It might help to adapt your program as indicated in this flowchart.

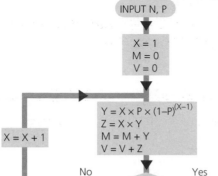

You will need larger values of N than were needed in finding the mean. The following table provides an indication of the sort of values needed.

p	N
$\tfrac{1}{2}$	25
$\tfrac{1}{6}$	100
0.8	15
0.75	15
0.6	25
$\tfrac{1}{3}$	40
$\tfrac{1}{4}$	75

The results you may obtain are given in this table.

p	Mean	Variance
0.8	$1\tfrac{1}{4}$	$\tfrac{5}{16}$
0.75	$1\tfrac{1}{3}$	$\tfrac{4}{9}$
0.6	$1\tfrac{2}{3}$	$1\tfrac{1}{9}$
$\tfrac{1}{2}$	2	2
$\tfrac{1}{3}$	3	6
$\tfrac{1}{4}$	4	12
$\tfrac{1}{6}$	6	30

What do you think is the relationship between the variance and the mean of Geo(p)? For a geometrically distributed random variable:

Variance = mean × (mean − 1)

Example 20.3

a) *If X is a random variable which is distributed* Geo(0.2), *find values for:*
   i) $E(X)$ ii) $\mathrm{Var}(X)$ iii) $P(X < \text{mean})$.
b) *The standard deviation of a geometric distribution is 6. What is its mean?*

Solution

a) i) *In general for* $\text{Geo}(p)$, *mean* $= \dfrac{1}{p}$, *so for* $\text{Geo}(0.2)$:

mean $= \dfrac{1}{0.2} = 5$

ii) *The variance is mean* $\times$ *(mean – 1), so for* $\text{Geo}(0.2)$:

variance $= 5 \times 4 = 20$

iii) $\text{P}(X < \text{mean}) = \text{P}(X < 5) = \text{P}(X = 1) + \text{P}(X = 2) + \text{P}(X = 3) + \text{P}(X = 4)$

$= 0.2 + 0.2 \times 0.8 + 0.2 \times 0.8^2 + 0.2 \times 0.8^3 = 0.5904$

b) *If the standard deviation is 6, then the variance is* 6^2, *i.e. 36. So, using the result variance = mean* $\times$ *(mean – 1):*

$36 = \text{mean} \times (\text{mean} - 1) \Rightarrow \text{mean}^2 - \text{mean} - 36 = 0$

This is a quadratic equation with solution:

mean $= \dfrac{1 \pm \sqrt{145}}{2} = 6.5208 \text{ or } -5.5208$

But a random variable which is geometrically distributed cannot be negative, hence the mean cannot be negative.

mean = 6.5208

EXERCISES

20.2 CLASSWORK

1 A random variable, X, is geometrically distributed with parameter $p = 0.7$.
   a) Write down the mode of X.
   b) State the mean of X.
   c) Write down the variance of X.

2 Illustrate $\text{Geo}(0.7)$ and $\text{Geo}(0.3)$ on a single diagram using a probability line graph.

3 Write down the mean and standard deviation of $\text{Geo}(0.9)$.

4 If X is known to be geometrically distributed with standard deviation $\frac{6}{5}$, what is its mean?

5 The mean of a geometric distribution is 1.21. Calculate its standard deviation.

EXERCISES

20.2 HOMEWORK

1 A random variable is geometrically distributed $\text{Geo}(0.2)$.
   a) Calculate the probability of the first success on the third attempt.
   b) Write down its mean.
   c) Calculate the variance of the random variable.

2 Illustrate $\text{Geo}(0.1)$ and $\text{Geo}(0.9)$ on the same probability diagram.

3 A random variable is modelled by $\text{Geo}(0.25)$. Write down its expected value and the expected value of its square.

4 The standard deviation of a random variable, Y, which is geometrically distributed is $\frac{3}{5}$. Calculate the probability: $\text{P}(Y = 1)$.

5 Calculate the mean of a random variable which is geometrically distributed with variance $\frac{15}{4}$.

MODELLING THE OCCURRENCE OF A RANDOM VARIABLE

We have used the term 'model' earlier, in connection with the probability distribution introduced in this chapter. The process of modelling a real-world situation can involve several different stages. These are shown as boxes in our modelling flowchart. The first of these is a description of that real situation or the real problem requiring a solution.

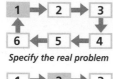

Specify the real problem

In the discussion at the start of this chapter, the real-world situation involved the number of rolls of two dice required to get a double in order for a player in a game to start playing.

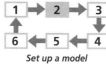

Set up a model

Once the real situation is grasped, the process of setting up an appropriate model can begin. $\text{Geo}(\frac{1}{6})$ was proposed as a model for the number of rolls of two dice required to get a double.

What assumptions led to this model?

The process which leads to $\text{Geo}(\frac{1}{6})$ might start like this.
1 A die can land with any one of six faces uppermost.
2 Each face is as likely as any other face.
3 For two dice, there are 36 possible equally likely outcomes.
4 Exactly six of these outcomes result in a double.

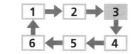

Formulate the mathematical problem

The next stage in the process is the formulation of the associated mathematical problem.

This leads us to assigning some numerical values to the likelihood of a 'double' being the outcome of rolling two dice.
5 The probability of a pair of dice landing as a double is $\frac{6}{36}$, i.e. $\frac{1}{6}$.
6 The probability that the dice do not land as a double is $1-\frac{1}{6}$, i.e. $\frac{5}{6}$.
7 The result of rolling the two dice is not affected by the result of any previous rolling, i.e. the outcomes are independent.

Having formulated the mathematical problem, the next step is to solve it.

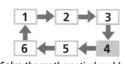

Solve the mathematical problem

8 The probability that a 'double' appears on the first roll of the dice is $\frac{1}{6}$.
9 To take exactly two rolls of the dice to get the first double means that the first roll was not a double but the second was a double. Since the outcomes are independent the probabilities can be multiplied to yield:
P(first double on second roll) $=\frac{5}{6}\times\frac{1}{6}$

10 The argument presented in (9) extends to:

P(first double on third roll) $=\frac{5}{6}\times\frac{5}{6}\times\frac{1}{6}=\left(\frac{5}{6}\right)^{2}\times\frac{1}{6}$

P(first double on fourth roll) $=\left(\frac{5}{6}\right)^{3}\times\frac{1}{6}$

...

P(first double on nth roll) $=\left(\frac{5}{6}\right)^{n-1}\times\frac{1}{6}$

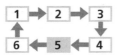
Interpret the solution

Compare with reality

We now need to interpret the solution of the mathematical problem. This suggests that in $\frac{1}{6}$, or about 16 per cent to 17 per cent, of the times a player has a go at rolling double he will be successful. It also indicates that he will need two attempts on between 13 per cent and 14 per cent $\left(\frac{5}{36}\right)$ of the occasions he has to roll a double to get started. Then, three attempts are required on about $11\frac{1}{2}$ per cent of the games. The model predicts that there is a reduction in the likely frequency as the number of attempts increases. The most likely number of attempts it predicts is 1. How these predictions and interpretations, compare with the reality is the next stage in the modelling process.

11 The model suggests that the modal number of attempts is 1. Is this borne out in reality?

12 The model suggests that the mean number of attempts is 6. Is this borne out in reality?

13 The model suggests that the variance of the number of attempts is 30. Is this borne out in reality?

14 The models suggests that the probability reduces at a constant rate. Again is this borne out in reality?

If the model seems to be appropriate then a report may be relevant. Otherwise it might be relevant to review the modelling process and to refine the proposed model. Thus the modelling process would be recommenced. Here, however, the model seems to be quite acceptable.

Exploration 20.7

Modelling

Look back at Example 20.1 and carry out the modelling process.
1   Specify the real world problem.
2   Set up the model.
3   Formulate the mathematical problem.
4   Solve the mathematical problem.
5   Interpret the implications of the solution.
6   Compare with reality.
7   Report.

Applying the geometric distribution

Example 20.4

A rowing club ran a stall during regatta week. The club offered a prize of £5 for a 20p stake to anyone who succeeded in rolling a double 6 with an ordinary pair of dice. If a contestant succeeded in rolling just one 6 they got a free go. A contestant who rolls a double 6 also gets their stake back. Is this a fair game?

Solution

In a 'fair game', the expected gain must be zero, where:
$$\text{E(gain)} = \sum \text{gain} \times \text{probability of the gain}$$
It is simple enough to identify the gain. A contestant who rolls a double 6 gains £5. Otherwise, the gain is –20p. But, what about the probability of these gains? We need to use the modelling process. The real-world situation has been specified. The model is based on symmetry and equal likelihood.

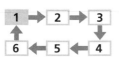
Specify the real problem

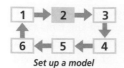

This leads to the familiar result which models the outcome space for a pair of dice as 36 equally likely events. Only one of these results in two 6s; ten result in exactly one 6; 25 have no 6. Hence, the model corresponds to:

P(double 6) = $\frac{1}{36}$

P(exactly one 6) = $\frac{10}{36}$

P(no 6) = $\frac{25}{36}$

The mathematical problem has already been formulated, i.e. E(gain) = 0. The solution of the mathematical problem requires us to establish the probabilities associated with each of the possible gains. The gain, £5, comes about when a contestant gets a double 6. The probability that this happens on the first roll of the dice is $\frac{1}{36}$. This is not the only opportunity that a contestant would conceivably have to get a double 6. How else could a contestant get a double 6?

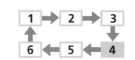

Imagine the contestant who rolls exactly one 6, then on the free go, gets a double 6. The probability that this happens is:

$\frac{10}{36} \times \frac{1}{36}$ *(What modelling has led to this result?)*

Then, there is the contestant who gets exactly one 6 on the free go and on the next free go gets a double 6. The probability for this is:

$\frac{10}{36} \times \frac{10}{36} \times \frac{1}{36}$

and so on. The possibilities can be illustrated in a tree diagram.

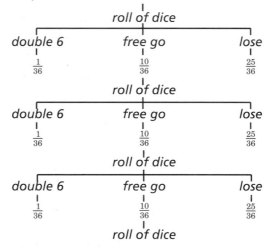

etc.

The probability of gaining £5 is modelled as:

$\frac{1}{36} + \frac{1}{36} \times \frac{10}{36} + \frac{1}{36} \times \left(\frac{10}{36}\right)^2 + \frac{1}{36} \times \left(\frac{10}{36}\right)^3 + \dots$

which is a geometric series with first term equal to $\frac{1}{36}$ and common ratio equal to $\frac{10}{36}$. The sum of the series is:

$$\frac{\frac{1}{36}}{\left(1 - \frac{10}{36}\right)} = \frac{1}{26}$$

The probability of gaining –20p must be $\frac{25}{26}$.
(This can be checked since it should be the sum of

$\frac{25}{36} + \frac{25}{36} \times \frac{10}{36} + \frac{25}{36} \times \left(\frac{10}{36}\right)^2 + \frac{25}{36} \times \left(\frac{10}{36}\right)^3 + \dots$ *)*

A summary of this is:

Gain	Probability
£5	$\frac{1}{26}$
−20p	$\frac{25}{26}$

Then, the expected gain for the game is: $= 500 \times \frac{1}{26} + -20 \times \frac{25}{26} = 0$
The interpretation which can be put on this solution is that the game is fair.
It would be interesting to compare this with reality, perhaps you can set up the game and get a few hundred players?
A brief report: the modelling undertaken here suggests that, on average, one contestant in every 26 will win the £5 prize. Twenty-five contestants will forfeit their stake money. The game is fair but it is not likely to lead to the rowing club making any money.

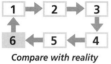

Compare with reality

EXERCISES

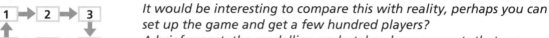

20.3 CLASSWORK

1   The organisers of a lottery claim that the chance of winning a prize with one ticket is 1 in 54. I decide to buy one ticket each week until I win a prize. Establish a probability model for the number of weeks. Use your model to:
   a) determine the expected number of weeks I have to wait for a prize,
   b) estimate the chance I will win a prize in less than four weeks,
   c) estimate the chance I will have to wait for more than a year,
   d) estimate the most likely number of weeks I have to wait.

2   An octahedral die with faces numbered 1, 2, ..., 8 is repeatedly rolled until a seven is obtained. Establish a model for the number of rolls required. Use your model to:
   a) determine the most likely number of rolls,
   b) estimate the mean number of rolls,
   c) predict the variance of the number of rolls,
   d) estimate the likelihood of requiring at least ten rolls.

3   I estimate that whenever I play a game of darts and I try to hit the bull my chance of success is $\frac{1}{8}$. What is the probability that I need:
   a) exactly eight attempts,
   b) fewer than eight attempts,
   c) more than eight attempts,
   to hit the bull.

4   If five per cent of the vehicles in your town are registered as taxis and you are waiting for a taxi to come into view, calculate the probability that:
   a) the first taxi is the sixth vehicle to come into view,
   b) the first taxi is not among the first six vehicles which come into view.

5   A game in an amusement park is played in which a contestant pays 25p for the privilege of rolling two dodecahedral dice each numbered 1, 2, 3, ..., 12. A prize of £10 is offered for any contestant getting a double 12. Contestants who get exactly one 12 are given a free go. All other contestants forfeit their stake money.
   a) Is this a fair game?
   b) Who stands to gain?
   c) What is the expected gain per go to the amusement park?

6   A fairground stall owner has two airguns, A and B. The guns are
    identical in appearance, but the chance that the pellet fired from gun
    A hits its target is $\frac{2}{3}$. For gun B the chance is $\frac{1}{2}$.
    a) I fire five pellets from gun A. What is the probability that:
        i)   none of them hit the target,
        ii) the first four miss the target but the fifth is successful,
        iii) at least one of them hits the target?
    b) If I use gun B, what is:
        i)   the most likely number of shots I need to hit the target,
        ii) the probability of needing more than five shots to hit the
             target?

EXERCISES

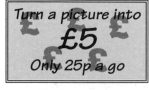

20.3 HOMEWORK

1   A woman decides she will give birth to one child each year until she
    bears a daughter. Establish a model for the number of children she has.
    a) What is the expected number of children?
    b) What is the modal number of children?
    c) Suggest a refinement you might make to your model so that it
        compares more favourably with reality.

2   A driving school claims that, on average, its pupils only need to take
    one driving test to qualify for a full driving licence. Establish a model
    for the number of tests a pupil needs assuming that the probability of
    a pupil passing the test is p.
    a) If the claim of the school is true, which 'average' is being quoted?
    b) Use your model to demonstrate that the claim is false if the school
        is using the mean number of tests.
    c) Suggest a reason why your model might need to be refined.

3   A tetrahedral die with its vertices numbered 1, 2, 3 and 4 is rolled
    respectively until a 2 is scored. What is the probability:
    a) that five rolls are required,
    b) that fewer than ten rolls are needed,
    c) that at least four rolls are required?

4   How many times does an ordinary die need to be rolled for the
    probability of getting at least one number greater than 4 to exceed 0.95?

5   The Beavers run a stall to raise funds. For a stake (non-returnable) of
    25p, contestants are invited to shuffle a pack of cards and cut the
    pack. If a picture (king, queen or jack) is cut, the contestant is given
    £5. If an ace is cut, the contestant is given a free go. Otherwise the
    contestant loses.
    a) Calculate the probability that a contestant loses.
    b) Calculate the probability that a contestant wins the £5.
    c) What is the expected win/loss to the Beavers per go?

6   A computer is programmed to produce single digits 0, 1, 2, ..., 9
    randomly.
    a) What proportion of the digits produced do you anticipate being
        zeros?
    b) What is the probability that none of the first 30 digits produced is
        a zero?
    c) What is the probability that two consecutive digits produced are
        zeros?

d) If the computer is programmed to produce double digits 00, 01, 02, ..., 99 randomly, what is the probability that none of the first:
  i) 30 pairs contain a double zero,
  ii) 300 pairs contain a double zero?

INTRODUCING THE BINOMIAL MODEL

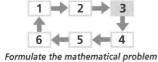

Specify the real problem

It has been estimated that 40 per cent of the world's population are of blood type A. What is the probability that, in a group of five people, exactly three will have type-A blood?

One approach to this problem is to work within a modelling framework. The real-world problem has been specified. A possible way of setting up the model is to let A represent a person with blood of type A and X represent a person who does not have blood of type A.

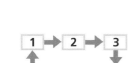

Set up a model

Then the sort of situation where exactly three people in a group of five have blood of type A can be represented by:

AAAXX   or   AXAXA   or   XAAXA   or ...

There are $_5C_3 = \dfrac{5!}{2!3!}$ arrangements of five people, three of whom have blood type A and two of whom do not.

In formulating this as a mathematical problem we have had to make certain assumptions about the people in the group. It might be reasonable to assume that:
- the blood type of one person is independent of that of any other person,
- the probability that a person's blood group is type A is constant – the same as the estimate given, i.e. 40 per cent or 0.4.

These assumptions are equivalent to saying that:

$P(A) = 0.4$ $P(X) = 0.6$ $P(AX) = P(A) \times P(X)$

So, the mathematical problem could be presented as:

If five letters are randomly chosen from a very large collection of As and Xs, what is the probability that the selection contains exactly three As when 40 per cent of the collection are As?

We are in a position to solve the mathematical problem. Consider one selection where the letters chosen are, in order:

AAAXX

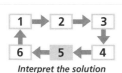

Solve the mathematical problem

The probability that this selection occurs is:
$$P(AAAXX) = P(A) \times P(A) \times P(A) \times P(X) \times P(X)$$
$$= 0.4 \times 0.4 \times 0.4 \times 0.6 \times 0.6 = 0.4^3 \times 0.6^2$$

However, this is just one of $\dfrac{5!}{2!3!}$ possible selections which result in exactly three As. Hence:

$$P(\text{exactly three As}) = \dfrac{5!}{2!3!} \times 0.4^3 \times 0.6^2 = 0.2304$$

Interpret the solution

An interpretation of this is that there is a probability of about 0.23 (23 per cent) that in a randomly selected group of five people there will be exactly three whose blood type is A.

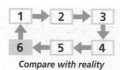

Compare with reality

Try comparing this result with reality. Your report should focus on how the proportion of groups of five people that include three whose blood type is A compares with the model's prediction of 23 per cent.

It is worth considering why there might be discrepancies. Possible reasons are:
- random variation,
- appropriateness of the assumption of independence,
- 40 per cent as the estimate of people with blood type A.

Example 20.5

Use the modelling framework to calculate the probability that, in a group of seven people, exactly two will have blood of type A.

Solution

The specification of the real problem is given above. The model can be set up as before, using A and X. Then the sort of situation sought with exactly two people having blood of type A in a group of seven can be represented by:

AAXXXXX or AXAXXXX or ...

There are $_7C_2 = \dfrac{7!}{(5!2!)} = 21$ arrangements with two As and five Xs.

The formulation assumes that the probability of A is constant and is 0.4. Assuming that one person's blood type is independent of the blood type of any other person (for example that there are no twins in the group) allows us to say that:

P(AAXXXXX) = (0.4)² × (0.6)⁵

It is only one step to the solution which says that there are $_7C_2 = 21$ possible outcomes where there are exactly two people of blood type A.

P(exactly two As) = 21 × 0.4² × 0.6⁵ ≈ 0.2613

The answer is given to four decimal places for convenience.

This can be interpreted to indicate that in just over a quarter (26 per cent) of all randomly-selected groups of seven people there will be exactly two who have type-A blood.

Exploration 20.8

Examining blood groups

Use the modelling framework to answer the following questions.
- What is the probability that, in a group of five people, exactly four will be of blood type A?
- What is the probability that in a group of seven people:
  a) exactly three have type-A blood,
  b) exactly four have type-A blood,
  c) exactly five have type-A blood?

The binomial distribution

In a group of five people, all five might be of blood type A; or there could be exactly four, or exactly three, or exactly two, or exactly one, or none of blood type A. Following the same modelling process as in the previous section leads to the following distribution of probabilities.

For a group of five people No. people with blood type A	Probability
0	$(0.6)^5 = 0.07776$
1	$5(0.4)(0.6)^4 = 0.2592$
2	$10(0.4)^2(0.6)^3 = 0.3456$
3	$10(0.4)^3(0.6)^2 = 0.2304$
4	$5(0.4)^4(0.6) = 0.0768$
5	$(0.4)^5 = 0.01024$

Note that the sum of the probabilities is 1. Why should this be so?

What we have done here is to list all possibilities when there are five people and so the total of the associated probabilities must be one. The resulting probability distribution is an example of a **binomial probability distribution**.

'Binomial' refers to there being only two possible blood types for each person, i.e. type A or not type A. In reality, there are many more blood types but it is still valid to regard blood as being either of one type or not of that type.

Another binomial probability distribution arises if we consider all the possibilities when there are seven people.

For a group of seven people No. people with blood type A	Probability
0	$(0.6)^7 = 0.0279936$
1	$7(0.4)(0.6)^6 = 0.1306368$
2	$21(0.4)^2(0.6)^5 = 0.2612736$
3	$35(0.4)^3(0.6)^4 = 0.290304$
4	$35(0.4)^4(0.6)^3 = 0.193536$
5	$21(0.4)^5(0.6)^2 = 0.0774144$
6	$7(0.4)^6(0.6) = 0.0172032$
7	$(0.4)^7 = 0.0016384$

The difference between the two distributions arises from the different numbers of people involved. In this case there were seven people, in the first there were five. The probability of an individual having blood type A is assumed to be constant.

Exploration 20.9

People with blood type O

It has been estimated that 45 per cent of the world's population have blood type O. Use an appropriate model to obtain the probability distribution for the number of people who have blood type O in a group of:
a) five people,
b) seven people,
c) four people.

Notation

The binomial distribution is usually written as B(n, p), where n is the number of people in the group, and p is the probability.

The number of people in a group of five who have blood of type O may be modelled by a binomial distribution similar to the blood type A example already considered. The difference is in the blood type. For 'type O' the probability is 0.45. The appropriate binomial distribution may be represented by B(5, 0.45).

This indicates that if a random variable, R, follows a binomial distribution, B(5, 0.45) then the following are the probabilities:
$P(R = 0) = {}_5C_0(0.45)^0(0.55)^5 \approx 0.050\,33$
$P(R = 1) = {}_5C_1(0.45)^1(0.55)^4 \approx 0.205\,89$
$P(R = 2) = {}_5C_2(0.45)^2(0.55)^3 \approx 0.336\,91$
$P(R = 3) = {}_5C_3(0.45)^3(0.55)^2 \approx 0.275\,65$
$P(R = 4) = {}_5C_4(0.45)^4(0.55)^1 \approx 0.112\,77$
$P(R = 5) = {}_5C_5(0.45)^5(0.55)^0 \approx 0.018\,45$

Note: The final probabilities have been given to five places of decimals.

Example 20.6

Identify the binomial distribution which is appropriate to model the following random variables:
a)   the number of heads which result when six coins are flipped,
b)   the number of 3s which result when five tetrahedral dice are rolled,
c)   the number of left-handed children in a class of 30 children if the proportion of left-handed people in the area is 15 per cent.

Solution
a)   Here, the probability that a coin lands head is $\frac{1}{2}$, and there are six coins, hence the binomial distribution is B(6, $\frac{1}{2}$).
b)   The probability that a tetrahedral die lands as a 3 is $\frac{1}{4}$ and there are five dice, hence, B(5, $\frac{1}{4}$).
c)   The appropriate distribution is B(30, 0.15) given there are 30 children, and the probability that any individual child is left-handed is assumed to be 0.15.

Probability function for the binomial distribution

Looking back at the probability distribution B(5, 0.45) we can see that the probability for each possibility can be written in a consistent way:

$$P(R = x) = {}_5C_x(0.45)^x(0.55)^{5-x}$$

This is the probability function for the random variable which is modelled by this binomial distribution. Previously the binomial distributions have had the following probability functions associated with them:
  B(5, 0.4): $P(R = x) = {}_5C_x(0.4)^x(0.6)^{5-x}$, and
  B(7, 0.4): $P(R = x) = {}_7C_x(0.4)^x(0.6)^{7-x}$
In the general case, a random variable which has the binomial distribution B(n, p) has probability function:
  $$P(R = x) = {}_nC_x\, p^x(1 - p)^{n-x}$$

EXERCISES

20.4 CLASSWORK   1   If 20 per cent of the population is left-handed, find the probability that a group of eight people contains:
a)   exactly two left-handers,

b) at least two left-handers,

c) not more than three left-handers.

2 Jane wins, on average, seven games of *Backgammon* in every ten games she plays.

 a) Find the probability that she wins exactly 14 games out of 20.

 b) Find the probability that she loses exactly two games out of ten.

 c) Find the probability that, in a match of six games, she wins more than she loses.

 d) What assumptions have been made in the solution of these problems?

3 In a certain school, 60 per cent of the pupils are brought to school by car, 30 per cent travel by public transport and the rest walk or cycle. Find the probability that a statistics class of ten contains:

 a) at least one person who walks or cycles,

 b) at least two who travel by public transport,

 c) not more than eight who are given a lift.

 What assumptions have been made in the consideration of the class?

4 Simon wins, on average, three-quarters of his tennis games. He loses one in ten and draws the rest. If he plays twelve games, find the probability that:

 a) he wins at least ten games,

 b) he loses not more than one game,

 c) he draws exactly two games.

5 Describe the conditions under which a binomial distribution may be used as a model for a random variable. State, with reasons, whether or not a binomial distribution would be an appropriate model for:

 a) the number of days on which rainfall is recorded in Paris during May,

 b) the number of rolls of a cubical die needed to get two successive 6s,

 c) the number of mathematics students in a group of 15 students chosen randomly from a university.

EXERCISES

20.4 HOMEWORK

1 In the winter term, 25 per cent of students have a cold at any one time. If nine students are selected at random, find the probability that:

 a) fewer than four have a cold,

 b) no one has a cold.

 Find the most likely number with a cold.

2 State the conditions under which a binomial distribution may be used as a model for a random variable. For each of the following, state if a binomial distribution is an appropriate model. Where you feel it is, state the value of n and p.

 a) In a given constituency, where 30 per cent of the electorate support the Liberals, the number of Liberal supporters in a household with four people on the electoral register.

 b) The number of doubles obtained when a pair of tetrahedral dice are rolled ten times.

 c) The number of 6s obtained when a cubical dice is rolled for five minutes.

3 A cinema manager records the occupancy figures for the last showing of the main film on Saturday evenings over a period of time. From the results he calculates the occupancy rate to be 80 per cent so inferring that the probability that any seat is occupied is 0.80. Use this to calculate the probability that in a row of eight seats:
a) seven are occupied,
b) six are occupied,
c) at least six are occupied,
d) at most five are occupied.
Detail the modelling assumptions you have made in calculating these probabilities. Do you consider them to be valid? Explain.

4 State the conditions under which a binomial distribution may be used as a model for a random variable.
For each of the following situations state whether a binomial distribution is a suitable model. If you think it is appropriate, give values for the parameters, n and p. If you think it is not appropriate, give your reasons.
a) In a large college where 25 per cent of all students study statistics, a count is made of the number who study statistics in a seminar group of 30 students.
b) A count is made of the number of green wine gums in a random sample of 40 gums, taken from a batch of 100 000 of which 8000 are green.
c) The output from a machine producing biro refills is known to contain five per cent defective refills, is recorded.
d) From a group of 25 workers of whom ten are in favour of a strike, a random sample of eight is taken and a count made of the number who are in favour of a strike.

5 Chocolate bars dispensed from a vending machine are either plain chocolate or milk chocolate, randomly in the ratio 3 : 2.
a) If three bars are bought, find the probability that at least one is milk chocolate.
b) If four bars are bought, find the probability that at least one is milk chocolate.
c) If six bars are bought, find the probability that at least one is milk chocolate.
d) How many bars need to be bought in order for the chance of obtaining at least one milk chocolate bar to be over 95 per cent?
e) How many bars need to be bought in order for the chance of obtaining at least one milk chocolate bar to be over 99 per cent?

THE RECURRENCE FORMULA FOR THE BINOMIAL DISTRIBUTION

It can be quite tedious producing the probabilities for a binomial distribution using the probability function. For a sequence of probabilities such as:
$$P(R = 0) \quad P(R = 1) \quad P(R = 2) \quad P(R = 3) \quad \dots$$
there is a convenient method which relates the probability of one event to the previous one. Consider B(7, 0.4), where:
$$P(R = 0) = {}_7C_0(0.4)^0(0.6)^7 = (0.6)^7$$

and

$$P(R = 1) = {}_7C_1(0.4)^1(0.6)^6 = \frac{7!}{1!6!}(0.4)^1(0.6)^6 = 7(0.4)^1(0.6)^6$$

Now, compare P(1) with P(0). What are the differences?

To get P(1) from P(0), we: multiply by 7, multiply by 0.4, divide by 0.6.

$$P(1) = 7 \times \frac{0.4}{0.6} \times P(0)$$

Now, consider P(R = 2):

$$P(R = 2) = {}_7C_2(0.4)^2(0.6)^5 = \frac{7!}{2!5!}(0.4)^2(0.6)^5 = \frac{7 \times 6}{1 \times 2}(0.4)^2(0.6)^5$$

(cancelling 5! in top and bottom, then expanding the 2!).

How can we get P(2) from P(1)? We need to multiply by 6, divide by 2, multiply by 0.4, divide by 0.6. This gives:

$$P(2) = \frac{6}{2} \times \frac{0.4}{0.6} \times P(1)$$

This is the same pattern as for getting P(1) from P(0), since that can be written as:

$$P(1) = \frac{7}{1} \times \frac{0.4}{0.6} \times P(0)$$

The $\frac{0.4}{0.6}$ is common, and the other factor, although it changes, has a common feature. Can you see what this feature is? Try writing P(3) in terms of P(2).

Consider:

$$P(R = 3) = {}_7C_3(0.4)^3(0.6)^4 = \frac{7!}{3!4!}(0.4)^3(0.6)^4 = \frac{7 \times 6 \times 5}{1 \times 2 \times 3}(0.4)^3(0.6)^4$$

$$= \frac{5}{3} \times \frac{0.4}{0.6} \times P(2)$$

Hence, the pattern continues. The factor $\frac{0.4}{0.6}$ is present and the changing factor has the same pattern.

One way of expressing this pattern is to say that the top and bottom add up to eight; the bottom is the value of the new event.

What factors are needed to produce P(4) from P(3), P(5) from P(4), P(6) from P(5), P(7) from P(6)?

In each case, the $\frac{0.4}{0.6}$ will appear, then there will be a factor $\frac{8-x}{x}$, where x is the new value of the random variable. Hence:

$$P(4) = \frac{4}{4} \times \frac{0.4}{0.6} \times P(3)$$

$$P(5) = \frac{3}{5} \times \frac{0.4}{0.6} \times P(4)$$

$$P(6) = \frac{2}{6} \times \frac{0.4}{0.6} \times P(5)$$

$$P(7) = \frac{1}{7} \times \frac{0.4}{0.6} \times P(6)$$

The pattern developed here is known as a recurrence formula for binomial probabilities. In general terms, for the distribution B(7, 0.4):

$$P(x) = \frac{8-x}{x} \times \frac{0.4}{0.6} \times P(x-1)$$

CALCULATOR ACTIVITY

Exploration 20.10   *Using the recurrence formula*

Try using your calculator to produce the probabilities for B(7, 0.4) using the recurrence formula. Start by producing $(0.6)^7$, then multiply this display by $\frac{0.4}{0.6}$ (you might want to simplify this constant factor) and by $\frac{7}{1}$. Then multiply the new display by $\frac{0.4}{0.6}$ and by $\frac{6}{2}$. Then ...

Continue the process. Check the successive probabilities with those on page 403.

CALCULATOR ACTIVITY

Exploration 20.11   *Programming probabilities*

If you have a programmable calculator you might like to write a program to display the successive probabilities. This flowchart might be used as a basis for the program.

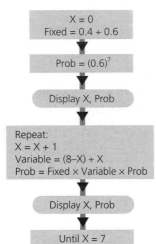

Is it possible to develop a recurrence formula for any binomial distribution? It ought to be. Consider the distribution B(30, 0.15), where: $P(0) = (0.85)^{30}$

and $P(1) = {}_{30}C_1 (0.15)^1 (0.85)^{29} = \frac{30!}{1!29!} \times (0.15)^1 \times (0.85)^{29} = \frac{30}{1} \times \frac{(0.15)}{(0.85)} \times P(0)$

This is a promising start. The fixed factor appears to be $\frac{0.15}{0.85}$, the variable factor looks promising with top and bottom adding up to 31 and the bottom being the new value of the random variable. How are these the features seen in the B(7, 0.4) case?

Can you predict the factors required to produce $P(2)$ from $P(1)$, $P(3)$ from $P(2)$, $P(x)$ from $P(x-1)$?

Using the probability function initially:
$P(2) = {}_{30}C_2 (0.15)^2 \times (0.85)^{28} = \frac{30!}{2!28!} \times (0.15)^2 \times (0.85)^{28}$

$= \frac{30 \times 29}{1 \times 2} \times (0.15)^2 \times (0.85)^{28}$

hence: $P(2) = \frac{29}{2} \times \frac{0.15}{0.85} \times P(1)$

similarly: $P(3) = \frac{28}{3} \times \frac{0.15}{0.85} \times P(2)$

These follow the pattern seen earlier and $P(x) = \frac{31-x}{x} \times \frac{0.15}{0.85} \times P(x-1)$

CALCULATOR ACTIVITY

Exploration 20.12   *Generating the probability distribution*

x	$P(R=x)$	x	$P(R=x)$
0	0.0076	9	0.0181
1	0.0404	10	0.0067
2	0.1034	11	0.0022
3	0.1703	12	0.0006
4	0.2028	13	0.0001
5	0.1861	14	0.0000
6	0.1368	15	0.0000
7	0.0828	⋮	
8	0.0420		

Generate the probability distribution B(30, 0.15) using the recurrence relation.

You might like to check your probabilities with those given below.

Note: All probabilities are given accurate to four decimal places.

Notice that the fixed factor is always related to the constant probability, p. How?

Fixed factor $= \dfrac{p}{1-p}$

The variable factor is related to the number of possible events, n, and to the new value of the random variable. What is this relationship?

Variable factor $= \dfrac{n+1-x}{x}$

The recurrence relation for B(n, p) is:

$$P(x) = \frac{n+1-x}{x} \times \frac{p}{1-p} \times P(x-1)$$

Exploration 20.13

Finding recurrence relationships

What are the recurrence relations for the following binomial distributions?

a) B(5, 0.45)   **b)** B(10, $\frac{1}{2}$)   **c)** B(15, $\frac{1}{4}$)   **d)** B(150, 0.01)

Using distribution tables

At the end of the book, there are binomial distribution tables. Look at these tables, and identify the section which refers to B(7, 0.40). Locate the table for the specific value of n, then the column corresponding to p = 0.4. Here is part of the appropriate extract from the table.

p	0.4	
r		$n = 7$
0	0.0280	
1	0.1586	
2	0.4199	
3	0.7102	
⋮	⋮	
7	1.0000	

Compare the values of the probabilities shown in the table and those given on page 403 for the number of people with blood type A in a group of seven people. Are the probabilities the same?

Perhaps the first thing to note is that the probabilities only coincide when referring to no one in the group of seven having blood of type A. Both values are 0.0280 (to four decimal places). Thereafter the tables are quite distinctly different. Why do you think this is?

Notice that for $r = 1$, the table has the probability 0.1586. However, the probability $P(R = 1)$ is 0.1306. The entry in the table against $r = 1$ represents $P(R = 0) + P(R = 1)$. So the entries in the table represent the sum of the probabilities from $R = 0$ up to $R = r$.

Checking that this is the case for $R = 2$ and $R = 3$ reveals:
$P(R = 0) + P(R = 1) + P(R = 2) = 0.4199$
$P(R = 0) + P(R = 1) + P(R = 2) + P(R = 3) = 0.7102$
which are the entries in the table.

The tables show the values of the **cumulative binomial distribution function**. The words 'cumulative' and 'function' are often dropped when referring to such tables. Using the binomial distribution tables yields the following:

$P(R \leq 4) = 0.9037$

$P(R \leq 5) = 0.9812$

$P(R \leq 6) = 0.9984$

$P(R \leq 7) = 1.0000$

when $R \sim B(7, 0.4)$.

The notation: $R \sim B(7, 0.4)$ means that R is a random variable which is binomially distributed with $n = 7$ and $p = 0.4$.

Clearly, using the tables saves time and effort when we are calculating cumulative probabilities. They can also be used to find approximations to individual probabilities, but both uses are limited in accuracy and, of course, to the (n, p) combinations tabulated.

Example 20.7

a) Calculate the probabilities of:
   i) three or fewer people in a group of ten having blood of type O,
   ii) exactly six people in a group of ten having blood of type O,
   iii) more than five people in a group of ten having blood of type O,
   iv) at least seven people in a group of ten having blood of type O.
b) It can be assumed that 20 per cent of people in the southern hemisphere have blood of type B. Calculate the probabilities of:
   i) in a group of 15 such people, five or fewer having blood of type B,
   ii) in a group of twelve such people, at least four having blood of type B,
   iii) in a group of eight such people, between three and five (inclusive) having type B blood.

Solution

a) The questions in this part refer to the B*(10, 0.45)* distribution (if Exploration 20.9 is correct).
   i) The event 'three or fewer' is required, hence:
      $P(R \leq 3) = 0.2660$
      can be read directly from the table for $n = 10$, the column $p = 0.45$, and the row corresponding to 3.
   ii) From the cumulative probabilities $P(R \leq 6)$ and $P(R \leq 5)$ the probability $P(R = 6)$ can be found.
      $P(R = 6) = P(R \leq 6) - P(R \leq 5) = 0.8980 - 0.7384 = 0.1596$
   iii) The event 'more than five' is the complement of the event 'five or fewer'. The tables yield $P(R \leq 5) = 0.7384$.
      The probability of the complement is:
      $1 - P(R \leq 5) = 1 - 0.7384 = 0.2616$
      Hence $P(R > 5) = 0.2616$
   iv) The event 'at least seven' corresponds to 'seven, eight, nine or ten'. This event is the complement of 'six or fewer', hence:
      $P(R \geq 7) = 1 - P(R \leq 6) = 1 - 0.8980 = 0.1020$
b) i) The appropriate probability distribution is B*(15, 0.2)*, and the event is $R \leq 5$. Hence, from the tables $P(R \leq 5) = 0.9389$.
   ii) This question requires the use of B*(12, 0.2)*. The event 'at least four' corresponds to 'four, five, six, ... or twelve' which is the complement of 'zero, one, two or three'.
      $P(R \geq 4) = 1 - P(R \leq 3) = 1 - 0.7946 = 0.2054$

iii) *Here, the binomial distribution required is B(8, 0.2). The probability of the event 'three, four or five' can be found from the probabilities:*
$P(R \leq 5), P(R \leq 2).$
$P(R = 3 \text{ or } R = 4 \text{ or } R = 5) = P(R \leq 5) - P(R \leq 2)$
$$= 0.9988 - 0.7969$$
$$= 0.2019$$

EXERCISES

20.5 CLASSWORK

1 A coin is biased and is twice as likely to come down heads than tails. If the coin is tossed eight times, use the recurrence formula to calculate the probability of obtaining fewer than four tails.

2 Use the appropriate recurrence formula to help you draw probability line diagrams for each of the following distributions.
a) B(5, 0.3) **b)** B(8, 0.6) **c)** B(8, 0.4) **d)** B(10, 0.2)
e) B(10, 0.5) **f)** B(12, 0.4)

3 Last year, 55 per cent of all school meals served were meat dishes, 20 per cent were fish and the rest were vegetarian. A group of 18 teachers takes lunch together. Find the probability, using tables, that:
a) at least six vegetarian meals are served,
b) no fish is served,
c) fewer than half the meals are meat.
What assumptions have you made?

4 On average two-fifths of films shown in a cinema are thrillers, and three-quarters of the rest are comedies; the remainder are science fiction. If eight films are selected from the programme at random, find the probability that:
a) at least four are comedies,
b) no more than two are science fiction,
c) the number of thrillers exceeds the number of other films.

5 On average, John correctly solves the newspaper brain teaser seven times out of ten. He attempts each puzzle over a two-week period (not including Sundays). Find the probability that:
a) he solves eight or fewer brain teasers,
b) he solves at least ten brain teasers,
c) he solves exactly seven brain teasers,
d) he solves fewer than six brain teasers.

EXERCISES

20.5 HOMEWORK

1 Suppose 30 per cent of school-age children wear spectacles. In a class of 15, what is the most likely number to wear spectacles?

2 Illustrate as probability line graphs the following distributions.
a) B (6, 0.3) **b)** B (7, 0.7) **c)** B (10, 0.45) **d)** B (18, 0.15)
e) B (20, 0.1) **f)** B (8, 0.3)

3 Answer Question 5 of the Classwork above for Jane, who is less proficient with brain teasers, and on average, correctly solves only four out of ten.

4 An examination consists of 20 multiple-choice questions each with four alternatives. Only one of the alternatives is correct.

X denotes the number of correct responses obtained by candidates who guess the answers to all 20 questions. Explain why X may be considered to have a binomial distribution. Hence determine:
a) $\mathrm{P}(X > 10)$ b) $\mathrm{P}(X \leq 5)$ c) $\mathrm{P}(X = 5)$.

5   Each of a group of 20 people flips a coin. What is the probability that:
a) fewer than half of them get a head,
b) at least a quarter of them get a tail,
c) fewer than three-quarters of them get a head?

BERNOULLI TRIALS

We are now going to discover some properties of the binomial distribution $\mathrm{B}(n, p)$. In particular, we are going to discover the relationship between the two parameters, n and p, and the mean and variance of the distribution.

Consider a decahedral die with its faces numbered $1, 2, 3, 4, 5, 6, 7, 8, 9, 10$.

The random variable we are going to model is the number of outcomes which can be described as a 'square' when a die is rolled once. The possible outcomes are 1, 4, 9.

Clearly, when a decahedral die is rolled, the outcome is either a 'square' or 'not a square'. An experiment which results in only one of two possible outcomes is often called a **Bernoulli trial** after the scientist and mathematician who pioneered it. The two possible outcomes in the trial are generally called 'success' and 'failure'.

The number of 'successes' in any given trial can only be 0 or 1. The distribution of the number of 'successes' is known as a **Bernoulli probability distribution**.

In this case, 'success' is the outcome a 'square', and 'failure' is 'not a square'. The probability of a 'square' is $\frac{3}{10}$ (since there are three faces with 'squares' and ten equally likely faces in total). Hence, the distribution of the number of 'successes' can be modelled by the Bernoulli distribution with probability $\frac{3}{10}$.

Notation

This result is written as: $\mathrm{Ber}(\frac{3}{10})$. It is tabulated below.

	x	$\mathrm{P}(B = x)$
No 'success'	0	$\frac{7}{10}$
One 'success'	1	$\frac{3}{10}$

The mean and variance of this random variable can readily be found using expectation.

x	p	xp	$x^2 p$
0	$\frac{7}{10}$	$0 \times \frac{7}{10}$	$0^2 \times \frac{7}{10}$
1	$\frac{3}{10}$	$1 \times \frac{3}{10}$	$1^2 \times \frac{3}{10}$

Mean of the Bernoulli distribution

Recall that the mean is the expected value of the random variable:

$$\mu = \Sigma xp = 0 + 1 \times \tfrac{3}{10} = \tfrac{3}{10}$$

This seems reasonable as we would anticipate there being three 'squares' in ten rolls of the die (on average).

Variance of the Bernoulli distribution

The variance can also be found using expectation.

$$\sigma^2 = \sum x^2 p - \mu^2 = \left(0 + 1^2 \times \tfrac{3}{10}\right) - \left(\tfrac{3}{10}\right)^2 = \tfrac{3}{10} - \left(\tfrac{3}{10}\right)^2 = \tfrac{21}{100}$$

So, to summarise this section: the number of 'squares' obtained on rolling a decahedral die can be modelled by Ber(0.3), the mean of this distribution is 0.3, and its variance is 0.21.

Exploration 20.14

A decahedral die

Imagine a decahedral die being rolled. What model is appropriate to describe the number of 'primes' which appear in a single roll? What are the mean and variance of the number of primes? (Remember, 2, 3, 5, 7 are prime numbers.)

The general Bernoulli distribution

The general Bernoulli distribution, Ber(p) can be tabulated (below).

x	0	1
P($B = x$)	$1 - p$	p

The mean is: $\mu = \sum xp = (0 \times (1 - p) + 1 \times p) = p$

The variance is:

$$\sigma^2 = \sum x^2 p - \mu^2 = (0^2 \times (1 - p) + 1^2 \times p) - \mu^2 = p - p^2 = p(1 \quad p)$$

Note the two cases:

- Ber(0.3) leads to $\mu_{\text{Ber}(0.3)} - 0.3$ and $\sigma^2_{\text{Ber}(0.3)} = 0.3 \times 0.7 = 0.21$ as we found earlier.
- Ber(0.4) leads to $\mu_{\text{Ber}(0.4)} = 0.4$ and $\sigma^2_{\text{Ber}(0.4)} = 0.4 \times 0.6 = 0.24$ as you may have found in Exploration 20.14.

Relating binomial and Bernoulli variables

In what way is a binomial variate related to a Bernoulli variate? Imagine rolling a decahedral die, say, five times and recording the number of 'squares' that occur. What distribution would be appropriate to model this random variable?

This situation is typical of B(5, 0.3). However, it could also be considered to be the sum of five Bernoulli distributions:

Ber(0.3) + Ber(0.3) + Ber(0.3) + Ber(0.3) + Ber(0.3)

What are the mean and variance of B(5, 0.3)? The simple answer is that its mean is the sum of five Bernoulli means:

$$= \mu_{\text{Ber}} + \mu_{\text{Ber}} + \mu_{\text{Ber}} + \mu_{\text{Ber}} + \mu_{\text{Ber}}$$
$$= 0.3 + 0.3 + 0.3 + 0.3 + 0.3 = 5 \times 0.3 = 1.5$$

and its variance is a similar sum:

$$= \sigma^2_{\text{Ber}} + \sigma^2_{\text{Ber}} + \ldots + \sigma^2_{\text{Ber}}$$
$$= 0.3 \times 0.7 + 0.3 \times 0.7 + \ldots + 0.3 \times 0.7$$
$$= 5 \times 0.3 \times 0.7 = 1.05$$

It is quite possible to test those conjectures using the results we discovered about the binomial distribution. Remember that if $X \sim \text{B}(5, 0.3)$ then the probability function is:

$$\text{P}(X = x) = {}_5\text{C}_x \, 0.3^x \, 0.7^{5-x}$$

This produces the following tabulation.

x	0	1	2	3	4	5
$\text{P}(X = x)$	0.168 07	0.360 15	0.308 70	0.132 30	0.028 35	0.002 43

Use expectation to calculate the mean and variance. Do your results agree with the above prediction?

Exploration 20.15

Mean and variance of Bernoulli variates

■ Use an argument based on linear combination of Bernoulli variates to predict the mean and variance of the binomial variate $X \sim \text{B}(5, 0.4)$.

■ Check your predictions using the appropriate probability function and expectation.

Mean and variance of the binomial distribution

In the previous section, we saw how a binomial variate could be considered to be the sum of n independent Bernoulli variates with the same probability of 'success'. Symbolically this can be written as:

$$X \sim \text{B}(n, p)$$

and this is equivalent to:

$$X \sim \text{Ber}(p) + \text{Ber}(p) + \ldots + \text{Ber}(p)$$

This equivalence leads readily to the mean and variance of a general binomial variate.

Mean
$$\mu_{\text{B}(n,p)} = \mu_{\text{Ber}} + \mu_{\text{Ber}} + \ldots + \mu_{\text{Ber}} \quad (n \text{ means})$$
$$= p + p + \ldots + p = np$$

Variance
$$\sigma^2_{\text{B}(n,p)} = \sigma^2_{\text{Ber}} + \sigma^2_{\text{Ber}} + \ldots + \sigma^2_{\text{Ber}}$$
$$= p(1 - p) + p(1 - p) + \ldots + p(1 - p) = np(1 - p)$$

Example 20.8

A survey indicates that 35 per cent of university students smoke cigarettes at least once a day. Describe how the number of smokers in a group of 18 students can be modelled using a sum of Bernoulli variates. What is the mean and variance of the number of smokers in groups of 18 university students?

Solution

A student either does or does not smoke at least one cigarette per day. This is a Bernoulli trial and the survey suggests:
P(smoke) = 0.35

The number of smokers in a group of 18 students can be modelled as the sum of 18 Bernoulli variates each having probability equal to 0.35. If X is the number of smokers, then: $X \sim B(18, 0.35)$

Hence, the mean of X is: $18 \times 0.35 = 6.3$

and, the variance of X is: $18 \times 0.35 \times 0.65 = 4.095$

EXERCISES

20.6 CLASSWORK

1 Thirty per cent of the members of a certain profession have an A-Level in Statistics. A random sample of ten members is obtained and the number, X, with an A-Level in Statistics is noted. Use a binomial distribution to model the occurrence of X. Estimate the probability that:
a) $X < 2$ b) $X =$ the expected value, μ c) $X > \mu + \sigma$.

2 A fair coin is tossed eight times.
a) Find the mean and variance of the number of heads obtained.
b) Repeat part a) for a biased coin for which the probability of getting a head is four times the probability of getting a tail.

3 Forty per cent of sixth-formers in a certain county study A-Level Mathematics. In a sixth-form group of 20, find the probability that:
a) exactly the expected number study A-Level Mathematics,
b) more than the expected number study A-Level Mathematics.
c) Calculate the variance of the number who do not study A-Level Mathematics.

4 In a sixth-form college, 45 per cent are in the Science department, 35 per cent in the Humanities department and the rest in the Languages department.
If a group of ten students is chosen at random,
a) calculate the mean and variance of the number in the Science department,
b) calculate the mean and variance of the number in the Languages department,
c) find the probability that more than half the group are in the Humanities department.

5 In a binomial distribution, the mean = 10.2 and the variance = 1.53.
a) Calculate n, p and q.
b) If p represents the probability of passing an exam, calculate the probability that more than the expected number pass the exam.

EXERCISES

20.6 HOMEWORK

1 Sixty per cent of the members of a profession have an A-Level in Mathematics. A random sample of ten members is obtained. The number, X, with A-Level Mathematics is recorded. Use a binomial distribution to model the occurrence of X. Estimate the probability that:
a) $X > 2$ b) $X = \mu$, the expected value of X c) $X < \mu + \sigma$.

2 In a particular area it has been established that 75 per cent of cars are fitted with some form of alarm system. A random sample of twelve cars from the area is selected. Deduce the distribution of the number of cars in the sample fitted with some form of alarm. Hence calculate the probability that the 'expected' number of cars are fitted with some form of alarm.

3 A test consists solely of questions requiring a 'Yes' or 'No' answer. State a distribution for the answer to a single question.

The test contains 18 questions.

a) For a candidate who simply guesses the answer to each question, state the distribution which describes his number of correct answers. Hence calculate the probability that he answers less than half the questions correctly.

b) Repeat a) for a candidate who has a 65 per cent chance of answering each question correctly.

4 On any given night the probability that each single room in a hotel is occupied is 0.80, and the probability that each double room is occupied is 0.74.

a) The hotel has five single rooms. If X denotes the number of single rooms occupied, deduce its probability model. Hence determine the mean and variance of X. Calculate the probability that on a given night, the mean number of single rooms are occupied.

b) The hotel has 15 double rooms. Explain how the number of double rooms occupied, Y, may be constructed as a sum of Bernoulli variables. State the mean, μ and variance, σ^2 of Y. Hence calculate the probability that Y is greater than $(\mu + \sigma)$.

5 a) The random variables $X_i \sim \text{Ber}(0.5)$. State the distribution of:

i) $Y = X_1 + X_2 + X_3$ ii) $Z = X_4 + X_5 + X_6 + X_7$ iii) $T = \sum_{i=1}^{7} X_i$

Hence show that $\mu_T = \mu_Y + \mu_Z$ and $\sigma_T^2 = \sigma_Y^2 + \sigma_Z^2$.

b) If $X_1, X_2, X_3 \sim \text{Ber}(0.3)$ and $X_4, X_5, X_6, X_7 \sim \text{Ber}(0.8)$ show that, although no distribution can be deduced for T (as defined in iii) above), the results for μ_T and σ_T^2 still hold.

CONSOLIDATION EXERCISES FOR CHAPTER 20

1 A random variable, X, has the probability distribution defined by:
$P(X = n) = p^n$ for $n = 1, 2, 3, ...$
a) Calculate p.   b) Find $P(X > 3)$.

2 In the game of *Monopoly*, players may find themselves in jail. There are a number of ways of getting out of jail: rolling a double with two ordinary dice; paying £50; or using a special 'Get out of jail' card. The rules of the game dictate that if a player elects to roll the dice and fails to get a double in the first three attempts then the player must use one of the other options.

a) Assume that, when I play *Monopoly*, I always elect to roll the dice if I find myself in jail. What is the probability:
   i) I get out of jail on my first attempt,
   ii) I need two attempts to roll a double
   iii) I fail to get out of jail using dice alone?

b) Suppose, when I find myself in situation iii), I always pay £50. Calculate the expected cost of my stays in jail.

3 Two players, X and Y, play a game. The probability that X wins the first game is 0.5. The probability for Y is 0.3. The probability that the first game is drawn is 0.2. If it is drawn another game is played, with the same probabilities. Calculate:
a) the probability that X is the first to win,
b) the probability that Y is the first to win,
c) the expected number of games played.

4 One plastic toy aeroplane is given away free in each packet of cornflakes. Equal numbers of red, yellow, green and blue aeroplanes are put into the packets.
Faye, a customer, has collected three colours of aeroplanes but still wants a yellow one. Find the probability that:
a) she gets a yellow aeroplane by opening just one packet,
b) she fails to get a yellow aeroplane in opening four packets,
c) she needs to open exactly five packets to get the yellow aeroplane she wants.

(MEI Question 3, Paper 1, January 1994)

5 Each packet of the breakfast cereal Fizz contains one plastic toy animal. There are five different animals in the set, and the cereal manufacturers use equal numbers of each. Without opening a packet it is impossible to tell which animal it contains. A family has already collected four different animals at the start of a year and they now need to collect an elephant to complete their set. The family is interested in how many packets they will need to buy before they complete their set.
a) Stating any necessary assumption, name an appropriate distribution with which to model this situation. What is the expected number of packets that the family will need to buy?
b) Find the probability that the family will complete their set with the third packet they buy after the start of the year.
c) Find the probability that, in order to complete their collection, the family will need to buy more than 4 packets after the start of the year.

(OCR Question 3, Specimen S1, 2000)

6 A cyclist has to make a right turn on a busy road on his way to work each weekday morning. The probability that he is able to turn without having to stop is 0.3.
a) Find the probability that on twenty consecutive weekday mornings
   i) he turns without having to stop, 4 or more times,
   ii) he turns without having to stop exactly five times.
The cyclist also makes the turn on Saturday and Sunday on the way to visit his invalid mother.
b) State, giving a reason, whether or not it is likely that the following random variables may be modelled by a binomial distribution:
   i) Y is the number of times the cyclist turns without having to stop on 20 consecutive days (i.e. including Saturdays and Sundays);
   ii) Z is the number of consecutive weekdays before the cyclist turns without having to stop on four occasions.

(AQA B Question 5, Specimen S1, 2000)

7 A manufacturer of chocolates produces 3 times as many soft centred chocolates as hard centred ones.
Assuming that chocolates are randomly distributed within boxes of chocolates, find the probability that in a box containing 20 chocolates there are:
a) equal numbers of soft centred and hard centred chocolates,
b) fewer than 5 hard centred chocolates.
A large box of chocolates contains 100 chocolates.
c) Write down the expected number of hard centred chocolates in a large box.

(EDEXCEL Question 3, Specimen S2, 2000)

8 A case of wine contains twelve bottles. A packing carton contains six cases. Seventy per cent of the bottles contain red wine; the rest contain white wine.

a) Find the probability that a case contains at least nine bottles of red wine.

b) Find the probability that all six cases in a carton contain at least nine bottles of red wine.

c) Find the probability that exactly five cases in a carton contain at least nine bottles of red wine.

d) Find the most likely number of cases in a carton which contain at least nine bottles of red wine.

9 A multiple choice test consists of four sections with three options for each answer. James selects his answers completely at random.

a) Find the probability that he scores no correct answers in section A.

b) Find the probability that he scores at least two correct answers in section A.

c) Find the probability that he scores no correct answers in exactly one section.

d) Find the probability that he scores at least two correct answers in exactly one section.

e) Find the probability that he scores no correct answers in at least two sections.

f) Find the probability that he scores at least two correct answers in at least two sections.

10 A test is applied to a certain type of component produced in a factory. The probability that a randomly chosen component fails is $\frac{1}{5}$. Ten components are tested. Find, correct to three significant figures the probability that:

a) none will fail,   b) exactly two will fail,

c) at most two will fail,   d) at least two will fail.

11 Three fair dice are thrown and 20 points are scored if all three dice show the same number; one point is scored if two of the dice show the same number.

a) Calculate the mean and variance of the number of points scored.

b) Calculate the mean and variance of the total number of points scored if the dice are thrown together four times.

12 If $X \sim B(n, p)$, write down expressions for μ_X and σ_X^2 in terms of n and p. You are told that $\mu_X = 1$, find the values of n and p if:

a) $\sigma^2 = 0.8$ b) $\sigma^2 = 0.9$ c) $\sigma^2 = 0.95$ d) $\sigma^2 = 0.995$.

13 The number of 'inners' scored by 150 archers at an archery contest is given in the table (each archer had five arrows to shoot at the target).

Number of inners	0	1	2	3	4	5
Number of archers	19	44	42	19	15	11

a) Calculate the mean number of hits per archer.

b) Assume that the number of hits may be modelled by a binomial distribution. What are the values of n and p?

c) Calculate the frequencies of each number of hits given by the binomial distribution.

d) Do you think the binomial is a good model?

14 Applicants for a sales job are tested on their knowledge of consumer protection legislation. The test consists of five multiple choice questions. The number of correct answers, X, follows the following distribution.

X	0	1	2	3	4	5
P($X = x$)	0.60	0.04	0.07	0.10	0.09	0.10

a) Find the mean and standard deviation of X.

A group of production staff, who had no knowledge of the subject, guessed all the answers. The probability of each answer being correct was 0.25. The random variable Y represents the distribution of the number of correct answers for this group.

b) i) Name the probability distribution which could provide a suitable model for Y.

ii) Determine the mean and standard deviation of Y.

c) Compare, and comment briefly on, the results of your calculations in parts **a)** and **b) ii)**.

(AQA B Question 1, Specimen S4, 2000)

15 In a certain game, a player throws five fair cubical dice together.

a) Identify the distribution of the number of 6s that will be obtained.

b) For each 6 obtained, the player receives 9 pence from his opponent but the player has to pay his opponent 3 pence for every score other than 6 that is obtained. Determine the mean and the standard deviation of the player's gain/loss per play.

(WJEC Question 5, Specimen S1, 2000)

Summary

- A probability distribution models the occurrence of a particular random variable.

- For a geometric probability distribution, Geo(p), where p is the probability of succeeding at the first event, $P(R = n) = p(1-p)^{n-1}$.

- The mean of Geo(p) = $\dfrac{1}{p}$.

- The variance of Geo(p) = mean (mean − 1) = $\dfrac{1}{p}\left(\dfrac{1}{p} - 1\right)$.

- You have discovered a model for a random variable which represents the number of successful events when a fixed number, n, of events occur, each of which can result in either a success or a failure; the events are independent, and the probability, p, that any event results in a success is constant.

- You have encountered the B(n, p) notation for the binomial probability distribution.

- You have discovered the distribution function and tables recording $P(R \leq x)$.

- If $X \sim B(n, p)$ then $\mu_X = np$ $\quad \sigma_X^2 = np(1-p)$

- X is the sum of n independent Bernoulli variates each with probability p.

The Poisson distribution

In this chapter we shall:

■ *discover a probability distribution which models the occurrence of random events,*
■ *validate the model in its use to approximate the occurrence of rare events.*

MODELLING RANDOM EVENTS

Gardeners are proud of the state of their gardens, and especially of the state of their grass – their lawn. They invest much time and effort into the appearance of their lawn. One of the reasons why so much effort is required is that weeds keep appearing. They crop up anywhere in the lawn. There doesn't seem to be any way of predicting where the next weed will appear. There's no particular part of the lawn favoured by the weeds nor is any part avoided. During the growing season, weeds seem to appear at about the same rate everywhere. Even in some of the most carefully attended lawns, weeds, or in particular, daisies, appear, at a rate of three daisies per square metre of lawn each week.

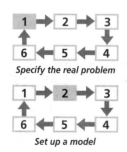

Specify the real problem

Set up a model

The gardener of a well-tended lawn decides to call in an expert to offer advice about the number of daisies she might find in any part of the lawn, to see if it is possible to reduce the amount of weedkiller that she is using.

Imagine that you are the lawn expert. How might you set about modelling the appearance of the daisies?

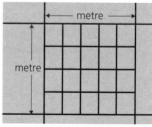

One possible approach is to imagine that a typical square metre of lawn is divided into a number of equal subdivisions. Let's start with 20 subdivisions.

What is the probability that none of the 20 subdivisions contains a daisy?

Suppose that a subdivision is big enough to contain one daisy but no more than one. We could then model the appearance of a daisy as a Bernoulli trial. The 'success' corresponds to a daisy appearing in the subdivision. The average number of daisies in a square metre (i.e. in 20 Bernoulli trials) is three. Hence, the probability of a 'success' is $\frac{3}{20}$, and the probability of a 'failure' is $\left(1-\frac{3}{20}\right)$.

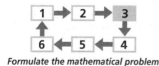

Formulate the mathematical problem

This leads to the conclusion:

P(no daisies in 20 subdivisions) = $\left(1-\frac{3}{20}\right)^{3} \approx 0.03876$

assuming that daisies occur independently. This assumption of independence enables us to use the multiplication law of independent events.

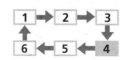

Solve the mathematical problem

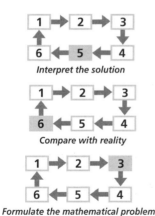

Interpret the solution

Compare with reality

Formulate the mathematical problem

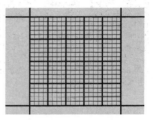

Is it realistic to suppose that a patch of ground, $\frac{1}{20}$ m^2 in area, is so small that it could not contain more than one daisy? Perhaps we need to subdivide the square metre of lawn further? We might divide each subdivision further into 20 equal parts, giving 400 new subdivisions in each square metre.

What is the probability that a square metre of lawn does not contain a daisy?

By developing an argument similar to the one above, we have 400 Bernoulli trials with a probability of 'success' equal to $\frac{3}{400}$. Hence:

P(failure) = $1 - \frac{3}{400}$

This leads to:

P(no daisies in a square metre) = $\left(1 - \frac{3}{400}\right)^{400} \approx 0.049\,23$

Clearly, this is a different result from that achieved by considering just 20 Bernoulli trials.

CALCULATOR ACTIVITY

Exploration 21.1

Evaluating the model

Explore the probability of getting no daisies in a square metre of lawn by using the model set up above, but with more subdivisions. You might try dividing each of the new subdivisions into 20 equal parts and repeating this process.

Recurrence formula

The sort of results you might expect are given in the table.

No. subdivisions	P(success)	P(failure)	P(no daisies in a square metre)
20	$\frac{3}{20}$	$1 - \frac{3}{20}$	0.038760
400	$\frac{3}{400}$	$1 - \frac{3}{400}$	0.049227
8000	$\frac{3}{8000}$	$1 - \frac{3}{8000}$	0.049759
160 000	$\frac{3}{160\,000}$	$1 - \frac{3}{160\,000}$	0.049786
3 200 000	$\frac{3}{3\,200\,000}$	$1 - \frac{3}{3\,200\,000}$	0.049787
64 000 000	$\frac{3}{64\,000\,000}$	$1 - \frac{3}{64\,000\,000}$	0.049787
1 000 000 000	$\frac{3}{1\,000\,000\,000}$	$1 - \frac{3}{1\,000\,000\,000}$	0.049787

So the likelihood of there being no daisies in a given square metre of lawn settles down to approximately 0.049 787.

Note: Some calculators give false results for this probability when there are more than 1000 million subdivisions.

It is worth reflecting, at this point, on what we have achieved. We have a model for the likelihood of there being no daisies in a square metre *when* there are, on average, three daisies. It will be useful to give this probability a label:

$P_{Av\,=\,3}(0)$

We have arrived at a value for $P_{Av=3}(0)$ using the limiting process:

$$P_{Av=3}(0) = \text{the limit of } \left\{\left(1-\tfrac{3}{n}\right)^n\right\} \text{ as } n \text{ increases}$$

$$\approx 0.049\,787 \text{ (to six decimal places)}$$

But we set out to model the *appearance* of daisies, so we ought to be trying to model the probability of finding one daisy, two daisies, three daisies, etc.

Let's return to the point where we set up 20 equal subdivisions of a square metre of lawn. We modelled the situation as 20 Bernoulli trials where the probability of success was $\tfrac{3}{20}$. We now want to know the probability of there being exactly one daisy, exactly two daisies, exactly three daisies, etc. in this square metre.

In Chapter 20, *Discrete probability distributions* we met the binomial distribution and the associated recurrence formula:

$$P(x) = \frac{p}{1-p} \times \frac{n+1-x}{x} \times P(x-1)$$

The situation that we are now considering could be modelled as $B(20, \tfrac{3}{20})$. Hence we could use the recurrence formula to work out the probability of there being exactly one daisy from our model for the probability of finding no daisies at all.

$$P(1) = \frac{\tfrac{3}{20}}{1-\tfrac{3}{20}} \times \frac{20+1-1}{1} \times P(0)$$

where $P(0)$ is $P_{Av=3}(0)$. As the model is refined, try considering, say, 400 subdivisions and using the recurrence formula for the binomial model $B(20, \tfrac{3}{400})$ which produces:

$$P(1) = \frac{\tfrac{3}{400}}{1-\tfrac{3}{400}} \times \frac{400+1-1}{1} \times P(0)$$

Further refinement will produce:

$$P(1) = \frac{\tfrac{3}{8000}}{1-\tfrac{3}{8000}} \times \frac{8000+1-1}{1} \times P(0)$$

and so on. The limit of this refinement process will lead to the probability we are seeking:

$$P_{Av=3}(1) = \text{limit}\left\{\frac{\tfrac{3}{n}}{1-\tfrac{3}{n}} \times \frac{n+1-1}{1}\right\} P_{Av=3}(0)$$

CALCULATOR ACTIVITY

Exploration 21.2

The value of the factor

Explore the value of the factor, in brackets, in the recurrence formula:

$$\left\{\frac{\tfrac{3}{n}}{1-\tfrac{3}{n}} \times n\right\}$$

as n increases.

If you have a programmable calculator, you could use a program based on this flowchart.

INPUT N

$P = \dfrac{3}{N}$

$\text{ratio} = \dfrac{P}{1-P}$

$\text{factor} = N \times \text{ratio}$

Display factor

Set up a model

Formulate the mathematical problem

The sort of results you might achieve are shown in the table below.

Values of n	Value of factor $\left\{\dfrac{\frac{3}{n}}{1-\frac{3}{n}} \times n\right\}$
20	3.53
400	3.023
8000	3.0011
160 000	3.00006
3 200 000	3.000003
64 000 000	3.0000001
1 000 000 000	3.000 000 009

***Note*:** This program does not seem to give false results even for values as large as a ten thousand million.

◼ What do you think the limiting value of the factor is?
◼ In what way is this limiting value related to the average number of daisies per square metre?

Interpreting the results

It seems that the limit value is the same as the mean, i.e. 3. This suggests that the probability of exactly one daisy is:

$$P_{Av=3}(1) = 3P_{Av=3}(0) \approx 0.149\,361 \text{ (to six decimal places.)}$$

The recurrence formula can be used to find the probability of finding exactly two daisies:

$$P_{Av=3}(2) = \text{limit}\left\{\frac{\frac{3}{n}}{1-\frac{3}{n}} \times \frac{n+1-2}{2}\right\}P_{Av=3}(1)$$

and the probability of exactly three daisies:

$$P_{Av=3}(3) = \text{limit}\left\{\frac{\frac{3}{n}}{1-\frac{3}{n}} \times \frac{n+1-3}{3}\right\}P_{Av=3}(2)$$

and the probability of exactly four daisies:

$$P_{Av=3}(4) = \text{limit}\left\{\frac{\frac{3}{n}}{1-\frac{3}{n}} \times \frac{n+1-4}{4}\right\}P_{Av=3}(3)$$

etc.

Before setting out to discover these probabilities, it is worth considering the similarities and differences between the successive factors. The part which changes in the limiting process is the part which contains n, i.e. the $\dfrac{\frac{3}{n}}{1-\frac{3}{n}} \times (n+1-x)$ part for $x = 2, 3, 4, \ldots$

CALCULATOR ACTIVITY

Exploration 21.3

The limiting value

Explore the limiting value of these factors for $x = 2$, $x = 3$, $x = 4$, ...
You could try adapting your previous program to allow for an input of x as well as n.

◼ What do you think the limit of this factor is?
◼ Does it depend on the value of x?

Expected results

The results you might have achieved are summarised in the table below where the value of this factor is given for $x = 2$, 3, 4 and 5 and for a range of values of n up to one thousand million.

Value of n	New value of random variable			
	$x = 2$	$x = 3$	$x = 4$	$x = 5$
20	3.35	3.18	3	2.82
400	3.015	3.008	3	2.992
8000	3.0008	3.0004	3	2.9996
160 000	3.00004	3.00002	3	2.99998
3 200 000	3.000002	3.0000009	3	2.9999991
64 000 000	3.0000009	3.00000005	3	2.99999995
1 000 000 000	3.000 000 006	3.000 000 003	3	2.999 999 997

This suggests that in every case the limit of the factor:

$$\frac{\frac{3}{n}}{1 - \frac{3}{n}} \times (n + 1 - x)$$

is 3, i.e. this factor gets closer to the average number of daisies per square metre the more extensive the subdivision of a square.

So, if you now interpret this result, the model suggests the following relationship between successive probabilities.

$$P_{Av=3}(1) = 3 \times P_{Av=3}(0)$$
$$P_{Av=3}(2) = \tfrac{3}{2} \times P_{Av=3}(1)$$
$$P_{Av=3}(3) = \tfrac{3}{3} \times P_{Av=3}(2)$$
$$P_{Av=3}(4) = \tfrac{3}{4} \times P_{Av=3}(3)$$
$$P_{Av=3}(5) = \tfrac{3}{5} \times P_{Av=3}(4) \quad \text{etc.}$$

This suggests that the recurrence formula for probabilities of successive numbers of events for this model is:

$$P_{Av=3}(x) = \tfrac{3}{x} \times P_{Av=3}(x - 1)$$

Probability distribution

You, the lawn expert, are now in a position to advise the gardener about the likelihood of her seeing various numbers of daisies in square metres of her lawn. We saw at the beginning of this chapter that $P_3(0) = 0.049\,787$ (this notation is less cumbersome than $P_{Av=3}(0)$).

Then we saw that:

$$P_3(1) = 3 \times P_3(0) \approx 0.149\,361$$
$$P_3(2) = \tfrac{3}{2} \times P_3(1) \approx 0.224\,042$$
$$P_3(3) = \tfrac{3}{3} \times P_3(2) \approx 0.224\,042$$
$$P_3(4) = \tfrac{3}{4} \times P_3(3) \approx 0.168\,031$$
$$P_3(5) = \tfrac{3}{5} \times P_3(4) \approx 0.100\,819$$

Extending the process:

$$P_3(6) = \tfrac{3}{6} \times P_3(5) \approx 0.050\,409$$

$$P_3(7) = \tfrac{3}{7} \times P_3(6) \approx 0.021\,604$$

$$P_3(8) = \tfrac{3}{8} \times P_3(7) \approx 0.008\,102$$

$$P_3(9) = \tfrac{3}{9} \times P_3(8) \approx 0.002\,701$$

$$P_3(10) = \tfrac{3}{10} \times P_3(9) \approx 0.000\,810$$

etc.

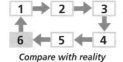

Compare with reality

How would you report your discoveries to the gardener? Suppose the garden is marked out in 100 metre squares. You might summarise your findings, briefly, by saying that she could expect to find five of the metre squares with no daisies; about 92 of them with between one and six daisies, and about three of the metre squares with more than six daisies.

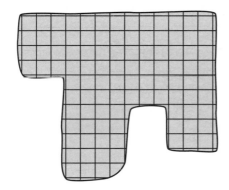

If you now reflect on the recurrence formula, it is quite possible to express the probability of the appearance of any given number of daisies in terms of the probability of none: $P_3(0)$. Try to express $P_3(4)$ in terms of $P_3(0)$. Consider the following argument.

$$P_3(1) = 3 \times P_3(0)$$

$$P_3(2) = \tfrac{3}{2} \times P_3(1) = \tfrac{3}{2} \times \left\{ 3 \times P_3(0) \right\} \quad \text{or} \quad \frac{3^2}{2} P_3(0)$$

Then:

$$P_3(3) = \tfrac{3}{3} \times P_3(2) = \tfrac{3}{3} \times \left\{ \frac{3^2}{2} \times P_3(0) \right\} = \frac{3^3}{3 \times 2} \times P_3(0)$$

and so:

$$P_3(4) = \tfrac{3}{4} \times P_3(3) = \tfrac{3}{4} \times \left\{ \frac{3^3}{312} \times P_3(0) \right\} = \frac{3^4}{4 \times 3 \times 2} \times P_3(0)$$

There seems to be an interesting pattern emerging in both the top and the bottom of the factor. The top appears to be:

3^x i.e. (average number)^x

But how can we rewrite the bottom of the factor? $4 \times 3 \times 2$ is the same as $4!$, so it appears that:

$$P_3(4) = \frac{3^4}{4!} \times P_3(3)$$

which suggests that the probability function is:

$$P_3(x) = \frac{3^x}{x!} \times P_3(0)$$

Exploration 21.4

Check the validity

Check the validity of this probability function by evaluating $P_3(x)$ for $x = 1, 2, 3, \ldots, 10$ using the function and comparing with the values found using the recurrence formula.

Poisson probability distribution

The model developed in this chapter has centred on the distribution of the number of daisies which might be found in metre squares of a lawn where there were, on average, three daisies per square metre. How would the probability function differ had there been an average of two daisies, or one daisy, or just $\frac{1}{2}$ a daisy per square metre?

This table summarises the probability function that would result from a similar modelling process.

Average	Probability function
3	$P_3(x) = \dfrac{3^x}{x!} \times P_3(0)$
2	$P_2(x) = \dfrac{2^x}{x!} \times P_2(0)$
1	$P_1(x) = \dfrac{1^x}{x!} \times P_1(0)$
$\frac{1}{2}$	$P_{\frac{1}{2}}(x) = \dfrac{\frac{1}{2}^x}{x!} \times P_{\frac{1}{2}}(0)$

Each of the functions rests on finding the appropriate probability of there being no daisies in a metre square, $P_\lambda(0)$ where the symbol, λ, (the Greek letter lambda) represents the average per square metre.

CALCULATOR ACTIVITY

Exploration 21.5

Relating probabilities

a) Use your calculator to evaluate $P_1(0)$ where:

$P_1(0) = $ limit of $\left(1 - \frac{1}{n}\right)^n$

b) Use your calculator to discover the relationship between:
$P_2(0)$ and $P_1(0)$
$P_3(0)$ and $P_1(0)$
$P_{\frac{1}{2}}(0)$ and $P_1(0)$.

c) Can you predict the relationship between $P_\lambda(0)$ and $P_1(0)$?

Expected results

You may have found that:

$P_1(0) \approx 0.367\,879$ (to six d.p.)

and:

$P_2(0) \approx 0.135\,335$

which is the square of $P_1(0)$, i.e.

$P_2(0) = \{P_1(0)\}^2$

and you know already that:

$P_3(0) \approx 0.049\,787$

so your calculator discoveries may have led you to:

$P_3(0) = \{P_1(0)\}^3$

further:

$P_{\frac{1}{2}}(0) = 0.606\,531 = \{P_1(0)\}^{\frac{1}{2}}$

It would seem reasonable to suggest that there is a power relationship between $P_\lambda(0)$ and $P_1(0)$.

$$P_\lambda(0) = \{P_1(0)\}^\lambda$$

As a result of this, all probabilities of events for which the occurrence may be modelled in this way can be expressed in terms of $P_1(0)$. The value of $P_1(0)$ is:

$$P_1(0) = 0.367\,879\,441\,2 \text{ (to ten d.p.).}$$

It is closely related to the natural number $e = 2.718\,281\,828\,5$ (to ten d.p.).

$$P_1(0) = \frac{1}{e} \text{ or } = e^{-1}$$

Hence, since $P_\lambda(0) = \{P_1(0)\}^\lambda$ then:

$$P_\lambda(0) = \{e^{-1}\}^\lambda = e^{-\lambda}$$

The probability function for this model is:

$$P_\lambda(x) = \frac{\lambda^x e^{-\lambda}}{x!}$$

This probability model was proposed by the 19th-century French mathematician, Siméon Poisson. It bears his name and the probability model is known as the **Poisson distribution**. He proposed that this modelled the number of random events which occur in a fixed interval of a continuous medium.

In the example about the lawn, the random event is the appearance of a daisy and the continuous medium is the lawn, with the fixed interval being a square metre per week.

Poisson also required the events to occur singly (i.e. no more than one daisy can appear at the same place in the garden at one time) and the occurrence to be at a uniform rate (e.g. in the garden we assumed that it was the growing season and the daisies grew at a weekly rate of three per square metre, on average). This assumption implies that there is no tendency for daisies to appear more densely in one part of the garden than another. It also assumes that there is no change of season. Clearly, in a different season, daisies are not going to grow at the same rate – they might not grow at all. Poisson also required the events to be independent (i.e. the presence of a daisy in one place is not going to attract others appearing, nor prevent others appearing nearby).

Using the Poisson distribution

Example 21.1

*A Geiger counter is used in recording radioactive events. Each radioactive event arriving at the counter shows as a number. The number of radioactive events recorded in a room is, on average, two events every five seconds. This is called the **background count**.*

a) *Which probability distribution is appropriate to model the number of radioactive events, which are recorded every five seconds, in the room?*

b) *Use the appropriate probability function to find:*
   i) the probability of exactly three events in five seconds,
   ii) the probability of more than three events in five seconds.

Solution

a) *Radioactive events can be regarded as 'random events' and here, the Geiger counter records the number of events occurring in five-second intervals. These are 'fixed intervals' (5s), in a 'continuous medium' (time). These events are recorded one at a time, i.e. singly, and may be assumed to occur independently and uniformly (two per five second interval, on average).*
This leads to the Poisson distribution with an average of 2.

b) *The probability model is:*

$$P_2(x) = \frac{2^x e^{-2}}{x!}$$

i) This requires you to find $P_2(3)$, i.e.

$$P_2(3) = \frac{2^x e^{-2}}{3!} \approx 0.1804$$

ii) Here, you need to find:

$$P_2(4) + P_2(5) + P_2(6) + ... \text{ etc.}$$

This can most readily be found by evaluating the probability of the 'complementary event', i.e. to find $P_2(0) + P_2(1) + P_2(2) + P_2(3)$.

$$P_2(0) + P_2(1) + P_2(2) + P_2(3) = e^{-2} + 2e^{-2} + \frac{2^2}{2!}e^{-2} + \frac{2^3}{3!}e^{-2} = 0.8571$$

Hence, the required probability is:
$$1 - 0.8571 = 0.1429$$

EXERCISES

21.1 CLASSWORK

1   The number of vehicles passing a traffic check-point every ten seconds is, on average, 5.3. Use the Poisson distribution to find the probability that in a ten-second iterval **a)** 4 vehicles pass, **b)** no vehicles pass, **c)** at least one vehicle passes, **d)** at most two vehicles pass the check point.

2   The random variable, X, has a Poisson distribution with mean 1.8. Evaluate:
a) $P(X = 1)$ **b)** $P(X \leq 2)$ **c)** $P(X \geq 1)$.

3   The number of broken eggs in a crate follows a Poisson distribution. If the probability of no broken eggs in a crate is $\approx 0.049\,787$, estmate the probability of:
a) one broken egg in a crate,   **b)** two broken eggs in a crate.

4   A car-hire firm owns two vehicles capable of taking a wheelchair. On average there is one request each day for the daily hire of one of these vehicles. On a particular day, find the probability that:
a) no such vehicle is demanded,
b) both vehicles are in use.

5   Two car-hire firms, A and B, each own two vehicles capable of taking a wheelchair. On average each firm receives one request each day for the daily hire of one of these vehicles. On a particular day, find the probability that:
a) no such vehicle is demanded,
b) firm A hires out both of its vehicles but firm B hires out neither of its vehicles,
c) exactly one of the four vehicles is demanded,
d) exactly two of the vehicles are demanded,
e) firm A cannot satisfy demand for such vehicles,
f) neither firm can satisfy demand for such vehicles.

6 The carpet in a hotel's corridors is 2 m wide. During production, small flaws occur at a mean rate of 2.3 per 20 m² area. Determine the probability that in 20 m² of the carpet there are:
a) more that two flaws,
b) exactly three flaws,
c) at most four flaws,
d) between three and five flaws, inclusive.

7 The number of cars travelling north under a motorway bridge during the hours of darkness may be modelled as a Poisson variate having a mean rate of 3.26 every ten seconds. Calculate the probability that in a ten-second interval during the hours of darkness, the number of cars passing under the bridge travelling north is:
a) exactly three, b) at least two, c) more than four.

EXERCISES

21.1 HOMEWORK

1 The random variable, Y, may be modelled as a Poisson variate with parameter $\lambda = 2.1$. Calculate:
a) $P(Y = 2)$ b) $P(Y \geq 2)$ c) $P(Y < 4)$ d) $P(2 < Y \leq 4)$.

2 Investigations have revealed that spelling mistakes occur in a local newspaper at an average rate of 1.37 per 100 words of text and that their occurrence may be modelled by a Poisson distribution. Calculate the probability that in 100 words of text, the number of spelling mistakes is:
a) exactly two, b) more than one,
c) at most two, d) between one and four, exclusive.

3 The number of faulty paving bricks in large batches has been shown to follow a Poisson distribution with mean 4.3. Evaluate the probability that in one of these batches the number of faulty bricks is:
a) exactly four, b) at most three,
c) at least two, d) between three and six, inclusive.

4 Explain why a Poisson distribution may be appropriate as a model for the *number* of faults per 20 m length of carpet.
Assume X may be modelled by a Poisson distribution with mean 0.98. Find the probability that in a randomly-selected 20 m length of this carpet:
a) there are no faults, b) there are at most two faults.

5 On average, there are two rotten apples in a box. Find the probability of finding:
a) exactly four rotten apples, b) at least two rotten apples,
c) not more than four rotten apples in a box.

6 A large computing facility is being designed to handle enquiries from all over the country. If enquiries are expected to arrive randomly at a mean rate of five per minute, determine the probability that:
a) no enquiry arrives in a minute,
b) at least two enquiries will arrive in a minute,
c) there will be two or three enquiries in a minute.

7 A field is sown with barley seed after the previous year's crop of wheat has been ploughed in. Unfortunately, the ploughing does not totally eliminate the wheat. Some wheat seeds remain and

germinate. Assume that the average number of wheat seeds which subsequently germinate is 2.3 per square metre. Calculate the probability that a randomly chosen square metre contains:
a) exactly one wheat seed,
b) two or three wheat seeds,
c) at least four wheat seeds which germinate.

VALIDATING THE MODEL

On page 424 we found the recurrence formula: $P_3(x) = \dfrac{3}{x} P_3(x-1)$

for the Poisson probability distribution where the average is 3. A convenient notation for a random variable, X, with occurrence that may be modelled in this way, is:

$X \sim \text{Poi}(3)$

In general, if a random variable, X, may be modelled with a Poisson distribution with average λ, then this is written:

$X \sim \text{Poi}(\lambda)$

The recurrence formula for this probability distribution is:

$$\mathbf{P}_\lambda(x) = \frac{\lambda}{x} \mathbf{P}_\lambda(x-1)$$

Just as in the case of a random variable which is binomially distributed, the recurrence formula is a very convenient way of calculating successive probabilities. We saw this on page 425, when we were calculating the probability of 0, 1, 2, 3, ..., 10 daisies in a metre square.

Example 21.2

Buttercups occur at an average rate of 1.8 per square metre per week. A gardener picks the buttercups that he finds in his garden once a week. What is the probability that he will collect:
a) up to five buttercups,
b) more than eight buttercups,
from an area of one square metre in a week?

Solution
If X is the number of buttercups found in a square metre in a week then it is reasonable to model X as a Poisson variate: $X \sim \text{Poi}(1.8)$
The recurrence formula for X is:

$$P_{1.8}(x) = \frac{1.8}{x} P_{1.8}(x-1)$$

and:
$P_{1.8}(0) = e^{-1.8} = 0.165\,299$
a) Hence, the required probability is:

$P_{1.8}(X \le 5) = P_{1.8}(0) + P_{1.8}(1) + P_{1.8}(2) + ... + P_{1.8}(5)$
and:

$P_{1.8}(1) = 1.8 \times P_{1.8}(0) \approx 0.297\,538$

$P_{1.8}(2) = \dfrac{1.8}{2} \times P_{1.8}(1) \approx 0.267\,784$

$P_{1.8}(3) = \dfrac{1.8}{3} \times P_{1.8}(2) \approx 0.160\,671$

$P_{1.8}(4) = \dfrac{1.8}{4} \times P_{1.8}(3) \approx 0.072\,302$

$P_{1.8}(5) = \dfrac{1.8}{5} \times P_{1.8}(4) \approx 0.026\,029$

Adding these probabilities produces: $P_{1.8}(X \le 5) = 0.989\,622$

b) *To find* $P_{1.8}(X > 8)$, *the property of complementary events can be used to good effect. Thus:*

$P_{1.8}(X > 8) = 1 - P_{1.8}(X \leq 8)$

We have already calculated the probabilities for 0, 1, 2, 3, 4 and 5, so all that needs to be done is to calculate:

$$P_{1.8}(6) = \frac{1.8}{6} \times P_{1.8}(5) \approx 0.007\,809$$

$$P_{1.8}(7) = \frac{1.8}{7} \times P_{1.8}(6) \approx 0.002\,008$$

$$P_{1.8}(8) = \frac{1.8}{8} \times P_{1.8}(7) \approx 0.000\,452$$

Adding the total of these to $P_{1.8}(X \leq 5)$ *gives:*

$P_{1.8}(X \leq 8) = 0.999\,890$

Hence: $P_{1.8}(X > 8) = 1 - 0.999\,890 = 0.000\,11$

The distribution function

In Chapter 20, *Discrete probability distributions* we encountered the cumulative probability distribution function and the associated tabular values. The same sort of tables exist for the Poisson probability model. Entries in these tables provide us with probabilities such as:

$$P_{1.8}(X \leq 5),\ P_{1.8}(X \leq 8),\ P_2(X \leq 3),\ P_3(X \leq 10)\ \text{etc.}$$

When there is no requirement for large numbers of decimal places, the tables provide a quick and easy way of obtaining probabilities for Poisson events.

Exploration 21.6

Using the Poisson distribution

a) Use the Poisson distribution tables to write down, to four places of decimals, the probabilities:
- $P_{1.8}(X < 5)$ ■ $P_{1.8}(X < 8)$
- $P_2(X \leq 3)$ ■ $P_3(X \leq 10)$.

b) Check your answers to part a), using the appropriate recurrence formula.

Example 21.3

A national newspaper has, on average, 3.6 misprints per page. Assume that the number of misprints on a page can be modelled as Poi(3.6). *Obtain, accurate to three places of decimals, the probabilities of the following events.*

a) *A page has fewer than six misprints.*
b) *A page is free from misprints.*
c) *A page has more than three misprints.*
d) *A page has exactly five misprints.*
e) *A page has between three and eight (inclusive) misprints.*

Solution

The degree of accuracy required allows the tables to be used.

a) $P_{3.6}(X < 6) = P_{3.6}(X \leq 5) = 0.8441 = 0.844$ *(three d.p.)*

b) $P(\text{page is free from misprints}) = P_{3.6}(X = 0) = 0.0273$
$$= 0.027\ \textit{(three d.p.)}$$

c) $P(\text{more than 3}) = 1 - P_{3.6}(X \leq 3) = 1 - 0.5152 = 0.485$ *(three d.p.)*

d) $P(\text{exactly 5}) = P_{3.6}(X \leq 5) - P_{3.6}(X \leq 4) = 0.8441 - 0.7064$
$$= 0.1377 = 0.138\ \textit{(three d.p.)}$$

e) P(between 3 and 8 inclusive) $= P_{3.6}(X \le 8) - P_{3.6}(X \le 2)$
$$= 0.9883 - 0.3027$$
$$= 0.6856 = 0.686 \text{ (three d.p.)}$$

Mean and variance

When we developed our model for the daisies, we started by assuming that there were, on average, three daisies per square metre. Does the model actually have a mean value equal to three? In other words, is the expected value equal to three?

Remember from the work you have done on expectation that the expected value of a random variable, X, was seen to be the sum:

$$\mu = \sum_{\text{all } x} x P(X = x)$$

In the case of this Poisson model, the possible values for the random variable are $x = 0, 1, 2, 3, 4, \ldots$ etc. This implies that the mean can be found from summing all products from $x = 0$.

$$\mu = \sum_{x=0} x P(X = x)$$

CALCULATOR ACTIVITY

Exploration 21.7

Find the mean number of daisies

Try one of the following suggestions, using your calculator to discover the mean number of daisies according to the probability model you developed.

a) Use a program based on this flowchart which makes use of the recurrence formula for Poisson probabilities. This program displays the expected value to an accuracy of about eight places of decimals for Poi(λ) when λ is less than four.
To improve the accuracy, or to explore the expected value for larger values of λ, you need to change the condition of the 'Repeat … Until' loop. If you change the stopping condition to 'Until $X > 40$' the program will display the expected value with a greater accuracy for λ up to the value 12.

b) You could use your calculator in 'Statistics' mode if it accepts probability distributions. See the advice offered in part **a)** on the limit needed on the value of X. If you are content with fewer than eight decimal places of accuracy, you could reduce the limit on X from 20 to 15 or fewer.

c) If you do not have an appropriate 'Statistics' mode calculator, you may be able to use its memory to evaluate the sum:

$$0 \times e^{-3} + 1 \times 3e^{-3} + 2 \times \frac{3^2}{2!}e^{-3} + 3 \times \frac{3^3}{3!}e^{-3} + 4 \times \frac{3^4}{4!}e^{-3} \times \ldots + 15 \times \frac{3^{15}}{15!}e^{-3} + \ldots$$

A bit of factorisation might reduce the effort required on keying in this sum:

$$3e^{-3}\left\{1 + 3 + \frac{3^2}{2!} + \frac{3^3}{3!} + \frac{3^4}{4!} + \ldots + \frac{3^{14}}{14!}\right\}$$

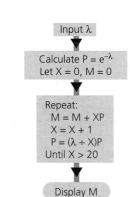

Input λ

Calculate $P = e^{-\lambda}$
Let $X = 0$, $M = 0$

Repeat:
$M = M + XP$
$X = X + 1$
$P = (\lambda \div X)P$
Until $X > 20$

Display M

Expected results

You should find that the mean of the Poisson model for the daisies is the same as the quoted average of three. This is a somewhat reassuring result since it is what you would want of the model! It is generally true that the mean of the Poisson model, Poi(λ), is the same as its parameter, λ.

Mean: $\mu = \lambda$

Example 21.4

A random variable, X, is believed to follow a Poisson distribution, Poi(λ). It is known that the probability, P(X = 0), is 0.1. What is the mean of the distribution?

Solution
We know that the probability, P(X = 0), is $e^{-\lambda}$. But the information says that this is 0.1. So we need to find λ when $e^{-\lambda} = 0.1$.
Using natural logs (since this is the inverse function):

$\log(e^{-\lambda}) = \log(0.1)$

Therefore $-\lambda \approx -2.303$ or, $\lambda \approx 2.30$
Hence the mean is about 2.30.
This can be checked by evaluating $e^{-2.30}$.

CALCULATOR ACTIVITY

Exploration 21.8

Relationship between the variance and the mean of the Poisson model

Develop the previous calculator activity to discover the relationship between the variance and the mean of the Poisson model. Recall that the variance, σ^2, can be found from the 'mean of the squares *minus* the square of the mean':

$$\sigma^2 = \left\{ \sum_{\text{all } x} x^2 P(X = x) \right\} - \mu^2$$

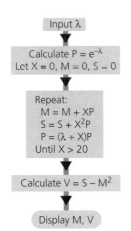

Input λ

Calculate $P = e^{-\lambda}$
Let $X = 0$, $M = 0$, $S = 0$

Repeat:
$M = M + XP$
$S = S + X^2P$
$P = (\lambda \div X)P$
Until $X > 20$

Calculate $V = S - M^2$

Display M, V

a) The previous flowchart can be adapted as shown.
    This program produces both the mean and variance.

b) If you have an appropriate statistics calculator, you should be able to put in the same probability distribution as in the previous calculator activity and extract the standard deviation. If you square the standard deviation you should get the variance.

c) Using the memory of a calculator you need to evaluate:

$$0^2 \times e^{-3} + 1^2 \times 3e^{-3} + 2^2 \times \frac{3^2}{2!}e^{-3} + 3^2 \times \frac{3^3}{3!}e^{-3} + ... + 15^2 \times \frac{3^{15}}{15!}e^{-3}$$

Factorising gives:

$$3e^{-3}\left\{ 1 + 2 \times 3 + 3 \times \frac{3^2}{2!} + 4 \times \frac{3^3}{3!} + 5 \times \frac{3^4}{4!} + ... + 15 \times \frac{3^{14}}{14!} \right\}$$

Once you evaluate this, you need to subtract the square of the mean.

The sort of results which emerge from a programmable calculator are summarised in the table that follows, for various values of the parameter λ and various limits for X.

λ	Limit on X	Mean	Variance
3	20	3	2.999 999 999
1.2	20	1.2	1.2
2	20	2	2
3.5	20	3.499 999 999	3.499 999 999
4	20	3.999 999 992	3.999 999 992
4	30	4	4
8	40	8	8
10	40	10	10
12	40	12	11.99 999 98

These results suggest that the variance of the Poisson model is the same as its mean.

Variance: $\sigma^2 = \lambda$

i.e. the variance has the same numerical value as the mean.

EXERCISES

21.2 CLASSWORK

1   If $X \sim$ Poi(4), use the Poisson tables to find the following.
    a) $P(X < 4)$ **b)** $P(X > 3)$ **c)** $P(X = 2)$ **d)** $P(3 < X < 7)$ **e)** $P(2 < X \le 8)$

2   A Mathematics student makes an average of three arithmetic errors on each homework assignment. Find the probability that, on a particular assignment, he made:
    a) more than three errors,   **b)** fewer than five errors,
    c) a number of errors between two and six inclusive.

3   A Poisson variable has a mean of 5. Find the probability that:
    a) $X < 5$ **b)** $X > 5$ **c)** $X \ge 5$

4   A Poisson variable is such that $P(X = 5) = 0.8\,P(X = 3)$. Find its mean and standard deviation.

5   A Poisson variable is such that $P(X = 3) = P(X = 4)$. Find $P(X = 5)$.

6   Sales of a particular pre-packed sandwich from a small shop follow a Poisson distribution with a mean of 9.4 per day. Calculate the probability that on a particular day, the number of pre-packed sandwiches sold:
    a) is fewer than eight,   **b)** exceeds ten,
    c) is between five and 15 exclusive.

7   The daily number, X, of items of crockery, broken in a hotel's kitchen may be modelled by a Poisson random variable with average 1.5.

x	$P(X = x)$	$f = 10\,000 \times P(X = x)$
0	0.2231	2231
≥ 8	0.0002	1
		1000

Complete the above table using $\lambda = 1.5$. Hence calculate the mean and variance of X. Approximate ≥ 8 by exactly 8. Comment on your two calculated values.

EXERCISES

1 A Poisson variable has a mean of 3.5. Find the probability that:
  a) $X \geq 3$ **b)** $X < 3$ **c)** $X \leq 6$

2 The random variable, Y, has a Poisson distribution with parameter $\lambda = 4.35$. Use the recurrence formula to evaluate $P(Y = 0)$, ..., $P(Y = 6)$. Hence state:
  a) $P(Y \leq 4)$ **b)** $P(Y \geq 6)$ **c)** $P(3 \leq Y \leq 6)$ **d)** $P(1 < Y < 4)$.

3 A Poisson variable is such that $P(X = 3) = 0.6P(X = 2)$. Find its mean and variance.

4 If $X \sim \text{Poi}(\lambda)$ and $P(X = 4) = 2\,P(X = 3)$, calculate the value of λ and hence $P(X = 5)$.

5 Show that if $P(Y = 5) = 1.8P(Y = 3)$ then $\lambda = 6$. Hence calculate $P(Y = 6)$.

6 The discrete random variable X is known to follow a Poisson distribution with mean 5.15. Use the recurrence formula to calculate $P(X = 0)$, ..., $P(X = 8)$. Hence determine:
  a) $P(2 \leq X \leq 7)$ **b)** $P(X \leq 6)$ **c)** $P(X > 5)$ **d)** $P(3 < X \leq 8)$.

7 A store's weekly number of sales of a particular make of hairdrier may be modelled by a Poisson random variable with mean 6.4. Use Poisson distribution tables to calculate the probability that sales in a particular week:
  a) exceed eight,   **b)** are fewer than four,
  c) are between five and ten inclusive,
  d) are less than eight but more than two.
If, at the beginning of the week, the store's stock of the hairdrier is ten, what is the probability that demand will exceed supply? Determine the minimum number of hairdriers that should be in stock at the start of the week if the probability of failing to meet demand is to be:
  e) at most ten per cent   **f)** at most five per cent
  g) at most one per cent.

ADDITIVE PROPERTY OF POISSON VARIATES

The lawn, which was the subject of expert investigation in the beginning of this chapter, sometimes has dandelions randomly appearing. They occur at a rate of about 0.6 per square metre per week. The growing seasons for daisies and dandelions overlap. If the only weeds which appear in the garden are daisies and dandelions, what is the weekly average number of weeds per square metre during the overlap period?

If we assume that the daisies and dandelions appear independently, it would seem reasonable to say that the weekly average number of weeds is $(3 + 0.6)$, i.e. 3.6. It seems reasonable to suggest that the conditions which are met by the daisies and the dandelions separately: random, independent, uniform rate, single occurance; are also met by them jointly as 'weeds'. Let X be the random variable 'the number of daisies in a square in one week' and let Y be the random variable 'the number of dandelions in a square metre in the same week'. Then, Z, which is the total number of weeds in a square metre in the week in question, can be expressed as the sum of X and Y:

$$Z = X + Y$$

The argument presented here indicates that if X and Y are independent Poisson variables, then this sum, $X + Y$, is also a Poisson variate.

The mean of Z will be the sum of the means of X and T, hence:

$$\mu_Z = \mu_X + \mu_Y$$

and since Z is a Poisson variate, its variance will be the same as the mean.

Example 21.5

In a physics laboratory, Geiger counter records indicate that the average count is one radioactive event every second. In a biology laboratory, the average count is four every five seconds. Use an appropriate probability model to calculate:

a) the average count per five seconds in the physics laboratory,
b) the probability of a count of at least four radioactive events, in a five-second interval:
  i) in the physics laboratory,
  ii) in the biology laboratory,
  iii) in total in the two laboratories.
Give your answers to three places of decimals.

Solution
a) The Poisson model is appropriate. This model requires that the random events occur at a constant rate. This implies that if the rate of occurrence is one per second, then in five seconds the average will be five.
b) This question requires you to calculate $P(X \geq 4)$ when X is a Poisson variate.
  i) In this part $X \sim \text{Poi}(5)$. The distribution tables indicate:
    $P(X < 4) = P(X \leq 3) = 0.2650$
    Hence:
    $P(X \geq 4) = 1 - P(X < 4) = 0.735$
  ii) Here, $X \sim \text{Poi}(3)$. From the tables:
    $P(X \geq 4) = 1 - P(X \leq 3) = 1 - 0.6472 \approx 0.353$
  iii) The random variable is the sum of the counts in each of the laboratories. The average count is therefore going to be $(5 + 3)$ i.e. 8. Hence, for this part of the question $X \sim \text{Poi}(8)$. The tables indicate:
    $P(X \geq 4) = 1 - P(X \leq 3) = 1 - 0.0424 \approx 0.959$

Example 21.6

A skilled word-processor operator produces documents with an average of 0.3 errors per page. What is the probability that a document consisting of 15 pages has:
a) no error,
b) at least one error,
c) fewer than five errors,
d) at least one error on each of five pages and none on the others?

Solution

It is reasonable to assume that the errors are random events. These occur in a page, i.e. in a fixed interval of a continuous medium. If it is also possible to assume that errors occur independently, singly and at a constant rate, a Poisson distribution is appropriate to model the number of errors which occur on a page. $\text{Poi}(0.3)$ *is the particular model for the errors on the page.*

a) *The model for the number of errors in a document of 15 pages is* $\text{Poi}(4.5)$. *Then:*

$$P(0) = e^{-4.5} \approx 0.0111$$

b) P(at least one error) $= 1 - P$(no error) ≈ 0.9889.

c) P(fewer than five errors) $= P(\leq 4) \approx 0.5321$.

d) *This question is quite demanding. Consider the situation being modelled. Suppose the first five pages have at least one error on each and there are no errors on any of the remaining ten pages.*

| ≥ 1 | ≥ 1 | ≥ 1 | ≥ 1 | ≥ 1 | 0 | 0 | ... | 0 |

The probability that this occurs is:

$$\{P(\geq 1)\}^5 \, \{P(0)\}^{10}$$

where $P(\geq 1)$ *refers to the chance that a single page has at least one error. Hence:*

$$P(\geq 1) = 1 - e^{-0.3} \approx 0.259\,18$$

and:

$$P(0) = e^{-0.3} \approx 0.740\,82$$

Hence, the probability that the first five pages each have at least one error and the rest have none is:

$$(0.259\,18)^5 (0.740\,82)^{10}$$

However, this is one way where five pages each have at least one error and none of the rest have any errors. There are $_{15}C_5$ *possible combination of pages which produce such a document. Hence, the probability required is:*

$$_{15}C_5 (0.25918)^5 (0.74082)^{10} \approx 0.1749$$

An alternative perspective on this part of the question identifies the conditions which give rise to a binomial probability model, in particular, the $B(15, 0.259\,18)$ and the requirement is to find $P(5)$.

EXERCISES

21.3 CLASSWORK

1   Faults occur in the manufacture of yarn at random and at a mean rate of 0.6 per 1000 m. Determine the probability that in a 1000 m roll there are:

a) no faults,   b) more than two faults.

Find also the probability that in a roll of 10 000 m the number of faults is:

c) exactly six,   d) fewer than ten,

e) between two and eight, inclusive.

2   The independent random variables, X, Y, Z, have Poisson distributions with means 2.6, 3.4 and 1.5 respectively. Evaluate:

a) $P(X + Y = 6)$ b) $P(X + Y \geq 8)$

c) $P(X + Z < 4)$ d) $P(X + Y + Z > 10)$

e) $P(Y + Z \leq 5)$ f) $P(3 \leq X + Z \leq 7)$.

3 Accidents occur on a process plant at an average of 2.1 per week. Determine the probability of:
   a) more than three accidents in a week,
   b) exactly two accidents in each of two successive weeks,
   c) exactly four accidents in a fortnight,
   d) more than eight accidents in a four week period.
   Explain why your answers to b) and c) differ.

4 A newspaper of 24 pages contains on average 36 misprints.
   a) On the leader page find the probability of:
      i) at least three misprints,
      ii) not more than four misprints.
   b On the two sports pages together, find the probability of:
      i) no misprints at all,
      ii) only one misprint,
      iii) two misprints in all.

5 A PC computer network which operates five days per week is subject to random crashes at an average rate of 0.9 per day. Use the Poisson distribution to estimate the probability of:
   a) exactly five crashes in a week,
   b) fewer than six crashes in a fortnight,
   c) between three and eight crashes inclusive in a fortnight,
   d) more than five crashes in a fortnight.

6 A newspaper of 24 pages contains, on average, 36 misprints. Find the probability of:
   a) no misprints on the front page,
   b) no misprints on any of the three Arts pages,
   c) exactly one misprint in the Arts section,
   d) exactly two misprints in the Arts section,
   e) no page in the newspaper being free of misprints.

EXERCISES

21.3 HOMEWORK

1 The demand for a certain spare part occurs randomly at an average rate of four per week. Find the probability that the demand is for:
   a) at least five in a week,
   b) exactly four in a week,
   c) at most six in a fortnight,
   d) exactly four in each of two successive weeks.
   What is the minimum number of this spare part which must be in stock at the beginning of each week so that the probability of failing to meet demand during the week is less than one per cent?

2 The independent Poisson random variables, R, S and T have parameters, 0.8, 2.6 and 5.6 respectively. Calculate the probability that:
   a) $R + S > 3$ b) $R + T \le 6$ c) $2 < S + T < 10$
   d) $R + S + T \ge 5$ e) $R + S + 7 = 10$.

3 For the period 6.30 a.m. to 8.30 a.m. the demand for a particular daily paper at a small newsagents may be modelled by a Poisson variate with mean 12.8. Calculate the probability that the demand for the paper:

a) exceeds five during the period 6.30 a.m. to 7.00 a.m.
b) is fewer that ten during the period 7.00 a.m. to 8.00 a.m.
c) is between five and 15, inclusive, during the period 6.30 a.m. to 8.00 a.m.
d) exceeds five during the period 7.15 a.m. to 7.45 a.m. and between 8.00 a.m. and 8.30 a.m.

4   On average a switchboard receives six calls in an hour.
a) Find the probability there are no calls in a five-minute period.
b) Find the probability there are no calls in a ten-minute period.
c) Find the probability of there being no calls between 4.05 p.m. and 4.10 p.m. given that there were no calls between 4.00 p.m. and 4.05 p.m.
d) Find the probability of there being no calls between 4.10 p.m. and 4.15 p.m. given there were no calls between 4.00 p.m. and 4.10 p.m.
e) What do you deduce from your answers to **c)** and **d)**?

5   A garage showroom has a demand for cars which is known to have a Poisson distribution with an average of 1.2 per day. Use the tables to answer the following questions.
a) What is the probability that four cars are sold in one day?
b) What is the probability that more than five cars are sold in a three-day period?
c) How many cars should the showroom have at the beginning of a five-day working week to be at least 95 per cent sure of meeting that week's demand?

6   The number of emergency admissions each day to a hospital is found to have a Poisson distribution with mean 2.
a) Evaluate the probability that on a particular day there are no emergency admissions.
b) At the beginning of one day the hospital has five beds available for emergencies. Calculate the probability that this will be insufficient to meet the demand for that particular day.
c) Calculate the probability that there will be a total of three admissions during a period of two consecutive days.
d) How many beds should be available at the beginning of a day for the hospital to be at least 95 per cent sure of coping with the demand for beds?

CONSOLIDATION EXERCISES FOR CHAPTER 21

1   The number of wrong notes hit by a pianist in a certain concerto is a Poisson variable with a mean of 1.6. If he plays the concerto twice, find the probability that:
a) he plays the concerto perfectly both times,
b) he plays the concerto perfectly once only,
c) he hits two wrong notes altogether,
d) he hits three wrong notes altogether,
e) he hits no more than two wrong notes in either concerto.

2   The number of double-yolked eggs in a crate is a Poisson variable with mean 1.5.
a) In one crate of eggs, find the probability of finding:
    i) more than three such eggs,
    ii) no more than two such eggs.

b) In two crates of eggs, find the probability of finding:
  i) exactly two such eggs altogether,
  ii) no more than two such eggs in either crate.

3   The number of faulty batteries in a box is a Poisson variable with a mean of 2.8.
a) Find the probability that a box is free of faulty batteries.
b) If there are three boxes, find the probability that exactly two of them are fault-free.
c) If there are five boxes, find the probability that not more than two are fault-free.

4   On average there are three orange Smarties in each packet. Find the probability of finding.
a) fewer than three orange Smarties in a packet,
b) more than three orange Smarties in a packet,
c) fewer than three orange Smarties in each of two packets,
d) exactly three orange Smarties in total, if two packets are bought.

5   A Poisson variable is such that its mean is equal to its standard deviation. Find the possible value of P(3).

6   On average an office receives three faxes an hour. Find the probability that they receive:
a) exactly two faxes in an hour,
b) exactly one fax in half an hour,
c) at least one fax in 15 minutes,
d) not more than two faces in a two-hour period.

7   The number of defective escalators each day in an underground system is a Poisson variable with a mean of 3 and the number of defective lifts in the system is a Poisson variable with a mean of 2. Find the probability that, on a given day:
a) there are one defective escalator and one defective lift,
b) there are at least two defective escalators and at least one defective lift,
c) there are not more than three defective machines altogether,
d) the system is operating perfectly.

8   A footballer has just been transferred from a Division 3 club to one in the Premier division. He has a scoring record of 0.8 goals per match.
a) Assuming that he maintains this record in the Premier division what is the chance that he will score two goals in a given game? State your assumptions.
b) What is the probability that he will have scored more than eight goals after twelve games?
c) Another striker with a scoring rate of 0.7 goals per game joins the Premier division club. The two strikers play together in a match. What is the probability they score four goals between them?

9   Every five minutes, two taxis, on average, pass a particular spot. Buses come past, on average, one every ten minutes. No other vehicles pass this spot. Find the probability that:
a) no buses or taxis pass in a ten-minute period,
b) exactly three vehicles pass in a five-minute period,
c) more taxis than buses pass in ten minutes.

10 The independent random variables X and Y have Poisson distributions with means λ and μ respectively. The random variable $Z = X + Y$.
Show that:
a) $P(Z = 0) = e^{-(\lambda + \mu)}$
b) $P(Z = 1) = (\lambda + \mu)\, e^{-(\lambda + \mu)}$.
Determine $P(Z = 2)$ and hence deduce the distribution of Z.
Verify your deduction by evaluating $P(Z = 3)$ directly, and by using appropriate combinations of probabilities for X and Y.

11 An insurance company employs agents who use their cars to travel a large number of miles each year. The company observes that the number of accidents involving each agent can be modelled by a Poisson distribution with mean 0.2 per year.
What is the probability that a particular agent is involved in:
a) two or fewer accidents in a particular year,
b) exactly three accidents in a particular year?

12 The independent Poisson random variables X and Y have means of 2.5 and 4.5 respectively. Obtain the mean and variance of the random variables:
a) $X - Y$ **b)** $2X + 5$.
For each of these random variables give a reason why the distribution is **not** Poisson.

13 The annual number of accidents at a certain road junction may be modelled by a Poisson distribution with mean 8.5. Improvements intended to reduce the accident rate are made at the junction. To test their effectiveness it is planned to monitor the number of accidents at the junction in the following year.
a) State suitable null and alternative hypotheses for the test,
b) If the improvements are to be considered effective when fewer than five accidents occur in the year, determine the significance level of the test.
c) If the improvements reduce the mean annual number of accidents at the junction to three, what is the probability of having five or more accidents?

14 Before being packed in boxes, apples in a fruit-packing plant have to be checked for bruising. The apples pass along a conveyor belt, and an inspector removes any of the apples that are badly bruised. Badly bruised apples arrive at random times, but at a constant average rate of 1.8 per minute.
i) Find the probability that at least one badly bruised apple arrives in a one-minute period.
ii) In a period of a minutes, the probability of at least one badly bruised apple arriving is 0.995. Find the value of a.
(OCR Question 1, Specimen Paper 2, 2000)

15 Two types of flaw, A and B, may occur in a manufactured cloth. The numbers of flaws of type A and type B occurring per metre length of the cloth are independent and have Poisson distributions with means 0.2 and 0.3, respectively.
a) Calculate the probability that a length of 1 metre of the cloth will have a **combined total** of exactly 4 flaws of types A and B.

b) A length of 1 metre of the cloth is found to have a **combined** total of exactly 3 flaws of types A and B. **Without using tables or a calculator**, calculate the conditional probability that exactly one of the 3 flaws was of type A.

c) Removing a type A flaw from the cloth costs 12 pence, and removing a type B flaw from the cloth costs 8 pence. Find the mean and the variance of the cost per metre of removing both types of flaw from the cloth.

(WJEC Question 1, Specimen Paper 2, 2000)

Summary

- The Poisson distribution models the number of random events which occur in a fixed interval of a continuous medium.

- $P_\lambda(x) = \dfrac{\lambda^x e^{-\lambda}}{x!}$

  mean of Poisson distribution $\mu = \lambda$

  variance of Poisson distribution $\sigma^2 = \lambda$

- Poisson variables are additive:
  $X \sim \text{Poi}(\mu_x)$, $Y \sim \text{Poi}(\mu_y)$.
  then: $X + Y \sim \text{Poi}(\mu_x + \mu_y)$

- Poisson distribution may be used to model events which can be described as rare.

Continuous random variables

STATISTICS 22

In this chapter we shall investigate:

- *how to model the occurrence of continuous random variables,*
- *how the summation process for discrete variables is paralleled by integration for continuous variables,*
- *how a review of the Poisson distribution leads to a new model of random events: the exponential distribution.*

MODELLING CONTINUOUS RANDOM VARIABLES

Exploration 22.1

Probability density function

A large retail DIY store sells planks of wood which it saws to the length the customer requires. The manager of the timber department is not prepared to sell any length less than 1.2 m. As a result she often has off-cuts of timber left over, which are put in a waste container. One of the customers of the store is the coordinator for Technology of a consortium of primary schools. He thinks there would be a use for these off-cuts but would like to know what lengths to expect in the container.

Imagine you are approached to offer the coordinator advice. You decide to obtain a random sample of off-cuts.

Length, x m	$0 \leq x < 0.2$	$0.2 \leq x < 0.4$	$0.4 \leq x < 0.5$
Number off-cuts, f	15	14	5

Length, x m	$0.5 \leq x < 0.6$	$0.6 \leq x < 1.0$	$1.0 \leq x < 1.2$
Number off-cuts, f	8	21	12

The lengths of your sample of 75 off-cuts are recorded in a table, and displayed in this histogram.

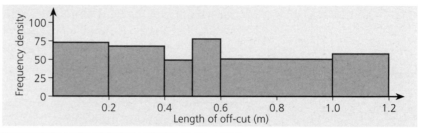

The coordinator asks you if this is typical of the lengths he might find and if you could tell him what proportion of the lengths are less than $\frac{3}{4}$ m. What do you think your reply is?

Planning an approach

You might talk to the coordinator about the nature of inherent random variability in data. You might also want a more appropriate presentation of the data, to respond to the question about proportion. The histogram concerns itself with **frequency** whereas **relative frequency** is more directly appropriate to **proportion**. Try presenting the data in a relative frequency histogram.

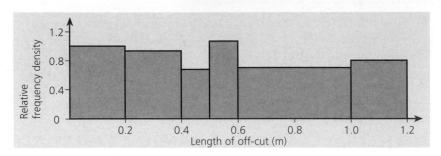

The relative frequency histogram is shown in this diagram. The Technology coordinator comments that the diagram looks no different from the first frequency histogram and asks how you can use it to answer his question on proportion. What is the main difference between the two diagrams?

You might point out that frequencies can be found from the first histogram, whereas the relative frequency histogram allows relative frequencies or proportions to be found from the areas. Suppose you invite the coordinator to estimate the proportion of off-cuts with lengths less than $\frac{3}{4}$ m. What do you think the estimate should be?

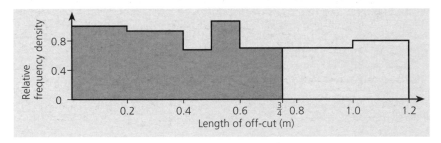

The area shaded in this diagram is an estimate of the proportion. This area consists of:

$$0.2 \times 1.0 + 0.2 \times 0.933 + 0.1 \times 0.667 + 0.1 \times 1.067 + 0.15 \times 0.7 = 0.665$$

So, a reasonable estimate of the proportion is 66.5 per cent or about $\frac{2}{3}$.

Reflecting on your discussion with the coordinator, you might mention that the relative frequency histogram you have used to estimate proportions is based on one random sample. You could suggest that you would prefer to obtain many more random samples so that you would be sure of the shape of the resulting relative frequency histogram.

If the sample of 75 lengths is representative of the off-cuts, then the relative frequency histogram is likely to be a smoother version of the first graph above. What model do you suggest might fit the **smoothed relative frequency density?**

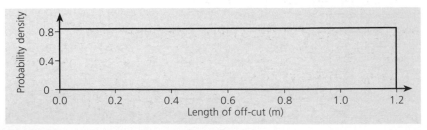

A possible model is shown in this diagram. Note that, since this is a model rather than actual data, relative frequency has been replaced by

probability. Hence, the diagram represents a **probability density function**. The area under the function represents probability in the same way that area represents relative frequency in a histogram.

Since all the off-cuts of timber have lengths between 0.0 and 1.2 m, what is the area under this probability density function? The area represents the probability of all possibilities, hence its value should be equal to 1. The region is rectangular and its area can be found from 'length × breadth'. Hence, the density function, $f(x)$, is:

$$f(x) = \frac{1}{1.2} \approx 0.833 \quad 0 \le x \le 1.2$$

Note: The word 'probability' is not always used in this context.

What does this model suggest is the proportion of off-cuts with length less than $\frac{3}{4}$ m? The proportion is modelled by the probability represented by the area shaded in this diagram. This is:

$$0.833 \times \frac{3}{4} \approx 0.625$$

or about $62\frac{1}{2}$ per cent which is close to the value obtained from the sample of 75 off-cuts.

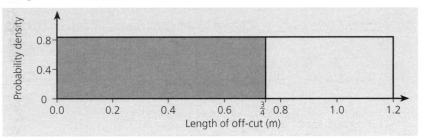

Exploration 22.2

Using the density function

Use the density function of the diagram showing the smoothed relative frequency density, above, to estimate the following proportions.

a) $0.3 \le x \le 0.6$ **b)** $x \ge 0.9$ **c)** $x < 0.8$

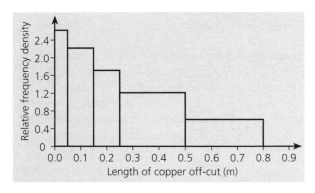

Distribution function

The plumbing department of the store sells copper pipe cut to any required length. There is no 'minimum length' policy. However, at the end of every day, the employee responsible for cutting copper pipe puts lengths he feels are unsaleable into a waste container. An examination of the container revealed a relative frequency histogram of the lengths as shown here.

Exploration 22.3

Using the relative frequency histogram

Use the relative frequency histogram above to calculate the following proportions of pipe lengths, x m.

a) $0 \le x \le 0.05$ **b)** $0.25 \le x \le 0.5$ **c)** $0.05 \le x \le 0.25$

A model for the probability density function of the length of copper pipe off-cuts is given in this diagram. The model proposed is a straight line joining the points with coordinates (0, 2.5) and (0.8, 0). Calculate the area between the density function and the horizontal axis. This area is equal to 1. Why?

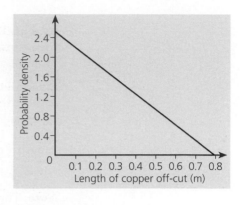

Interpreting the results

Since the density function is a straight line, it is relatively simple to find its equation. Using $y = mx + c$, the density function, $f(x)$, is:

$$f(x) = -\frac{2.5}{0.8}x + 2.5$$

and simplifying this gives: $f(x) = 2.5 - 3.125x \quad 0 \leq x \leq 0.8$

The area between the density function and the horizontal axis can be found by integrating $f(x)$ between $x = 0$ and $x = 0.8$.

$$\begin{aligned}
\text{Area} &= \int_0^{0.8}(2.5 - 3.125x)\,dx \\
&= \left[2.5x - 3.125 \times \tfrac{1}{2}x^2\right]_0^{0.8} \\
&= (2.0 - 1.0) - 0 = 1.0
\end{aligned}$$

Integration is used to find the area under a density function. Integration is used to find areas and hence to find probabilities with many density functions. This is because few density functions produce shapes with areas that can accurately be found by other methods. Evaluating integrals can be a time-consuming, tedious, difficult process. However, it is possible to address these issues by using the **cumulative probability distribution function**.

You may recall that the concept of a distribution function:

$$F(x) = P(X \leq x)$$

was introduced in Chapter 20, *Discrete probability distributions*. In the same way, we can use this concept for continuous random variables. There is a difference between the approach adopted for a discrete random variable, such as one which is binomially distributed, and the variables under discussion now. That difference is in the way that the cumulative probabilities are evaluated. Rather than adding up probabilities of consecutive events, we use integration. For example, the probability that the length of an off-cut of copper pipe is less than x m is the area under the density function between 0 and x m. This area can be found, using integration, as:

$$\begin{aligned}
P(X \leq x) &= \int_0^x(2.5 - 3.125x)\,dx \\
&= \left[2.5x - 3.125 \times \tfrac{1}{2}x^2\right]_0^x \\
&= 2.5x - \frac{3.125}{2}x^2
\end{aligned}$$

Note that this is the same integral as was needed to show that the total area under the curve was equal to 1.

Note: The standard notation for the distribution function is to use a capital letter, $F(x)$.

Now that the form of the distribution function for the length of copper off-cuts has been found, there should be no need to do any more integration to evaluate probabilities. Some quite high level mathematics has been used to develop $F(x)$ and it is reasonable to question the validity of the proposed model. In Exploration 22.3, you calculated proportions of off-cuts in particular ranges of lengths. What are the estimates of those proportions suggested by the model?

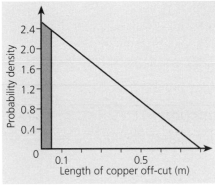

a) The first proportion you calculated can be estimated by:

$$P(0 \leq x \leq 0.05)$$

which is available directly from the distribution function as:

$$F(0.05) = 2.5x - \frac{3.125}{2}x^2 \quad \text{for } x = 0.05$$
$$= 2.5 \times 0.05 - \frac{3.125}{2} \times 0.05^2$$
$$\approx 0.121$$

which compares with the proportion, obtained from the relative frequency histogram, $2.6 \times 0.05 \approx 0.13$.

b) The second proportion:

$$P(0.25 \leq x \leq 0.5)$$

can also be found using the distribution function as a difference between two cumulative proportions.

$$P(0.25 \leq x \leq 0.5) = P(x \leq 0.5) - P(x \leq 0.25)$$
$$= F(0.5) - F(0.25)$$
$$\approx 0.8594 - 0.5273$$
$$= 0.332$$

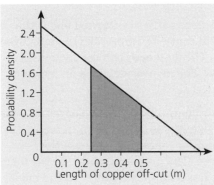

This compares with, $1.2 \times (0.5 - 0.25) = 0.3$, from the histogram.

c) The third proportion can be found in a similar way:

$$P(0.05 \leq x \leq 0.25) = F(0.25) - F(0.05)$$
$$= 0.5273 - 0.1211$$
$$\approx 0.406$$

The relative frequency was $2.2 \times (0.15 - 0.05) + 1.7 \times (0.25 - 0.15) = 0.39$.

The table below summarises the observed relative frequencies and the probabilities expected by the proposed model.

Length, x m	Relative frequency	Probability
$0.0 \leq x \leq 0.05$	0.13	0.12
$0.25 \leq x \leq 0.5$	0.3	0.33
$0.05 \leq x \leq 0.25$	0.39	0.41

There appears to be reasonable agreement between the model and the observed data. What do you think is the probability of the length of an off-cut of pipe being less than −0.5 m? Clearly, it is impossible for the length of the pipe to be negative. This has implications for the value of the distribution function for negative values of x. The distribution function, under these circumstances, must be zero, i.e:

$F(x) = 0$ when $x < 0$

According to the density function model proposed, what is the probability of getting an off-cut of length less than 1.5 m? Since no off-cuts are longer than 0.8 m, this probability must be 1, i.e:

$F(x) = 1$ when $x > 0.8$

These considerations lead to the **full definition** of the distribution function for the length of copper pipes.

$$F(x) = \begin{cases} 0 & \text{when } x < 0 \\ 2.5x - \frac{3.125}{2}x^2 & \text{when } 0 \le x \le 0.8 \\ 1 & \text{when } x > 0.8 \end{cases}$$

Exploration 22.4

Defining the distribution function

Try giving a full definition of the distribution function for the length of off-cuts of wood.

Median and mode

The general manager of the DIY store is rather concerned about the quantity of pipe going into the waste container. She asks the employee what the average length of pipe is. The employee said he thought it was a bit less than $\frac{1}{4}$ m. Is he right? The answer depends on which average he was giving.

The **mode** is the length which occurs most often. The relative frequency histogram suggests that lengths less than 0.05 m occur relatively more often than other lengths, since this is where the relative frequency density is greatest. The proposed model, in the form of the probability density function, has a similar feature. In the model the density function takes its largest value at $x = 0$. This suggests that zero is the mode. It does not appear that this is the average being quoted by the employee.

The **median** is the middle length, i.e. the length of pipe such that half the pipes are longer and half are shorter. This suggest that:

$P(X \le \text{median}) = \frac{1}{2}$

or, in terms of the distribution function:

$F(\text{median}) = \frac{1}{2}$

This leads to the quadratic equation:

$2.5 \times \text{median} - \frac{3.125}{2} \times (\text{median})^2 = \frac{1}{2}$

The equation can be rearranged into:

$1.5625 \times (\text{median})^2 - 2.5 \times \text{median} + 0.5 = 0$

What is the solution of the equation? Most quadratic equations have two solutions and this is no exception. Its solutions are:

median ≈ 1.366 or 0.234

but only one of these values is possible. Since no pipe length is more than 0.8 m, the 1.366 m length is not possible. Hence:

median ≈ 0.234 m

This suggests that the employee *could* have been referring to the median. A glance at the table on page 447 suggests that this is not an unreasonable value for the median. The table indicates that the relative frequency for lengths between 0 m and 0.25 m is $(0.13 + 0.39)$ and is just over $\frac{1}{2}$.

Example 22.1

A refined model is proposed for the distribution of lengths of the copper pipe off-cuts. The density function is:

$$f(x) = \frac{a}{(x+1)^2} - 1.5625 \quad \text{when } 0 \le x \le 0.8$$

a) *What is the value of a?*
b) *Obtain the full definition for the distribution function, $F(x)$.*
c) *Use your distribution function to estimate the following probabilities.*

   i) $P(0 \le x \le 0.05)$
   ii) $P(0.25 \le x \le 0.5)$
   iii) $P(0.05 \le x \le 0.25)$

d) **i)** *Write down the mode.*
   ii) *Show that the median is one of the roots of the equation:*
   $1.5625x^2 - 3x + 0.5 = 0$
   and hence identify the median of the model.

Solution

a) *If $f(x)$ is a density function for this continuous random variable, then the integral of $f(x)$ over the range $x = 0$ to $x = 0.8$ must equal 1. Hence:*

$$\int_0^{0.8} \left(\frac{a}{(x+1)^2} - 1.5625 \right) dx = 1$$

Integrating produces:

$$\left[-\frac{a}{(x+1)} - 1.5625x \right]_0^{0.8} = 1$$

Evaluating, by putting in the limits:

$$\left(-\frac{a}{1.8} - 1.5625 \times 0.08 \right) - \left(-\frac{a}{1} \right) = 1$$

$$\Rightarrow -\frac{a}{1.8} - 1.25 + a = 1$$

Rearranging produces:
$a = 5.0625$

b) *There are three parts to the full definition of $F(x)$.*
   For $x < 0$: $F(x) = 0$
   For $x > 0.8$: $F(x) = 1$

For x between 0 and 0.8:

$$F(x) = \int_0^x \left(\frac{5.0625}{(x+1)^2} - 1.5625 \right) dx$$

$$= \left[-\frac{5.0625}{(x+1)} - 1.5625x \right]_0^x$$

$$= \left(-\frac{5.0625}{(x+1)} - 1.5625x \right) - \left(-\frac{5.0625}{1} \right)$$

$$= 5.0625 - 1.5625x - \frac{5.0625}{(x+1)}$$

c) **i)** $P(0 \le x \le 0.05) = F(0.05) \approx 0.163$

ii) $P(0.25 \le x \le 0.5) = F(0.5) - F(0.25)$
$$\approx 0.9063 - 0.6219$$
$$\approx 0.284$$

iii) $P(0.05 \le x \le 0.25) = F(0.25) - F(0.05)$
$$\approx 0.6219 - 0.1629$$
$$\approx 0.459$$

d) **i)**   *A sketch of the density function may help to identify the mode. A graphics calculator might help to produce a sketch like this.*
This suggests that the mode is 0.0 metres.

ii)   *The median is the value of x which satisfies:*
$$F(x) = \tfrac{1}{2}$$
Hence:
$$5.0625 - 1.5625x - \frac{5.0625}{1+x} = 0.5$$
Subtracting 0.5 gives:
$$4.5625 - 1.5625x - \frac{5.0625}{1+x} = 0$$
Multiplying by $(1 + x)$ *gives:*
$4.5625(1 + x) - 1.5625x(1 + x) - 5.0626 = 0$
Expanding and collecting like terms:
$3x - 1.5625x^2 - 0.5 = 0$
Rearranging gives the quadratic equation:
$1.5625x^2 - 3x + 0.5 = 0$
as required.
The solutions to these equations are x = 1.736 or 0.1844.
Hence the median is 0.184 metres.

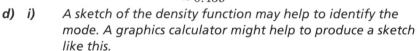

Probability density vs Length of off-cut (m)

EXERCISES

22.1 CLASSWORK

1 The table shows the take-home pay for a group of 1000 people.

Pay : £ x	Frequency
$0 \le x < 25$	41
$25 \le x < 50$	43
$50 \le x < 75$	51
$75 \le x < 125$	142
$125 \le x < 200$	231
$200 \le x < 275$	212
$275 \le x < 350$	175
$350 \le x < 425$	105

a) Illustrate these data in a relative frequency histogram. Use your histogram to estimate the proportion of people whose pay lies between £150 and £250.
b) Devise a model for your histogram in the form of a probability density function.
c) Use your model to estimate the probability of someone having take-home pay between £150 and £250.

2 The relative frequency of occurrence of a random variable, X, is modelled by the probability density function:

$$f(x) = \begin{cases} a(1-x) & \text{when } 0 \le x \le 1 \\ 0 & \text{for all other values of } x \end{cases}$$

where a is constant.
a) Calculate the value of a.
b) Derive the cumulative distribution function of X.
c) Determine the median of X.
d) Calculate the probability that X lies between 0.3 and 0.7.

3 The money, £x, set aside each week by a small company for future investment is modelled using the density function, $f(x)$, where:

$$f(x) = \begin{cases} k(1-0.001x) & \text{when } 0 \le x \le 1000 \\ 0 & \text{for all other values of } x \end{cases}$$

a) Calculate the value of the constant k.
b) Sketch the density function and state the modal amount of money set aside each week.
c) Obtain the distribution function, $F(x)$, and use it to estimate:
   i) $P(0 \le x \le 200)$ ii) $P(x > 400)$ iii) the median.

4 A random variable, X, has probability density function:

$$f(x) = \begin{cases} kx^2(1-x) & \text{when } 0 \le x \le 1 \\ 0 & \text{for all other values of } x \end{cases}$$

a) Determine the value of the constant k.
b) Sketch $f(x)$ and state the mode of X.
c) Calculate the distribution function $F(x)$.
d) Using your calculator, determine the median.

5 A continuous random variable, T, has probability density function:

$$f(t) = \begin{cases} at & \text{when } 0 \le t \le 8 \\ 8a & \text{when } 8 < t \le 9 \\ 0 & \text{elsewhere} \end{cases}$$

a) Sketch $f(t)$.
b) Determine the value of the constant a.
c) Obtain the distribution function $F(t)$.
d) Determine the median value of T.
e) Calculate the probability $P(t > 7)$.

6 A model for the relative frequency of a continuous random variable, X, is proposed as:

$$f(x) = \begin{cases} ax & \text{when } 0 < x \le 2 \\ a(4-x) & \text{when } 2 < x \le 4 \\ 0 & \text{elsewhere} \end{cases}$$

a) Sketch the graph of $f(x)$ and state the mode.
b) Determine the value of the constant a.
c) Obtain the distribution function $F(x)$.
d) Estimate the relative frequency for the event: $1 < X < 3$.

7 Observations are made on a random variable, X. The table records 170 observations.

Observation	Frequency
$0 \leq x < 2$	4
$2 \leq x < 4$	20
$4 \leq x < 6$	26
$6 \leq x < 8$	48
$8 \leq x < 10$	72

a) Illustrate these data in a relative frequency histogram.
b) Use your histogram to estimate the proportion of observations lying between 3 and 7.
c) Devise a model for the histogram in the form of a density function.
d) Use your model to estimate the probability that an observation lies between 3 and 7.

EXERCISES

22.1 HOMEWORK

1 The table shows the age, in years, of a group of 4000 sports cars owned by members of an international enthusiasts' club.

Age, x years	Number of cars
$16 \leq x < 18$	450
$18 \leq x < 21$	499
$21 \leq x < 24$	507
$24 \leq x < 27$	588
$27 \leq x < 30$	601
$30 \leq x < 32$	463
$32 \leq x < 34$	389
$34 \leq x < 36$	503

a) Display the information in a relative frequency histogram.
b) Use your histogram to estimate the proportion of cars which are between 25 and 35 years old.
c) Determine a probability density function to model your histogram.
d) Use your model to estimate the probability of a randomly selected car being between 35 and 25 years old.

2 A group of 165 people were asked to record the time, t hours, since they last ate a meal. The results are shown in the table below.

Time, t hours	Number of people
$0 \leq t < 2$	41
$2 \leq t < 4$	35
$4 \leq t < 8$	52
$8 \leq t < 12$	29
$12 \leq t < 16$	8

a) Display the information in a relative frequency histogram.
b) Use your histogram to estimate the proportion of people who had last eaten between five and ten hours ago.
c) Devise a density function to model the relative frequency.
d) Use your model to estimate the probability of a randomly selected person having last eaten between five and ten hours ago.

3   A random variable, T, may be modelled using the density function:

$$f(t) = \begin{cases} b(1+t) & \text{when } 1 \le t \le 3 \\ 0 & \text{for all other values of } t \end{cases}$$

a) Sketch the graph of $f(t)$.
b) Determine the value of the constant, b.
c) Obtain the distribution function, $F(t)$.
d) Calculate the probability $P(t > 2)$.

4   A random variable, X, is modelled using the density function:

$$f(x) = \begin{cases} b & \text{when } 0 \le x \le 20 \\ \dfrac{b(40 - x)}{20} & \text{when } 20 < x \le 40 \\ 0 & \text{elsewhere} \end{cases}$$

a) Sketch the graph of $f(x)$ and determine the value of b.
b) Calculate the median of x.

5   A survey is conducted of makers of 'home-produced' jam. The quantity, X, of jam left over after filling all the 500 g jars available is recorded. The following model for the density function is proposed.

$$f(x) = \begin{cases} k(1 - 0.002x) & \text{when } 0 \le x \le 500 \\ 0 & \text{elsewhere} \end{cases}$$

a) Determine the value of the constant, k.
b) Sketch the density function and state the modal value.
c) Obtain the distribution function, $F(x)$.
d) Use $F(x)$ to determine:
   i) $P(0 \le x \le 100)$ ii) $P(100 \le x \le 200)$
e) Write down the median and confirm your answer using the distribution function.

6   I use the following density function to model my journey time, t hours, to work.

$$f(t) = \begin{cases} kt^2 & \text{when } 0.1 \le t \le 0.25 \\ 0.25k(0.5 - t) & \text{when } 0.25 < t \le 0.5 \\ 0 & \text{elsewhere} \end{cases}$$

a) Sketch $f(t)$ and determine the value of the constant, k.
b) Write down the mode.
c) Estimate the probability that my journey takes:
   i) more than 15 minutes,   ii) between 12 and 24 minutes.

7   The monthly fuel consumption, X, in thousands of litres, of a road haulage company may be modelled by the density function:

$$f(x) = \begin{cases} \dfrac{k}{x^2} & \text{when } 2 \le x \le 4 \\ 0 & \text{elsewhere} \end{cases}$$

a) Sketch $f(x)$ and determine the value of the constant, k.
b) Determine the distribution function $F(x)$.
c) Use $F(x)$ to estimate the probabilities:
   i) $P(x > 3.5)$ ii) $P(x < 2.5)$.
d) Determine the median and quartiles of the fuel consumption; hence write down the quartile spread.
e) Find the level of consumption exceeded, on average, in only one month in ten.

EXPECTED VALUE

We have already used the concept of the expected value of a random variable. The focus was on discrete variables and its expected value was the same as the mean:

$$\text{mean} = E(X) = \sum_{\text{all } x} x\, P(x)$$

for discrete variables.

In the case of continuous variables, the mean is similarly defined as the expected value. The difference is that summation is replaced by integration, and probability is replaced by probability density:

$$\text{mean} = E(X) = \int_{\text{all } x} x\, f(x)\, dx$$

for continuous variables.

In the case of the copper pipe off-cuts, the employee may have given his general manager his estimate of the mean. Recall that the density function for the length of the off-cuts is:

$$f(x) = \begin{cases} 2.5 - 3.125x & 0 \le x \le 0.8 \\ 0 & \text{elsewhere} \end{cases}$$

Hence, the mean, μ, for this model is found by integration.

$$\text{mean length of pipe, } \mu = \int_0^{0.8} x(2.5 - 3.125x)\, dx$$

$$= \int_0^{0.8} \left(2.5x - 3.125x^2\right) dx$$

$$= \left[2.5 \times \frac{x^2}{2} - 3.125 \times \frac{x^3}{3}\right]_0^{0.8}$$

$$= 0.267$$

Thus, this average, the mean, is a bit more than $\frac{1}{4}$ m.

Exploration 22.5

Using integration to find the mean length

Try using integration to find the mean length of timber off-cut for the model shown in the diagram on page 445.

Variance

You may recall that one of the measures, variance, associated with spread can be defined in expectation terms:

$$\text{Var}(X) = \text{E}(X^2) - \mu^2$$

For a continuous random variable, calculation of the expected value of the square, $\text{E}(X^2)$, involves integration:

$$\text{E}(X^2) = \int_{\text{all } x} x^2 \text{f}(x)\,dx$$

Hence, the variance of the lengths of pipe off-cuts according to the model is:

$$\text{variance} = \int_0^{0.8} x^2 (2.5 - 3.125x)\,dx - 0.267^2$$

$$= \left[2.5 \times \frac{x^3}{3} - 3.125 \times \frac{x^4}{4} \right]_0^{0.8} - 0.267^2$$

$$= 0.1067 - 0.0711 = 0.0356$$

Exploration 22.6

Calculating the variance

Try calculating the variance of the lengths of timber off-cuts according to the model of the histogram on page 445.

Example 22.2

The DIY store employs a customer information assistant on Saturdays. The assistant offers customers advice about the location of goods in the store. The general manager is interested in the time the assistant spends answering customers' enquiries. A model for the time is proposed. Here is a diagrammatic representation of the model.

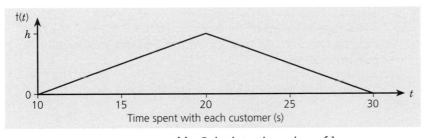
Time spent with each customer (s)

a) *Study the diagram and, without any calculation, estimate each of the following averages.*
  i) *modal time*
  ii) *median time*
  iii) *mean time*

b) *Calculate the value of h.*
c) *i)* *Show that for $10 \le t \le 20$, the probability density function, $\text{f}(t)$, has the equation: $\text{f}(t) = 0.01t - 0.1$.*
   ii) *Find the form of $\text{f}(t)$ for $20 \le t \le 30$.*
d) *Use your expressions for $\text{f}(t)$ to determine:*
   i) *the mean,*   *ii)* *the standard deviation,*
   of the constant times as indicated by the model.

Solution
a) *i)* *The modal time is where the density function takes its greatest value. This is for 20 seconds.*
   ii) *The density function is symmetric about $t = 20$. This indicates that the area under the function is divided into two equal parts at $t = 20$. Hence, the median is 20 seconds.*

iii) *The symmetry of the density function suggests that the mean may also be 20 seconds.*

b) *The area under the function must be equal to 1. The shape is a triangle and its area can be found from 'half base × height'. Hence, the area is:*

$\frac{1}{2} \times 20 \times h = 1$

$\Rightarrow h = 0.1$

c) i) *Between $t = 10$ and $t = 20$, the density function is linear passing through points with coordinates (10, 0) and (20, 0.1). The gradient of the line representing $f(t)$ is:*

$$\frac{0.1}{20 - 10} = 0.01$$

Hence, $f(t)$ is of the form: $f(t) = 0.01t + constant$
The constant can be found from either of the points through which the line passes, e.g. finding it for (10, 0) suggests:
$0 = 0.01 \times 10 + constant$
which implies that the constant is −0.1. Check by finding the constant for the line through (20, 0.1). Hence:
$f(t) = 0.01t - 0.1$ when $10 \le t \le 20$.

ii) *Between $t = 20$ and $t = 30$, $f(t)$ is linear and passes through points (20, 0.1) and (30, 0). The gradient is:*

$$\frac{-0.1}{30 - 20} = -0.01$$

Hence, $f(t)$ is of the form: $f(t) = -0.01t + constant$
Ensuring that the line passes through (20, 0.1), say, implies that:
$0.1 = -0.01 \times 20 + constant$
This suggests that the constant is 0.3. Hence:
$f(t) = -0.01t + 0.3$ when $20 \le t \le 30$.

d) i) *The mean can be calculated from:*

$$\int_{\text{all } t} t\,f(t)\,dt$$

The range of values of t is from $t = 10$ to $t = 30$. But, the form of t changes at $t = 20$ and this must be taken into account in the integral. So:

$$\text{mean} = \int_{10}^{20} t(0.01t - 0.1)\,dt + \int_{20}^{30} t(0.3 - 0.01t)\,dt$$

$$= \left[0.01 \times \frac{t^3}{3} - 0.1 \times \frac{t^2}{2}\right]_{10}^{20} + \left[0.3 \times \frac{t^2}{2} - 0.01 \times \frac{t^3}{3}\right]_{20}^{30}$$

$$= 8.333 + 11.667$$

$$= 20$$

*as anticipated in **a**).*

ii) *The standard deviation may be found from the variance.*

$$\text{variance} = \int_{10}^{20} t^2(0.01t - 0.1)\,dt + \int_{20}^{30} t^2(0.3 - 0.01t)\,dt - 20^2$$

$$= \left[0.01 \times \frac{t^4}{4} - 0.1 \times \frac{t^3}{3}\right]_{10}^{20} + \left[0.3 \times \frac{t^2}{2} - 0.01 \times \frac{t^4}{4}\right]_{20}^{30} - 400$$

$$= 141.667 + 275 - 400$$

$$= 16.667$$

Hence, the standard deviation is $\sqrt{16.667} \approx 4.08$.

Rectangular distribution

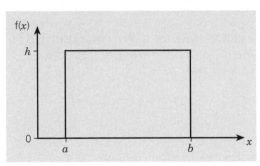

The model proposed for the length of timber off-cuts is an example of a **rectangular probability distribution**. It is characterised by a density function which resembles a rectangle.

Consider a random variable which is rectangularly distributed on $a \leq x \leq b$. The density function is a constant, h, for this set of values of x. The area of the rectangle must be 1, hence:

$$h \times (b - a) = 1$$

which implies that the **density function** is:

$$f(x) = h = \frac{1}{b-a} \quad \text{when } a \leq x \leq b.$$

The mean value of X is:

$$
\begin{aligned}
E(x) &= \int_a^b x\, f(x)\, dx \\
&= \int_a^b x \times \frac{1}{b-a}\, dx \\
&= \left[\frac{1}{b-a} \times \frac{x^2}{2} \right]_a^b \\
&= \frac{1}{b-a} \left(\frac{b^2}{2} - \frac{a^2}{2} \right) \\
&= \frac{1}{2(b-a)} \left(b^2 - a^2 \right) \\
&= \frac{1}{2(b-a)} (b-a)(b+a) \\
&= \tfrac{1}{2}(b+a)
\end{aligned}
$$

The variance is:

$$
\begin{aligned}
\int_a^b x^2 \times \frac{1}{b-a}\, dx - \left(\frac{b+a}{2} \right)^2 &= \left[\frac{1}{b-a} \times \frac{x^3}{3} \right]_a^b - \frac{(b+a)^2}{4} \\
&= \frac{1}{3(b-a)} \left(b^3 - a^3 \right) - \frac{(b+a)^2}{4} \\
&= \frac{1}{3(b-a)} (b-a)\left(b^2 + ab + a^2 \right) - \frac{b^2 + 2ab + a^2}{4} \\
&= \frac{b^2 + ab + a^2}{3} - \frac{b^2 + 2ab + a^2}{4} \\
&= \frac{4\left(b^2 + ab + a^2 \right) - 3\left(b^2 + 2ab + a^2 \right)}{12} \\
&= \frac{b^2 - 2ab + a^2}{12} \\
&= \frac{(b-a)^2}{12}
\end{aligned}
$$

Exploration 22.7

Check your results

Check your values for the mean and variance which you calculated in Explorations 22.4 and 22.5. The rectangular distribution for the timber off-cuts has $a = 0$, $b = 1.2$ hence:

$$\text{mean} = \frac{1.2 + 0}{2} = 0.6 \text{ metres}$$

and variance $= \dfrac{(1.2 + 0)^2}{12} = 0.12$

Note: $X \sim \text{Rect}(a, b)$ indicates that the random variable, X, is rectangularly distributed on $a \le x \le b$.

Triangular distribution

Adding together two independent observations of a uniformly distributed variate results in a triangularly distributed variate. The relationship between the means of the distributions and the relationship between the variances of the distributions is comforting.

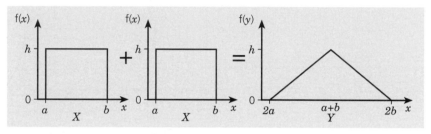

If $X \sim \text{Rect}(a, b)$ and X_1, X_2 are independent observations on X, then the distribution of $Y = X_1 + X_2$ is a triangular distribution symmetric about $y = (a + b)$ as shown in the diagram.

The mean of Y is μ_Y where:

$$\mu_Y = \mu_X + \mu_X = \tfrac{1}{2}(a + b) + \tfrac{1}{2}(a + b) = (a + b)$$

and the variance of Y is $\sigma_Y{}^2$ where:

$$\sigma_Y{}^2 = \sigma_X{}^2 + \sigma_X{}^2 = \frac{(b - a)^2}{12} + \frac{(b - a)^2}{12} = \frac{(b - a)^2}{6}$$

Example 22.3

A model for the distribution of length of time, in minutes, it takes a customer of the DIY store to pay for purchases has density function:

$$f(t) = At(8 - 3t) \quad \text{when } 0 \le t \le 2\tfrac{2}{3}$$

a) *Calculate the value of A.*
b) *Sketch a graph of the density function.*
c) *Calculate the mean time to pay for purchases, as indicated by the model.*
d) *What is the standard deviation of the time?*
e) *Estimate the probability that it takes a customer longer than two minutes to pay.*

Solution

a) The area under the density function must be 1. Hence:

$$\int_0^{2\frac{2}{3}} At(8-3t)\,\mathrm{d}t = 1$$

Expanding and integrating gives:

$$A\left[4t^2 - t^3\right]_0^{2\frac{2}{3}} = 1$$

Evaluating: $\frac{256}{27}A = 1 \Rightarrow A = \frac{27}{256}$

b)

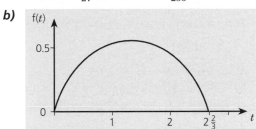

c) The mean is:

$$\int_0^{2\frac{2}{3}} t \times \frac{27}{256} t(8-3t)\,\mathrm{d}t = \frac{27}{256}\left[\frac{8t^3}{3} - \frac{3t^4}{4}\right]_0^{2\frac{2}{3}}$$
$$= 1.333$$

Note: *We might have found this value without integration, basing our argument on symmetry.*

d) To calculate the standard deviation, we need to find the variance.

$$\int_0^{2\frac{2}{3}} t^2 \times \frac{27}{256}t(8-3t)\,\mathrm{d}t - (1.333)^2 = \frac{27}{256}\left[4t^4 - \frac{3t^5}{5}\right]_0^{2\frac{2}{3}} - (1.333)^2$$
$$= 2.1333 - 1.7778$$
$$\approx 0.3556$$

Hence the standard deviation of times is $\sqrt{0.3556} \approx 0.596$ minutes.

e) $P(T>2) = \int_2^{2\frac{2}{3}} \frac{27}{256}t(8-3t)\,\mathrm{d}t$

$$= \frac{27}{256}\left[4t^4 - t^3\right]_2^{2\frac{2}{3}}$$
$$\approx 0.156$$

EXERCISES

22.2 CLASSWORK

1 The density function for a random variable, X, is given by:

$$f(x) = \begin{cases} \dfrac{k}{x^3} & \text{when } 3 \le x \le 6 \\ 0 & \text{elsewhere} \end{cases}$$

a) Calculate the value of the constant, k.
b) Calculate the mean and the variance of X.
c) Calculate the median of X.
d) What is the probability that each of two observations of X are greater than 5?

e) Three observations on X are made. Calculate the probability that exactly one observation is less than 4 and the other two are greater than 4.

2   The distribution of lengths, in cm, of off-cuts of wood is modelled as a rectangular distribution, Rect(5, 10).

a) Write down the mean length and determine the variance of the length.

b) Three randomly chosen off-cuts are measured. Calculate the probability that at least two of them are more than 8 cm.

3   The random variable, X, is distributed rectangularly:

$$X \sim \text{Rect}\left(-\frac{1}{2}\pi, \frac{1}{2}\pi\right)$$

a) Calculate the mean of X.

b) Calculate the variance of X.

c) Determine the distribution function, $\text{F}(x)$.

4   A random variable, T, is modelled using the density function:

$$\text{f}(t) = \begin{cases} k(7-2t) & \text{when } 0 \le t \le 3 \\ 0 & \text{elsewhere} \end{cases}$$

a) Calculate the value of k.

b) Determine the median of T.

c) Calculate the mean and variance of T.

d) Three independent observations are made on T. Estimate the probability that at least one of these is less than 2.

5   A random variable, X, is distributed rectangularly:

$$X \sim \text{Rect}(-1, 1)$$

a) Write down the density function, $\text{f}(x)$.

b) Calculate the mean and variance of X.

c) Describe the distribution of the sum, Y, of two independent observations on X.

d) Determine the density function, $\text{f}(Y)$.

e) Estimate the probability, $\text{P}(y > 0.5)$.

6   A random variable, X, has density function:

$$\text{f}(x) = \begin{cases} kx(4-x) & \text{when } 0 \le x \le 2 \\ 0 & \text{elsewhere} \end{cases}$$

a) Determine the value of the constant, k.

b) Show that the mean is 1.25.

c) Calculate the variance of X.

d) Estimate the proportion of observations on X which will be within one standard deviation of the mean.

EXERCISES

22.2 HOMEWORK

1   A random variable, T, has density function:

$$\text{f}(t) = \begin{cases} (2k)^{-1} & \text{when } 0 \le t \le 2k \\ 0 & \text{elsewhere} \end{cases}$$

a) Determine the value of the mean in terms of k.

b) Calculate the variance as a function of k.

2 A random variable, X, is rectangularly distributed:

$$X \sim \text{Rect}(a, b)$$

a) Write down the density function, $f(x)$.
b) Determine the distribution function, $F(x)$.

3 The density function for a random variable, X, is given by:

$$f(x) = \begin{cases} kx(4-x) & \text{when } 0 \le x < 4 \\ 0 & \text{elsewhere} \end{cases}$$

a) Use calculus to obtain the value of the constant, k.
b) Determine the mean of X.
c) Calculate the standard deviation of X.
d) Estimate the probability, $P(x < 1)$.

4 A random variable, X, is modelled as being rectangularly distributed:

$$X \sim \text{Rect}(a^2, 4a^2)$$

a) Write down the density function for X.
b) X represents the area of a square which is randomly generated by a computer. What is the mean area of the random square?
c) Calculate the probability that the length of the side of a square is less than $1.5a$.

5 A model for the distribution of mass, W, in grams, of grade II strawberries has density function:

$$f(w) = \begin{cases} k(30w - w^2 - 200) & \text{when } 10 \le w < 20 \\ 0 & \text{elsewhere} \end{cases}$$

where k is constant.
a) Calculate the value of k and sketch the graph of $f(w)$.
b) Calculate the mean mass of grade II strawberries.
c) Calculate the standard deviation of the mass.
d) Four strawberries are chosen at random. Calculate the probability that each weighs over 13 g.

6 A university lecturer estimates that most of her students will spend between two and five hours on a particular piece of coursework. Very few spend less than two hours and none spends in excess of five hours. She models the time, T, in hours spent using the density function:

$$f(t) = \begin{cases} kt & \text{when } 0 \le t < 2 \\ \frac{2}{3}k(5-x) & \text{when } 2 \le t \le 5 \\ 0 & \text{elsewhere} \end{cases}$$

a) Find the value of k.
b) Sketch the graph of the density function.
c) Calculate the mean and variance of T.
d) Determine the probability that a student spends more than four hours on the coursework.
e) Estimate the proportion of students who spend less than an hour on the work.

MATHEMATICAL MODELLING ACTIVITY
THE EXPONENTIAL DISTRIBUTION

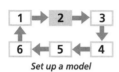
Specify the real problem

Specify the real problem

The DIY store's general manager is concerned about the queues that build up at the checkouts. She decides that she needs to collect information about the pattern of arrivals of customers. An A-level student who works at the store on Saturdays, said that the Poisson distribution was a useful model for the number of people arriving at the store in a fixed period of time. Under what circumstances is this an appropriate model?

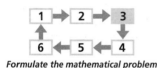
Set up a model

Set up a model

Records of the number of people entering the store on Saturdays indicate that there are, on average, 1500 during the ten hours that the store is open for trading. The manager offers this information to the student. He says that this is equivalent to an average of 150 people per hour or 2.5 people per minute.

The manager says she needs to know something about the time gap between arrivals.

Formulate the mathematical problem

Formulate the mathematical problem

The student says about 92 per cent of the times between arrivals will be one minute or less. The manager asked him how he reached that conclusion.

Solve the mathematical problem

Solve the mathematical problem

The student told her that the Poisson model indicates the probability of no person arriving in a given one minute period is $e^{-2.5}$ which is about eight per cent.

Interpret the solution

Interpret the solution

He says this is therefore the chance of waiting for more than a minute for the next person to arrive in the store. Hence, 92 per cent of times between arrivals will be less than one minute. The manager says she thinks she understands, but she really wants to know more about the distribution of the possible time gap rather than just the likelihood of the time being less than one minute.

The student says that the Poisson model can still help. If there are 2.5 people, on average every minute, then in a two-minute period there would be an average of five. This suggests that in a period of t minutes, there would be an average of $2.5t$ people. Then, if the manager follows the same argument as above:

P(time gap between arrivals $\leq t$ minutes) = 1 − P(no arrival in t minutes)
$$= 1 - e^{-2.5t}$$
He says that this can be shortened to: $P(T \leq t) = 1 - e^{-2.5t}$

where T is the random variable which models the time between people arriving at the store.

This random variable, T, is a continuous variate, and the probability, $P(T \le t)$, is a cumulative probability which implies that the distribution function for T is:

$$F(t) = 1 - e^{-2.5t} \quad \text{when } t \ge 0$$

It is quite possible to use the distribution function to determine probabilities. For example, the manager asks what the chance is that there will be less than 20 seconds between arrivals. The student says that this is equivalent to asking for the probability:

$$P(T \le \tfrac{1}{3}) = 1 - e^{-\frac{2.5}{3}} \approx 0.565$$

And the chance that the time gap is somewhere between one and two minutes? The student says this is:

$$
\begin{aligned}
P(1 \le T \le 2) &= F(2) - F(1) \\
&= \left(1 - e^{-5}\right) - \left(1 - e^{-2.5}\right) \\
&= (1 - 0.0067) - (1 - 0.0831) \\
&\approx 0.0075 \quad \text{i.e. } 7.5\%
\end{aligned}
$$

The manager asks if it is possible to use this distribution function to find the mean time gap indicated by the model. The student tells her that the density function is needed for that. Normally a distribution function, $F(t)$, is found by integrating a density function, $f(t)$. However, in this case the distribution function is available. So to get the density function required for the mean it is necessary to differentiate $F(t)$.

$$
\begin{aligned}
f(t) &= \frac{d}{dt} F(t) \\
&= \frac{d}{dt} \left(1 - e^{-2.5t}\right) \\
&= 2.5 e^{-2.5t}
\end{aligned}
$$

Hence, the density function for the time gap is:

$$f(t) = 2.5 e^{-2.5t} \quad \text{when } t \ge 0$$

thus the mean can be found:

$$\text{mean} = \int_0^\infty t \times 2.5 e^{-2.5t}\, dt$$

using integration by parts:

$$\int_0^\infty t \times 2.5 e^{-2.5t}\, dt = \left[-t e^{-2.5t}\right]_0^\infty - \left[\frac{1}{2.5} e^{-2.5t}\right]_0^\infty$$

Clearly, it is not really possible to replace t by 'infinity', however, putting a large value in place of infinity gives:

$$\left[-t e^{-2.5t}\right]_0^\infty - \left[\frac{1}{2.5} e^{-2.5t}\right]_0^\infty = [0 - 0] - \frac{1}{2.5}[0 - 1] = \frac{1}{2.5}$$

Hence, the mean time is 0.4 minute or 24 seconds.

The time gap considered here is an example of a continuous random variable which has an **exponential distribution**. The modelling assumptions:

- random events
- occurring singly and independently

- in a continuous medium
- at a uniform rate

are necessary as they are required for the discrete Poisson distribution. The random variable of the exponential distribution is the interval of continuous medium between each random event.

Where the random events occur at the uniform rate, λ per unit continuous medium, then if X is the variate measuring the gap between events:

distribution function: $F(x) = 1 - e^{-\lambda x} \quad x \geq 0$

density function: $f(x) = \lambda e^{-\lambda x} \quad x \geq 0$

mean of X: $\mu = \dfrac{1}{\lambda}$

Example 22.4

The DIY store sells tape measures supplied by one manufacturer. The tapes are supplied in various lengths: 1 m, 2 m, 5 m, 10 m and 50 m. The manufacturer claims that the number of flaws in any 250 m of the material used in making the tape measure is less than 1.

a) *Estimate the probability:*
  i) *of a 10 m tape being free from flaws,*
  ii) *of having at least one flaw in a 50 m tape,*
  iii) *of having no tape measure with a flaw in a box of 100 2-metre tapes.*
b) *A DIY enthusiast, who bought a 5 m tape complains to the manager that it was flawed. The manager asks to see it, but the customer has disposed of it. The manager is somewhat suspicious and seeks statistical advice from the student. What advice would you offer?*

Solution
a) *In order to estimate probabilities it is necessary to set up a model. It seems reasonable to consider 'flaws in tape material' as random events in a continuous medium. Provided the assumptions of singularity, independence and uniform rate of occurrence are appropriate, then an exponential model is relevant. The claim of the manufacturer might be interpreted in a 'worst case scenario' as indicating that the average number of flaws is one per 250 m. In other words, the rate of occurrence is $\frac{1}{250}$ flaw per m, i.e. 0.004 flaw per metre. Thus, the distribution function is:*

$F(x) = 1 - e^{-0.004x}, x \geq 0$

  i) P*(10 m tape being free from flaws)*
    $= P(X > 10) = e^{-0.004 \times 10} \approx 0.961$
  ii) P*(at least one flaw in a 50 m tape)*
    $= P(x \leq 50) = 1 - e^{-0.004 \times 50} \approx 0.181$
  iii) *It will help to estimate the probability of a 2 m tape being free from flaws.*
    This is $e^{-0.0004 \times 2} \approx 0.992\ 03.$
    Hence, P*(all 100 tapes free from flaws)* $\approx (0.992\ 03)^{100} \approx 0.449.$
b) *The probability that a 5 m tape is unflawed is 0.9802. Hence, the chance that a tape is flawed is about two per cent. So the student*

may well report that, under the assumption that flaws occur at an average rate of one per 250 metres, it is unlikely that a 5 m tape will contain a flaw. The manager's suspicions may be appropriate, depending on how many 5 m tapes have been sold.

CONSOLIDATION EXERCISES FOR CHAPTER 22

1   A random variable is modelled using an exponential distribution with mean equal to 1.

  a) Obtain the cumulative distribution function $F(x)$.
  b) By appropriate use of $F(x)$, determine:
   i) the median,
   ii) the probability that a random observation is between the median and the mean.

2   The life, X hours, of a high-intensity projector bulb may be modelled by an exponential distribution where the distribution is:

$$f(x) = \begin{cases} 1 - e^{-\frac{x}{10}} & \text{when } x \geq 0 \\ 0 & \text{otherwise} \end{cases}$$

  a) Calculate the median life.
  b) Calculate the probability that a bulb lasts between five and ten hours.
  c) Derive the density function.
  d) Calculate the mean and variance of the life of a bulb.

3   The time, T days, between successive notifications of a rare disease may be modelled by an exponential distribution. The mean time is observed to be 80 days. Calculate the probability that the time between two successive notifications is:

  a) less than 30 days,   **b)** between 50 and 100 days.

4   The number of breakdowns of a computer in a month may be modelled as a Poisson variate with mean equal to 2. Assume that a month has 30 days.

  a) Calculate the probability that there is no further breakdown until the 16th day, given that there was a breakdown on the first.
  b) Determine the probability that the time between breakdowns is:
   i) less than ten days,   **ii)** between ten and 20 days,
   iii) between 20 and 30 days.
  c) Given that there is no breakdown during the first ten days of one month, calculate the probability that there will be a breakdown during the next ten days.

5   The time, T, between the arrival of successive vehicles on a country road may be modelled using an exponential variate with $\lambda = 0.01$ per second.

  a) Calculate the mean and variance of T.
  b) A heavily laden pedestrian tries to cross the road. She sets off just as one vehicles passes. Assume that, unhindered, she would take 50 seconds to cross the road. Calculate the probability that she succeeds before another vehicle appears.

6 The probability that at least t metres of curtain material is free from flaws is $e^{-\frac{t}{a}}$.

   a) Find the density function for the flaw-free length of material.
   b) Prove that the mean length is a metres.
   c) If the mean length is 15 m, what is the probability that there is a 30 m length free of flaws?

7 The density function for a random variable, X, is:

$$f(x) = \begin{cases} \frac{1}{2} - \frac{1}{8}x & \text{when } 0 \le x \le b \\ 0 & \text{otherwise} \end{cases}$$

   a) Calculate the value of b.
   b) Find the mean and variance of X.
   c) Sketch the density function and state the modal value of X.
   d) Determine the median and the quartiles of X.

8 A random variable, T, may be modelled using the density function:

$$f(t) = \begin{cases} k(1-t^2) & \text{when } -1 \le t < 1 \\ 0 & \text{otherwise} \end{cases}$$

   a) Calculate k and sketch the graph of $f(t)$.
   b) Determine the distribution function for T.
   c) Calculate the probabilities:
      i) $P(X > \frac{1}{2})$ **ii)** $P(-\frac{1}{2} < X < \frac{1}{2})$
   d) Determine the mean and variance of X.

9 A random variable, X, may be modelled using the rectangular distribution:

   $X \sim \text{Rect}(5,10)$

   a) Write down the mean and variance of X.
   b) Determine the mean and variance of the sum of two independent observations on X.
   c) Calculate the probability that the sum of two independent observations on X is more than 12.

10 Lengths of off-cuts of copper piping in a builder's yard are rectangularly distributed between 5 cm and 30 cm. State the mean and variance of the lengths of off-cuts.

   Calculate the probability that, out of four randomly chosen off-cuts, exactly two are more than 20 cm long.

11 The number of telephone calls per minute received by the switchboard is modelled by a Poisson distribution with mean 15.

   Calculate the probability that the time between two successive calls is:
   a) at most 6 seconds,   **b)** between 5 and 10 seconds.

12 The lifetime, X hours, of a certain type of lightbulb in a given environment has an exponential distribution with mean lifetime 100 hours.

   a) Write down the probability density function of X and obtain the cumulative distribution function X.
   b) Find the probability that a lightbulb chosen at random lasts less than 50 hours.

13 The continuous random variable X has probability density function f given by:

$$f(x) = \begin{cases} kx^2(3-x) & 0 \le x \le 3 \\ 0 & \text{otherwise} \end{cases}$$

where k is a constant.
  i) Show that $k = \frac{4}{27}$, and find $\mathrm{E}(X)$.
  ii) Find $\mathrm{P}(X < 2)$.
  iii) Use your answer to part **ii)** to state, with a reason, whether the median of X is less than 2, equal to 2 or greater than 2.

(OCR Question 5, Specimen paper 2, 2000)

14 The lifetime (x years) of a particular make of electric light bulb is modelled by the probability density function f(x), where:

$$f(x) = \begin{cases} cx(5-x), & \text{where } c \text{ is a constant, for } 0 < x < 5 \\ 0, \text{otherwise} \end{cases}$$

a) A standard lamp has just been fitted with a new bulb. Calculate the probability that the bulb will fail within 2 years.
b) Calculate the mean and variance of the life of a bulb.

(AQA A Question 7, Specimen paper 2, 2000)

15 The continuous random variable X, which is restricted to values in the interval from 2 to 4, inclusive, has cumulative distribution function F given by:

$$\mathrm{F}(x) = ax^2 + bx, \text{ for } 2 \le x \le 4.$$

a) Giving a clear indication of your method, show that $a = \frac{1}{8}$ and $b = -\frac{1}{4}$.
b) Find the value of c such that $\mathrm{P}(X > c) = 0.88$.
c) Determine the mean value of X.

(WJEC Question 3, Specimen paper 2, 2000)

16 The continuous random variable X has probability density function f(x) given by:

$$f(x) = \begin{cases} \frac{1}{20}x^3, & 1 \le x \le 3 \\ 0, & \text{otherwise} \end{cases}$$

a) Sketch f(x) for all values of x.
b) Calculate $\mathrm{E}(X)$.
c) Show that the standard deviation of X is 0.459 to three decimal places.
d) Show that for $1 \le x \le 3$, $\mathrm{P}(X \le x)$ is given by $\frac{1}{80}(x^4 - 1)$ and specify fully the cumulative distribution function of X.
e) Find the interquartile range for the random variable X.

Some statisticians use the following formula to estimate the interquartile range:

  interquartile range = $\frac{4}{3} \times$ standard deviation

f) Use this formula to estimate the interquartile range in this case, and comment.

(EDEXCEL Question 7, Specimen paper 2, 2000)

Summary

■ The probability density function is used as a model for relative frequency.

■ If f(x) is a probability density function then:

$$\int\limits_{\text{all } x} f(x)\mathrm{d}x = 1$$

$$\text{mean} = \mathrm{E}(X) = \int\limits_{\text{all } x} x\,f(x)\mathrm{d}x$$

$$\text{variance} = \mathrm{Var}(X) = \int\limits_{\text{all } x} x^2\,f(x)\mathrm{d}x - \mu^2$$

■ The rectangular probability distribution is:

$$f(x) = \frac{1}{b-a} \quad \text{for } a \le x \le b$$

It has mean $\mathrm{E}(X) = \frac{1}{2}(a+b)$ and variance $\frac{1}{12}(b-a)^2$

■ The exponential probability distribution is:

$$f(x) = \lambda \mathrm{e}^{-\lambda x} \quad x \ge 0$$

It has a mean $\mathrm{E}(X) = \dfrac{1}{\lambda}$

Samples and populations

In this chapter we shall investigate:

■ *random sampling,*
■ *systematic, stratified, quota and cluster sampling,*
■ *sampling from distributions,*
■ *the role of distribution functions.*

We shall now find out how to explore characteristics of data where we are unable to gain access to all the data. The exploration process can be refined to improve its accuracy, to improve its efficiency, to make it easier to use; however there are drawbacks. These refinements are introduced in this chapter. Finally, we shall consider how models for data may be simulated using related processes.

SUBJECTIVE AND RANDOM SAMPLING

Have a look at the diagram and, in no more time than it takes you to finish this sentence, select one value from the display which you feel is representative of all 200 numbers.

	A	B	C	D	E	F	G	H	I	J	K	L	M	N	O	P	Q	R	S	T
1	8.8	6.6	9.2	6.0	11.1	15.3	7.0	6.0	6.0	6.8	7.9	12.2	6.9	8.1	9.8	11.1	6.2	9.0	7.1	7.7
2	6.4	8.2	6.6	7.0	9.8	6.1	12.2	6.8	6.6	6.9	9.5	8.6	8.0	6.0	7.8	6.6	11.7	7.1	11.7	12.2
3	17.4	8.0	12.8	13.8	9.5	7.4	7.7	16.6	5.8	6.5	7.0	19.3	9.9	7.9	11.4	10.8	8.3	6.4	5.7	16.2
4	8.4	7.9	7.5	7.2	11.0	19.5	6.2	9.3	13.1	15.5	7.1	9.4	10.8	10.2	10.7	13.4	7.2	12.0	9.4	9.4
5	13.6	6.8	8.2	12.6	13.1	14.2	8.4	8.4	5.9	9.0	7.8	10.1	11.8	7.2	7.2	6.7	17.2	9.7	8.9	10.4
6	18.9	11.5	6.7	6.3	7.8	5.5	6.2	13.3	14.7	15.2	13.3	7.2	6.4	8.9	9.6	10.4	6.5	13.0	10.7	7.3
7	12.1	7.7	10.7	16.0	8.5	10.8	10.3	11.4	9.6	11.9	10.7	7.7	15.7	7.3	11.1	8.5	8.1	8.4	8.1	8.6
8	8.7	8.3	6.3	6.7	9.6	8.1	6.1	11.0	10.9	6.0	15.7	8.9	6.0	8.3	15.5	8.7	8.7	17.8	11.6	5.8
9	6.5	18.5	6.5	8.6	6.7	6.8	7.9	6.1	12.2	11.2	6.8	15.8	9.6	8.6	10.5	9.2	8.7	13.2	6.2	7.8
10	9.1	11.0	8.1	8.6	7.6	9.0	7.7	8.5	11.6	8.3	10.3	8.6	7.4	7.9	6.2	8.6	9.3	7.7	12.1	15.0

You might think that was a pretty tall order, i.e. you might think you were being asked to carry out a virtually impossible task. In a way, you would be right.

There are many occasions where we need to know something about the characteristics of data but our access is restricted in some way. Consider a company that manufactures fireworks. Fireworks need a fuse that must burn for a sufficiently long time to allow the organiser to be out of the way when the firework goes off, or explodes, or ... .

A responsible manufacturer would want to use only those fuses with a sufficiently long burn time. So, how do they check the burn time of all fuses? The only sure way is to set every fuse alight and time it – but then they wouldn't have any fuses left to put on the fireworks!

They need a reliable method of **sampling** from the entire stock of fuses available. This entire stock is known as the **population** of fuses. The firework manufacturer needs to obtain a **representative sample** of fuses, i.e. a small collection of fuses, having the characteristics of the whole stock. Why would taking a sample of just one fuse and testing this not be of much benefit? Clearly, this would give no indication of the variation there might be in the times. A larger sample is needed.

Return to the data in the diagram above and select a **sample of size 6**, i.e. a sample of six items of data, that you think is **representative** of the population of 200. (Carry out your selection without doing any calculations.)

There are many thousands of possible samples, including:

  5.5   6.5   7.5   8.5   18.5   19.5

In what way do you think this sample is representative of the population? If you scan the population you will see that it only contains numbers in this range, so it is representative in one sense.

In what ways may the sample not be representative of the population? The mean of the sample may not be the same as the population mean, the variances may differ, the sample does not have a unique mode, the distributions of frequencies are not the same, ...

Reflect on your own sample. In what ways is it representative, and in what ways may it not be representative of the population?

It is rather unrealistic to expect a sample of size 6 to be wholly representative of a population, even a population of such limited size. It is more reasonable to require that the sampling method is not subjective and introduces no bias in the selection. One method of achieving this is called **random sampling**. This process gives every member of the population the same chance of being in the sample and does not exclude any sections of the population at any stage of the process.

One approach at random sampling is through **random numbers** such as those found on some calculators, on computers or in tables. This involves setting up a one-to-one correspondence between the random numbers and the members of the population, i.e. there is a unique pairing between each member of the population and a unique collection of random numbers. A fairly obvious approach, in the case of the population of 200 on the previous page, is to use three-digit random numbers and the one-to-one correspondence, as shown here.

Random number	Member of population
001	1st
002	2nd
003	3rd
...	...
...	...
200	200th

The correspondence is unique and each member has an equal chance of being selected. Selecting a sample in this way requires a list of the population. Such a list is known as a **sampling frame**. The list must be complete, up to date, and contain only the population.

CALCULATOR ACTIVITY

Exploration 23.1

The random number facility

Use the random number facility on your calculator to select a sample of size 6 from the population listed above. It might be convenient to number the members of the population so that column A contains the 1st to 10th members; column B contains the 11th to 20th members, etc.

Evaluating the results

What difficulties did you encounter in the calculator activity? Suppose your calculator produced the following random numbers:

$$0.588 \quad 0.269 \quad 0.117 \quad 0.002 \quad 0.824 \quad 0.715 \quad 0.513$$

If the method suggested is followed, 0.588 and 0.269 would correspond to the 588th and 269th members of the population. But these do not exist, so these random numbers would be ignored. Many other random numbers would also be ignored, so clearly this is an inefficient way of using random numbers.

Efficiency

There are many ways of improving the efficiency and trying to use all of the random numbers.

Casting out

In this method, the random numbers giving rise to 201, 202, 203, etc. have the 200s removed. This would produce the following results.

Random number	Remove	Position in sampling frame	Member
269	200	69th	7.9
588	400	188th	11.6
824	800	24th	7.5
117	0	117th	7.7

Grouping

An equivalent procedure which works very well if a computer or calculator is available, but is rather awkward to use manually, is to group the random numbers into, in this case, fives. This means we allow 0.001, 0.002, 0.003, 0.004, 0.005 to correspond to the first entry in the sampling frame, and 0.006, 0.007, ..., 0.010 to correspond to the second entry in the sampling frame, etc. We need to consider which random numbers will correspond to the 200th entry, since it seems as if only 0.996, 0.997, 0.998, 0.999 are available once the others have been assigned. So the 200th member of the population is associated with only four random numbers, unlike the five for every other. (A way of overcoming this is to include 0.000.)

Try to identify which members of the population would be selected using the 'grouping' approach.

Pure random sampling

You may have found that grouping was not very easy. One way of simplifying it is to divide the three-digit random number by the group size, and use the next integer (unless the result is already a whole number). This is illustrated in this table.

Random number	Divide by group size	Position in sampling frame	Member
588	$588 \div 5 = 117.6$	118th	8.9
269	$269 \div 5 = 53.8$	54th	19.5
117	$117 \div 5 = 23.6$	24th	7.5
002	$2 \div 5 = 0.4$	1st	6.6
824	$824 \div 5 = 164.8$	165th	17.2
715	$715 \div 5 = 143$	143rd	11.4
513	$513 \div 5 = 102.6$	103rd	7.0

One very real reservation about this and the previous procedure is that we have to treat the random number 000 (i.e. 0.000) in a special way and convert the random decimals from our calculator into integers. This can be overcome by using a function know as **the integer part of** ... or INT(x).

To get 588 from the random decimal 0.588 we have effectively multiplied it by 1000; the process involved here requires us to divide the result by 5. A short-cut to this is to do the multiplication ($\times 1000$)) and division ($\div 5$) in one move, i.e. to multiply the calculator random decimal by 200. For example:

$$\text{INT}(200 \times 0.588) = \text{INT}(117.6) = 117$$
and $\quad \text{INT}(200 \times 0.715) = \text{INT}(143) = 143$
and $\quad \text{INT}(200 \times 0.002) = \text{INT}(0.4) = 0$

but this does not give quite the same results. The major concern is that 0.002 corresponds to a position 'zero' in the sampling frame. This is a little difficult to work with, so a convenient alteration to the procedure is to *add one* to the result of the multiplication. This leads to the results in the following table.

Random decimal	Conversion	Position in sampling frame
0.588	$\text{INT}(200 \times 0.588 + 1)$	118th
0.269	$\text{INT}(200 \times 0.269 + 1)$	54th
0.117	$\text{INT}(200 \times 0.117 + 1)$	24th
0.002	$\text{INT}(200 \times 0.002 + 1)$	1st
0.824	$\text{INT}(200 \times 0.824 + 1)$	165th
0.715	$\text{INT}(200 \times 0.715 + 1)$	144th
0.513	$\text{INT}(200 \times 0.513 + 1)$	103rd

There is only one difference between the positions here and those found previously. This is illustrated below where 0.000 is not treated any differently.

Random decimal	Correspondence in sampling frame
0.000, 0.001. .... 0.004	1
0.005, 0.006, ..., 0.009	2
0.100, ..., 0.104	3
...	...
...	...
0.995, 0.996, 0.997, 0.998, 0.999	200

Now each member of the population has an equal chance of being in the random sample.

Sampling populations of any size

The method just described is readily adaptable to populations of other sizes. For instance, if the population has 82 members then:

INT(82 × random decimal + 1)

will generate appropriate positions in the sampling frame.

The number of places in the random decimal affects the randomness of this process. The greater the number of digits in the decimal the better. If you are dependent on a calculator which produces random three-digit decimals, it is possible to extend these to six places, nine places, ... For example, the two three-digit decimals 0.588, 0.269 can be computed as:

0.588 + (0.269 ÷ 1000) to give the six-digit decimal 0.588 269.

Random decimals with six places should be sufficient to sample from sampling frames with tens of thousands of elements.

The above discussion indicates that an efficient way of using calculator random decimals to sample from populations of size N is to use:

INT($N \times (r + r \div 1000) + 1$) where r is a three-digit random decimal.

In most practical situations, sample sizes are quite small, so duplication is not allowed in a sample. This means that if the same position in the sampling frame is selected more than once, then it is ignored on the second and subsequent occasions. In short, no repeats are allowed in small samples. For example, when using the 'casting out' manual technique of selecting a sample from the data on page 471, the first few random decimals which appear may be:

0.517   0.317   0.991.

These correspond to:

Random number	Remove	Position in frame	Member
517	400	117	7.7
317	200	117	7.7
991	800	191	7.7

The random numbers 517, 317 correspond to the same position in the sampling frame, hence 317 is ignored and only the member of the population selected by 517 is allowed. The random number 991 corresponds to a different position and so the corresponding member of the population is accepted in the sample, even though it is the same in value.

Exploration 23.2

A sample of size 10

The following is a collection of calculator random decimals.

0.431	0.214	0.143	0.596	0.475
0.423	0.270	0.606	0.313	0.309
0.928	0.378	0.851	0.238	0.734
0.200	0.190	0.525	0.933	0.278
0.064	0.821	0.209	0.888	0.808

Obtain a random sample of burn times of size 10 using:
a) casting out,
b) grouping,
c) Pure random sampling using:
   i) three decimal places,   ii) six decimal places.
Calculate the mean burn time for each sample.

Example 23.1

A shopkeeper, each year, sells 200 packets of sparklers. Each packet contains five sparklers.

Last year she had many complaints that the sparklers were difficult to light. She receives her supply of 200 packets to sell this year and decides to use a sample of five per cent of the packets to establish the proportion of sparklers which are difficult to light.
a) How would you advise the shopkeeper to undertake this task?
b) The shopkeeper obtains a sample of ten packets and finds the number of sparklers in each packet that are difficult to light. The results are:
2, 1, 5, 2, 2, 2, 2, 3, 1, 0.
What proportion of the sparklers do you estimate to be difficult to light?

Solution
a) The shopkeeper needs to establish a sampling frame. She could do this by numbering the packets: 1, 2, 3, ... , 200. Having done this she needs to obtain a random sample. She wants a sample of five per cent of the packets, so she needs ten packets in her sample. A random sample may be obtained using a random number generator, e.g. programming a calculator to identify which packets to include in the sample. The calculator could be programmed to produce the following:
$$\text{INT}(200 \times (\text{random decimal}) + 1)$$
until ten distinct numbers are obtained. Then the ten packets of sparklers can be selected. Having selected the packets, she needs to open each of them and test the contents, to see how many are difficult to light. The problem, of course is that once alight they are impossible to stop, hence the sparklers will be destroyed.
b) The sample indicates that 2 + 1 + 5 + ... + 1 + 0, i.e. 20 sparklers were difficult to light. The ten packets each had five sparklers. So, 20 sparklers out of 50 were difficult to light. This suggests that an estimate of the proportion is:
$$\frac{20}{50} \text{ or } \frac{2}{5} \text{ or } 0.4$$

EXERCISES

23.1 CLASSWORK

1 A population has N members. A calculator produces the following random decimals.

0.687, 0.802, 0.070, 0.802, 0.212, 0.974. 0.562, 0.297, 0.179, 0.395

A sample of size five is selected from a sampling frame listing the population. The position in the frame of each member of the sample is found using:
$$\text{INT}(N(r_1 + r_2 \div 1000) + 1)$$

where r_1, r_2 are consecutive three-digit random numbers. Identify which members of the frame would be selected if:

a) $N = 400$ **b)** $N = 5000$ **c)** $N = 147$ **d)** $N = 60\,000$ **e)** $N = 200\,000$.

2 Describe how you would use random numbers to select a random sample of 15 members from a population of 438 members.

3 State which of the following are subjective samples and which may be random samples.
   a) a sample of patients chosen as participants in a drug test
   b) the winners in a lottery
   c) the top Year 10 mathematics set
   d) the children whose surnames begin with B in a primary school

4 A partnership of GPs would like to obtain a sample of patients on their register to investigate their level of satisfaction with the management of the practice. Discuss the problems they would face in simply assigning random numbers to each name on their register.

5 Indicate an appropriate sampling frame for each of the following.
   a) a sample to survey local attitudes to the building of a new local supermarket on green belt land
   b) children's attitudes in a secondary school to a shortened lunch break
   c) change of a region's telephone dialling code
   d) proposed merger of two pharmaceutical companies

EXERCISES

23.1 HOMEWORK

1 A sample of 20 is to be taken from a school with 470 students. Describe how you would use random numbers to select the sample. Explain how you would ensure efficiency in your selection process.

2 It is required to sample the population of a certain town. Discuss the suitability of the following sampling frames.
   a) names in the telephone directory
   b) names on the electoral roll
   c) membership of the local civic society

3 Identify, where possible, an existing sampling frame for each of the following populations.
   a) households with telephones in the Birmingham area
   b) employees at a factory
   c) lions in Africa
   d) guests in a large hotel
   e) visitors to a free art exhibition

4 For each of the following investigations, detail the population from which the sample should be taken.
   a) proportion of people displaying an allergy to a new treatment for hay fever
   b) proportion of winners on the football pools
   c) number of households with outstanding gas accounts
   d) number of cars without a valid MOT certificate

5 A research study into prostate problems in men involved sending a questionnaire to 552 men aged over 50 who were registered with a general practice.

a) Suggest one advantage and one disadvantage of this sampling method.
b) Of the men contacted, 358 returned the questionnaire. Of these, 273 reported that they had undergone treatment for prostate problems. Obtain an estimate of the proportion of men aged over 50 who experience prostate difficulties.
c) Criticise the method of obtaining the estimate in **b)** and suggest an alternative method.

SYSTEMATIC, STRATIFIED, QUOTA AND CLUSTER SAMPLING

So far we have considered reasons why it is sometimes necessary to use a sampling procedure to obtain information about the population from which the sample is taken. Sometimes, data are obtained from an entire population, even as large as the population of people in a country. This is a **census.** Although it has the distinct advantage of presenting a complete picture of the population, a census is time-consuming and expensive to carry out. It is out of date before completion. The accuracy of the data decreases with time that elapses after the data are collected. The amount of data collected is usually so extensive that it is virtually impossible to analyse every bit of it. Often, census information is actually sampled after it has been collected in order to identify characteristics effectively.

Stratified sampling

Simple random sampling does not guarantee a **representative** sample. In random sampling any collection is possible. An approach which tries to enhance this aspect without reintroducing subjectivity is **stratified sampling**. Sub-samples are taken randomly from distinct sections or **strata** of data. The size of the sub-samples are in proportion to the size of the strata in the population.

Suppose we return to the firework scenario. The shopkeeper wants to improve her sampling procedure, so she decides to use a stratified random sampling method. Her supplier tells her that he classifies the fuses as short, medium and long. These have burn times, t seconds, such that $t < 7$, $7 \leq t < 10$, $t \geq 10$, respectively. The fuse manufacturer says that the fuses are produced in the ratio $1 : 2 : 2$.

A stratified sample would contain burn times in these ratios. Why is it not possible to have a stratified sample of size six? Clearly, the sample size should be a multiple of five.

The shopkeeper decides to take a stratified sample of ten fuses to estimate the mean burn time. So, she needs *two* short, *four* medium and *four* long burn time fuses in her sample. The sampling is to be done randomly. One approach is to generate random numbers until she has selected the two short-burn fuses, then to generate random numbers until she has selected the four medium burn times etc. This is rather inefficient. How might she improve efficiency? She could generate the random numbers, select the fuse and not reject any unless the stratum is complete.

Suppose the random numbers generated are those in the table. The fuse times selected and strata to which they belong would also be recorded in the table.

Random decimal	Position	Time	Action	Stratum
0.641	129	9.6	Keep	M
0.894	179	13.2	Keep	L
0.509	102	9.5	Keep	M
0.956	192	12.2	Keep	L
0.288	58	8.1	Keep	M
0.066	14	7.9	Keep	M
0.839	168	8.7	Reject	
0.957	192		Reject	
0.202	41	11.1	Keep	L
0.292	59	6.8	Keep	S
0.434	87	10.9	Keep	L
0.849	170	8.6	Reject	
0.935	188	6.2	Keep	S

The stratified random sample contains:

Time	Stratum
6.8, 6.2	short
9.6, 9.5, 8.1, 7.9	medium
13.2, 12.2, 11.1, 10.9	long

The mean burn time is 9.55 seconds.

Exploration 23.3

Mean burn times

Obtain a stratified random sample of fuse burn times of size 10 using your calculator to generate random decimals. Calculate the mean burn time for your sample.

Quota sampling, cluster sampling

Randomising the sampling process is highly desirable. However when the population under investigation is large or spread widely, e.g. in investigating consumer spending habits or seeking opinion from owners of cafés, it has cost and time implications. Subjective alternatives are sometimes used for pragmatic reasons. **Quota sampling** is a subjective alternative to stratified sampling.

Sub-samples must be in the appropriate proportion but the selection of the member for the sub-sample is left up to the sampler. Often the method used is on a 'first come, first in' basis.

Cluster sampling is another approach to gauging characteristics of a large, widely-spread population. A small area, often geographical, where typical members of the population are to be found is identified. Then, every member of the population is recorded in this cluster. In the case of the firework display, you might choose a firework party nearby and record the fuse burn time of all the fireworks let off at the party. Why might this sample not be representative of the population?

Exploration 23.4

Quota sampling burn times

Conduct a five per cent quota sampling survey of the burn times, starting by going down column A. Calculate the mean time of your sample. In what way do you anticipate that your sample differs from the sample obtained by anyone else conducting this survey in this way?

Systematic sampling

A very convenient form of sampling which gives every member of a population the same chance of being included *before* the process begins, but one which excludes large sections of the population the moment the process begins, is **systematic sampling**. If the sample is to contain five per cent of a population, then systematic sampling would involve selecting every 20th member of the population. If a ten per cent sample is sought then every tenth member of the population is selected. Clearly, this process effectively excludes 19 out of every 20, or nine out of every ten in the case of the ten per cent sample. However, if the first item to be included in the sample is chosen randomly then every member of the population has an equal chance of being included.

Exploration 23.5

Systematic sampling

Obtain a five per cent systematic sample of burn times using a randomly-generated start point. (You need not restrict your start point to one of the first 20 times since you can always go back to the beginning.)

Consider the situation where 21 students carry out the exploration. How likely is it that there will be at least two identical samples? Can you think of any other reasons why systematic sampling is undesirable?

EXERCISES

23.2 CLASSWORK

1   The principal of a college asks members of a statistics class to suggest an appropriate sampling method for seeking student opinion on the refurbishing of the main hall.

Proposal 1: Select every 20th student from the college's alphabetical listing of all students.
Proposal 2: Select students at random from each year's listing and in proportion to the number on the list.
Proposal 3: Simply select students as they enter the dining hall.
Proposal 4: Select students as they arrive at college, but ensure representative proportions with respect to year and to gender.

In each case identify the sampling method and list its advantages and disadvantages. Which proposal would you recommend to the principal?

2   A school has 210 sixth-formers, 30 doing arts foundation courses, 80 doing science A-Levels and the rest doing humanities A-Levels. Describe how you would obtain a ten per cent stratified sample. Explain how this differs from a simple random sample.

3 **a)** Explain briefly what is meant by a random sample.
A college has 2580 students. A survey into student attitudes to work, using a questionnaire, is being carried out. The questionnaire is to be given to a sample of 250 students. The following three methods of selecting the sample are proposed:
A: Ask for volunteers.
B: Ask every fifth student entering the college on a certain morning.
C: Use the alphabetical list of students in the college, taking every tenth student on the list.

   b) Discuss briefly the advantages and drawbacks of each of the proposed methods of selection.

   c) Explain in detail a method which could be used to obtain a random sample of 250 students from the population of the college.

4 Explain why it is often necessary to sample, and state the properties that are considered essential for a statistically acceptable sample.

   A district councillor decides to investigate the attitudes of residents on a large housing estate towards the proposed building of a new light industrial estate. If a sample of residents is to be selected, state, with reasons, the method of sampling you would recommend the councillor to use.

5 A town has a population of 60 000. The water company is interested in how many households own dishwashers.

   a) What are the advantages of a sampling method of enquiry over a census?

   b) Describe briefly how you would select a suitable sample in this situation. Your answer should include details of the sampling frame, the type of sample to be used and how you would calculate your estimate based on your sample information.

6 Return to the data on page 477 and present them in a two-part stem-and-leaf display. Estimate the mean burn time. Compare with the means obtained in the various sampling processes discussed in this chapter. How accurate do you feel the fuse manufacturer is in his ratio 1 : 2 : 2 for short : medium : long burn times?

EXERCISES

23.2 HOMEWORK

1 It is required to assess opinions about the management of a town centre shopping mall. Describe which method of sampling is used in each of the following proposals, and discuss the advantages and disadvantages of each.

   a) Give a questionnaire to the driver of every tenth car in the nearby shoppers' car park.

   b) Give a questionnaire to people emerging from the supermarket check-out, taking account of their sex and age.

   c) Give a questionnaire to anyone walking about the shopping mall who will accept one.

   d) Send a questionnaire to local residents selected from the electoral roll using random numbers.

2 Distinguish between:
   a) random and subjective sampling,
   b) random and representative sampling,
   c) random and systematic sampling.

3 A school has tickets for 48 of its students to go to an international art exhibition. There are 1200 students at the college. There are the following numbers in each year group.

Year	7	8	9	10	11	12/13
Number	200	225	224	226	150	175

If the 48 are chosen from all 1200 students, describe how you would select a representative group using:
a) pure random sampling, **b)** stratified sampling,
c) quota sampling.
State which of these methods is the most appropriate.

4 Describe, briefly, how you would obtain a representative sample of the opinion of the 5374 students at a tertiary college on having a totally non-smoking campus.

5 The total numbers of goals scored in 100 hockey matches are recorded in the table.

3	4	2	5	3	4	6	4	5	4	5	6	5	4	5	3	4	5	2	5
6	1	6	4	5	4	4	4	6	4	4	4	5	3	5	5	5	6	5	3
4	3	5	2	4	3	4	1	5	6	4	6	5	5	4	5	5	6	5	3
5	2	6	3	5	6	2	4	5	5	4	6	5	4	4	5	4	6	3	4
5	5	4	6	2	5	4	3	5	2	3	6	6	3	5	3	4	6	4	6

a) Represent the data in a stem-and-leaf diagram.
b) Calculate the mean number of goals per match.
c) **i)** Use a simple random sampling method to select a sample of size 5. Calculate the mean of the sample.
   ii) Repeat this process until you have ten sample means. Calculate the mean of the sample means.
d) **i)** Use a systematic sampling method to select a sample of size five. Calculate the mean of the sample.
   ii) Repeat this process until you have ten sample means. Calculate the mean of the sample means.
e) **i)** Use your stem-and-leaf diagram to identify three strata in the data. Use a stratified sampling procedure to select a sample of size 5. Calculate the mean of the sample.
   ii) Repeat until you have ten sample means. Calculate the mean of the sample means.
f) Comment on the results in **b)**, **c)**, **d)** and **e)**.

6 The diagram represents the number of sparklers which prove to be difficult to light in packets of five, sold by a corner shop.

	A	B	C	D	E	F	G	H	I	J	K	L	M	N	O	P	Q	R	S	T
1	2	3	1	2	3	1	2	4	1	2	0	2	3	1	2	3	1	2	4	1
2	2	0	2	3	1	2	3	1	2	4	1	2	0	2	3	1	2	3	1	2
3	4	1	3	0	2	3	1	2	3	1	2	4	2	3	0	2	3	1	2	3
4	1	2	5	2	3	1	2	3	1	2	3	1	2	0	2	3	1	2	3	1
5	2	4	1	2	0	2	3	1	2	3	1	2	4	1	2	0	2	3	1	2
6	3	1	2	4	1	3	0	2	3	1	2	3	1	2	4	1	3	0	2	3
7	1	2	3	1	2	4	2	3	1	2	3	1	2	3	1	2	0	2	3	1
8	2	3	1	2	4	1	2	0	2	3	1	2	3	1	2	4	1	2	0	2
9	3	1	2	3	1	2	4	1	2	0	2	3	1	2	3	1	2	4	1	3
10	0	2	3	1	2	3	1	2	4	2	3	0	2	3	1	2	3	1	2	5

The shopkeeper decided to use a systematic sampling procedure by opening every 20th packet and setting the contents aside for testing. He decided to use random numbers to determine which of the 20 packets he would start with. How might he do this?

Carry out the following process which represents a simulation of the experience of the shopkeeper.
a) Obtain a five per cent systematic sample by randomly choosing a starting point from the row labelled 1. Record the mean of the sample.
b) Repeat the process in a).
c) Examine the columns of data and offer a criticism of this process of sampling.

SAMPLING FROM PROBABILITY DISTRIBUTIONS ▮

Reflect on the 'sparklers' data in question 6 above. If these came from the same source as the sparklers as the shopkeeper's in Example 22.1, then 40 per cent of the sparklers are difficult to light. What probability distribution is appropriate to model the number of the sparklers which are difficult to light in packets of five?

Provided the assumptions which led to the binomial model are valid then B(5, 0.40) would be appropriate. This suggests that the data in question 6 are from this distribution. You may have noticed elements of a pattern in the systematic sample you obtained in tackling question 6. Is this pattern inevitable or is it merely a feature of the sparkler production? One way of tackling questions like this is to simulate observations of a random variable, i.e. to obtain random samples from probability distributions.

A common way of doing this makes use of the cumulative distribution function appropriate to the random variable. Then it uses random decimals to represent a cumulative probability. The observation selected is the one which corresponds to this cumulative probability. This process is analogous, in the sparkler example, to having the entire production, say 10 000 packets of sparklers, in a long line. The packets are arranged so that all those with none that are hard to light are at the front of the line, followed by those with one, then those with two etc. Then random numbers between 1 and 10 000 are generated, to select packets.

Sampling from binomial and Poisson distributions

The cumulative distribution for the random variable X where $X \sim B(5, 0.4)$, is shown in the table below.

x	0	1	2	3	4	5
$P(X \le x)$	0.077 76	0.336 96	0.682 56	0.912 96	0.989 76	1.000 00

Since there are five places of decimals in this display of the distribution function, it would be appropriate to use random five-place decimals to obtain observations of X. Suppose the following random decimals are generated.

0.306 90, 0.592 52, 0.041 96, 0.958 58

The observations corresponding to these random decimals can be found by locating the decimals on a diagram like this, which is equivalent to the cumulative distribution.

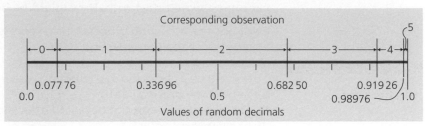

Hence:

0.306 90 corresponds to 1
0.592 52 corresponds to 2
0.041 96 corresponds to 0
0.958 58 corresponds to 4.

Exploration 23.6

Observations

Use you calculator or the random number tables in this book to obtain five observations of the random variable X where:

a) $X \sim B(5, 0.4)$,
b) $X \sim B(10, 0.2)$, (if you use the distributions tables then four-place decimals)
c) $X \sim Poi(3.2)$, (again four-place decimals are appropriate in using the tables)
d) $X \sim Poi(7.9)$.

Sampling from other distributions

Where distributions tables are not available, we can use our knowledge of the probability function and hence the cumulative probability function to obtain random samples.

Imagine you are working in a firework factory and your job is to ensure that the 'volcanoes' are standing on their base rather than lying on their side as they travel along the production line. On average, 20 per cent of the volcanoes lie on their side. Whenever you see a volcano on its side, you stand it upright and then count the number of volcanoes up to the next one lying on its side, and so on. Why might a geometric distribution be an appropriate model for this count?

From the information available, Geo(0.2) would seem to be appropriate. The distribution function can be tabulated.

x	1	2	3	4	5	
$P(X \le x)$	0.2	$1 - 0.8^2$ $= 0.36$	$1 - 0.8^3$ $= 0.488$	$1 - 0.8^4$ $= 0.5904$	$1 - 0.8^5$ $= 0.672\,32$	etc. etc.

So, a random decimal less than 0.2 corresponds to the value 1,
a random decimal between 0.2 and 0.36 corresponds to the value 2,
a random decimal between 0.36 and 0.488 corresponds to the value 3, etc.

Exploration 23.7

Finding observations

Find the observations on X, where $X \sim \text{Geo}(0.2)$, which correspond to the following decimals.

0.126 57, 0.339 93, 0.988 83, 0.515 64, 0.782 98

Example 23.2

Simulate the outcome of rolling a tetrahedral die three times using these random numbers.
482 51   735 46   821 43

Solution
The distribution function can be given in linear form as shown.
Then considering the random numbers as five-digit random decimals:
0.482 51 corresponds to the outcome 2,
0.735 46 corresponds to the outcome 3,
0.821 43 corresponds to the outcome 4.

EXERCISES

23.3 CLASSWORK

1 A trial consists of simultaneously rolling twelve fair cubical dice and counting the number of sixes obtained.
Use random numbers and the table of the appropriate distribution function to simulate an experiment which consists of 20 such independent trials.

2 The weekly number of accidents on a particular stretch of road is known to be a Poisson variate with a mean rate of 1.6. Use random numbers and distribution function tables to simulate 26 weeks' accident figures.

Calculate the mean and variance of your simulated values. Compare with the values you would expect.

3 The number of Smarties in a mini pack takes one of the values 9, 10 and 11, all of which are equally likely.
 a) Andrea always eats exactly one box of Smarties a day. Simulate the daily number of Smarties eaten by Andrea over a 28-day period.
 b) Brian always eats exactly two boxes of Smarties a day. Simulate the daily number of Smarties eaten by Brian over a 28-day period.

In each case compare the simulated totals eaten over the period with that expected.

4 As part of a factory's quality control procedures, random samples of ten items are selected from large batches and a count made of the number which are defective.
 a) When the process is operating adequately two per cent of items are defective. Simulate the counts recorded from sampling 20 batches. Use your results to then estimate the proportion that are defective.
 b) Repeat **a)**, when the process is producing 15 per cent defective items due to an unidentified malfunction.

EXERCISES

23.3 HOMEWORK

1 Use random numbers to simulate the scores obtained when a fair six-sided die is rolled 36 times.
Repeat the simulation when the die is biased such that:
$P(1) = P(2) = P(3) = P(4) = P(5) = \frac{1}{9}$ and $P(6) = \frac{4}{9}$

In each case compare your simulated results with those you would expect.

2 A trial consists of tossing two fair coins simultaneously and counting the number of heads, H, observed.

Specify completely the distribution of H.

Using random number tables, simulate 50 observations of H. Estimate the probability of a head in a single toss of one of the coins. Comment.

3 The weekly number of word-processors sold by Shop A may be modelled by a Poisson distribution with mean 5. Independently, the weekly number of word-processors sold by Shop B may also be modelled by a Poisson distribution, but with mean 4.
a) Simulate 20 weeks' sales for shop A.
b) Simulate 20 weeks' sales for Shop B
c) Simulate 20 weeks' sales for Shops A and B combined

Compare the combined results for a) and b) with those obtained in c).

4 A fair tetrahedral die is repeatedly rolled until a score of 4 is observed. If R denotes the number of rolls required, specify completely the distribution of R. Copy and complete the following probability table for R.

r	1	2	3	4	5	6	7	≥ 8
$P(R = r)$								

Hence, using random numbers, simulate 48 observations of R. Using your results construct an empirical probability table for R and compare it with the theoretical probability table.

CONSOLIDATION EXERCISES FOR CHAPTER 23

1 Explain what is meant by:
a) a stratified sample, b) a cluster sample,
c) a quota sample.

For each case outline a situation where it may be considered to be the most appropriate sampling method.

2 a) Describe how you would use the random number 48 722 obtained from a table of random digits arranged in groups of five digits to obtain a single sample from a population of 3027 members.
b) Use random numbers from tables to select a five per cent stratified sample from a population of size 360 divided into three strata of sizes 40, 120 and 200 respectively.

3 The daily demand for a particular spare part from a garage's stores is known to be a random event with an average of 2.5.
a) Use random numbers and appropriate distribution tables to simulate 50 days' demands.

b) If there are five of these spare parts in stock at the beginning of each day, use your results to estimate the probability of being out of stock.

c) Compare this estimate with that given by the appropriate probability model.

4 As part of a traffic investigation, a count, X, is made of the number of cars passing a checkpoint between each successive alternative type of motor vehicle.

a) Given that 80 per cent of vehicles passing the check point are cars, identify a possible probability model for X, stating any further assumptions that are necessary.

b) Construct a probability table for X and hence use random numbers to simulate 30 observed values of X.

5 Describe how you could obtain representative samples of the following.

a) the opinion of students, in a school, on government education policy

b) the distribution of daisies in a hockey pitch

c) the diameter of trees in a 20 acre woodland

d) the make of car driven by teachers in primary schools in Cornwall

e) the ownership of telephone answering machines in private households in Yorkshire

f) the size of carrots sold in supermarkets

g) the size of farms in Wales

6 Describe two methods by which you might be able to determine the pattern of membership of professional associations by teachers. Carry out one of these and report your findings. In what way might your findings differ from those you may have obtained using your other method?

7 Describe a method which you could use to determine ownership of computers by households in a town of about 25 000 people. Explain why you chose your approach rather than other methods.

8 Use the random decimals 0.4751, 0.8230, 0.1308 to obtain three observations for each of the following random variables.

a) $X, X \sim \mathrm{B}(12, 0.4)$

b) $Y, Y \sim \mathrm{Poi}(4.8)$

c) $Z, Z \sim \mathrm{Ber}(0.6)$

9 Use the random decimals:

0.5862, 0.1037, 0.0049, 0.8540, 0.9500

to obtain five observations from a random variable which is distributed $\mathrm{Geo}(0.1)$.

10 Describe how you could use computer-generated random decimals to simulate outcomes of rolling:

a) a tetrahedral die,

b) a cubical die,

c) an icosahedral die.

11 Describe how you might conduct a survey of the opinions of concerned people about the wearing of uniforms in school.

12 Describe how you could conduct a survey into the readability of daily newspapers.

13 **a)** Explain briefly:
  i) why it is often desirable to take samples,
  ii) what you understand by a sampling frame.
  b) State two circumstances when you would consider using:
  i) clustering, **ii)** stratification,
  when sampling from a population.
  c) Give two advantages and two disadvantages associated with quota sampling.

(ULEAC Question 10, Statistics paper 2, June 1992)

14 A school held a disco for years 9, 10 and 11 which was attended by 500 pupils. The pupils were registered as they entered the disco. The disco organisers were keen to assess the success of the event. They designed a questionnaire to obtain information from those who attended.
  a) State one advantage and one disadvantage of using a sample survey rather than a census.
  b) Suggest a suitable sampling frame.
  c) Identify the sampling unit.

(EDEXCEL Question 1, Specimen paper 2, 2000)

15 Give one example of a sample survey in each of the cases where:
  a) a stratified sample would be appropriate,
  b) a cluster sample would be appropriate.

(WJEC Question 1, Specimen paper 1, 2000)

16 Following a spell of particularly bad weather, an insurance company received 42 claims for storm damage on the same day. Sufficient staff were available to investigate only six of these claims. The others would be paid in full without investigation. The claims were numbered 00 to 41 and the following suggestions were made as to the method used to select the six. In each case six different claims are required, so any repeats would be ignored.

Method 1	Choose the six largest claims.
Method 2	Select two-digit random numbers, ignoring any greater than 41. When six have been obtained choose the corresponding claims.
Method 3	Select two-digit random numbers. Divide each one by 42, take the remainder and choose the corresponding claims (e.g. if 44 is selected claim number 02 would be chosen).
Method 4	As 3, but when selecting the random numbers ignore 84 and over.
Method 5	Select a single digit at random, ignoring 7 and over. Choose this and every seventh claim thereafter (e.g. if 3 is selected, choose claims numbered 03, 10, 17, 24, 31 and 38).

Comment on each of the methods, including an explanation of whether it would yield a random sample or not.

(AEB Question 4, Specimen paper 2, 1994)

17 Members of a public library may borrow up to four books at any one time. The number of books borrowed by a member on each visit to the library is a random variable X, with the following probability distribution.

X	0	1	2	3	4
probability	0.24	0.12	0.20	0.28	0.16

a) Find the mean and the standard deviation of X.

This distribution is unknown to the librarian. In order to estimate the mean number of books borrowed by members she decides to record the number of books borrowed by a sample of 40 members using the library. She chooses the first member of the sample by selecting a random integer, r, between 1 and 5 inclusive. She then includes in her sample the rth member to leave the library one morning and every fifth member to leave after that until her sample of 40 is complete. Thus if $r = 3$ she chooses the third, eighth, 13th, ... 198th members leaving the library as her sample.

b) **i)** Is each of the first 200 people leaving the library equally likely to be included in the sample?

 ii) Does the sample constitute a random sample of the first 200 people leaving the library? Give a reason.

 iii) Comment on whether the sample will provide a useful estimate of the mean number of books borrowed by members.

 A list of names of 8950 members of the library is available.

c) Describe how random sampling numbers could be used to select a random sample (without replacement) of 40 of these names.

(AEB Question 5 (part), Paper 9, Winter 1994)

Summary

In this chapter we have discussed:

- the process of simple random sampling

- the use of the integer part function $\text{INT}(x)$ in converting random decimals into selections

- the importance of sampling frame

- how sampling can be made representative

- how to simulate random variables.

Approximating distributions

In this chapter, we discover:

■ *how certain well-tabulated probability models may be used to approximate the probabilities of other models,*

■ *the use of a continuity correction when approximating discrete random variables with continuous random variables.*

POISSON APPROXIMATION TO BINOMIAL

The **binomial distribution** provides an appropriate model when we are counting the number of successes in a fixed number of Bernoulli trials. In Chapter 20, *Discrete probability distributions* we discovered the **probability function** for $X \sim B(n, p)$:

$$P(X = r) = {}_nC_r \, p^r \left(1 - p\right)^{n-r}$$

and the recurrence relation:

$$P(X = r) = \frac{n + r - 1}{r} \times \frac{p}{1 - p} \times P(X = r - 1)$$

Recall also the **Poisson distribution** which is an appropriate model to use when we are counting the number of random events in a fixed interval. The probability for $X \sim Poi(\lambda)$ is:

$$P(X = r) = \frac{e^{-\lambda} \lambda^r}{r!}$$

and the recurrence formula is:

$$P(X = r) = \frac{\lambda}{r} \times P(X = r - 1)$$

Consider the binomial distribution: $X \sim B(50, 0.03)$.

What is the mean of X? The probabilities, $P(0)$, $P(1)$, $P(2)$ are shown below.

	B(50, 0.03)	Poi(1.5)
X	$P(X)$	$P(X)$
0	0.218 065	0.223 130
1	0.337 214	0.334 695
2	0.255 518	0.251 021

Try calculating $P(X = r)$ for $r = 3, 4, ..., 9$.

The mean of X is $50 \times 0.03 = 1.5$. The probabilities for a Poisson variable with the same mean as the binomial variate are also shown in the table above.

Try calculating $P(X = r)$ for $r = 3, 4, ..., 9$ for the Poisson variable.

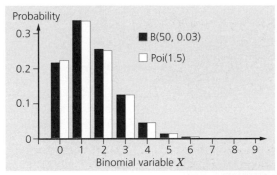

Probability

■ B(50, 0.03)
□ Poi(1.5)

Binomial variable *X*

A graphical comparison of the two sets of probabilities is shown in this diagram.

Do you feel that the Poisson probabilities are approximately the same as the binomial probabilities? A numerical comparison of the probabilities displayed in the diagram is shown in the following table, where the **absolute difference** is the numerical difference between the values.

	B(50, 0.03)	Poi(1.5)	
X	P(*X*)	P(*X*)	Absolute difference
0	0.218 065	0.223 130	0.005 065
1	0.337 214	0.334 695	0.002 519
2	0.255 518	0.251 021	0.004 497
3	0.126 442	0.125 511	0.000 931
4	0.045 949	0.047 067	0.001 117
5	0.013 074	0.014 12	0.001 046
6	0.003 033	0.003 530	0.000 497
7	0.000 590	0.000 756	0.000 167
8	0.000 098	0.000 142	0.000 044
9	0.000 014	0.000 024	0.000 009

One way of evaluating the quality of the approximation is to find the individual absolute differences in the binomial and Poisson probabilities, then to sum these absolute differences. If this is done when using Poi(1.5) to approximate B(50, 0.03), then the total obtained is 0.0159 (to four decimal places). This is a small value but remember that we are dealing with probabilities. Since absolute differences have been used, this total is larger than any error in the calculation of B(50, 0.03) probabilities using Poi(1.5).

The maximum error in approximating an individual probability is less than 0.005. This occurs in using $e^{-1.5}$ in place of $(0.97)^{50}$ for P(*X* = 0).

Clearly, it is possible to approximate binomial probabilities using the Poisson distribution – but which binomial distributions?

If you have access to a programmable calculator you might like to try the following calculator activity. If you have a spreadsheet available, you could carry out a similar comparison between the B(*n*, *p*) and Poi(*np*) probabilities.

CALCULATOR ACTIVITY

Exploration 24.1

$Poi(1.5) \approx B(n, \frac{1.5}{n})$

The purpose of this activity is to give you a feeling for the binomial distributions which may reasonably be approximated by Poi(1.5). The program calculates P(*X* = *r*) for both B(*n*, *p*) and Poi(1.5) until the absolute difference in the exact and approximate probabilities is less than 10^{-6}.

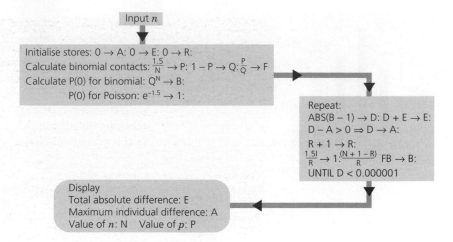

Interpreting the results

The sort of results that you might obtain are shown in the following table.

n	p	Total absolute difference	Maximum difference
10	0.15	0.0839	0.0262
20	0.075	0.0405	0.0128
75	0.02	0.0106	0.0034
100	0.015	0.0079	0.0025
500	0.003	0.0016	0.0005

These results suggest that the larger the value of n and, consequently, the smaller the value of p, the closer the Poisson probabilities are.

How could you adapt the program shown above to find out if other Poisson distributions can be used to approximate binomial probabilities? One approach would be to input the mean and then replace 1.5 by the input mean.

CALCULATOR ACTIVITY

Exploration 24.2

Poi(λ) $\approx$ B(n, $\frac{\lambda}{n}$)

Now try to find out how well appropriate Poisson distributions can be used to approximate binomial distributions.

Interpreting the results

The sort of results that you might obtain are summarised in the following table.

	Binomial		Total ABS difference	Maximum difference
	n	p		
Poi(3)	10	0.3	0.1728	0.0428
	50	0.06	0.0308	0.0076
	100	0.03	0.0152	0.0034
	150	0.02	0.0101	0.0023
	200	0.015	0.0076	0.0017
Poi(5)	100	0.04	0.0205	0.0040
	250	0.02	0.0099	0.0018
	1000	0.005	0.0025	0.0004
Poi(10)	100	0.1	0.0517	0.0068
	250	0.04	0.0200	0.0026
	500	0.02	0.0099	0.0013
	1000	0.01	0.0049	0.0006

It is increasingly evident that the value of p plays a crucial part in determining if Poi(np) probabilities are going to be a close approximation to B(n, p) probabilities. The binomial parameter, p, must be very small. How small it is depends to some extent on whether we want to approximate individual probabilities, e.g. P($X = 4$), or whether we want to approximate an accumulation of probabilities, e.g. P($X > 4$) or P($2 < X \leq 8$).

When $p \leq 0.02$ the approximations are generally very good, regardless of the event. When $0.02 < p \leq 0.05$, approximations for individual probabilities are generally reliable but accumulations of probabilities need to be viewed with caution. We should avoid approximating binomial probabilities, other than for individual events when $p > 0.05$.

Rare events

When we discussed the Poisson distribution previously, it was used as a model for the number of random events occurring in a continuous medium. We now know that it can be used to model binomial variables when p is very small. Such situations are often called **rare events**. This leads to the application of the Poisson distribution in modelling the occurrence of rare events.

Example 24.1

A school has 1200 students. On average, three students per year receive national recognition for their sporting achievements. Let X be the number of students receiving some recognition in one particular year.

a) *Obtain estimates for:*
   i) P($X = 0$)   **ii)** P($X \leq 5$).
b) *What is the probability that there would be 7 or more students receiving recognition?*

Solution

a) It may be reasonable to model the distribution of X as Poi(3) since this appears to be a 'rare event'. Under this assumption:

   i) $P(X = 0) = e^{-3} \approx 0.0498$

   ii) $P(X \le 5) = 0.9161$ *(from tables)*

b) $P(X \ge 7) = 1 - P(X \le 6)$

$$= 1 - 0.9665 = 0.0335$$

EXERCISES

24.1 CLASSWORK

1 A telesales representative makes 40 calls per evening and on average makes two sales. Let X be the number of sales per evening.

  a) Obtain estimates for:
    i) $P(X > 4)$ **ii)** $P(X < 6)$.
  Let Y be the number of sales in a two-day period.
  b) Obtain estimates for:
    i) $P(Y < 1)$ **ii)** $P(3 \le Y \le 4)$.

2 On average two applicants each year wanting to train as pilots are colour-blind. Let X be the number of colour-blind applicants in one year.

  a) Obtain estimates for:
    i) $P(X = 3)$ **ii)** $P(X > 3)$ **iii)** $P(X \ge 4)$.
  b) Find the probability of fewer than two colour-blind applicants in:
    i) each of four successive years,
    ii) just one of four successive years.

3 A football team has 34 players including reserves. On average only one player fails to appear for a match.

  a) Estimate the probability that fewer than three would fail to appear for a match.
  b) Estimate the probability that, in a series of four matches, there would be more than two absences in total.

4 State which approach to use to calculate the following probabilities and then use it to find the required probability.

  a) $P(X \ge 3)$ when $n = 200$ and $p = 0.006$.
  b) $P(X \le 2)$ when $n = 5$ and $p = 0.24$.
  c) The probability of more than one faulty floppy disc in a box of 40 discs, if on average each box contains only one faulty disc.

EXERCISES

24.1 HOMEWORK

1 A literary editor reads 60 manuscripts a month and, on average, recommends one for future publication. Let X be the number of manuscripts recommended on one month.

  a) Obtain estimates for:
    i) $P(X > 2)$ **ii)** $P(X < 4)$.
  Let Y be the number of manuscripts recommended in six months.
  b) Obtain estimates for:
    i) $P(Y < 8)$ **ii)** $P(11 \le Y \le 13)$.

2 On average, five out of the 300 new students at a college each year are left-handed. Let X be the number of new left-handed students in one year.

a) Obtain estimates for:
   i) $P(X = 5)$ **ii)** $P(X > 5)$ **iii)** $P(X \geq 6)$.

b) Find the probability of fewer than four new left-handed students:
   i) in each of three successive years,
   ii) in just one of three successive years.

3 An orchestra has 80 members. On average only one fails to attend a rehearsal.

a) Estimate the likelihood that four or more will fail to attend a rehearsal.

b) In a series of six rehearsals, what is the probability that there would be three or fewer absentees?

4 Which model would you use to evaluate the following probabilities?

a) $P(X \leq 4)$ where $n = 100$ and $p = 0.01$

b) $P(X \leq 4)$ where $n = 10$ and $p = 0.1$

c) The probability of there being not more than four broken eggs in a crate if, on average, a crate contains only one broken egg.

NORMAL APPROXIMATION TO POISSON

Consider this diagram, which shows the distribution $X \sim \mathrm{Poi}(9)$. How could we describe the shape of the graph?

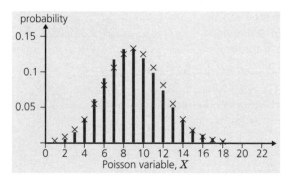

probability

Poisson variable, X

It is symmetric. It is bell-shaped. It tails off in both directions.

This description is very like the one used in the normal probability model, to describe the normal distribution's **density curve**.

Notice in this graph that the points marked with a cross do not quite coincide with the ends of the vertical lines representing the Poisson probabilities. These points correspond to the normal distribution $N(9, 3^2)$ with the same mean and variance as the Poisson variable. It appears that the normal distribution provides reasonably accurate approximations to Poisson probabilities – but under what circumstances? And how are the approximations obtained?

The circumstances are easily identified – it occurs when the Poisson distribution has the symmetric bell-shape of the normal distribution. This is when the mean of the Poisson is large. To determine what is meant by 'large' we need to address the second question – how the approximations are made.

Continuity correction

The difficulty with this is in the fundamental difference between the variates. A Poisson variate is discrete and a normal variate is continuous. If $X \sim \text{Poi}(9)$, then the probability of X being equal to 15 is readily obtained.

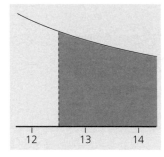

$$P(X = 15) = \frac{e^{-9} \times 9^{15}}{15!} = 0.019\,43$$

However, if $X \sim \text{N}(9, 9)$, then the probability that X is 15 has to be found as the area under the density curve between $X = 15.5$ and $X = 14.5$. The diagram illustrates this. Try finding the value of this area.

The process of finding the value is:

$$
\begin{aligned}
P(X = 15) &= P(X \le 15.5) - P(X \le 14.5) \\
&= \Phi\!\left(\frac{15.5 - 9}{\sqrt{9}}\right) - \Phi\!\left(\frac{14.5 - 9}{\sqrt{9}}\right) \\
&= 0.984\,89 - 0.966\,60 \\
&= 0.0183
\end{aligned}
$$

There is quite a lot of work involved in calculating an individual probability using the normal distribution. Calculating cumulative probabilities is often less work! For instance, to evaluate $P(X > 12)$ using the normal approximation, we need firstly to notice that we are interested in the event 'greater than 12' which does not include 12, hence the region under the normal curve is the area from 12.5 onwards.

So we have to apply a continuity correction to the discrete event being approximated as a continuous event.

$$
\begin{aligned}
P(x > 12) &\approx 1 - P(x \le 12) \\
&= 1 - 0.878\,42 \\
&= 0.1216
\end{aligned}
$$

This compares favourably with the Poisson exact value from tables.

$$
\begin{aligned}
P(x > 12) &= 1 - P(x \le 12) \\
&= 1 - 0.8758 \\
&= 0.1242
\end{aligned}
$$

The diagram and the two probability calculations in this section seem to indicate that $\text{N}(9, 9)$ may be used to approximate $\text{Poi}(9)$ probabilities. However, we need to explore the approximations over a much wider range of values of X. Exploration 24.3 is designed for this.

CALCULATOR ACTIVITY

Exploration 24.3

$N(9, 9) \approx Poi(9)$

The format of the program for Exploration 24.2 can be followed here. The difference between the two situations lies in evaluating the normal probabilities. The subroutine evaluates $\Phi(z)$ by adapting the programs developed for the normal probability model.

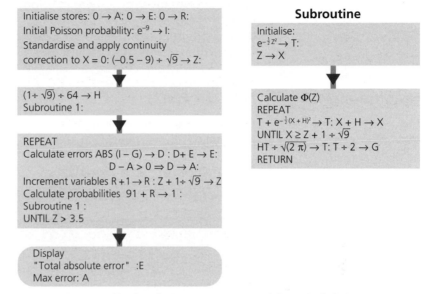

Initialise stores: $0 \to A$: $0 \to E$: $0 \to R$:
Initial Poisson probability: $e^{-9} \to I$:
Standardise and apply continuity
correction to $X = 0$: $(-0.5 - 9) \div \sqrt{9} \to Z$:

$(1 \div \sqrt{9}) \div 64 \to H$
Subroutine 1:

REPEAT
Calculate errors ABS $(I - G) \to D$: $D + E \to E$:
$D - A > 0 \Rightarrow D \to A$:
Increment variables $R + 1 \to R$: $Z + 1 \div \sqrt{9} \to Z$
Calculate probabilities $9I + R \to I$:
Subroutine 1 :
UNTIL $Z > 3.5$

Display
"Total absolute error" :E
Max error: A

Subroutine

Initialise:
$e^{-\frac{1}{2}Z^2} \to T$:
$Z \to X$

Calculate $\Phi(Z)$
REPEAT
$T + e^{-\frac{1}{2}(X + H)^2} \to T$: $X + H \to X$
UNTIL $X \geq Z + 1 \div \sqrt{9}$
$HT \div \sqrt{(2\pi)} \to T$: $T \div 2 \to G$
RETURN

Discover how well $N(9, 9)$ approximates $Poi(9)$ probabilities.

Interpreting the results

You should discover that the maximum difference between a $Poi(9)$ probability and the $N(9, 9)$ approximation is 0.01. The total absolute difference is about 0.08.

These errors are rather larger than were acceptable at the beginning of this chapter. It is useful to explore the actual errors, which seem to show a pattern. For $X = 0$ to 3, the approximations are overestimates. For $X = 4$ to 8 they are underestimates. Then, for $X = 9$ to 13 they are overestimates and for all $X \geq 14$ they are underestimates. You may be able to see this in the graph on page 425.

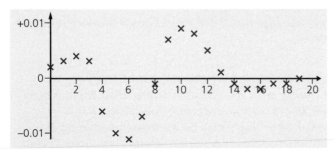

Alternatively, you might like to adapt your calculator program to display the actual error for each probability. This diagram is a graph of the actual errors.

Interpreting these errors in approximating Poisson probabilities is fairly straightforward. If the Poisson event is reasonably symmetric about the mean, e.g. $P(4 < X \leq 12)$, the positive and negative differences tend to cancel out, leading to reasonable accuracy. If the event is largely in the upper tail e.g. $P(X > 14)$, then the approximation is an underestimate. The reverse is true in a lower tail.

Exploration 24.4

Poi(9)

- Demonstrate that for $X \sim \text{Poi}(9)$:
a) $P(4 < X \leq 12) = 0.821$ and that when this probability is approximated using N(9, 9) the result is 0.812,
b) $P(X > 14) = 0.0415$ and that the normal approximation is 0.0334.
What percentage error is there in using the normal approximation in each of these cases?
- Explore the percentage error in using the normal approximation for other events of $X \sim \text{Poi}(9)$.

Exploration 24.5

N(λ, λ) $\approx$ Poi(λ)

Explore the accuracy of using N(λ, λ) to approximate Poi(λ) probabilities for various λ, e.g. λ = 5, 10, 15, ...

Interpreting the results

You might expect results such as those in the following table.

	Absolute difference	Maximum difference
5	0.11	0.015
10	0.08	0.010
15	0.06	0.005
25	0.05	0.003
50	0.04	0.002

Clearly, the total difference and maximum individual difference decrease as the mean of the Poisson distribution becomes larger. A pattern of errors emerges that is similar to that for Poi(9) for upper and lower tail probabilities and for events symmetrically located around the mean.

Example 24.2

The school in Example 24.1 has, on average, 75 students per year given county recognition. Two hundred and forty of the 1200 students are in the sixth form.
a) How many of the sixth form would you expect to receive county recognition each year?
b) Estimate the probability that there would be 24 or more selected for county awards.

Solution
a) If it is reasonable to assume that the number of students recognised at county level is a Poisson variate, then there would be, on average, 75 ÷ 5 = 15 sixth-formers per year.
b) The probability of 24 or more may be approximated using the normal distribution and the appropriate continuity correction so that 24 is included:

$$P(X \geq 24) \approx P\left(z \geq \frac{23.5 - 15}{\sqrt{15}} \right)$$

$$= 1 - \Phi(2.195)$$

$$\approx 0.014$$

EXERCISES

24.2 CLASSWORK

1 On average, an estate agent sells 30 houses per month. In the last month 25 were sold. Was this significantly fewer than usual?

2 The number of responses to an advertisement in a local newspaper follows a Poisson distribution with a mean of 8.

a) Find the probability that there are fewer than five responses.
b) Find the probability that there are more than 50 responses to five consecutive daily advertisements.

3 On average, an angler catches four fish per fishing trip. Estimate:

a) the probability he would catch less than three fish on a trip,
b) the likelihood of his catching four or fewer fish in two trips,
c) the chance that he would have less than nine fish from four trips.

4 A computer crashes, on average, twelve times a month.

a) Find the probability of more than 15 crashes in a month.
b) Find the probability of less than 30 crashes in a three-month period.
c) Find the probability of exactly twelve crashes in a month.
d) Find the probability of exactly 36 crashes in a three-month period.
e) Compare your answers to **d)** and **c)**.

EXERCISES

24.2 HOMEWORK

1 On average, a company appoints 20 new trainees each year. Last year, 15 were appointed. Was this significantly fewer than usual?

2 The number of full-page advertisements placed in a monthly magazine follows a Poisson distribution with a mean of 5.

a) Find the probability that there are fewer than four full-page advertisements in an issue.
b) Find the probability of at least 50 full-page advertisements in a year's run of the magazine.

3 a) A salesman finalises, on average, 25 new contracts per month. What is the probability that he would complete no more than 20 next month?
b) Estimate the likelihood that the salesman would finalise 40 or fewer contracts in the next two months.
c) Determine the chance that he completes no more than 80 in the next four months.

4 The number of train cancellations per week on a certain line has an average of 10.

a) Find the probability of at least twelve cancellations in a week.
b) Find the probability of fewer than 50 cancellations in a four-week period.
c) Find the probability of exactly ten cancellations in a week.
d) Find the probability of exactly 40 cancellations in four weeks.
e) Compare your solutions to **c)** and **d)**.

NORMAL APPROXIMATION TO THE BINOMIAL

Consider this diagram, which shows the binomial distributions B(20, 0.5) and B(50, 0.2). How could we describe the similarities between the distributions?

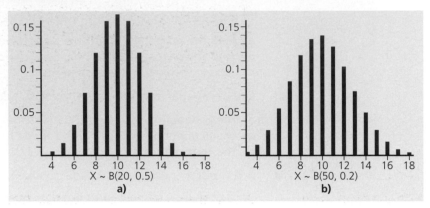

Clearly the distributions appear symmetric, although there is an element of asymmetry in B(50, 0.2). This distribution is more spread than B(20, 0.5). Their variances are 5 and 8 using the result $\sigma^2 = np(1-p)$ that we discovered in Chapter 20, *Discrete probability distributions*. They look as if they could be approximated by a normal distribution. For which do you think will the normal approximation be better?

Recall that the normal distribution is symmetric. This implies that if the actual distribution is also symmetric then the approximation is likely to be better than if it were not symmetric. The appropriate normal distribution to choose to approximate binomial probabilities must have the correct mean and variance. So N(10, 5) is appropriate to approximate B(20, 0.5).

Consider the probabilities P(X = 8), P(X = 9), ..., P(X = 12). The normal approximations to these can be evaluated using the continuity correction, as in the case of approximating Poisson probabilities. Below is an illustration of the calculation of P(X = 12).

B(20, 0.5)	N(10, 5)
0.120	$\Phi\left(\dfrac{12.5-10}{\sqrt{5}}\right) - \Phi\left(\dfrac{11.5-10}{\sqrt{5}}\right) \approx \Phi(1.118) - \Phi(0.671)$
	$\approx 0.868\,15 - 0.748\,89$
	≈ 0.119

B(50,0.2)	N(10,8)
0.103	$\Phi\left(\dfrac{12.5-10}{\sqrt{8}}\right) - \Phi\left(\dfrac{11.5-10}{\sqrt{8}}\right) \approx \Phi(0.884) - \Phi(0.530)$
	$\approx 0.811\,68 - 0.701\,94$
	≈ 0.110

The normal approximation to the perfectly symmetric binomial distribution B(20, 0.5), is much closer than to the less symmetric B(50, 0.2). Compare B(20, 0.5) probabilities and their approximations using N(10, 5).

You should have found that the comparison between the symmetric binomial distribution B(20,0.5) and its approximating distribution is much closer. A summary of the measures of closeness for the two cases is given in this table.

Binomial				Normal approximation	
n	p	μ	σ^2	Σ (absolute difference)	Maximum difference
20	0.5	10	5	0.008	0.001
50	0.2	10	8	0.053	0.007

You can see that the approximation to the symmetric binomial distribution is definitely the better of the two.

Exploration 24.6

Normal and binomial distributions with mean 10

■ Find out how well appropriate normal distributions approximate binomial distributions where the mean is equal to 10. You might like to develop a calculator activity or to use a spreadsheet for this.

■ Now repeat the investigation when the mean is larger than 10.

Interpreting the results

Some results you might have discovered are given in the table below.

	Binomial		Normal approximation	
Mean	n	p	Σ (absolute difference)	Maximum difference
10	30	0.333	0.033	0.005
	40	0.25	0.046	0.007
15	30	0.5	0.005	0.001
	45	0.333	0.027	0.003
	60	0.25	0.038	0.004
	75	0.2	0.043	0.005
20	40	0.5	0.004	0.000
	50	0.4	0.015	0.002
	80	0.25	0.033	0.003
	100	0.2	0.037	0.004

It is clear that symmetry is also the crucial factor in determining the closeness of the normal approximation to binomial probabilities.
A binomial distribution is perfectly symmetric when $p = 0.5$. So if p is close to 0.5, then the normal distribution with mean np and variance = $np(1-p)$ will provide a reasonable approximation to B(n, p) probabilities.

Example 24.3

The random variable, X, is distributed binomially with parameters n = 50, p = 0.2.

a) Calculate the probability that X ≤ 5 using the actual binomial probability function.

b) *Obtain an estimate for the probability that $X \leq 5$, using the normal approximation.*

c) *Calculate the relative percentage error in using the normal approximation compared to the correct probability function. Comment on your answer.*

Solution

a) $P(X \leq 5) = 0.8^{50} + 50 \times 0.2 \times 0.8^{49} + \ldots$

$= 0.0480$

b) *The mean is $50 \times 0.2 = 10$, and the variance is $50 \times 0.2 \times 0.8 = 8$, hence the appoximation using a continuity correction comes from:*

$$P(X \leq 5) = \Phi\left(\frac{5.5 - 10}{\sqrt{8}}\right)$$

$$\approx 1 - \Phi(1.591)$$

$$\approx 1 - 0.9442$$

$$= 0.0558$$

c) *Relative percentage error is* $\dfrac{0.0558 - 0.0480}{0.0480} \times 100\% \approx 16\%$

This is a relatively large error, and it is likely to be because p is not very close to 0.2.

Exploration 24.7

Appropriation of N(np, npq)

Example 24.3 provides an illustration that probabilities obtained using the normal approximation can be relatively different from the true values. Clearly, the work involved in using the approximation is potentially far less than using the exact distribution. However, if p is not close to 0.5 then use of the normal approximation can be far from the mark!

The following table arose from using $N(0.2n, 0.16n)$ for $B(n, 0.2)$.

B(n, 0.2)		Normal approximation	
Mean	n	Σ (absolute difference)	Maximum difference
10	50	0.053	0.007
15	75	0.043	0.005
20	100	0.037	0.004
25	125	0.034	0.003
30	150	0.031	0.002
40	200	0.027	0.002
50	250	0.024	0.001

Under what circumstances does the line of this approximation appear to be sound?

We can see that the measure of error reduces as the value of n increases. Clearly, since p is fixed in this compilation, increasing n has the effect of increasing the mean.

The message is that if p is not close to 0.5, then n needs to be large to reduce the potential for error in using the normal approximation.

Example 24.4

Obtain an estimate of the probability that there will be more than 60 left-handed students among the 240 sixth-formers at the school in Example 24.1, if it is reasonable to assume that 23 per cent of people are left-handed.

Solution
The number of left-handed students may be modelled by the binomial B(240, 0.23). The value of p is not close to 0.5 but 240 is a fairly large value and the mean, 55.2, is large.
Under these circumstances it is reasonable to approximate the required probability using the normal distribution as N(55.2, 42.504). Hence:

$$P(X > 60) \approx P\left(z \le \frac{60.5 - 55.2}{\sqrt{42.504}} \right)$$
$$= 1 - \Phi(0.813)$$
$$= 0.208$$

EXERCISES

24.3 CLASSWORK

1   A politician visits houses during the run-up to an election. She finds that at 40 per cent of homes the occupants agree with her party's policies.
   a) Find the probability that if five houses are visited all will have occupants that agree with her.
   b) Estimate the probability that at least half the occupants of 20 houses will agree with the politician.
   c) Repeat **b)** for 50 homes and comment on the two probabilities.

2   It has been estimated that 35 per cent of all households own a computer. One hundred households in a new town are sampled. What is the likelihood that at least 45 of these own a computer?

3   If 70 per cent of university students take out student loans, find the probabilities that:

   a) at least 50 in a group of 90 students have taken out student loans,
   b) more than 60 in a group of 100 students have taken out student loans.
   Two groups of 100 students are following different courses. Find the probability that:
   c) at least 75 students in both groups have taken out student loans.

4   It is assumed that 20 per cent of people who are classified as unemployed remain unemployed after attending a job preparation scheme.

   a) If a total of 400 unemployed people attend a scheme, what is the likelihood that at least 100 of them will remain unemployed?
   b) If a total of 100 unemployed attend a scheme, what is the probability that 25 or more remain unemployed?

EXERCISES

1   A charity usually receives donations from about 60 per cent of households in a door-to-door collection.
    a) Find the probability that every household in a street of five makes a donation.
    b) Estimate the probability that at least half the households in a street of 20 make a donation.
    c) Estimate the probability that a least half the households in a street of 50 make a donation.

2   It is estimated that 28 per cent of households have a pet animal. A survey is conducted in a rural area. What is the likelihood of at least 35 of the 100 households surveyed having a pet?

3   If 65 per cent of students play sport at least once a week, estimate the probability that:

    a) at least 45 in a group of 60 play sport in a given week,
    b) more than 50 in a group of 80 play sport in a given week.
    A college has five houses, each with 120 students. Estimate the probability that:
    c) at least 80 in each house play sport in a given week,
    d) only two of the houses have at least 80 students who play sport that week.

4   The winter 'flu vaccination programme is known to be ineffective with 25 per cent of adults.

    a) If a random sample of 200 adults are vaccinated, what is the probability that 72 or fewer will catch 'flu?
    b) If a random sample of 50 adults are vaccinated, what is the probability that 18 or fewer will catch 'flu?

OTHER DISTRIBUTIONS

Exploration 24.8

Distributions of continuous or discrete random variables which have the characteristic bell-shape of the normal distribution may be approximated using $N(\mu, s^2)$. You have discovered this in the case of two discrete random variables. Consider the continuous variate, X, which is the sum of three independent observations of a rectangularly distributed variate: Rect(0, 1). The mean of the rectangular distribution is 0.5 and its variance is $\frac{1}{12}$. Hence:

$$\mu = 0.5 + 0.5 + 0.5 = 1.5 \text{ and } \sigma^2 = \frac{1}{12} + \frac{1}{12} + \frac{1}{12} = \frac{1}{4}$$

Recall that the sum of two independent observations from Rect(0, 1) produces a symmetric triangular distribution. It is reasonable to suppose that X will be symmetrically distributed. You could obtain a sample of observations on X using your calculator repeatedly to produce and add up three random decimals.

Observations

The following is a five-part stem-and-leaf of 300 observations of X.

Leaf depth		Unit = 0.10
4	0T	2233
16	0F	444555555555
28	0S	677777777777
48	0E	888888888888889999999
81	1O	000000000000000001111111111111111111
124	1T	2222222222222222222222223333333333333333333333333
(48)	1F	444444444444444444444444444444455555555555555555555555
128	1S	666666666666666666666666666666677777777777777777777777
78	1E	888888888999999999999999999999999
48	2O	000000000000001111111
29	2T	222222222233333
14	2F	4444445555
4	2S	67
2	2E	88

These observations appear reasonably symmetrically distributed, but how well does a normal distribution provide a fit? One approach to addressing this question is to determine the frequencies predicted for each 'branch' of the stem-and-leaf display. The appropriate normal distribution is N(1.5, 0.25). The following are examples of determining the frequency for branches.

■ The normal approximation to $P(X < 0.4)$ is:

$$\Phi\left(\frac{0.4 - 1.5}{\sqrt{0.25}}\right) = \Phi(-2.2)$$
$$= 1 - \Phi(2.2)$$
$$= 0.013\,90$$

Hence, the expected frequency is 4.17.

■ The normal approximation to $P(0.4 \leq X < 0.6)$ is:

$$\Phi\left(\frac{0.6 - 1.5}{\sqrt{0.25}}\right) - \Phi(-2.2) = \Phi(2.2) - \Phi(1.8)$$
$$= 0.022\,03$$

Hence the expected frequency is 6.609. Continue this process of obtaining expected frequencies corresponding to the branches of the stem-and-leaf diagram above.

The table below represents the sort of outcome that might be achieved (note that the final branch has been treated as $X \leq 2.6$).

O	4	12	12	20	33	43	48	50	30	19	15	10	4
E	4.17	6.609	13.449	23.37	34.677	43.947	47.556	43.947	34.677	23.37	13.449	6.609	4.17

A simple subjective impression of the appropriateness of this normal approximation can be obtained graphically. This is left to the reader.

This is an example of a more general result leading to the use of the normal distribution in approximating the distribution obtained by summing repeated observations of a random variable.

Example 24.5

Describe the distribution which could be used to model the total time for the swings of a pendulum.

Solution
The time for one swing may be assumed to be a random variable, T, with mean, μ_T and variance σ_T^2. The time for ten swings is equivalent to the sum of ten observations on T. Hence, the time for ten swings may be modelled by a normal distribution $\mathrm{N}(10\mu_T, 10\sigma_T^2)$.

EXERCISES

24.4 CLASSWORK

1 A company executive travels on the underground to his office in central London. The journey has a mean length of 42 minutes and a standard deviation of twelve minutes.

   a) State the distribution that would model the total time spent travelling to and from work in a five-day week.
   b) Estimate the probability that he spends less than six hours per week travelling.
   c) Estimate the probability that he spends between 6.5 and 7.5 hours per week travelling.

2 The mass of a good-quality banana is a random variable with mean 200 grams and standard deviation 30 grams.

   a) What would be the distribution of the mass of a bunch of twelve bananas?
   b) Estimate the probability that a bunch of twelve bananas has a mass between 2.2 and 2.5 kilograms.

3 The quantity of apples put in a plastic bags by customers at a supermarket has a mean mass of 1.5 kg with a standard deviation of 0.4 kg.

   a) Estimate the probability that the next 20 customers buy more than 32 kg of apples.
   b) Estimate the probability that the next 200 customers buy more than 320 kg of apples.

4 The four continuous random variables X_1, X_2, X_3 and X_4 are rectangularly distributed on the interval [10, 20]. Let X be the sum of these four random variables.

   a) Estimate the probability that $X > 70$.
   b) Find the value of k if the probability that $X > k$ is 0.90.

EXERCISES

24.4 HOMEWORK

1 A student's journey time to and from school has a mean of 23 minutes and standard deviation of three minutes.

   a) Describe the distribution which could be used to model the total time spent travelling in a school week.
   b) Estimate the probability that he spends over 4 hours travelling in a given week.
   c) Estimate the probability that he spends between 3.5 hours and 4 hours travelling in a given week.

2 The mass of a grade A apple is a random variable with a mean of 120 g and a standard deviation of 8 g.

    a) Describe the distribution which could be used to model the total mass of a bag of twelve grade A apples.

    b) Estimate the probability that this total mass lies between 1.42 kg and 1.45 kg.

3 The amount spent in a supermarket may be assumed to be a random variable with a mean of £10.52 and a standard deviation of £4.20.

    a) Estimate the probability that the next 20 customers spend over £200 in total.

    b) Estimate the probability that the next 100 customers spend over £1000 in total.

4 The continuous variate X is the sum of five independent observations of a rectangularly distributed variate Rect (0, 10).

    a) Estimate the probability that $X > 30$.

    b) Find the value k such that the probability $(X > k) = 0.95$.

CONSOLIDATION EXERCISES FOR CHAPTER 24

1 Market research suggests that 40 per cent of a newspaper's readers look at the arts pages, but only two per cent of these read the dance reviews. If 1000 readers are selected at random, estimate the probability that:
a) at least 380 read the arts pages,
b) at least ten read the dance reviews.

2 At a certain university, 15 per cent of the new intake of students are mature students. In previous years, ten per cent of mature students have been over 50. If a random sample of 80 new students is taken:

    a) find the probability that at least ten are mature students,
    b) find the most likely number of students over 50.

3 State the conditions under which a binomial distribution may be approximated by a Poisson distribution.

The probability that an adult suffers an allergic reaction to a particular inoculation is 0.0018. If 5000 adults are given the inoculation, estimate the probability that:

    a) at most ten suffer an allergic reaction,
    b) from five to 15, inclusive, suffer an allergic reaction.

(NEAB Question 3, Specimen paper 9, 1996)

4 A factory mass-produces certain items, four per cent of which are defective. A random sample of n items is chosen from a day's total output.

    a) Calculate the smallest value of n for which the probability that the sample contains at least one defective item is greater than 0.99.
    b) When $n = 100$, find an approximate value for the probability that the sample contains five or more defective items.

5   The number of plants found in squares of equal area on a large moor follows a Poisson distribution with mean 27. Using a suitable approximation, find the probability that a particular square contains 30 or more plants.

(AEB Question 5 (part), Paper 9, June 1994)

6   'Bob's your uncle' is a familiar saying. In an extensive survey of a large number of pupils it was found that only 4 per cent of them had an uncle called Bob.

   a) Without referring to tables, calculate the probability that exactly 3 of 10 randomly chosen pupils have an uncle called Bob.
   b) Using tables, or otherwise, find the probability that exactly 2 or 3 of 50 randomly chosen pupils have an uncle called Bob.
   c) Find an approximate value for the probability that, in a random sample of 150 pupils, exactly 7 will have an uncle called Bob.

(WJEC Question 4, Specimen paper 1 2000)

7   It is given that 93 per cent of children in the UK have been immunised against whooping cough. The number of children in a random sample of 60 UK children who have been immunised is X, and the number who have not been immunised is Y. State, with reasons, which of X or Y has a distribution which can be approximated by a Poisson distribution.

   Using a Poisson approximation, find the probability that at least 58 children in the sample of 60 have been immunised against whooping cough.

   Three random samples, each of 60 UK children, are taken. Find the probability that in one of these samples exactly 59 children have been immunised while in each of the other two samples exactly 58 children have been immunised. Give your answer correct to 1 significant figure.

(OCR Question 4, Specimen paper 2 2000)

8   On average 5 per cent of the items from a particular production line are found to be faulty. A random sample of 100 items is taken and X are found to be faulty.

   a) Assuming that $X \approx \mathrm{B}(n, p)$, write down the mean and variance of X and calculate $\mathrm{P}(X = 1)$.
   b) Explain why it is reasonable to use a Poisson model to approximate the distribution of X. Use an appropriate Poisson model to calculate the probability of finding one faulty item.

(AQA A Question 2, Specimen paper 2 2000)

9   A biologist is studying the behaviour of sheep in a large field. The field is divided up into a number of equally sized squares and the average number of sheep per square is 2.25. The sheep are randomly spread throughout the field.

   a) Suggest a suitable model for the number of sheep in a square and give a value for any parameter or parameters required.
   Calculate the probability that a randomly selected sample square contains:
   b) no sheep,
   c) more than 2 sheep.
   A sheepdog has been sent into the field to round up the sheep.

d) Explain why the model may no longer be applicable.
In another field, the average number of sheep per square is 20 and the sheep are randomly scattered throughout the field.
e) Using a suitable approximation, find the probability that a randomly selected square contains fewer than 15 sheep.

(EDEXCEL, Question 6, Specimen paper 2, 2000)

10   In parts **a)**, **b)** and **c)** of this question use the binomial, Poisson and normal distributions, according to which you think is the most appropriate. In each case, draw attention to any feature of the data which supports or casts doubt on the suitability of the model you have chosen. Indicate, where appropriate, that you are using one distribution as an approximation to another.

a) The annual income of all employees of a large firm has a mean of £14 500 with a standard deviation of £2200. What is the probability that a mean income of 100 employees selected at random is between £14 000 and £15 000?

b) A technician looks after a large number of machines on a night shift. She has to make frequent minor adjustments. The necessity for these occurs at random at a constant average rate of eight per hour. What is the probability that:
   i) in a particular hour she will have to make five or fewer adjustments,
   ii) in an eight hour shift she will have to make 70 or more adjustments?

c) A number of neighbouring allotment tenants bought a large quantity of courgette seeds which they shared among them. Overall 15 per cent failed to germinate. What is the probability that a tenant who planted 20 seeds would have:
   i) five or more failing to germinate,
   ii) at least 17 germinating?

(AEB Question 7, Specimen paper 2, 1996)

Summary

It is possible, under appropriate circumstances, to approximate probabilities of one model by those of another.

Description	Approximation	Condition
$B(n, p)$	$Poi(np)$	large n, small p $p < 0.02$ usually good
$Poi(\lambda)$	$N(\lambda, \lambda)$	large λ, at least 10 with care $\lambda \geq 25$ reasonable
$B(n, p)$	$N(np, np(1-p))$	symmetry is key issue ideally $p \approx 0.5$ otherwise n must be large
ΣXi	$N(n\mu_x, n\sigma^2)$	sums of repeated observations

Hypothesis testing

In this chapter, we:

■ *discover more of the versatility of the nomal distribution,*
■ *discover how probability is used in testing hypotheses,*
■ *learn about possible errors,*
■ *interpret the outcome of tests,*
■ *explore the limitations of statistical testing,*
■ *learn more of correlations.*

STATISTICAL TESTS

Binomial

Suppose that a group of 16 teachers had their blood tested. How many should we expect to have blood of type O? Recall from Chapter 20, *Discrete probability distributions* that 45 per cent of the world's population have blood of that type, so it would seem reasonable to expect that about half of the group, say seven or eight, would have type-O blood.

What if none of the group had type-O blood? We might be tempted to conclude that there was a lower likelihood that teachers had blood of that type than in the population at large. But why might we come to this conclusion? It is, of course, quite possible for a group to have no one with that blood type even when the chance for any individual in the group is 0.45. What is the probability? Making the modelling assumptions of the earlier part of the chapter leads to the number of people being a binomial variable, B(16, 0.45).

Hence $P(0) = (0.55)^{16} \approx 0.000\ 07$

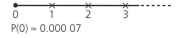

$P(0) \approx 0.000\ 07$

An interpretation of this suggests that fewer than one occasion in ten thousand would result in there being no one with blood of type O when there is actually a 45 per cent chance of finding a person with such blood. So, this result is highly unlikely.

It would seem to suggest that type-O blood is less commonly found in teachers than in the general population. Would we draw the same conclusion if there had been one teacher with type-O blood in this group of 16? We have decided already that if none of the 16 had type-O blood, then we would be suggesting that the blood type occurred less frequently. The chance that either one teacher or no teacher is found, in the 16, with type-O blood is:

$P(0) + P(1) = P(R \le 1) \approx 0.0010$

according to the binomial distribution tables for B(16, 0.45).

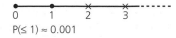

$P(\le 1) \approx 0.001$

This indicates that such an event would occur about once in a thousand times of testing groups of 16 people. Again, it is a very rare occurrence and it would be reasonable to draw the same conclusion.

$P(\leq 2) \approx 0.0066$

What conclusion would you draw if you found two type-O teachers in the group? Using, the same model B(16, 0.45), leads to $P(R \leq 2) \approx 0.0066$. This indicates that on fewer than seven occasions in a thousand would we find two or fewer people with type-O blood. Again, it is something which is rarely likely to occur, and we could reasonably justify concluding that there is a lower incidence of blood type-O found in teachers than in the general population.

Exploration 25.1

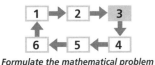

Formulate the mathematical problem

Blood groups among teachers

What conclusions would you reach about the occurrence of type-O blood when:
a) three people are found, **b)** four people are found,
c) five people are found,
with type-O blood in a group of 16 teachers?

Interpreting the results

The modelling activity in Exploration 25.1 leads to B(16, 0.45) in each case. The mathematical problem formulated varies.

In part **a)** it was necessary to evaluate the likelihood of observing three or fewer people, since we have already decided that observing zero, one or two people would lead us to draw the same conclusion.

$P(R \leq 3) = 0.0281$

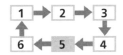

Interpret the solution

This indicates that we observe such a result on fewer than three occasions out of 100. Again, this is an unlikely event, and it seems reasonable to conclude that teachers are less likely to have type-O blood than the general population.

In parts **b)** and **c)**, $P(R \leq 4) \sim 0.0853$;

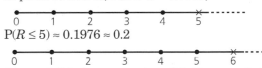

$P(R \leq 5) \approx 0.1976 \approx 0.2$

A reasonable interpretation of the last result is that on about 20 per cent of the occasions we should find five or fewer people with type-O blood. This does not seem to be terribly rare. It might be difficult to justify the conclusion that the teachers are any different from the general population, so which of these results do we take to be significant?

Significance level

The case of four or fewer people is less clear cut and depends on what probability is considered to be associated with an unlikely or rare event. The probability is referred to as the **alpha** or **significance level** of the test. A common significance level is **five per cent**.

It is worth reflecting on the meaning of the significance level. This is the likelihood of observing a 'rare' event even when the proportion within the teachers is 0.45. This is the chance of wrongly concluding that the proportion of type-O blood group in teachers is less than in the population.

If the significance level is chosen to be five per cent, then since $P(R \leq 4) \approx 8\frac{1}{2}\%$ is greater than five per cent, the conclusion we should reach is that the incidence of four people is not one of the rare events.

Critical region

The group of observations which we consider to be rare events is called the **critical region**. Clearly, the critical region depends on the significance level chosen. For the model being explored here B(16, 0.45) and a significance level of five per cent, we have discovered that an observation lying in the critical region $R \leq 3$ leads to the conclusion that the proportion of teachers with type-O blood is lower than in the population at large.

Example 25.1

a) *Sixteen teachers are asked about their blood type. What critical region is associated with the conclusion that teachers are less likely to have type-O blood than the population at large when the significance level is:*
   i) *10%*   *ii)* *2%*   *iii)* *1%?*

b) *A researcher wants to address the question, 'Are scientists less likely to have type-A blood than the general population?' The researcher performs blood tests on 20 scientists. What critical region should the researcher use if the test is conducted at:*
   i) *the 10% level,*   *ii)* *the 2% level?*

Solution

a) *The model used here is B(16, 0.45).*
   i) *Tables indicate that* $P(R \leq 5) \approx 0.2 \approx 20\%$
       $P(R \leq 4) \approx 0.085 \approx 8\frac{1}{2}\%$
       Hence the critical region at 10% level is $R \leq 4$.
   ii) *The tables indicate that* $P(R \leq 3) \approx 0.028 \approx 3\%$
       $P(R \leq 2) \approx 0.007 \approx 1\%$
       Hence the 2% critical region is $R \leq 2$.
   iii) *The 1% critical region is also* $R \leq 2$.

b) *The model used in this case is B(20, 0.4).*
   i) *The distribution tables indicate that* $P(R \leq 5) = 0.1256 \approx 12\frac{1}{2}\%$
       $P(R \leq 4) = 0.0510 \approx 5\%$
       Hence the 10% critical region is $R \leq 4$.
   ii) *The tables indicate that* $P(R \leq 4) = 0.0510 \approx 5\%$
       $P(R \leq 3) = 0.0160 \approx 1\frac{1}{2}\%$
       Hence the 2% critical region is $R \leq 3$.

The alternative and null hypotheses

What do we mean by the term 'significance level'? It is the maximum probability of getting an observation in the critical region when the model used is appropriate. However, if we do get an observation in the critical region, we are going to conclude that the model is not appropriate. So using the **significance level** inevitably offers **the chance of wrongly rejecting the model** used. Clearly, 'getting something wrong' is not what is in mind, and so the significance level is usually chosen to be a small probability. The error associated with the significance level is called a '**type I error**.'

In statistical tests, the two models involved are the underlying set of assumptions from which the probability distribution is formulated, and the alternative set of assumptions which will be accepted if the test results in an observation in the critical region. These models are called **hypotheses**. The set of assumptions which underpin the model used is called the **null hypothesis**. The alternative set is known as the **alternative hypothesis**.

In common with much of mathematics, a short notation for presenting the concepts of these hypotheses is adopted. The null hypothesis, in the case of the 16 teachers and the type-O blood would be presented as:

$$H_0: p = 0.45$$

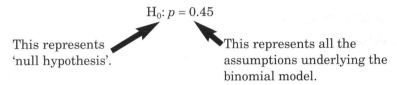

This represents 'null hypothesis'.

This represents all the assumptions underlying the binomial model.

The alternative hypothesis would be presented as:

$$H_1: p < 0.45$$

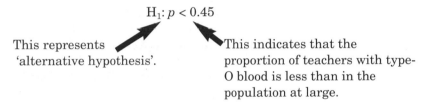

This represents 'alternative hypothesis'.

This indicates that the proportion of teachers with type-O blood is less than in the population at large.

Example 25.2

What are the appropriate hypotheses for Example 25.1b?

Solution
The model used to develop the probability distribution and to establish the critical region is B*(20, 0.4). The set of assumptions which give rise to this model constitute the null hypothesis. The alternative hypothesis concerns itself with scientists being less likely than the general population to have type-A blood. Hence, the two hypotheses can be summarised as:* $H_0: p = 0.4;$ $H_1: p < 0.4$.

One-tailed tests

What would the alternative hypothesis be if a particular blood type occurred with greater frequency in one group of people than in the general population? Suppose we assume that ten per cent of the general population have type-B blood. What alternative hypothesis could we use if we wished to respond to the question: Is type-B blood found more frequently among Australian mathematicians than in the general population?

The null hypothesis would be: $H_0: p = 0.10$

and the alternative hypothesis would be: $H_1: p > 0.10$.

With this alternative hypothesis, we need to consider the probability of getting large numbers of people in a group with type-B blood rather than the small numbers we have considered so far. We need to examine the 'upper tail' of the probability distribution involved. This information can be gained from the distribution tables, but not directly.

Suppose the blood types of a group of 17 Australian mathematicians are recorded. What critical region would be appropriate for a hypothesis test with a five per cent significance level against the alternative hypothesis $H_1: p > 0.10$?

Examining the distribution function for B(17, 0.1) shows:
$P(R \leq 3) = 0.9174$ and $P(R \leq 4) = 0.9779$.

The first of these implies $P(R \geq 4) = 1 - 0.9174 = 0.0826 \approx 8\frac{1}{4}\%$ which is more than the significance level of five per cent. Hence, an occurrence of four is not in the critical region.

The second of these implies that $P(R \geq 5) = 1 - 0.9779 = 0.0221 \approx 2\frac{1}{4}\%$ which is less than the significance level. Hence, the critical region is $R \geq 5$.

Example 25.3

Twenty Australian mathematicians had their blood types identified. Eight of them were found to have type-B blood.

a) *Write down appropriate null and alternative hypotheses to respond to the question: Is there sufficient evidence, at the five per cent level of significance, to support the view that Australian mathematicians are more likely to have type-B blood than the general population?*

b) *Calculate the five per cent upper-tail critical region.*

c) *Conduct the test and report your findings.*

Solution

a) *Assuming that in the general population the proportion of people with type B blood is 10% leads to the hypotheses $H_0: p = 0.1$; $H_1: p > 0.1$.*

b) *The appropriate distribution tables are those for the probability model B(20, 0.1).*
Examining the table yields:
$P(R \leq 3) = 0.8670$
$P(R \leq 4) = 0.9568$
$P(R \leq 5) = 0.9887$
These cumulative probabilities lead to:
$P(R \geq 4) = 1 - 0.8670 \approx 13.3\%$
$P(R \geq 5) = 1 - 0.9568 \approx 4.3\%$
$P(R \geq 6) = 1 - 0.9887 \approx 1.1\%$
Now 13.3% is larger than the significance level, but 4.3% is smaller than the significance level (and 1.1% is considerably smaller!). Hence, the critical region is $R \geq 5$.

c) *The critical region is $R \geq 5$, and in the group there were eight people with type-B blood. This is unlikely to occur under the null hypothesis, hence it is reasonable to conclude that we are more likely to find people with type-B blood among Australian mathematicians than in the general population.*

Two-tailed tests

The two types of alternative hypothesis we have considered so far have been:

■ $H_1: p < ...$
■ $H_1: p > ...$

Both of these are 'one-tailed', which means the critical region is either:

■ a low set of values of the random variable, or
■ a high set.

The question that led to the test being done asked:

    i) are the occurrences less likely, or
    ii) are the occurrences more likely?

A question of the type, 'Is the occurrence different ...?' does not require a specific direction or tendency to be given. This sort of question leads to an alternative hypothesis such as $H_1: p \neq ...$.

The critical region needs to take into account both the upper and lower tails. An hypothesis test with this sort of alternative hypothesis is called a **two-tailed test**. The significance level is generally divided equally between the upper and lower tails.

Suppose that quarter of American scientists have type-O blood. Twenty Mexican scientists are going to have their blood type identified to see if there is any difference between them and the American scientists. A five per cent significance level is chosen for the test. The critical region will consist of a lower tail of up to $2\frac{1}{2}$ per cent and an upper of up to $2\frac{1}{2}$ per cent.

An examination of the tables for the model B(20, $\frac{1}{4}$) yields:
$P(R \leq 1) = 0.0243 \approx 2.4\%$ and $P(R \geq 10) = 1 - 0.9861 = 0.0139 \approx 1.4\%$.

Note: $P(R \leq 2) \approx 9\%$ and $P(R \geq 9) \approx 4\%$ each of which is much larger than the allowed $2\frac{1}{2}$ per cent contribution to the significance level.

Hence, the two parts of the critical region are $R \leq 1$ and $R \geq 10$.

Now suppose that there are eight Mexicans with type-O blood in the group. The result 'eight' does not lie in either part of the critical region, hence the test indicates that there is no difference in the proportion of Mexican and American scientists with type-O blood. If, however, there had been twelve Mexicans with type-O blood, we could justifiably conclude that there was a difference. It is worth noting that we would not be justified in saying that proportionately more Mexicans had that blood type; this is not justified because this was not the question posed and consequently the alternative hypothesis and its critical region did not correspond to such a question.

Example 25.4

Suppose that 30 per cent of Western males have type-A blood. A test is carried out to see if the proportion of Western females with type-A blood is different. A group of 20 females have their blood types identified.

a) Write down appropriate hypotheses and identify the critical region appropriate to a ten per cent significance level.

b) *What conclusion would you draw if the test revealed that two females had type-A blood?*

Solution

a) *The hypotheses are* $H_0: p = 0.30$; $H_1: p \neq 0.30$.
The appropriate probability model is B(20, 0.30). *The size of the tails are, at most, 5%. An examination of the distribution table yields:*
$P(R \leq 2) = 0.0355 \approx 3.6\%$ *and* $P(R \geq 10) = 1 - 0.9520 \approx 4.8\%$.
$(P(R \leq 3) \approx 11\%$ *and* $P(R \geq 9) \approx 11\%$, *both of which are too large. Hence, the critical region is* $R \leq 2$ *and* $R \geq 10$.

b) *The result 'two' is in the critical region. Hence, it is reasonable to conclude that the proportion of Western females with type-A blood is different from that of Western males.*

Type I and type II errors

We have already met a type I error i.e. the process of rejecting the null hypothesis in favour of the alternative when in fact the null hypothesis actually holds true. The likelihood of committing a type I error is chosen by the experimenter since this is the significance level. Clearly, in the interests of accuracy, it is important to keep this likelihood small.

However, this is not the only possible error that can be made. It is possible to accept the null hypothesis when in fact the alternative hypothesis holds! This sort of error is called a **type II error**. Once again, the chance of doing this needs to be minimised. Unfortunately, it is a distinctly challenging task to provide an accurate evaluation of the probability of committing type II errors. In order to evaluate the probability of a type II error we would need to know the alternative proportion precisely – and, of course, that is not possible.

Example 25.5

A new drug is being trialled. A group of 20 volunteer patients is involved in the trial. The role of recovery from the ailment of which they are showing symptoms is usually 50 per cent.

a) *State suitable null and alternative hypotheses for the test.*

b) *Suppose that the number of patients who recover under the new drug treatment is X. The drug company decides that their new product is a success if $X \geq 14$. What is the probability of committing a type I error?*

c) *What is the probability of committing a type II error if the actual rate of recovery under the new drug is 85 per cent?*

Solutions

a) $H_0: p = 0.50$, H, : $p > 0.50$ in B(20, p)

b) $P(X \geq 14)$ *under* B(20, 0.50) *is 0.0577.*

c) *A type II error would be committed when $X \leq 13$ but the recovery rate is per cent. Thus the probability of a type II error is* $P(x \leq B)$ *under* B(20, 0.85) *which is 0.0219.*

EXERCISES

1 A coin is tossed three times and shows heads each time.
   a) Is there evidence, at the five per cent level, that the coin is biased towards heads?
   b) If the coin shows six heads on six tosses, is there evidence, at the five per cent level, that it is biased towards heads?
   c) Repeat **b)** at the one per cent level of significance. Comment.

2 An independent weather forecaster predicted that the probability of rain on any day in Wimbledon fortnight (twelve days) was 0.5. In the event it rained on two days out of the twelve.
   a) Does this provide evidence, at the five per cent level, that his theory was incorrect?
   b) Does this provide evidence, at the one per cent level, that his theory was incorrect?
   c) What assumptions were made by the forecaster? Were these realistic assumptions?

3 A driving instructor claims that 80 per cent of his pupils pass the driving test at their first attempt.
   a) In a month when ten of his pupils took the test for the first time, only four passed. Does this evidence tend to disprove his claim?
   b) Repeat **a)** assuming two passes out of five attempts.
   c) Repeat **a)** assuming eight passes out of 20 attempts.
   d) Compare **a)**, **b)** and **c)**.
   Conduct your tests at the five per cent level.

4 Explain the terms 'critical region', 'significance level' and 'null hypothesis'.
   a) A new waterproof material is introduced which is claimed to be better than existing materials. A group of 20 volunteers try out jackets made of the new material. The number, X, of these people who report that the new material is an improvement is recorded. Assume that X is binomially distributed: B $(20, p)$.
   A statistical test is proposed in which the hypotheses are:
   $$H_0: p = \tfrac{1}{2}, \quad H_1: p > \tfrac{1}{2},$$
   and the critical region is $X \geq 14$. What is the significance level of the test?
   b) What is the critical region if the significance level is one per cent?
   c) If p is actually 0.7, what is the probability that $X \geq 14$?
   d) Why is a one-tailed test preferred to a two-tailed test in this case?

5 A researcher claimed that 30 per cent of chicken sandwiches are contaminated with listeria. A school canteen refuted this claim and sent 20 of its chicken sandwiches to be tested. The canteen manager decided that he would sue the researcher if fewer than three of the 20 sandwiches were contaminated.
   a) State suitable hypotheses for the test.
   b) What is the critical region?
   c) What is the significance level?
   d) If in fact 15 per cent of the canteen's sandwiches were contaminated, what is the probability of fewer than three of the 20 being found to have listeria?

EXERCISES

1   A national charity organised a raffle and claimed that 20 per cent of the tickets sold would win a small prize. Susan bought twelve tickets but won no prizes.

   a) Does this evidence suggest, at the five per cent significance level, that the number of prizes won was lower than expected?
   b) Repeat a) for 30 per cent of tickets sold.
   d) Repeat b) for 10 per cent of tickets sold.

2   In previous years, sixth-formers have been equally likely to choose drama or photography as their extra class. This year, 14 out of 20 have chosen drama.
   a) Does this provide evidence of a change in preferences? Use the two per cent significance level.
   b) In previous years, 70 per cent of sixth-formers have chosen drama. This year, only ten out of 20 have done so. Does this provide evidence of a change in preferences? Use the two per cent significance level.

3   A lottery offered a choice of one number from the integers 1 to 25 inclusive. Mary selected the number 7 on 50 consecutive entries but 7 was never the winning number.
   a) Does this evidence suggest, at the five per cent significance level, that the lottery was biased against the number 7?
   b) What if Mary had made 100 consecutive entries?

4   State what you understand by the terms 'critical region' and 'significance level'.
   a) A drug for treating a certain medical condition has side-effects in 40 per cent of patients. A new drug is introduced which it is claimed reduces the risk of side-effects.
   State suitable null and alternative hypotheses to test this claim.
   b) A consultant agrees to use the new drug in treating 20 patients. She decides to accept the claim if fewer than four patients suffer side-effects. State the critical region and find the significance level of the test.
   c) On average the new drug actually causes side-effects in 20 per cent of patients, calculate the probability of fewer than four patients, in a group of 20, suffering from side-effects whilst on the new drug.

5   Under what circumstances would you use a one-tailed test rather than a two-tailed test? An international bank proposes to take over an insurance company. The bank claims that the proposal has the backing of over one half of the company's investors. The directors of the company claim that their investors are evenly split. Independent arbitrators are brought in to test the validity of these claims. They decide to obtain the opinions of 20 investors randomly chosen.
   a) State suitable null and alternative hypotheses.
   b) The number of investors in favour of the proposals is X. The arbitrators decide to accept the bank's opinion of $X \geq 13$. What is the significance level of the test?
   c) What is the critical value if the significance level is $2\frac{1}{2}$ per cent?
   d) What is the probability of rejecting the company's claim if the actual proportion if its investors in favour of the take-over is 75 per cent?

POISSON DISTRIBUTION

A gardener notes one week that a particular metre square in the south-east corner of the garden contained seven daisies. She asks the expert if this means that the daisy population is more dense in this part of the garden. How would you set about answering the query and what advice would you offer the gardener?

Statistically speaking, the gardener is asking her lawn expert to conduct an **hypothesis test**. We know that we need to set up an appropriate model in order to determine probabilities. The modelling assumptions are those that lead to the Poisson model Poi(3), which assumes that daisies occur at the same rate throughout the lawn including the south-east corner. This model is summarised as the **null hypothesis**, $H_0: \mu = 3$.

The question asks whether daisies occur at a greater rate in the south east corner, this is the alternative hypothesis, $H_1: \mu > 3$.

Since there is a distinct direction in H_1, the test to be conducted is one-tailed. The direction indicates that 'large' observations would be considered unusual under the null hypothesis.

Suppose we conduct the test at the five per cent level of significance, so that if the observed number of daisies lies in an upper tail of five per cent then it would be considered as 'significant' under the null hypothesis. The distribution tables for Poi(3) indicate that:

$$P(X \geq 7) = 1 - P(X \leq 6) = 1 - 0.9665 = 0.0335$$

Hence:

$$P(X \geq 7) = 3.35\% < 5\%$$

which suggests that an observation of seven or more will occur in less than five per cent of the metres squares on average.

It is appropriate to report to the gardener that this is an unusually high number of daisies. It is not impossible when the average is actually three, but it is reasonable to conclude that the mean occurrence of daisies in the south-east corner of the garden is higher than three.

Briefly, the expert might say that the daisies are more dense there than elsewhere.

Example 25.6

The number of accidents that occur on a particular section of road in a one month period is modelled by a Poisson distribution with mean 4.8
a) *Determine the probability that there is more than one accident on this section of the road in any given month.*
A speed camera is introduced in view of the users of this section of road. There was exactly one accident on this stretch of road in the month immediately following the introduction of the speed camera.
b) *Test, at the five per cent level, the claim that speed cameras improve road safety. State the hypotheses and conditions clearly.*

Solutions

a) Let X represent the number of accidents in a given month, then $X \sim \text{Poi}(4.8)$. The question wants the probability:
$$P(X > 1) = 1 - \{P(X = 0) + P(X = 1)\}$$
$$= 1 - 0.0477, \text{ from tables}$$
$$= 0.9523$$

b) The null hypothesis for this test is that the introduction of the speed camera has had no effect, i.e. $H_0: \mu = 4.8$. The claim to be tested is clearly indicative of a one-tailed test in the direction of a reduction in the mean number of accidents, i.e. $H_1: \mu < 4.8$. We know that only one accident occurred in the following month, hence we can determine the probability of one or fewer accidents occurring under the assumption of no change:
$$P(X \leq 1) = 0.0477.$$
This probability is less than 5 per cent, hence it is a 'significant' event. It is reasonable to conclude that the claim is justified.

EXERCISES

25.2 CLASSWORK

1. The number of students dropping out of a university course each year follows a Poisson distribution with a mean of 6.4. Last year, only two students dropped out. Does this provide evidence, at the five per cent significance level, of a change in behaviour?

2. The number of serious accidents on a certain stretch of road averages three each year. Last year there were seven accidents on this stretch. Does this provide evidence, at the five per cent significance level, that the situation has deteriorated?

3. A traffic survey has established that the number of vehicles passing a school's entrance has a Poisson distribution with mean 9.6 per minute. Following the operating of a new alternative route, five vehicles pass the school's entrance in a one-minute interval. Test the hypothesis that the opening of the alternative route has made no difference to the mean number of vehicles passing the school's entrance. Suggest how the test could be improved.

4. A single observation is to be taken from a Poisson distribution with mean μ and used to test $H_0: \mu = 6$ against $H_1: \mu < 6$. The critical region is chosen to be $x \leq 2$. What is the significance level of the test?

5. A football team has 34 players including reserves. On average only one player fails to turn up for a match.

   a) If three fail to turn up for a match is there evidence that the number of players failing to turn up has increased?

   b) In a series of four matches there were only two absences in total. Is there evidence that the number of players failing to turn up for matches is decreasing?

EXERCISES

1 Explain briefly, referring to your practical work if possible, the role of the null hypothesis and of the alternative hypothesis in a test of significance.

Over a long period, John has found that the bus taking him to school arrives late, on average, nine times per month. In the month following the start of new summer schedules, John finds that his bus arrives late 13 times. Assuming that the number of times that the bus is late has a Poisson distribution, test, at the five per cent level of significance, whether the new schedules have, in fact, increased the number of times on which the bus is late. State clearly your null and alternative hypotheses.

2 If in question 1 there were five accidents in a particular week, would this suggest that the average weekly rate had increased? (Use a five per cent level of significance.)

3 Small bubbles in a particular type of glass occur at random. When the production process is operating satisfactorily, the mean number is 0.2 per square metre. A random sample of 20 pieces of glass, each 1 m^2 in area, reveals a total of seven bubbles. Investigate the claim that the process is not operating satisfactorily as it is producing too many small bubbles.

4 Two independent observations, x_1 and x_2, are taken from a Poisson distribution with mean μ in order to test the hypothesis $H_0: \mu = 5$ against $H_1: \mu < 5$. The critical region selected is $x_1 + x_2 \leq 4$.
a) State the distribution of the random variable $Y = X_1 + X_1$.
b) Find the significance level of the test.

5 a) A salesman wins, on average, 25 new contracts each month. One month he won only 20 new contracts. Does this indicate a deterioration in his efficiency?
b) If the salesman won only 40 new contracts in two months, would this indicate that his performance had deteriorated?
c) If the salesman won only 80 new contracts in four months, would this indicate a deterioration?

MEANS OF SAMPLES FOR A NORMAL DISTRIBUTION

By the end of Chapter 24, *Approximating distributions* we were using the normal distribution in connection with sums of observations of a random variable. It is a simple step from summing observations to finding their average. The normal distribution plays an important role in modelling the distribution of the mean of a sample of data.

We know that if the independent random variables, X and Y, are normally distributed, then linear combinations such as $X + Y$, $\frac{1}{2}X + \frac{1}{2}Y$, $\frac{1}{2}(X + Y)$, etc. are also normally distributed. In particular, consider the case where:

$$X \sim N(\mu_X, \sigma_X^{\ 2})$$

and

$$Y \sim N(\mu_Y, \sigma_Y^{\ 2})$$

What is the mean of the random variable, R, where:

$$R = \tfrac{1}{2}(X + Y)?$$

R can be considered as a linear combination:

$$\tfrac{1}{2}X + \tfrac{1}{2}Y$$

of X and Y. Hence, the mean of R is the same linear combination of the means of X and Y:

$$\mu_R = \tfrac{1}{2}\mu_X + \tfrac{1}{2}\mu_Y = \tfrac{1}{2}(\mu_X + \mu_Y)$$

i.e. the average of the mean of X and Y. But, what about the variance of R?

Recall that variance is a squared measure of spread and this prompts the familiar results:

$$\sigma_R{}^2 = \left(\tfrac{1}{2}\right)^2 \sigma_X{}^2 + \left(\tfrac{1}{2}\right)^2 \sigma_Y{}^2$$
$$= \frac{\sigma_X{}^2 + \sigma_Y{}^2}{2^2}$$

This can be thought of as half the average of the variances.

If X and Y have the same normal distribution, then $\tfrac{1}{2}(X + Y)$ is the distribution of the mean of samples of size 2 taken randomly from that normal distribution. What do our discoveries imply about the distribution of the mean of samples of size 2?

Under these circumstances, X and Y have the same distribution, say $X \sim N(\mu, \sigma^2)$ (dropping the distinguishing subscripts). Then the distribution of $\tfrac{1}{2}(X + Y)$ can conveniently be written as the random variable, $\overline{X}_2$ representing the mean of a sample of size 2. The results suggest that the mean of the distribution of $\overline{X}_2$ is the average of the means of X and Y. So in other words the mean of $\overline{X}_2$ is $\tfrac{1}{2}(\mu + \mu) = \mu$. The variance of $\overline{X}_2$ is half the average of the variances, i.e:

$$\frac{1}{2}\left(\frac{\sigma^2 + \sigma^2}{2}\right) = \frac{\sigma^2}{2}$$

Hence, the distribution of the mean of a sample of size 2 is:

$$\overline{X} \sim N\left(\mu, \tfrac{1}{2}\sigma^2\right)$$

Exploration 25.2

Distribution of the mean of a sample

- Assume that the random variables, U, V, W are normally distributed as:
  $U \sim N(\mu_U, \sigma_U{}^2)$, $V \sim N(\mu_V, \sigma_V{}^2)$, $W \sim N(\mu_W, \sigma_W{}^2)$.

  Consider the random variable, R, where
  $R = \tfrac{1}{3}(U + V + W)$

  Describe its distribution and use this to explore the distribution of the mean of a sample of size 3 drawn from a normal distribution, $N(\mu, \sigma^2)$.

- Explore the distribution of the mean of a sample of size 4 drawn from $N(\mu, \sigma^2)$. Make a conjecture about the distribution of means of samples of size n drawn from a normal distribution.

Interpreting the results

Your exploration may have revealed that the mean of the distribution of sample means, or the mean of $\overline{X}_n$, is the same as the mean of X. You may have found that the variance of the distribution of $\overline{X}_n$ gets smaller as the sample size increases. The variance of $\overline{X}_n$ is inversely proportional to the size of the sample.

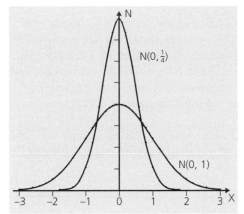

This is summarised in the diagram, which shows the distribution of means of samples of size 4 drawn from the standard normal distribution N(0, 1). The distribution of sample means is clearly considerably less spread than the standard distribution.

So if $X \sim N(\mu, \sigma^2)$ then means of samples of size n are:

$$\overline{X}_n \sim N\left(\mu, \frac{\sigma^2}{n}\right)$$

Standard error

The variance of the sample means is $\dfrac{\sigma^2}{n}$. Hence, the standard deviation of the sample means is:

$$\sqrt{\frac{\sigma^2}{n}} = \frac{\sigma}{\sqrt{n}}$$

The standard deviation of the distribution of means is known as the **standard error of the mean**. The term 'standard error' is given to the standard deviation of the distribution of a sample statistic.

Example 25.7

The energy in one portion of muesli served at breakfast in a large hotel may be modelled as a random variable with a mean of 125 calories. The variance may be assumed to be 100.

a) *Calculate the probability that a serving of muesli will contain more than 140 calories.*

b) *Each of a family of five has a serving of muesli. Calculate the probability that the mean energy that each of them has is more than 140 calories. Comment on the results.*

Solution

a) *Suppose X is the random variable representing the energy in a serving of muesli. Then $X \sim N(125, 100)$. The question is seeking:*

$$P(X > 140) = 1 - \Phi\left(\frac{140 - 125}{10}\right) = 0.0668$$

b) *This part of the example concerns the distribution of the mean energy in a sample of five servings. The distribution of the mean of a sample of size 5 is:*

$$\overline{X}_5 \sim N\left(125, \frac{10^2}{5}\right) = N(125, 20)$$

Hence: $P\left(\overline{X}_5 > 140\right) = 1 - \Phi\left(\dfrac{140 - 125}{\sqrt{20}}\right) = 0.000\,39$

Clearly there is considerably less chance of the mean serving having over 140 calories than an individual serving.

Distribution of sample mean

We have now seen that the distribution of the mean of a sample of a normal variate is itself normal. The **central limit theorem** says that it does not generally matter from which distribution we take samples. The distribution of the sample mean can be approximated by a normal distribution. The approximation improves as the size of the sample gets larger. More strictly, the central limit theorem (CLT) states:

> Given the random variable, X, with mean, μ, and variance σ^2, then the distribution of the mean, $\overline{X}_n$, of independent samples of size n approaches $N\left(\mu, \dfrac{\sigma^2}{n}\right)$.

Notice that the central limit theorem requires that μ and σ^2 merely exist. It does not demand that X is symmetric nor that it is continuous. This implies that the distribution of the mean of a sample drawn from, say a Poisson distribution, $\text{Poi}(\lambda)$, can be approximated by $N\left(\lambda, \dfrac{\lambda}{n}\right)$ where n is the size of the sample. This approximation is valid irrespective of the value of λ, in contrast with the sort of approximations considered in Chapter 24, *Approximating distributions*.

The question which so far remains unanswered is, 'What size of sample is sufficient?' There is no exact answer. Let us consider the following illustration. Suppose random samples of size 5 are drawn from the binomial distribution, $X \sim B(4, 0.2)$. This binomial variate has mean, $\mu = 0.8$, and variance, $\sigma^2 = 0.64$. The means $\overline{X}_5$, of samples of size 5, should be distributed with a mean also equal to 0.8, and variance $\frac{1}{5}(0.64) = 0.128$. This table contains the results of obtaining 200 samples of size 5 and records the means of those samples.

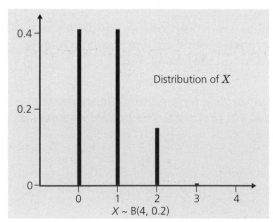

Distribution of X

$X \sim B(4, 0.2)$

Mean of sample	Frequency
0.0	2
0.2	9
0.4	30
0.6	34
0.8	43
1.0	36
1.2	26
1.4	12
1.6	5
1.8	3
2.0	0

Does the normal distribution: $N\left(0.8, \dfrac{0.64}{5}\right)$ fit these data?

Since X is discrete, then a **continuity correction** should be applied in considering the means of samples of observations of X.

Recall that the continuity correction, ±0.5, is used in approximating exact probabilities associated with a random variable which takes integer values. In this case, the sample mean is the variate and so the continuity correction becomes $\pm\dfrac{0.5}{n}$, where n is the sample size, i.e. 0.1 here. Hence, the probability $P(\overline{X}_5 = 0.2)$ is approximated by the standardised variates probability:

$$P\left(z \le \frac{0.3-0.8}{\sqrt{0.128}}\right) - P\left(z \le \frac{0.1-0.8}{\sqrt{0.128}}\right) \approx 0.0558$$

Try calculating some of the approximate probabilities for the values of $\overline{X}_5$ in the table above.

The table below shows the probabilities and expected frequencies.

$\overline{X}_5$	Observed	Approximate probability	Expected
0.0	2	0.0252	5.04
0.2	9	0.0558	11.16
0.4	30	0.1198	23.96
0.6	34	0.1890	37.80
0.8	43	0.2204	44.08
1.0	36	0.1890	37.80
1.2	26	0.1198	23.96
1.4	12	0.0558	11.16
≥ 1.6	8	0.0252	5.04

How close are these predicted frequencies to the actual frequencies? A casual inspection reveals that most are within 3 or thereabouts. Is this a close enough fit to accept that the normal distribution is a reasonable model for the distribution of these sample means? It is left to the reader to graph the frequencies and obtain a subjective answer.

We have seen that the sample size may be as small as 5, even if the variate is discrete. But we should use the appropriate continuity correction matched to the size of the samples when the sample size is small. When n is large, e.g. in excess of 10, and X is a discrete variate there is no need to use the continuity correction.

Exploration 25.3

A collection of activities on the central limit theorem

■ Return to the data in the table on page 522. Calculate:

a) the mean,   b) the variance,
of the means of the samples of size 5. Compare the calculated values with the values suggested by the central limit theorem.

■ Remind yourself about the distribution of random decimals. What is the mean of the distribution? What is the variance of the distribution? This table represents the results of obtaining a sample of four random decimals from a computer and calculating its mean. There are results for 300 samples.

$\overline{X}_4$	Frequency
$\overline{X}_4 < 0.25$	17
$0.25 \leq \overline{X}_4 < 0.3$	12
$0.3 \leq \overline{X}_4 < 0.35$	19
$0.35 \leq \overline{X}_4 < 0.4$	26
$0.4 \leq \overline{X}_4 < 0.45$	34
$0.45 \leq \overline{X}_4 < 0.55$	89
$0.55 \leq \overline{X}_4 < 0.6$	36
$0.6 \leq \overline{X}_4 < 0.65$	27
$0.65 \leq \overline{X}_4 < 0.7$	15
$0.7 \leq \overline{X}_4 < 0.75$	14
$\overline{X}_4 \geq 0.75$	17

a) Calculate estimates of the mean and variance of the empirical distribution of sample means and compare that with the values anticipated by the central limit theorem.

b) Compare the expected frequencies based on the hypothesis:
$$\overline{X}_4 \sim N\left(0.5, \tfrac{1}{48}\right)$$
with the observed frequencies.

■ Devise a program for a calculator or a spreadsheet which obtains samples of size 5 from a Poisson distribution, say Poi (1.0) and calculates their means. Carry out a comparison to determine if the normal distribution suggested by the central limit theorem provides a reasonable fit for the distribution of means.

Example 25.8

The life of a cut-price light bulb is a random variable which may be modelled by an exponential distribution with mean 300 hours. Hence, its variance is 300^2. These cut-price bulbs are sold in special packs of nine. Use the central limit theorem to estimate the probability that the average life of the bulbs in a special pack is in excess of 500 hours.

Solution
The central limit theorem suggests that the mean life of a pack of nine bulbs is distributed:

$$N\left(300, \frac{300^2}{9}\right) = N\left(300, 100^2\right)$$

Hence: $P(\overline{X}_9 > 500) = 1 - \Phi\left(\dfrac{500 - 300}{100}\right)$
$$= 0.022\,75$$

Example 25.9

A sample of ten jars of home-made marmalade were weighed. The total mass of the marmalade was 4663 g. Assume that the standard deviation of the mass of marmalade in a jar is 12 g. Test at the five per cent level of significance if there is evidence to support the view that the mean mass of marmalade per jar is less than 470 g.

Solution

Appropriate hypotheses for the test are:

$H_0: \mu = 470 \quad H_1: \mu < 470$

It is reasonable to assume that the mean mass of a sample of size 10 is normally distributed: $N (470, \frac{144}{10})$.

The observed sample mean is $\frac{4663}{10}$, *hence its standardised value is:*

$$\frac{466.3 - 470}{\sqrt{\frac{144}{10}}} \approx -0.975$$

The appropriate critical value for this one-tailed test conducted at the five per cent level of significance is –1.645. Hence the test statistic is not significant.

Thus it is reasonable to conclude that there is not sufficient evidence to support the view that the mean mass of marmalade is less than 470 g.

EXERCISES

25.3 CLASSWORK

1 The daily takings from a corner shop is a normal variate with a mean of £800 and a variance of 2500.

a) Find the probability that the takings for one day exceed £900.
b) Find the probability that the mean daily takings for a five-day period are greater than £850.
c) Find the probability that the mean daily takings for a six-day period lie between £780 and £820.
d) Find the interquartile range for the mean daily sales over five days.

2 The time taken to serve customers at a post office can be modelled as a random variable with a mean of 3 minutes and a variance of 4.

a) Find the probability that a transaction takes less than two minutes.
b) Find the probability that the mean time for ten transactions is greater than 3.5 minutes.
c) When Rachel joins the queue one person is about to be served and three others are standing in front of her in the queue. Find the probability that she will reach the counter in less than ten minutes.
d) Emma is standing behind Rachel in the queue. Find the probability that Emma is served within 14 minutes.

3 The length of straws is a random variable that is uniformly distributed between 20 and 21 cm.

a) Find the mean and variance of this random variable.
b) Estimate the probability that the average length of 40 straws exceeds 20.6 cm.
c) Estimate the probability that the total length of ten straws is less than 202 cm.

4 An organic food store buys apples that are described as 'Top grade'. The mass of these apples is a random variable with mean 200 grams and variance 100. Apples from other grades are lighter.

a) The mean mass of apples from a box of 20 is 195 grams. Carry out a test to investigate whether these are 'Top grade' apples or some other grade.

b) Repeat the test for another box of 20 apples with a mean mass of 198 grams.

c) What is the minimum mass for a box of 20 apples which could satisfy an inspector that they are 'Top grade'?

EXERCISES

25.3 HOMEWORK

1   The quantity of cheese sold each week in a grocery shop is a normal variate with a mean of 60 kg and a variance of 225.

a) Find the probability that less than 40 kg will be sold in a week.

b) Find the probability that the mean weekly sales in a five-week period are less than 55 kg.

c) Find the probability that mean weekly sales over eight weeks lie between 58 kg and 62 kg.

d) Find the interquartile range for mean weekly sales over eight weeks.

2   The time taken to conduct a foreign exchange transaction may be modelled as a random variable with a mean of 8 minutes. The variance may be assumed to be 4.

a) Find the probability that a transaction will take longer than ten minutes.

b) Find the probability that the mean time taken for the next four transactions is over 10 minutes.

c) Jean is standing fourth in the queue. Find the probability that she will reach the counter in less than 20 minutes.

d) Jane is standing seventh in the queue. Find the probability that she will reach the counter in less than an hour.

3   The length of wood off-cuts is a random variable, uniformly distributed between 0 and 0.5 m.

a) Estimate the probability that the average length of 20 off-cuts is over 0.3 m.

b) Estimate the probability that the combined length of ten off-cuts exceeds 2 m.

c) Miscellaneous lots of 100 off-cuts are sold. Find the interquartile range for the average length of off-cut in each lot.

4   The weight of 'A' grade oranges is a random variable with a mean of 150 g and a variance of 25. Other grades of oranges weigh less.

a) The mean weight of oranges from a bag of twelve is 140 g. Carry out a test to investigate whether these oranges are grade 'A' or another grade of orange.

b) Repeat the test for a bag of twelve oranges with a mean weight of 145 g.

c) What is the minimum weight for a bag of twelve oranges which would reasonably satisfy an investigator that the bag does consist of grade 'A' oranges?

BIVARIATE DATA

Pearson's product moment correlation coefficient (PPMCC)

We know that if a value of r is close to unity (either $+1$ or -1), then there is evidence in the data of a linear correlation between the variables. But when is a value of the product moment correlation coefficient 'close to unity'? Clearly, the answer to this question is very important.

One approach to this is to set up bivariate populations which do not show linear correlation and then obtain random samples for which the value of r is calculated. If this process is repeated a large number of times it ought to be possible to obtain an empirical distribution for r.

A simple way of generating a bivariate distribution is to use pairs of random decimals as (x, y) observations. We could generate eight pairs and then calculate the corresponding value of the product moment correlation coefficient. This gives one value of r. Try it yourself, using the tables of random digits, say in groups of five, to represent random digits, say in groups of five, to represent random decimals. Select sixteen groups and pair them off. Now treat the resulting eight pairs as coordinates of eight points from a bivariate distribution. Calculate the value of the product moment correlation coefficient, r where:

$$r = \frac{s_{xy}}{\left(s_x s_y\right)}$$

This gives us one value for r, and can be assumed to be an observation of the product moment correlation coefficient for eight uncorrelated data pairs.

To obtain a distribution of observations we need to repeat this process a large number of times, say 100 or more. You may like to use your calculator in this process as described in the following exploration.

CALCULATOR ACTIVITY

Exploration 25.4

Bivariate data – Sample size 8

a) Try programming your calculator to run a program based on this flowchart. It is intended to produce a value of the product moment correlation coefficient for a sample of size 8 from a bivariate population in which there is no correlation.

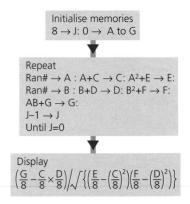

Record the output each time the program is run. Use a stem-and-leaf display with a unit equal to 0.01.

b) Once you have a 100 or more values of r recorded, you will have a reasonable impression of the distribution of r for eight pairs of data. Describe the distribution and try to identify ten per cent two-tailed (or five per cent one-tailed) critical values.

PPMCC

Exploration 25.5

Empirical critical values for the PPMCC

The following stem-and-leaf display represents the outcome obtained by running the above program a total of 131 times.

Units 0.01

```
−8 | 0
−7 | 8 8 4
−6 | 5 3 2 2 2
−5 | 7 6 6 3 2
−4 | 8 7 4 2 2 2
−3 | 9 9 4 3 2 1 1
−2 | 9 9 8 5 5 5 5 4 0
−1 | 9 9 8 8 7 7 6 6 4 4 1
−0 | 8 7 5 4 2 2 2 1 0 0 0 0 0
 0 | 0 0 0 0 1 1 2 2 3 5 7 7 9 9
 1 | 0 1 1 2 4 4 5 6 7 7 7 7
 2 | 1 1 2 2 2 4 6 7 8 9 9
 3 | 0 2 2 3 3 4 8 8 9 9
 4 | 0 0 3 3 5 7 8 9
 5 | 3 3 4 7 7 8 9
 6 | 0 1 2 3 5 8
 7 | 4 6
 8 | 3
```

To use this empirical distribution to determine critical values for r is perhaps optimistic. However, the following three examples show how we might use the display to obtain critical values.

a) H_0: product moment correlation coefficient = 0;
H_1: product moment correlation coefficient > 0

The null hypothesis reflects the way the distribution was obtained i.e. no linear correlation. The alternative hypothesis reflects an interest in positive linear correlation. H_1, therefore, indicates that you should be considering the upper tail. The five per cent upper-tail critical value has a depth of $0.05 \times (131 + 1) = 6.6$ which suggests that it is between 0.63 and 0.62.

b) H_0: product moment correlation coefficient = 0;
H_1: product moment correlation coefficient < 0

The interest in this as in the lower tail and the five per cent critical value is between −0.63 and −0.62. This agrees closely with the upper-tail value.

c) H_0: product moment correlation coefficient = 0;
H_1: product moment correlation coefficient ≠ 0

The alternative hypothesis addresses the issue of whether the data show linear correlation without any concern over positive or negative. Examining the tails of the distribution suggests that the five per cent critical values are between 0.74 and 0.68, and between −0.78 and −0.74.

Reflection

In Chapter 33, *Bivariable data*, of AS Mathematics, we met the following data for eight young runners in similar races under different conditions.

	Time (minutes)	
Conditions:	Dry	Wet
Runner	X	Y
A	35.5	37.4
B	40.4	40.5
C	38.8	39.6
D	39.9	39.8
E	38.0	37.1
F	37.2	36.1
G	34.7	36.7
H	37.9	36.8

Is there sufficient evidence in these data to support the hypothesis that the times in the two conditions are positively correlated?

The hypotheses relevent to this text are:

H_0: product moment correlation coefficient = 0;
H_1: product moment correlation coefficient > 0

and the sample of eight pairs of race times had a correlation coefficient of about 0.774. This value is closer to +1 than the critical value, 0.62 to 0.63, found in part **a)**. It is reasonable to conclude at the five per cent level, that the null hypothesis of no correlation can be rejected in favour of the alternative hypothesis of positive correlation. Hence, there seems to be evidence to support the view of a positive correlation between the times obtained in the dry and in the wet on all-weather tracks.

Tables of critical values for *r*

So far we have discovered properties of the sample correlation coefficient for eight data pairs. Clearly the distribution of values of r will differ with more than eight or fewer than eight data pairs. We have also obtained only an empirical distribution for r.

Tables of critical values are produced for a range of values of n (the number of pairs). These tables indicate the following upper-tail five per cent critical values.

n	Critical value of r
6	0.7293
8	0.6215
10	0.5494

The experimental distributions obtained are in close agreement with these tabulated values.

Example 25.10

a) Is there evidence to support the view, at the five per cent level, that the following data are positively linearly correlated?

X	2.71	5.09	4.27	3.36	3.99	4.52
Y	1.50	2.49	1.81	1.01	1.63	1.58

b) The ten members of a rugby club's squad who consider themselves as forwards took part in out-of-season training. Part of this training involved running 100 metres. In another part, they ran 10 km across country. Their times are shown in the table.

Distance	Time										
100 m	X (seconds)	22.4	23.5	12.5	22.2	15.5	19.1	23.8	21.9	22.2	19.9
10 km	Y (minutes)	46.9	44.5	49.8	40.3	43.7	52.0	46.9	35.0	41.6	40.8

Do these data support the view that those players who are fast over 100 m tend to be slow over 10 km and vice versa? Conduct your test at the five per cent level.

Solution

a) Appropriate hypothesis are:
   H_0: product moment correlation coefficient = 0;
   H_1: product moment correlation coefficient > 0.
   The value of r is 0.7447 which is closer to +1 than the critical value, 0.7293, for six pairs. It is reasonable to conclude that the data are positively linearly correlated.

b) Appropriate hypothesis are:
   H_0: product moment correlation coefficient = 0;
   H_1: product moment correlation coefficient < 0.
   The value of r for these ten pairs of data is – 0.3633. The tables do not give 'lower-tail' critical values, but the distribution of r is symmetric about r = 0. This means that the five per cent lower-tail critical value is – 0.5494. We can see that, for this data, r is not closer to –1 than the critical value. Hence there is insufficient evidence to support the negative correlation of the times over 100 m and 10 km. So the data do not support the view that the players who are faster over 100 m tend to be slower over 10 km. The data suggest that there is no linear correlation.

EXERCISES

25.4 CLASSWORK

1 The maize crop over a six-year period from a farming cooperative is recorded in the table, along with the corresponding rainfall.

Maize crop (tonnes)	69	86	67	80	72	68
Rainfall (mm)	50	65	42	55	60	35

Is there evidence in these data to support the hypothesis, at the ten per cent level, that the maize crop is linearly correlated to rainfall? State your alternative hypothesis.

2 Records of nine randomly-selected births were examined to determine if there is any evidence of a correlation between gestation period and the acidity (measured as pH level) of the mother's blood during labour.

The data are shown in the table.

Gestation	34	42	37	40	34	38	41	39	36
Blood pH	7.36	7.28	7.38	7.34	7.35	7.32	7.30	7.36	7.21

State suitable hypotheses and conduct a test of the correlation coefficient for these data. Make your conclusions clear.

3 The times of the births recorded in question **2** are given below.

Blood pH	7.36	7.28	7.38	7.34	7.35	7.32	7.30	7.36	7.21
Time of birth	20:15	00:30	13:45	18:00	10:15	03:00	15:30	21:15	14:00

The times are given using the 24-hour clock in hours : minutes.
i) a) Plot a scattergraph of these data.
  b) Comment on the extent of correlation you feel is evident from your scattergraphs.
  c) Conduct a test at the five per cent level of significance to determine if there is a positive correlation between blood pH and time of birth.
ii) Determine if there is any correlation between time of birth and gestation period.

4 Is there evidence in the following car production figures to support the view that car production and steel production are negatively correlated?

Year	1	2	3	4	5	6	7	8	9	10	11
Cars (000s)	9.8	19	27	32.1	43.8	41.1	37.8	43.1	61.1	78	71.8
Steel production	634	690	530	645	730	655	437	380	570	320	300

Justify your response.

5 The table records the average daily hours of sunshine each month for two years.

Month		Jan	Feb	Mar	Apr	May	June	July	Aug	Sept	Oct	Nov	Dec
Average	Y1	2.0	1.63	2.78	5.64	7.32	5.5	5.0	4.77	4.66	3.58	1.92	1.75
Sunshine	Y2	1.64	2.48	2.13	4.37	4.61	5.23	5.0	6.08	5.28	3.71	1.71	1.48

a) Plot a scattergraph of these data. Are the data correlated?
b) Justify your responses in **a)** by carrying out an appropriate hypothesis test.

6 The table contains production figures claimed by industry and the seasonally adjusted figures put out by a government.

Actual	42.1	30.7	37.4	25.8	35.2	35.2	36.2	34.1	36.6	35.6	32.5	31.0	31.2	31.6	21
Government	42.4	37.9	35.6	35.2	35.2	35.2	35.3	35.4	35.1	34.3	33.0	32.0	31.6	31.7	31.8

Test the claim that these data are positively correlated.

EXERCISES

1   The following are the percentage shares of the vote predicted for eight election candidates, x, and the percentage shares actually obtained, y.

x	57	70	46	35	15	44	30	55
y	71	72	49	41	16	39	58	77

Is there evidence to support the hypothesis that the data are positively linearly correlated? Use a five per cent level of significance.

2   Calculate the product moment correlation coefficient for these data:

x	1002	1003	997	995	1000	1006
y	63	66	52	52	57	70

a) between the given values of x and y,
b) between the transformed values of x and y:
$X = x - 1000$ and $Y = y - 50$.

3   An experiment produced the following results.
Product moment correlation coefficient between x and $y = 0.73$
Product moment correlation coefficient between x and $z = -0.64$
Product moment correlation coefficient between y and $z = 0.79$
Explain why there must be an error in these results.

4   a) Test the following set of bivariate data to see whether there is a significant negative correlation.

x	4.1	4.5	5.2	5.7	6.3	7.2
y	9.2	7.3	3.1	3.4	2.9	2.1

b) Draw a scattergraph of the data. Does this confirm your calculation in a)?

5   The prices of two commodities x and y were recorded each December for a period of twelve years. The results are given in the table below.

Price of x (£)	1.20	1.50	2.00	2.50	3.30	3.00	3.10	3.70	4.00	4.80	5.00	5.50
Price of y (£)	3.20	4.50	2.20	5.80	3.00	4.60	5.70	5.70	3.50	3.60	5.90	4.40

a) Draw a scatter diagram to illustrate the data.
b) State with reasons whether you would believe that the two prices were correlated.
c) Conduct a test at the five per cent level to determine whether there is a significant non-zero correlation between the two variates.

6   Consider the following set of data.

x	−3	−2	−1	0	1	2	3
y	9	4	1	0	1	4	9

a) Calculate the product moment correlation coefficient for these data.
b) Draw a scattergraph of the data.
c) Comment on your results.

RANK CORRELATION

In the section above, we discussed the **product moment correlation coefficient** (PMCC) and the way in which it is used to assess evidence of linear association. The value of the sample product moment correlation coefficient, r, for a collection of data pairs is not a reliable guide for assessing evidence of **non-linear** association. Neither is r reliable when one or both of the original variables has been replaced by positions or ranks (1st, 2nd, 3rd, ... etc.).

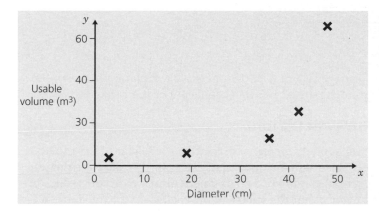

x Diameter (cm)	y Usable wood (m^3)
3	5.78
19	8.98
36	19.56
42	38.65
48	69.20

Study the scattergraph above. Do the data appear to be linearly related or might there be some other sort of relationship? Calculate the product moment correlation coefficient for these data.

You should find that $r = 0.8464$. A test, conducted at the five per cent level, of the hypothesis that the population correlation coefficient, ρ, is positive would suggest that this value is significant. The five per cent one-tailed critical value is 0.8054. This supports the view that there is a positive linear correlation in these data. This contrasts with the appearance of a 'curved' relationship.

Non-linear relationship

The data in the diagram and table above represent the base diameter of a tree and the usable wood in the tree, for five trees of different ages. It is reasonable to expect a positive association between the diameter of a tree and the wood in the tree. But it is not plausible for the relationship to be linear. There is a need for a measure of correlation that supports a positive (or negative) association, where appropriate, and that can be used for non-linear relationships.

Product moment correlation coefficient of the ranks

The simplest answer is to replace the data by their individual positions or ranks. For example, the smallest value of x is 3, so this is replaced by the rank 1. The next smallest x-value is 19, so this is replaced by the rank 2 and so on. The smallest y-value is 5.78 and this is replaced by the rank 1 and so on. The result of this is shown in the following tables.

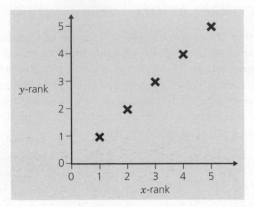

x-rank	y-rank
1	1
2	2
3	3
4	4
5	5

It is quite clear that there is perfect positive correlation between the ranks. What might the correlation coefficient of the ranks be?

Spearman's coefficient

Calculating the product moment correlation coefficient of the ranks rather than of the original values is an example of **rank correlation**. The resulting coefficient is known as **Spearman's rank correlation coefficient**. Notice that the values of the coefficient for the data and for the ranks are different. This is an indication that the distribution of the product moment correlation coefficient and Spearman's correlation coefficient are different. Try Exploration 25.6 to discover something of the distribution of r_S (r_S is the notation used for Spearman's coefficient).

Exploration 25.6

Distribution of r_S

The value of r_S for the ranks in the diagram and table above is exactly 1. Is this sufficient evidence at the five per cent level to support the assertion that the ranks are perfectly positively correlated?

- Show that there are 5! possible distinct arrangement of the five ranks, 1, 2, 3, 4, 5.
- Under the hypothesis that all arrangements of ranks are equally likely show:
  a) $P(r_S = 1) \approx 0.083$ **b)** $P(r_S \leq 0.9) \approx 0.042$ **c)** $P(r_S \leq 0.8) \approx 0.067$.
- Show that the five per cent critical value is 0.9.
- Conduct the hypothesis test and consider your interpretation.

Critical values

Tables of critical values of r_S may be found after the tables for the product moment correlation coefficient. The five per cent critical value for five pairs of ranks is 0.9. The value, 1, for the ranks in the diagram and data above is greater than this and so it is reasonable to conclude that there is a positive correlation between tree diameter and usable wood in the tree.

These tables may also be used to test two-sided hypotheses and to test for negative correlation.

Example 25.11

Forestry officials claim that, on mountains, trees grow at a slower rate the higher up the mountain they are planted. The evidence they put forward is in the table below. They measured the growth rate of trees in six plantations at different altitudes. A growth rate of 1 represents a faster growing tree than rate 2 etc. Test, at five per cent, the claims of the officials.

	Lowest altitude				Highest altitude	
Plantation	A	B	C	D	E	F
Growth rate	1	4	2	3	5	6

Solution

The six plantations are at different heights and so can be positioned. We can give the highest plantation the rank 1 and so on. This produces the following pairs of ranks.

x	6	5	4	3	2	1
y	1	4	2	3	5	6

The hypotheses for the test are:

H_0: no correlation; H_1: negative correlation.

The value of r_S (i.e. the product moment correlation coefficient for the ranks) is:

$$r_S = \left(\frac{\sum xy}{6} - 3.5 \times 3.5 \right) \div \left(\sqrt{\frac{35}{12}} \sqrt{\frac{35}{12}} \right)$$

$$\approx -0.8286$$

The tables of critical values for Spearman's coefficient indicate that 0.8286 is the upper five per cent one-sided critical value. This has to be interpreted as −0.8286 for the lower five per cent critical value. Hence, the result is significant indicating that there is evidence against the null hypothesis. The forestry officials seem to be justified in making their claim.

An alternative method of calculation

In calculating the product moment correlation coefficient for n pairs, (x, y), of ranks, the means and the variances can be pre-determined. The n ranks are going to be 1, 2, 3, ..., n in some order. Hence:

the mean of ranks = $\dfrac{n+1}{2}$

and the variance of ranks = $\dfrac{n^2 - 1}{12}$

This can be put to good use in calculating the product moment correlation coefficient of ranks.

$$r_S = s_{xy} \div s_x s_y$$

But $s_{xy} = \dfrac{1}{n}\sum xy - \left(\dfrac{n+1}{2}\right) \times \left(\dfrac{n+1}{2}\right)$

$= \sum \dfrac{xy}{n} - \left(\dfrac{n+1}{2}\right)^2$

and $s_x s_y = \sqrt{\dfrac{n^2-1}{12}} \sqrt{\dfrac{n^2-1}{12}} = \dfrac{n^2-1}{12}$

Hence the only variable in this is xy, the sum of the products of the ranks. This results in:

$$r_S = \dfrac{12\sum xy - 3n(n+1)^2}{n(n^2-1)}$$

which does not seem to be much of an improvement over using the familiar approach. However, Σxy can be expressed fairly simply in terms of the sum of the squares of the differences between the individual ranks. Consider defining the difference:

$d = x - y$

for each pair of ranks. Then:

$\Sigma d^2 = \Sigma(x-y)^2 = \Sigma x^2 + \Sigma y^2 - 2\Sigma xy.$

But $\Sigma x^2 = \Sigma y^2 = \frac{1}{6}n(n+1)(2n+1)$

Hence $2\Sigma xy = \frac{1}{3}n(n+1)(2n+1) - 2\Sigma d^2$

Then:

$12\Sigma xy - 3n(n+1)^2 = 2n(n+1)(2n+1) - 3n(n+1)^2 - 6\Sigma d^2$
$= n(n^2-1) - 6\Sigma d^2$

Hence:

$$r_S = \dfrac{n(n^2-1) - 6\sum d^2}{n(n^2-1)}$$

$$= 1 - \dfrac{6\sum d^2}{n^3 - n}$$

This alternative way of calculating Spearman's coefficient is preferred by some statisticians. However, you need to consider the facilities you may have available on your calculator to determine if indeed this is a preferred method for you. Notice, also the cautionary point about 'ties' following Example 25.12.

Example 25.12

Two judges at a horticultural show placed entries in the 'miniature tree' class in the order shown in the table. Test at the five per cent level, if there is evidence of agreement between the judges.

Entry	A	B	C	D	E	F	G
Judge X	3	5	1	2	7	4	6
Judge Y	2	7	3	1	5	4	6

Solution

Appropriate hypotheses for the test are:
H_0: no correlation; H_1: positive correlation.
The differences, d, in the ranks are shown below.

	A	B	C	D	E	F	G
d	+1	−2	−2	+1	+2	0	0

Hence, $d^2 = 14$ and Spearman's rank correlation coefficient is:

$$r_S = 1 - \frac{6 \times 14}{343 - 7} = 0.75$$

The five per cent critical value for seven pairs of ranks is 0.7143, the calculated value for the judges is closer to +1, hence the judges are in agreement.

A cautionary note – what do you do when there are ties?

Suppose that judge X could not decide between her top two miniature trees and so made them 'equal first'. To make the average of her ranks come to 4 as it ought to be, you need to give each of the 'equal first' the *average*, $1\frac{1}{2}$, *of the two ranks*, 1 and 2, which would otherwise have been the case.

Suppose that judge Y could not decide between the last three and so made them all 'equal fifth'. The average of his ranks must also be kept at 4, and so his final three trees would get the *average*, 6, *of the three ranks*, 5, 6 and 7.

The new table would now look like this.

Entry	A	B	C	D	E	F	G
Judge X	3	5	$1\frac{1}{2}$	$1\frac{1}{2}$	7	4	6
Judge Y	2	6	3	1	6	4	6

The value of Σd^2 is 5.5, hence the value of $1 - \dfrac{6 \Sigma d^2}{n^3 - n}$ is 0.9018.

However, calculation of r_S using the product moment correlation coefficient of the ranks produces 0.8976. The correct value is the latter. So there is not much difference between the values and it is acceptable to use the Σd^2 result provided there are not too many ties. However, it is far better to use the product moment correlation coefficient of the ranks at all times.

EXERCISES

25.5 CLASSWORK

1   A group of students gained the following marks in their Pure Mathematics and Statistics Modular examinations.

Student	A	B	C	D	E	F	G	H
Pure Mathematics	62	52	48	79	36	47	44	42
Statistics	74	66	52	71	56	73	40	57

a) Rank each set of marks.
b) Calculate Spearman's rank correlation coefficient.

c) Test at five per cent the hypothesis that there is a positive correlation between relative performance in the two examinations.

2   Five 200-metre runners kept a record of the times achieved in training in dry and in wet conditions. The table records the average times.

Competition	A	B	C	D	E
Dry	25.5	25.7	26.2	25.8	23.4
Wet	24.4	25.3	24.8	25.4	26.3

a) Rank these times.
b) Calculate the value of r_S for the ranks.
c) Is there evidence at the ten per cent level that there is a correlation between their relative performance in different conditions?

3   The mass and length of eight pine cones were recorded. The table shows the rank of the data. Low ranks correspond to high mass and great length.

a) Calculate the value of r_S.

Cone	A	B	C	D	E	F	G	H
Mass	2	6	1	5	3	4	7	8
Length	1	5	2	8	3	4	6	7

b) Is there evidence of positive correlation between the mass and length of pine cones?

4   In a ski-jumping contest each competitor made two jumps. The orders of merit for the ten competitors who completed both jumps are shown below.

Ski-jumper	A	B	C	D	E	F	G	H	I	J
First jump	2	9	7	4	10	8	6	5	1	3
Second jump	4	10	5	1	8	9	2	7	3	6

a) Calculate Spearman's rank correlation coefficient for the performances of the ski-jumpers in the two jumps.
b) Using a five per cent level of significance, interpret your result.
(ULEAC Question 4, Specimen paper T2, 1994)

5   A building society analyst used a combination of twelve ratios to measure the overall performance during 1992 of each of Britain's top ten building societies. The table below ranks these societies according to their performance rating. The table also indicates the size of each society as measured by its assets.

Building society	Performance rating	Assets (£million)
Cheltenham & Gloucester	1	14 789
Halifax	2	58 710
Leeds Permanent	3	16 631
National & Provincial	4	10 708
Bradford & Bingley	5	11 910
Britannia	6	8 524
Woolwich	7	20 165
Nationwide	8	34 119
Alliance & Leicester	9	20 479
Bristol & West	10	7 141

Sources: Wrigglesworth, J., 'Major Players' (UBS) 1993
Building Societies Yearbook 1993

Calculate an appropriate measure of correlation for these two sets of data, justifying your choice of measure. Interpret the value you obtain.

(NEAB Question 6, Specimen paper 8, 1996)

EXERCISES

25.5 HOMEWORK

1 Two judges independently judge the exhibits of five contestants in a flower show. The judges rank them as follows.

Contestant	A	B	C	D	E
Judge X	4	3	1	2	5
Judge Y	4	1	2	3	5

Calculate Spearman's rank correlation coefficient for these data and state, in general terms, how your answers confirms that the two judges agree reasonably closely.

(UCLES Question 3, Specimen paper S1, 1992)

2 In an investigation into the relationship between the speed of athletes and their IQ, nine athletes were timed over a measured distance, and their times and their IQs were recorded, as shown below.

Athlete	A	B	C	D	E	F	G	H	I
Time	12.1	12.5	14.2	13.5	12.1	14.1	14.6	13.4	12.6
IQ	114	110	120	117	102	121	115	109	91

a) Rank the times and the IQs.
b) Calculate the value of Spearman's rank correlation coefficient.
c) Do these data support the view that IQ and speed of an athlete are correlated?

3 Top-Exec is a recruitment agency which specialises in recruiting executives for top management positions. One management vacancy that was advertised attracted 94 applications. The ten best applicants were invited to attend for a day's activities, and were each subsequently given scores according to their performance in interview

(I), past experience (P) and performance in a short examination (E) designed to test their professional knowledge. The scores in the interview (I) and the examination (E) were as follows.

Applicant	1	2	3	4	5	6	7	8	9	10
Interview, I	6	4	5	8	9	3	4	9	10	2
Examination, E	3	5	7	7	6	8	7	10	9	4

Calculate the value of Spearman's rank correlation coefficient for these data and comment on your result.

The rank order correlation coefficient obtained between interview (I) and past experience (P) was 0.91 and between past experience (P) and examination (E) was 0.32.

Top-Exec was contemplating dropping the examination in future. Considering the three rank correlation coefficient values, comment on the wisdom of taking this action.

(NEAB Question 3, Paper AS, June 1994)

4   Three judges independently adjudicate the eight finalists in a piano competition. The orders of merit awarded to the pianists by each judge are given on the following page.

Pianist	A	B	C	D	E	F	G	H
Judge X	7	5	3	6	1	2	4	8
Judge Y	2	5	3	6	4	1	8	7
Judge Z	5	2	3	1	6	4	7	8

a) Calculate Spearman's coefficient of rank correlation between:
   i) X and Y,   ii) Y and Z,   iii) Z and X.
b) Comment on the results you find in a).

8   As part of a survey, two students were selected, randomly, from each of Years 7 to 12 in a large school. One of the questions asked concerned the pocket money they received. The answers were ranked and the results are given in the table.

Child	A	B	C	D	E	F	G	H	I	J	K	L
Year	7	7	8	8	9	9	10	10	11	11	12	12
Pocket money	10	9	8	7	2	6	5	1	4	3	11.5	11.5

a) Rank the years of the students.
b) Calculate the value of r_S.
c) Test the hypothesis that there is a negative correlation between school year and pocket money.
d) Repeat the above test with students K and L excluded. Comment.

SAMPLE PROPORTION

Point estimate

A random sample of 13 felled trees produces the following quantities of useable wood:
11.3, 8.8, 6.4, 8.7, 14.6, 16.2, 12.4, 7.1, 15.2, 10.3, 9.5, 17.2 and $7.8\,\mathrm{m}^3$.

You can see that three of the trees had more than 15 m³ of usable wood. What does this tell us about the proportion of such useful trees? The most immediate response is quite simply 'three out of 13', which works out as about 23 per cent.

Distribution of sample proportion

Assume that the proportion of trees of this species which are this productive is p. The number, X, of productive trees in a sample of size n may then be modelled by a binomial distribution.

$$X \sim \mathrm{B}\,(n, p)$$

Under the circumstances discussed in Chapter 24, *Approximating distributions*, binomial probabilities may be approximated using the normal distribution with mean equal to np and variance equal to $np(1-p)$. It is a short step from knowing the distribution of the number of productive trees in a sample of given size, to working out a reasonable model for the distribution of the proportion. Recall that the proportion, $\frac{3}{13}$, of productive trees was found by dividing the number, 3, by the sample size, 13. Thus in a general case, sample proportion is found in the same way, i.e. by dividing the number observed, X, by the size of the sample, n. Since, $X \approx \mathrm{N}(np, np(1-p))$, it means that sample proportion, $\frac{x}{n}$, is distributed approximately normally.

$$\frac{x}{n} \approx \mathrm{N}\left(\frac{np}{n}, \frac{np(1-p)}{n^2}\right)$$

$$= \mathrm{N}\left(p, \frac{p(1-p)}{n}\right)$$

This indicates that the distribution of the sample proportion is approximately normal, and has mean equal to the population proportion, p, and variance equal to $\dfrac{p(1-p)}{n}$, which depends on the size of the sample and on p.

Example 25.13

Test, at the two per cent level of significance, the hypothesis that the proportion of trees with more than $15\,m^3$ of usable wood is under half.

Solution
Appropriate hypotheses for the test are:

H_0: $p = 0.5$ H_1: $p < 0.5$

The observed proportion is $\frac{3}{13}$, its distribution may be assumed to be normal with mean equal to 0.5 and variance $\frac{0.25}{13}$. The test statistic is:

$$\frac{\frac{3}{13} - 0.5}{\sqrt{\frac{0.25}{13}}} \approx -1.941$$

The critical region for this test is $Z < 2.054$, hence the result is not significant. It is reasonable to conclude that there is insufficient evidence to assume that the proportion of such trees is under half.

EXERCISES

1   A random sample of 12 apples on sale in supermarkets is inspected and 4 apples are found to be bruised. Conduct a test, at the five per cent level of significance, to determine if the proportion of all apples in the supermarket could be as high as $\frac{1}{2}$.

2   Nationally, 28 per cent of households own a pet. In a certain region, five households in a random sample of ten own a pet. Is there evidence that pet ownership is significantly above average in this region?

3   It is claimed that, after vaccination, only 25 per cent of adults will catch 'flu during the winter.

   a) In a random sample of 200, 80 caught 'flu. Test the claim at the five per cent significance level.
   b) In a random sample of 5, 2 caught 'flu. Test the claim at the five per cent significance level.
   c) Compare your answers to a) and b).

4   A survey of 1225 people showed that 283 had changed their car in the previous twelve months. Is this sufficient evidence, at the one per cent level, to justify the claim that a quarter of car owners change their car each year?

EXERCISES

1   A sample of 200 nails produced by a machine is carefully measured, and 43 of the nails are found to be undersized. Conduct a test, at the five per cent level of significance, to determine if it is fair to claim that a quarter of all nails are undersized.

2   It is estimated that nationally 35 per cent of households have a computer. In a certain town 45 households out of a sample of 100 had a computer. Is there evidence that the level of ownership of computers is above average for this town?

3   It is claimed that only 20 per cent of the longterm unemployed remain unemployed after attending a job preparation scheme.

   a) In a sample of 400, 100 remained unemployed. Test the claim at the five per cent significance level.
   b) In a sample of 100, 25 remained unemployed. Test the claim at the five per cent significance level.
   c) Compare your answers to a) and b).

4   Out of a random sample of 200 people asked, 54 said that they travelled by train regularly. Is this sufficient evidence, at the five per cent level, to support the claim that a quarter of the population travel by train regularly?

CONSOLIDATION EXERCISES FOR CHAPTER 25

1 A coin is tossed five times and no heads are obtained.
   a) Is there evidence, at the one per cent significance level, that the coin is biased against heads?
   b) Is there evidence, at the five per cent level, that the coin is biased against heads?
   Discuss the usefulness of each of these tests.

2 **a)** A coin is tossed five times and one head is obtained. Is there evidence at the two per cent level of significance that the coin is biased against heads?
   b) Repeat **a)** when the coin is tossed ten times and two heads are obtained.
   c) Repeat **a)** when the coin is tossed 15 times and three heads are obtained.
   d) Discuss **a)**, **b)**, **c)**.

3 The national pass rate of an examination is 70 per cent. A teacher finds that six out of the twelve children in his class pass. Is there evidence at the five per cent level that this group did significantly worse than average?

4 **a)** Give proof that the mean and variance of a random variable, X, which is binomially distributed are np and $np(1-p)$ with the conventional notation.
   A disease for which there is yet no known cure has a natural recovery rate of 30 per cent, that is to say that 30 per cent of the patients who suffer from this disease recover. A group of ten patients suffering from the disease are to receive a new drug. The drug will be given more extensive trialling if four or more of this group recover.
   b) What is the probability that a drug which in fact has no effect is given further trialling?
   c) Find also the probability that the new treatment will be rejected even if it increases the recovery rate to 70 per cent.

5 I suspect that a cubical die is biased against coming up as a 6. I decide to conduct a statistical test.
   a) Explain why $H_1: p < \frac{1}{6}$ is an appropriate alternative hypothesis.
   b) I decide to conduct my test at the five per cent level. My experiment consists of rolling the die 16 times and recording the number of 6s which occur. What conclusion should I reach if the number is zero?
   c) Suppose, instead, I had chosen to roll the die 26 times. What is the critical region?

6 A trainer claims that one of her squad of gymnasts has improved her performance on the vault. Last season, the gymnast had perfect scores on 70 per cent of her vaults. This season she has had a perfect score on 18 of the 20 vaults she has done. Test the claim of the trainer at the five per cent level.

7 A packet contains 20 seeds, and on average, 75 per cent of this variety of seed germinate. Calculate the probability that 18, 19 or 20 of the seeds will germinate. A new way of packaging seeds becomes available and it is claimed that this results in higher germination rate. What is the critical region if the level of significance is:
   a) 10%   **b)** 5%   **c)** 2%?

8 In Manuel's restaurant the probability of a customer asking for a vegetarian meal is 0.30. During one particular day in a random sample of 20 customers at the restaurant three ordered a vegetarian meal.

a) Stating your hypotheses clearly, test, at the five per cent level of significance, whether or not the proportion of vegetarian means ordered that day is unusually low.

Manuel's chef believes that the probability of a customer ordering a vegetarian meal is 0.10. The chef proposes to take a random sample of 100 customers to test whether or not there is evidence that the proportion of vegetarian meals ordered is different from 0.10.

b) Stating your hypotheses clearly, use a suitable approximation to find the critical region for this test. The probability for each tail of the region should be as close as possible to 2.5%.

c) State the significance level of this test giving your answer to two significant figures.

(EDEXCEL Question 5, Specimen paper 2, 2000)

9 A student answers a test consisting of 16 multiple-choice questions, in each of which the correct response has to be selected from the four possible answers given. The student only gets two of the questions correct, and the teacher remarks that this 'shows that the student did worse than anyone would do just by guessing the answers'. The probability of the student answering a question correctly is denoted by p, assumed to be the same for all the question in the test.

i) State suitable null and alternative hypotheses, in terms of p, for a test to examine whether the teacher's remark is justified.

ii) Carry out the test, using a ten per cent significance level, and state your conclusion clearly.

(OCR Question 2, Specimen paper 2, 2000)

10 Inspection of 100 metres of curtain material revealed a total of four flaws. Using a suitable Poisson distribution as a model, test at the two per cent significance level the null hypothesis that the mean number of flaws per 10 metres of the material is equal to 1, against the alternative that it is less than 1.

(WJEC Question 3, Specimen paper A3, 1994)

11 A company director monitored the number of errors on each page of typing done by her new secretary and obtained the following results:

No. of errors	0	1	2	3	4	5
No. of pages	37	65	60	49	27	12

a) Show that the mean number of errors per page in this sample of pages is 2.

b) Find the variance of the number of errors per page in this sample.

c) Explain how your answers to parts a) and b) might support the director's belief that the number of errors per page could be modelled by a Poisson distribution.

Some time later the director notices that a four-page report which the secretary has just typed contains only three errors. The director wishes to test whether or not this represents evidence that the number of errors per page made by the secretary is now less than 2.

d) Assuming a Poisson distribution and stating your hypothesis clearly, carry out this test. Use a five per cent level of significance.

(EDEXCEL *Question 4, Specimen paper 2, 2000*)

12 A fisherman catches, on average, four fish, when he fishes at a certain lake.

a) On one visit to the lake he caught only two fish. Does this indicate that it has become more difficult to catch fish at this lake?
b) If he caught four fish from two visits, does this suggest that it has become more difficult to catch fish at this lake?
c) How would you respond if he caught eight fish in four visits?

13 An orchestra has 80 members. On average only one fails to attend a concert.

a) If four members fail to attend a concert, is there evidence that absentee numbers have increased?
b) In a special series of six concerts, there were only three absences in total. Is there evidence that the number of absences significantly declined for this series?

14 A school has 1200 students. On average each year three of them receive national honours. One year there were seven students given national recognition. Is there evidence that the average number of nationally-recognised students is on the increase?

15 The total number of train cancellations in a certain region, in a 30-day month was 47. Assume that, from previous studies, the variance of the number of cancellations is 1.4.

a) Test, at the one per cent level of significance, if the evidence is consistent with the claim that, on average, fewer than one cancellation per day occurs.
b) Estimate the probability of at least 60 cancellations in a 30-day month.

16 The number of accidents on a certain stretch of road in each of the last five years was:
19, 22, 23, 14, 22.

a) What probability distribution might be appropriate to model the number of road accidents each year on a given stretch of road? State its mean and variance in this case.
b) Test, at the five per cent significance level, the claim that on average there are fewer than 24 accidents per year.
c) Test this claim at the one per cent significance level.
d) Compare and comment on your answers to **b)** and **c)**.

17 A chamber of commerce claims that the average take-home pay of manual workers in full-time employment in its area is £140 per week. A sample of 125 such workers had mean take-home pay of £148 with a standard deviation of £28.

a) Test, at the five per cent significance level, the hypothesis that the mean take-home pay of all manual workers in the area is £140. Assume that the sample is random and that the distribution of take-home pay is normal. State clearly your null and alternative hypotheses.

b) How would your conclusion be affected if you later discovered that:

   i) the distribution of take-home pay was not normal but the sample was random,

   ii) the sample as not random but the distribution of take-home pay was normal?

Give a brief justification for each of your answers.

(AQA B Question 2, Specimen paper 4, 2000)

18 It is thought that the heights of a population of plants are normally distributed with a mean of 55 cm and a standard deviation of 9 cm. The mean height of a group of 20 of these plants is 51.2 cm.

   a) Test the hypothesis that, at the five per cent significance level, the mean of the population is less than 55 cm.

   b) Describe a type I error in the context of this test and give the probability of making such an error.

(AQA A Question 4, Specimen paper 2, 2000)

19 Lessons in a school are supposed to last for 40 minutes. However, a Mathematics teacher finds that pupils are usually late in arriving for his lessons, and that the actual length of teaching time available can be modelled by a normal distribution with mean 34.8 minutes and standard deviation 1.6 minutes.

   i) Find the probability that the length of teaching time available will be less than 37.0 minutes.

   ii) The probability that the length of teaching time available exceeds m minutes is 0.75, Find m.

The teacher has a weekly allocation of 5 lessons with a particular class. Assuming that these 5 lessons can be regarded as a random sample, find the probability that the mean length of teaching time available in these 5 lessons will lie between 34.0 and 36.0 minutes.

(OCR Question 3, Specimen paper 2, 2000)

20 The 'reading age' of children about to start secondary school is a measure of how good they are at reading and understanding printed text. A child's reading age, measured in years, is denoted by the random variable X. The distribution of X is assumed to be N(μ, σ^2). The reading ages of a random sample of 80 children were measured, and the data obtained is summarised by $\Sigma x = 892.7$, $\Sigma x^2 = 10\,266.82$.

   i) Calculate unbiased estimates of μ and σ^2, giving your answers correct to two decimal places,

   ii) Previous research has suggested that the value of μ was 10.75. Determine whether the evidence of this sample indicates that the value of μ is now different from 10.75. Use a ten per cent significance level for your test.

   iii) State, giving a brief reason, whether your conclusion in part **ii)** would remain valid if:

   a) the distribution of X could not be assumed to be normal,

   b) the 80 children were all chosen from those starting at one particular secondary school.

(OCR Question 6, Specimen paper 2, 2000)

21 The breaking strength of a certain type of fishing line has a normal distribution with standard deviation 0.24 kN. A random sample of 10 lines is tested. The mean breaking strengths of the sample and of the population are $\bar{x}$ kN and μ kN respectively. The null hypothesis $\mu = 8.75$ is tested against the alternative hypothesis $\mu < 8.75$ at the $2\frac{1}{2}$ per cent significance level.

   i) Show that the range of values of $\bar{x}$ for which the null hypothesis is rejected is given by $\bar{x} < 8.60$, correct to two decimal places.
   ii) Explain briefly what is meant, in the context of this question, by a type I error, and state the probability of making a type I error.
   iii) Explain briefly what is meant, in the context of this question, by a type II error, and state the probability of making a type II error when $\mu = 8.50$.

   (OCR Question 7, Specimen paper 2, 2000)

22 A particular brand of electric light bulbs have lifetimes that are normally distributed with mean 1200 hours and standard deviation 150 hours. It is suspected that a particular batch of these bulbs is sub-standard in that the mean lifetime is less that 1200 hours. To test this suspicion a random sample of 25 bulbs is to be taken from the batch and their lifetimes measured.

   a) Determine the significance level of the decision rule which will conclude that the batch is sub-standard if the sample mean lifetime is less than 1173 hours.
   b) Determine the decision rule that should be used for the significance level to be five per cent.
   c) Using the rule in **b)** what conclusion should be drawn if the sample mean lifetime is equal to 1145 hours?

   (WJEC Question 2, Specimen paper 2, 2000)

23

Age	4:5	5:6	6:8	8:7	9:7	10:1	11:1	12:5
Hours	14	14.2	14.4	15.5	15.5	15.8	15.9	18.0

The ages of eight randomly-selected children are recorded (years:months) together with an estimate of the time (in hours) they spent awake the previous day.

   a) Calculate the product moment correlation coefficient for these data.
   b) Test, at the five per cent level, whether the data are positively linearly related.
   c) Plot a graph of the data and comment.

24

Preservative	0.25	0.35	0.40	0.60	0.65	0.80	0.95	1.00
pH	7.5	7.4	7.3	7.3	7.4	7.6	7.7	7.9

   a) Calculate the product moment correlation coefficient for these data and interpret its value.
   b) Plot a scattergraph of the data and review your interpretation.
   c) Investigate whether (preservative)^2 is a better independent variable.

25 A technician monitoring water purity believes that there is a relationship between the hardness of the water and its alkalinity. Over a period of ten days, she recorded the data in this table.

Alkalinity (mg/l)	33.8	29.1	22.8	26.2	31.8	31.9	29.4	26.1	28.0	27.2
Hardness (mg/l)	51.0	45.0	41.3	46.0	48.0	50.0	46.3	45.0	45.3	43.0

a) Plot the data on graph paper with 'Alkalinity' on the horizontal axis.

b) Carry out an appropriate test to assess whether a straight line is an appropriate model for the relationship between alkalinity and hardness.

26 The marks awarded by two judges to ten contestants are given in the table.

Contestant	1	2	3	4	5	6	7	8	9	10
Judge X	5	6	8	4	7	5	9	4	6	5
Judge Y	8	7	8	6	9	8	9	7	8	7

a) Rank the marks given by each judge taking care over the tied ranks.

b) Obtain the value of Spearman's rank correlation coefficient.

c) Test, at five per cent, the hypothesis that there is positive agreement between the judges.

27 Eight children took a mathematics test and an English test. The marks they each got are shown in the table.

Child	A	B	C	D	E	F	G	H
Mathematics	9	6	9	5	9	5	8	0
English	4	6	9	2	1	9	4	1

a) Carefully rank the marks in each test.

b) Obtain the value of r_S.

c) Test the hypothesis that there is positive correlation between their relative performance in the subjects.

28 An experiment was conducted to see if there is a correlation between the colour of paint and its drying time. The results, for the 'seven colours of the rainbow' are shown in the table.

Colour	R	O	Y	G	B	I	V
Drying time	10.6	7.3	9.9	9.6	8.8	8.2	9.2

a) Rank the colours and their drying times.

b) Test the data to determine if there is correlation.

29 Two independent assessors awarded marks to each of five projects. The results were as shown in the table.

Project	A	B	C	D	E
First assessor	38	91	62	83	61
Second assessor	56	84	41	85	62

Calculate Spearman's rank correlation coefficient for the data.

Show, by sketching a suitable scatter diagram, how two assessors might have assessed five projects in such a way that Spearman's rank correlation coefficient for their marks was +1 while the product moment correlation coefficient for their marks was not +1. (Your scatter diagram need not be drawn accurately to scale.)

(OCR Question 2, Specimen paper 1, 2000)

30 In a national survey into whether low death rates are associated with greater prosperity, a random sample of 14 areas was taken. The areas, arranged in order of their prosperity, are shown in the table below, together with their death rates. The death rates are on a scale for which 100 is the national average.

Area	A	B	C	D	E	F	G	H	I	J	K	L	M	N
Death rate	66	76	84	83	102	78	100	110	105	112	122	131	165	138

a) Calculate an appropriate correlation coefficient and use it to test, at the five per cent level of significance, whether or not there is such an association. State your hypotheses and your conclusion carefully.

b) A newspaper carried this story under the headline, 'Poverty causes increased deaths'. Explain carefully whether or not the data justify this headline.

c) The data include no information of the age distributions in the different areas. Why would such additional information be relevant?

(MEI Question 1, Paper S2, January 1995)

31 Write down appropriate null and alternative hypotheses when testing the unbiasedness of a coin.

In 50 tosses of a particular coin a head occurred in 29 of the tosses. Determine the p-value of this result when testing the unbiasedness of the coin. State the conclusions you draw from the p-value.

(WJEC Question 4, Paper S2, 2000)

32 In an election there are two candidates, A and B. A random sample of 1000 voters is taken and, of these, 545 say they will vote for A. State a point estimate for the fraction of A-voters in the whole population. Determine if there is sufficient evidence to say that over half the voters would support candidate A (conduct your test at the two per cent level).

33 After a young child was knocked down outside her home by a speeding stolen car, a group of neighbours conducted a vigorous campaign to have speed bumps introduced on all roads in their large estate. The local evening newspaper sampled local opinion and, from a random sample of 90 adult residents of the estate, found that 34 out of the 50 women and 16 out of the 40 men in the sample supported the introduction of speed bumps. Test at the five per cent level, the claim:

a) that more than half of women

b) that fewer than half of men

are in favour of speed calming bumps in the road.

34 An observer at a railway station records whether trains arrive on time (which he defines as within two minutes of the scheduled arrival time). The results from a random sample of 25 trains follow (where L indicates late and O indicates on time).

O, O, L, O, O, L, L, O, O, L, O, L, O, O, O, O, O, O, O, L, O, O, L, O, L, L

Assume that the probability, p, of a train arriving late is a constant and that the arrival times of all trains are independent.

a) **i)** Estimate p.
    ii) Are these data indicative of the claim that more than 15 per cent of trains are late? Conduct your test at $2\frac{1}{2}$ per cent level.)

The timetable is revised in an attempt to improve the situation. Following this revision 28 out of a random sample of 200 trains are observed to arrive late.

b) **i)** Estimate the value of p after the timetable revision.
    ii) Using the value of p estimated in **b)i)**, test the claim that fewer than 15 per cent of trains are late.

35 A new drug cure for the common cold is being trialled. The pharmaceutical company tests the new drug on 40 volunteers. Within one week of taking the new product, 36 of the volunteers report that their cold symptoms have disappeared. The company cautiously claims that the drug cures at least 75 per cent of all colds. Test this claim.

Summary

In this chapter we have explored:

- some of the issues of statistical testing:
  hypotheses,
  critical regions and values,
  significance levels,
  one-and two-tailed tests,
  type I and type II errors.

- 8 tests in the context of:
  the binomial distribution,
  the Poisson distribution,
  the normal distribution,
  distributions of correlation coefficients.

- non-linear correlations:
  r_s = product moment correlations coefficient of ranks,
  $$r_s = 1 - \frac{6\sum d^2}{n^3 - n}, \text{ except when there are ties}$$

- the distribution of sample proportion
  $$\hat{p} \approx N\left(p, \frac{p(1-p)}{n}\right)$$

Validating models – the chi-squared distribution

In this chapter we shall:

- *reflect on the models discussed so far and find out how well they fit observed data,*
- *investigate an intuitive way of measuring the quality of the fit by considering the difference between the frequencies observed and those expected by the model.*

Exploration 26.1

Observed frequencies

You need two cubical dice, each numbered 1, 2, 3, 4, 5, 6. Roll the dice and record the number of **even** numbers (this will be 2, 1 or 0) in the outcome. Now repeat this process until you have recorded the outcomes for 20 rolls of the two dice. Record your results in a table like this.

No. of evens	Observed frequency
0	
1	
2	

Display your results in a frequency block graph.

EXPECTED FREQUENCIES

Let X represent the random variable 'the number of even numbers displayed when two dice are rolled'. What probability distribution is appropriate to model the relative frequency of the outcomes? We can assume that the dice are symmetrical and each face is equally likely to appear uppermost. Hence the probability that an even number results is $\frac{1}{2}$ for each die and for each roll. We can also assume that the outcome on one die is independent of the outcome on the other. The number of evens seen on each roll of the pair of dice may thus be modelled by a binomial distribution:

$$X \sim B(2, \tfrac{1}{2})$$

This model suggest the following probabilities:

$$P(X = 0) = {}_2C_0\left(\tfrac{1}{2}\right)^0\left(\tfrac{1}{2}\right)^2 = \tfrac{1}{4}$$

$$P(X = 1) = {}_2C_1\left(\tfrac{1}{2}\right)^1\left(\tfrac{1}{2}\right)^1 = \tfrac{1}{2}$$

$$P(X = 2) = {}_2C_2\left(\tfrac{1}{2}\right)^0\left(\tfrac{1}{2}\right)^2 = \tfrac{1}{4}$$

How well does this model fit your observed data?

Compare with reality

A first attempt at answering this might be to compare these probabilities with the frequencies you observed. But, if you do, you are not comparing like with like. The quantities you are comparing should be like quantities, either both frequencies or both probabilities. In this chapter we concentrate on comparing frequencies. We need to convert the probabilities suggested by the model into **expected frequencies**.

The model suggests that if a quarter of outcomes result in no evens, a quarter of the 20 rolls of the dice are expected to result in no evens. The model suggests the following results.

X	Expected frequency in 20 rolls
0	5
1	10
2	5

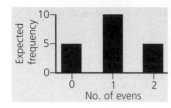

A graphical display of these expected frequencies is shown here. Compare these expected frequencies with your observed frequencies.

A measure of the quality of fit

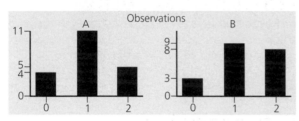

We are now in a better position to address the issue of how well a model fits observed results. Consider the two collections of observations displayed in this diagram. Do you think that:

- either
- neither
- both

are reasonably modelled by the display above?

Intuitively, it seems reasonable to say that observations A are very well modelled, but that the fit of the model is less good for observations B.

Descriptions of the fit such as 'good', 'poor' or 'perfect' are **qualitative**. In this chapter we are interested in **quantifying** the fit of providing a *measure of the quality of the fit* provided by a model. A simplistic approach to this is to find the total **differences between the observed frequency and the frequency expected** by the model. For observations A, this is shown here.

Outcome	$X = 0$	$X = 1$	$X = 2$
Observations A: O	4	11	5
Expected frequencies: E	5	10	5
Difference: $O - E$	–1	1	0

The total of the differences is zero. Try calculating the total of the differences between observations B and the expected frequencies. You should find that the total of the differences is also zero despite the fit appearing to be poorer. Unfortunately, the result will always be zero, regardless of the quality of the fit. The total of the positive differences will always be balanced by the total of the negative differences.

To overcome this we can **square the differences**. However, there is a further consideration. In observations A, the model expected five occurrences of $X = 0$ whereas four were observed, and ten occurrences of $X = 1$ when eleven were observed. In each case, the squared difference:

$$(0 - E)^2 = 1$$

is the same. But this squared differences is a much larger proportion of the expected frequency in the case $X = 0$ than in the case $X = 1$. It is $\frac{1}{5}$ i.e. 20 per cent, compared with $\frac{1}{10}$ i.e. ten per cent. This **relative difference** should be taken into consideration. A measure of the quality of fit can be found by the following process.

1   **Find the difference: $(O - E)$**
2   **Square the differences: $(O - E)^2$**
3   **Express these as a proportion of the expected frequency: $\frac{(O-E)^2}{E}$**
4   **Find the total of these relative differences: $\sum \frac{(O-E)^2}{E}$**

Applying this process to observations A produces this table.

Outcome	O	E	$(O - E)^2$	$\frac{(O-E)^2}{E}$
$X = 0$	4	5	$(-1)^2$	$\frac{1}{5} = 0.2$
$X = 1$	11	10	$(1)^2$	$\frac{1}{10} = 0.1$
$X = 2$	5	5	$(0)^2$	$\frac{0}{5} = 0.0$

Hence, the measure of the quality of the fit is:

$$\sum \frac{(O-E)^2}{E} = 0.3$$

Exploration 26.2

Measure of fit for observations B

Find the measure of fit of the model to the observation B.
The results you may have found are shown below.

Outcome	O	E	$(O - E)^2$	$\frac{(O-E)^2}{E}$
$X = 0$	3	5	$(-2)^2$	0.8
$X = 1$	9	10	$(-1)^2$	0.1
$X = 2$	8	5	$(3)^2$	1.8

This produces: $\sum \frac{(O-E)^2}{E} = 2.7$

Interpreting the measure of fit

It is worth reflecting on these measures. The binomial model seemed to fit observations A better than it fitted observations B. The measures of fit are 0.3 and 2.7 respectively. These measures are associated with the difference between the observations and the model. When the difference is large then the measure is large. The reverse is also true – when the difference is small the measure is small. A simple interpretation of the measure of fit is possible.

Value of $\sum \frac{(O-E)^2}{E}$		Quality of fit
small	small difference	good
large	large difference	poor

Exploration 26.3

An experiment

You need two cubical dice again. Roll the two dice and record the number of square numbers (i.e. 1 or 4) in the outcome.

- Repeat the process until you have recorded the results of 50 rolls of the two dice.
- Record your results in a frequency table.
- Try to explain why the binomial model B(2, $\frac{1}{3}$) is appropriate to model the relative frequencies.
- Use the probabilities of the model to find the expected frequencies of observing 0, 1, 2 squares.
- Obtain the measure of the quality of the fit.
- Interpret the measure.

Note: The expected frequencies are 22.222..., 22.222..., 5.555... in this case. It is reasonable to use these to three decimal places of accuracy. Although they are taken to represent frequencies, we do not use integers because these are the average frequencies expected by the model. Sticking to integers introduces errors which can cause confusion in the interpretation of the measure of fit.

Empirical distribution of the measure of fit

The table above provides a very simple way of interpreting the measure of fit for a particular model. A large value indicates a poor fit. The larger the value, the poorer the fit – but how large is large? We need to discover the distribution of possible values of this measure of fit. From this we ought to be able to determine which values might be considered to be large. One way of doing this is to generate some, say 20, observations of a random variable, X, where:

$$X \sim B(2, \tfrac{1}{2})$$

as in Exploration 26.1. Having obtained the observed frequencies, we need to calculate the corresponding measure of fit:

$$\sum \frac{(O-E)^2}{E}$$

This process needs to be repeated a large number of times. The sort of results you might obtain are shown below. This display represents the values of the measure of fit for 84 sets of 20 observations of X.

Unit = 0.1

```
0 | 4 3 4 3 3 3 8 0 3 3 3 3 3 8 3 3 8 3 0 4 3 8
1 | 2 2 1 5 1 1 9 5 0 9 2 9 2 9 2 9 9 2 2 2 9 6 1 1 9 1 6
2 | 7 7 4 7 7 4 7 4 7 7 7 4
3 | 6 6 6 2 6 6 6 6 6 2
4 | 8 8 4 8 8 4
5 | 1 1 9
6 | 8 8
7 | 2
8 | 9
```

The 84 values span 0.0 to 8.9. Their distribution is highly skewed and positively skewed. Each value has arisen as the measure of fit of the binomial model B(2, 0.5) to collections of observations generated in the same way. The aim here is to determine what is meant by a 'large' value of the measure of fit. It is worth reflecting on the concept of hypothesis testing and significance.

Now we shall test the null hypothesis: 'A model provides a good fit for observed frequencies' against the alternative hypothesis: 'It is not a good fit'. In brief:

H_0: model fits; H_1: model doesn't fit.

Using the measure we have discovered in this chapter, we can state the parallel hypothesis:

H_0: $\sum \frac{(O-E)^2}{E}$ is small; H_1: $\sum \frac{(O-E)^2}{E}$ is large.

If you use a five per cent significance level, you are prepared to take a five per cent chance of wrongly rejecting the null hypothesis.

Five per cent of the $\sum \frac{(O-E)^2}{E}$ values in the stem-and-leaf diagram

above are larger than 5.9, and the next largest value is 6.8. It is reasonable, on this evidence, to conclude that the five per cent critical value lies somewhere between 5.9 and 6.8.

Flipping coins

Exploration 26.4

Each of two boys had a coin and was flipping it. They recorded the number of heads showing each time after each had flipped his coin. The results are shown in the table.

Number of heads	Number of times
0	11
1	32
2	17

■ One boy proposed the following model: 'There are three possibilities i.e. no head, one head, or two heads, so you would expect to see each of these outcomes equally often'. This led him to suggest that the expected frequencies are: 20, 20, 20.

  Calculate a measure of fit for this model and comment on the result.

■ Propose your own model and test how well it fits the observed frequencies.

Likely results

The measure of fit for the equally likely model is:

$$\sum \frac{(O-E)^2}{E} = \frac{(11-20)^2}{20} + \frac{(32-20)^2}{20} + \frac{(17-20)^2}{20}$$
$$= 11.7$$

Appropriate hypotheses are:
H_0: equal likelihood is an appropriate model;
H_1: the model is not appropriate

The critical value for the measure of fit under these circumstances is

6.0, but the calculated value, 11.7, is much larger. Hence, the model is a poor fit. It is reasonable to conclude that the proposed model is inappropriate.

For the second part, a binomial model B(2, 0.5) is a reasonable proposal. This would have expected frequencies 15, 30, 15. Hence, the measure of fit would be:

$$\frac{(11-15)^2}{15} + \frac{(32-30)^2}{30} + \frac{(17-15)^2}{15} = 1.47$$

This measure is smaller than the critical value of 6.0. Hence, it is reasonable to conclude that the binomial distribution is a reasonable fit for these frequencies.

The chi-squared statistic and degrees of freedom

The measure, $\sum \frac{(O-E)^2}{E}$, we are using to judge the appropriateness of a probability distribution to model a collection of observed frequencies is know as a **chi-squared statistic** (from the Greek χ^2). Its distribution, hence the critical values, is dependent on the number of frequency cells in the model. More strictly, the distribution is dependent on the **degrees of freedom** of the model.

Degrees of freedom and frequency cells are very closely linked. In the case of the binomial model with $n = 2$, there are three possible frequency cells representing the cases:

$X = 0; X = 1; X = 2.$

The model will predict expected frequencies for each of the cells, but the total of these expected frequencies must be exactly the same as in the observed frequencies. Thus the model is free to predict expected frequencies for two cells but it is **constrained**, by the need to ensure that the total frequency is correct, as far as the third cell is concerned.

This leads to the definition:

degrees of freedom = number of frequency cells − number of constraints.

Example 26.1

Each of four children has a coin and flips it. They count the total number of heads showing. They repeat this until they have a total of 80 counts. The results are recorded in the table.

Number of heads, X	0	1	2	3	4
Expected frequency	3	27	25	23	2

a) *What probability model is appropriate as a basis for predicting expected frequencies?*

b) *Determine the expected frequencies and use these to find the value of $\sum \frac{(O-E)^2}{E}$ for these data.*

c) *State the number of degrees of freedom of the χ^2 statistic in this case.*

Solution

a) *Each coin can land either head or tail with probability equal to $\frac{1}{2}$. There are four children. Hence an appropriate model is the binomial: B(4, 0.5).*

b) *The frequencies predicted by this model are:*

Number of heads, X	0	1	2	3	4
Observed frequency	5	20	30	20	5

c) *The total of the expected frequencies must be 80. There are five frequency cells and one constraint, hence there are $5 - 1 = 4$ degrees of freedom.*

Critical values of the chi-squared statistic

We have already stated that the distribution of the χ^2 statistic depends on its degrees of freedom The Greek letter for n i.e. ν (nu) is used to represent the number of degrees of freedom of the χ^2 statistic. It is often written as a subscript, hence χ^2_4 represents a chi-squared statistic with $\nu = 4$ (i.e. four degrees of freedom).

The table represents a modest extract from tables of critical vales of the χ^2_ν statistic:

ν	1.0%	5%	10%	90%	95%	99%
2	0.0201	0.1026	0.211	4.605	5.991	9.210
4	0.297	0.711	1.064	7.779	9.488	13.277

The first thing to note about this presentation is that the percentages quoted are cumulative. Thus the given percentage represents the probability of observing a value of χ^2_ν which is less than or equal to the quoted value e.g.

$$P(\chi^2_2 \leq 5.991) = 95\%$$

Thus, 5.991 or above, represents the upper five per cent of the χ^2_2 statistic's distribution. This results in 5.991 as the upper-tail five per cent critical value for a chi-squared test with two degrees of freedom.

The second thing to notice is that the critical values for the χ^2_4 statistic are consistently larger than for the χ^2_2 statistic. For example, the upper-tail five per cent critical value for a chi-squared test with four degrees of freedom is 9.488.

The third thing to notice is that the lower-tail critical values are small, or perhaps very small, numbers. Recall the earlier interpretation table in which small values of the measure of fit indicated a small difference between model and observation. So, if you obtain a value of $\sum \frac{(O-E)^2}{E}$ which is smaller than the lower-tail critical values of χ^2_ν you are justified in concluding that there is an extremely close fit between the model and the observations. Some researchers feel drawn to say that under these circumstances the fit is 'suspiciously close, the implication being that the results are in some sense, too good to be true.

Exploration 26.5

Exploring χ^2

Explore the χ^2_v critical value tables at the end of the book. Identify the upper-tail two per cent critical value for:

a) χ^2_2 **b)** χ^2_4.

Example 26.2

A medical researcher investigated the blood type found in 1500 people. He chose 300 families each with five people and recorded the number of people with type-O blood in each family. His results are shown in the table.

No. of people with type O	0	1	2	3	4	5
No. of families	18	81	85	70	38	8

a) *Assume that a binomial distribution is appropriate to model the occurrence of people with type-O blood. If 45 per cent of the world's population have blood of this type, use the binomial model to determine the expected frequencies of occurrence of 0, 1, 2, 3, 4 people with type-O blood in families of five people.*

b) *Explain why it is not necessary to use the model to determine the expected frequency of five people.*

c) *Obtain the value of the measure of fit:*

$$\sum \frac{(O-E)^2}{E} \text{ for the data.}$$

d) *Conduct an appropriate hypothesis test at the five per cent level of significance and make your conclusions clear.*

Solution

a) *The binomial model is B(5, 0.45) and so the expected frequencies are:*
$X = \quad 300 \times (0.55)^5 = 15.099$
$X = 1 \ 300 \times 5(0.45)(0.55)^4 = 61.767$
$X = 2 \ 300 \times 10(0.45)^2(0.55)^3 = 101.073$
$X = 3 \ 300 \times 15(0.45)^3(0.55)^2 = 82.695$
$X = 4 \ 300 \times 5(0.45)^4(0.55) = 33.831$

b) *We know that there were a total of 300 families investigated, so the expected frequencies must come to 300. This means that the final frequency cell is constrained to contain:*
300 – (15.099 + 61.767 + ... + 33.831) = 5.535

c)

Observed	18	81	85	70	38	8
Expected	15.099	61.767	101.073	82.695	33.831	5.535
$\frac{(O-E)^2}{E}$	0.5574	5.9888	2.5560	1.9489	0.5137	1.0978

Hence,
$$\sum \frac{(O-E)^2}{E} = 12.6626$$

d) *Appropriate hypothesis are:*

H_0: *binomial model is a good fit for these data;*
H_1: *the model does not fit.*

Approximate five per cent critical value for the $\sum \frac{(O-E)^2}{E}$ statistic can be found by consulting the chi-squared tables. The number of degrees of freedom in this case is:

number of cells	minus	constraints	
i.e. 6	–	1	= 5

and the five per cent χ_5^2 (upper-tail) is 11.070. Since the test statistic, 12.6626, is larger then the critical value, there is a large difference between observed and expected frequencies. We can conclude that the binomial model is not appropriate for these data.

EXERCISES

26.1 CLASSWORK

1 Observations made on a discrete random variable, X, are shown in the table.

x	0	1	2	3	4
Observed frequency	35	76	62	21	6

a) Assume that the binomial distribution, B(4, 0.3), is an appropriate model for these data. Determine the frequencies expected by this model.

b) Explain why it is not necessary to use the model to determine the expected frequency of observation of the value $x = 4$.

c) Obtain the value of the measure of fit, $\sum \frac{(O-E)^2}{E}$, and conduct a χ^2 test at the five per cent level of significance.

d) What are your conclusions?

2 Two dice are rolled 216 times. The number of sixes appearing after each roll is recorded. The results are shown in the table.

Number of sixes	0	1	2
Observed frequency	128	78	10

a) Obtain the frequencies expected by the binomial model B(2, $\frac{1}{6}$).

b) Carry out a chi-squared test at the five per cent level of significance making your hypotheses and conclusion clear.

3 A survey was conducted with 500 economists. Each was asked five questions about economic indicators. The numbers of positive responses are recorded in the table.

No. of positive responses	0	1	2	3	4	5
No. of economists	7	22	128	167	133	44

a) Explain what assumptions would be needed in order to model the number of positive responses using a binomial distribution.

b) Determine the frequencies expected in using the binomial distribution, B(5, 0.6), to model the positive responses.

c) Conduct a chi-squared test at the ten per cent level of significance to determine if this binomial model fits the observed data. Make your conclusions clear.

d) What conclusion would you have drawn if the test had been conducted at the five per cent level?

4 Some students are conducting an experiment where they drop 20 coins on a large sheet of graph paper. They record the number of coins which land clearly in a grid square of the paper. They repeat this process 50 times.

No. coins landing clearly	≤ 5	6	7	8	≥ 9
Frequency	9	7	17	8	9

a) Explain why a binomial distribution may be an appropriate model for the number of coins landing clearly each time.
b) Assume that the distribution, B(20, 0.33), is appropriate and obtain the frequencies expected by this model for the classes indicated in the table.
c) Conduct a chi-squared test at the two per cent level to determine if this model fits. Report your findings.

EXERCISES

26.1 HOMEWORK

1 A student throws four coins and records the number of coins landing heads. She repeats this until she has a total of 160 recordings. The results are shown in the table.

Number of heads	0	1	2	3	4
Frequency	5	32	68	42	13

a) Explain why the binomial model, B(4, 0.5), may be appropriate to provide a fit for these data.
b) Conduct an appropriate test at the five per cent level of significance and report your findings.

2 On each of 200 days, a potter throws four plates and records the following data.

No. of exhibition plates produced	0	1	2	3	4
No. of days	9	35	69	71	16

a) Assume that the quality of the potter's work is such that 60 per cent of his plates are of exhibition standard. Use an appropriate model to determine expected frequencies.
b) Conduct a chi-squared test at the one per cent level of significance to determine if your model provides a reasonable fit for the data. Report your findings.

3 A calculator is programmed to produce random digits, from the range 0 to 9, in pairs. The number of even digits in each pair is noted until 50 pairs have been produced. The results are shown in the table.

No. of even digits	0	1	2
No. of pairs	13	17	20

a) Determine an appropriate model to fit these data.
b) Obtain the frequencies expected by your model and conduct an appropriate hypothesis test at the two per cent level of significance. Report your findings.
c) What conclusion would you have reached had you conducted your test at the:
   i) ten per cent level   ii) 0.5 per cent level?
d) Is there evidence in these data to suggest that the calculator is biased in its production of random digits?

4   The binomial model, B(8, 0.2), is proposed to fit the 200 observations in the table.

x	0	1	2	3	≥4
Frequency	31	65	60	31	13

a) Determine the frequencies expected by the model.
b) Conduct a chi-squared test at the ten per cent level of significance and report your findings.
c) Which one of the following descriptions would you use to describe the quality of the fit?
   very poor, poor, reasonable, good, very good

GOODNESS OF FIT

The χ^2 statistic may often be referred to as the **chi-squared goodness of fit**. We shall now develop its use in judging the fit of other models, where the expected frequencies give rise to concerns and where additional constraints are imposed.

Expected frequency convention

First, we consider the situation where each of a group of twelve children rolls a ten-faced die. The faces are numbered 0, 1, 2, ... , 9 and the number of zeros which result is counted. The experiment is repeated until the children have recorded a total of 50 counts. We need an appropriate model which could be used to determine the expected frequencies of occurrence of the possible counts of zeros.

The random variable, X, is the number of zeros recorded each time. We could use a binomial model:

$$X \sim B(12, 0.1)$$

The frequencies expected by this model are:

Outcome	$50 \times P(X)$		E
$X = 0$	$50 \times (0.9)^{12}$	=	14.122
$X = 1$	$50 \times 12(0.1)(0.9)^{11}$	=	18.829
$X = 2$	$50 \times 66(0.1)^2(0.9)^{10}$	=	11.506
$X = 3$	$50 \times 220(0.1)^3(0.9)^9$	=	4.262
$X = 4$	$50 \times 495(0.1)^4(0.9)^8$	=	1.065
$X = 5$	$50 \times 792(0.1)^5(0.9)^7$	=	0.189
$X = 6$	$50 \times 924(0.1)^6(0.9)^6$	=	0.025

etc.

The expected frequencies have been given to three decimal places. Clearly it is possible to continue calculating expected frequencies for the remaining possible outcomes. The frequencies are getting smaller each time. Suppose that the results obtained by the children are as given in this table.

Outcome, X	0	1	2	3	4	5	≥ 6
Observed, O	14	19	12	4	0	0	1
Expected, E	14.122	18.829	11.506	4.262	1.065	0.189	0.027

Are the expected frequencies close to the observed frequencies?

It seems that there is very little difference between any corresponding pair of O and E. Is this view born out by the measure of fit?

$$\sum \frac{(O-E)^2}{E} \approx 36.36$$

This seems to indicate an enormous difference between the observed and expected frequencies. What gives rise to this large value? The differences in the first four cells:

$$\sum_{X=0}^{X=3} \frac{(O-E)^2}{E} \approx 0.04$$

contribute about 0.1 per cent of the total measure of fit. This seems to agree with the closeness between the observed and expected frequencies. The problem lies with the remaining cells.

In these cells, the expected frequencies are comparatively small, at 1.065, 0.189, 0.025, ... and the measure of fit, $\sum \frac{(O-E)^2}{E}$, involves dividing these small quantities. The contributions from these cells are 1.065, 0.189, 35.064. To avoid wrongly rejecting the null hypothesis more often than anticipated by the significance level, it is necessary to *amalgamate frequency cells* so that the expected frequency is no longer small. It is generally agreed that *expected frequencies should not be less than 5.*

In this case, the sum of the expected frequencies for the first three outcomes, $X = 0$, $X = 1$, $X = 2$ comes to:

$$\sum_{X=0}^{X=2} E = 44.456$$

This means that the total for all the remaining outcomes:

$$\sum_{X=3}^{X=12} E = 50 - 44.456 = 5.544$$

is just over 5. So, to conduct a chi-squared goodness-of-fit test for these data based on fitting the model, B(12,0.1), it is necessary to reduce the number of frequency cells to just four.

Outcome, X	0	1	2	3 or more
Observed, O	14	19	12	5
Expected, E	14.122	18.829	11.506	5.543

Then the measure of fit:

$$\sum \frac{(O-E)^2}{E} \approx 0.077$$

is much more in line with the very reasonable view that a binomial model fits the observed frequencies. To confirm this, we consult the chi-squared statistic for the five per cent upper tail critical value for three degrees of freedom, i.e. 7.815.

There are three degrees of freedom because the number of frequency cells has been reduced to four. The total frequency must be 50 and this imposes the additional constraint on the model.

Generally, frequency cells should be amalgamated unless all expected frequencies are at least 5. This is not an unbreakable rule. Somewhat greater flexibility in testing models can be obtained by adopting the following convention. Amalgamate frequency cells until at least 80 per cent of the expected frequencies are at least 5 and no expected frequency is less than 2.

Fitting other models

The process of amalgamating cells opens the way to testing the fit of models such as the **Poisson distribution**, **geometric, or other distributions**. These distributions allow for exceedingly large values of the random variable which may never be observed in practical situations.

Suppose the headteacher of the infant school gave all 55 children in Year 2 a piece of written work. The numbers of errors made by the children are summarised below.

No. of errors, X	0	1	2	3	4	5	6	7	8
No. of children, O	4	12	15	13	6	4	0	1	0

The headteacher's experience suggests that children make 2.5 errors, on average, doing this piece of work and that the errors occur randomly. Does a Poisson model provide a reasonable fit for these frequencies?

The Poisson model Poi(2.5) indicates that the expected frequencies are:

X	0	1	2	3	4	5	6	7	8...
E	4.515	11.287	14.108	11.757	7.348	3.674	1.531	0.547	0.171...

The cells which might be amalgamated are those where the expected frequencies are small i.e. the cells corresponding to $X = 0$, $X = 5$, $X = 6$, etc. There is no need to amalgamate the cell corresponding to $X = 0$, particularly if the cells corresponding to $X = 5$, $X = 6$, etc are amalgamated. This gives the following table:

X	0	1	2	3	4	≥ 5
O	4	12	15	13	6	5
E	4.515	11.287	14.108	11.757	7.348	5.985

and the value of the measure of fit:

$$\sum \frac{(O-E)^2}{E} \approx 0.745$$

This compares favourably with the five per cent critical value of the statistic with five degrees of freedom, 11.070. It is reasonable to conclude that the Poisson model provides a good fit for the observed frequencies.

Additional constraints

Suppose that, in the infant school just considered, the headteacher was new. This might be the first time that the piece of writing had been set. The average would not be known, so the only way that a reasonable average could be obtained is by using the average from the data. This imposes a further constraint on the model and reduces further the degrees of freedom.

The mean, $\bar{x}$, number of errors per child for the data given initially is $\frac{132}{55} \approx 2.4$. Using the model Poi(2.4) produces the following expected frequencies.

X	0	1	2	3	4	≥ 5
O	4	12	15	13	6	5
E	4.989	11.975	14.370	11.496	6.897	5.273

The measure of fit works out to be 0.551. This time the number of degrees of freedom is:

$$6 \qquad - \qquad (1 \qquad + \qquad 1) \qquad = \qquad 4$$

frequency cells   less   (total to   +   mean obtained   = 4
be 55   +   from data)

Hence, the appropriate critical value of consider is the χ_4^2 statistic i.e. 9.488. We conclude that there is no reason to reject the Poi(2.4) model.

Exploration 26.6

Mind the gap

You need eight 2p coins, a large sheet of paper ruled with lines 4 cm apart, and some means of randomly projecting the coins onto the paper. A coin is described as a clear if, having landed on the paper, no part of it touches or covers any of the ruled lines. Your experiment consists of randomly projecting the eight coins onto the paper and counting the number of clears. Then repeat this process until you have a total of 40 counts. Now tackle the following model fitting processes.

■ Decide what probability distribution you feel is appropriate to model the occurrence of the number of clears when eight coins are randomly dropped on the paper. Determine the appropriate parameters from your experimental data and conduct a chi-squared goodness-of-fit test. Report on your findings.

■ Test the appropriateness of the model B(8, $\frac{1}{3}$) as providing a basis to model your observed frequencies. Report your findings.

Example 26.3

The fabric department of a large department store sells material from which curtains are made. The material is supplied to the store in rolls containing 50 m. When the departmental manager notices that there is no more than 3 m left on a roll, she checks the length. If she finds there is less than 1 m remaining, the material is discarded. If there is between 1 m and 3 m the material is sold at a reduced price as a 'remnant'. A model of the length of material offered for sale as remnant material is proposed. The density function, f(x), of the model is:

$$f(x) = \begin{cases} x-1 & 1 \le x \le 2 \\ 3-x & 2 \le x \le 3 \\ 0 & \text{elsewhere} \end{cases}$$

a) *If 40 remnants are measured, determine the expected number which will be found in the following length classes.*

$1.0 \le x \le 1.25$ $\qquad$ $1.25 \le x \le 1.5$
$1.5 \le x \le 1.75$ $\qquad$ $1.75 \le x \le 2.0$
$2.0 \le x \le 3.0$

b) *An examination of 40 remnants reveals the following data.*

Class	$1.0 \le x \le 1.25$	$1.25 \le x \le 1.5$	$1.5 \le x \le 1.75$	$1.75 \le x \le 2.0$	$2.0 \le x \le 3.0$
Observed	3	4	6	6	21

Carry out a goodness-of-fit test at the five per cent level to determine if there is sufficient evidence to support the proposed model.

Solution

a) *A sketch of the density is shown. It is apparent that the graph of the function is symmetric about x = 2. The probability, determined by the model, that a remnant will lie in a given range can be found from consideration of symmetry or by integration e.g.*

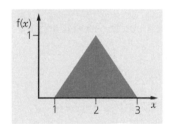

$$P(1.0 \le x \le 1.25) = \int_{1.0}^{1.25} f(x)\,dx$$

$$= \left[\tfrac{1}{2}x^2 - x \right]_{1.0}^{1.25} = 0.031\,25$$

which is $\frac{1}{32}$. Multiplying this by 40 produces the expected frequency of 1.25.

Other expected frequencies can be found as:

Class	$1.0 \le x \le 1.25$	$1.25 \le x \le 1.5$	$1.5 \le x \le 1.75$	$1.75 \le x \le 2.0$	$2.0 \le x \le 3.0$
Expected	1.25	3.75	6.25	8.75	20

b) *The first two cells should be amalgamated since the expected frequencies are low. This results in the following table.*

Class	$1.0 \le x \le 1.5$	$1.5 \le x \le 1.75$	$1.75 \le x \le 2.0$	$2.0 \le x \le 3.0$
E	5	6.25	8.75	20
O	7	6	6	21

The value of the measure of fit:

$$\sum \frac{(O-E)^2}{E} = 1.724$$

There are four frequency cells and one constraint (the total frequency must be 40), hence, the number of degrees of freedom for the chi-squared statistic is 3. The five per cent upper-tail critical value is 7.815. Clearly, the test result is much less than this, which suggests that the model is reasonable.

EXERCISES

26.2 CLASSWORK

1   A Geiger counter is a device for recording the number of radioactive particles emitted by an appropriate source. The numbers of emissions recorded by a Geiger counter in each of 100 one-second intervals are shown in the table.

Number recorded	0	1	2	3	4	≥ 5
Frequency	20	19	29	13	13	6

a) Explain briefly why a Poisson distribution may be appropriate to model the number of particles recorded in one second.
b) Determine the mean number of emissions in one second. Use this to derive the frequencies expected by the Poisson model. (Assume, for the mean, that 5.5 is representative of the '≥ 5' class.)
c) Test at the five per cent level whether the Poisson model is appropriate. Report your findings carefully.

2   The number of fraudulent claims received each day by an insurance company is shown in the table.

Number of frauds	0	1	2	3	≥ 4
Frequency	29	38	21	10	2

a) Assume that the mean number of fraudulent claims that the company has usually received is 1.1 per day. Determine an appropriate probability model for these data.
b) Carefully conduct a chi-squared goodness-of-fit test at the two per cent level.
c) Interpret your findings.

3   The librarian of a college library wanted to know if the number of books borrowed each day (of a six-day week) was uniformly distributed. She collected the following records.

Day	Mon	Tue	Wed	Thu	Fri	Sat
No. borrowed	308	292	243	229	226	202

a) Determine the daily number of books expected by a uniform model.
b) Conduct a goodness-of-fit test at the two per cent level.
c) Interpret your findings.

4 A model is proposed for a continuous random variable. The proposed density function is given below.

$$f(x) = \begin{cases} \frac{(6-x)}{18} & \text{when } 0 \leq x < 6 \\ 0 & \text{otherwise} \end{cases}$$

Test if this model is an appropriate fit for the 100 items of data in the table. Conduct your test at the five per cent level.

Class	$0 \leq x < 1$	$1 \leq x < 2$	$2 \leq x < 4$	$4 \leq x < 6$
Frequency	36	29	22	13

5 A manuscript in an unknown hand is discovered. It is suggested that it is the work of a well-known 19th-century novelist. It is known that 23 per cent of the novelist's sentences contain fewer than 20 words and 13 per cent contain at least 40 words. The unidentified manuscript contains 171 sentences under 20 words, 110 sentences with at least 40 words and there are 519 remaining sentences.

a) Write down suitable null and alternative hypotheses for a goodness-of-fit test.
b) Calculate the expected number of sentences, in the three classes identified, under the null hypothesis.
c) Carry out the test at ten per cent and interpret your outcome.

EXERCISES

26.2 HOMEWORK

1 In 400 ten-minute intervals, a taxi firm received the following numbers of calls.

No. of calls	0	1	2	3	4	5	6	7	≥ 8
No. of intervals	3	11	56	74	70	73	48	40	25

a) Carry out a goodness-of-fit test at the five per cent significance level to determine if the Poisson distribution with mean 4.5 is a suitable model for the data.
b) Repeat the test for Poi(4).
c) Describe, but do not carry out, how you would modify your procedure if you used the mean obtained from the given data.

2 The numbers of letters of complaint received by a major radio station each day over a period of 200 days are shown in the table.

No. of complaints	0	1	2	3	4	5	≥ 6
No. of days	34	78	60	20	5	3	0

Use a chi-squared test, with a five per cent level of significance, to determine if a Poisson distribution is an appropriate model for these data.

3 A successful local rugby team has five entrances to its grounds. The numbers of spectators using each entrance one Saturday are recorded in the table.

Entrance	N	S	E	W	M
No. of spectators	620	685	644	639	767

Use an appropriate test to determine if there is sufficient evidence to support the view that the same number of people, on average, use each entrance.

4 There are four common blood types: O, A, B and AB. The proportions of people in one north European country in each of these blood-type groups are assumed to be 48 : 40 : 8 : 4. The records of 200 pre-school children reveal the data shown in the table.

Blood type	O	A	B	AB
No. of children	113	62	13	12

Do these data support the hypothesis that the distribution of blood type among pre-school children is different from the assumed distribution?

5 A model is proposed for the weight distribution of trout in a fish farm. The density function of the model is:

$$f(x) = \begin{cases} \frac{1}{36} w(6 - w) & \text{when } 0 \le w \le 6 \\ 0 & \text{elsewhere} \end{cases}$$

A sample of 80 fish is obtained and their weights are recorded. The table contains a summary of the data.

Class of weight	$0 \le x < 1$	$1 \le x < 2$	$2 \le x < 4$	$4 \le x < 6$
No. of fish	6	14	39	21

a) Use the model to determine the expected number of fish in each weight class.
b) Conduct a goodness-of-fit test at the ten per cent level to determine if the model is appropriate for these data. Make your conclusions clear.

CONTINGENCY TABLES AND INDEPENDENCE

The concept of **independence** is important in developing probability models. Recall that if two events, A, B are independent then the probability, $P(A \text{ and } B)$, that they both occur is the product, $P(A) \times P(B)$, of their individual probabilities.

Consider a survey carried out with 100 primary school children. There are 60 boys and 40 girls in the survey. The children are asked to state their first choice among various makes of car 'British' or 'European' and 'Other country' of origin.

The assumption that gender and preference are independent would indicate for instance that the proportion of boys among those who state a preference for 'British' cars is the same as the proportion $\frac{60}{100}$

of boys taking part in the survey. Equally, $\frac{60}{100}$ of those stating 'European' as their preference would be boys.

Suppose that 50 of the children state a preference for European cars. How many of these 50 would you expect to be boys? Assuming independence leads to $\frac{60}{100} \times 50$ i.e. 30 boys preferring European cars. This leaves 20 (50 – 30) girls expected to have chosen European.

If 30 children state a preference for British cars, how many of these do you expect to be boys, and how many does this suggest will be girls? The independence model suggest that the expected number of boys is $\frac{60}{100} \times 30 = 18$ and the expected number of girls must be $30 - 18 = 12$.

These expected values can conveniently be summarised in a table known as a **contingency table**.

		Preference			
		European	**British**	**Other**	**Subtotal**
Gender	**Boy**	$\frac{60}{100} \times 50 = 30$	$\frac{60}{100} \times 30 = 18$		60
	Girl	$50 - 30 = 20$	$30 - 18 = 12$		40
	Subtotal	50	30	20	100

How many boys and how many girls do you expect to choose cars of 'other' country of origin? Since 48 boys are already accounted for out of 60, there must be twelve expected and this indicates that eight girls are expected to prefer 'other' manufacturers.

A summary of the numbers of children expected to be found in each possible cell is shown below.

	Expected frequencies		
	European	**British**	**Other**
Boy	30	18	12
Girl	20	12	8

The preferences actually stated by the children are shown in the 'observed frequencies' table below.

	Observed frequencies		
	European	**British**	**Other**
Boy	25	20	15
Girl	25	10	5

We can use the measure of fit developed so far to judge whether there is evidence to support the independence model assumed to derive the expected frequencies above.

$$\sum_{all\,cells} \frac{(O-E)^2}{E} = \frac{(25-30)^2}{30} + \frac{(25-20)^2}{20} + \frac{(20-18)^2}{18} + \frac{(10-12)^2}{12} + \frac{(15-12)^2}{12} + \frac{(5-8)^2}{8}$$
$$\approx 4.514$$

Again, we can approximate the critical values of this statistic using the chi-squared distribution. However, first we need to find the number of degrees of freedom of the model. Refer back to the table of expected frequencies. Only 30 and 18 are determined by the assumed model, the remaining cell frequencies are constrained by column sub-totals, row sub-totals and the total frequency.

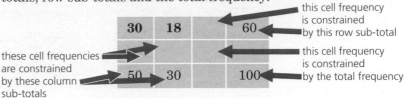

Hence, the number of degrees of freedom is:

$$3 \times 2 \quad - \quad (2 \quad + \quad 1 \quad + \quad 1) \quad = \quad 2$$
cells in the table   column   row   total

The five per cent critical value for a χ^2_2 statistic is 5.991. The test statistic for these data is 4.514, which is smaller than the critical value indicating a reasonable fit. Hence, the independence of gender and preference of car manufacturer is supported by these data.

Contingency tables and association

The model we used to determine the expected frequencies in the 'gender and car manufacturer' study was independence. When that probability model is used and the **measure of fit** turns out to be **large**, indicating that the model does not fit, the appropriate conclusion is that the row factor and the column factor are *not independent*. When the factors are not independent, they are said to be **associated**. Hence, the process explored previously can be used to determine whether two factors are associated.

Consider a survey conducted among all the overseas students at a large English university. The survey included a question in which the students were asked which of three car styles they preferred. They were asked to choose between hatchbacks, estates and sports versions. The students were identified by their year of study: first year, second year, third year or postgraduate.

There were 343 students altogether. The largest group was made up of the 108 first-year students. There were 87 second years, 88 in the third year and 60 postgraduates. Use the assumption that choice of style and year of study are independent, to determine the proportion of students in the first year who choose hatchbacks.

The assumption of independence implies that the proportion of first years who choose hatchbacks is the same as in the survey i.e. $\frac{108}{343}$. Similarly, of those choosing estates the proportion of first years is expected to be $\frac{108}{343}$. The proportion of second-year students among those choosing hatchbacks is expected to be $\frac{87}{343}$ and so on.

The actual numbers of students who choose each car style are given in the table.

	Hatchback	Estates	Sports
No. of students	185	102	56

We can use the information we have to explain how these six expected frequencies have been obtained.

		Expected Car Choice			
		Hatchback	Estate	Sports	Sub-total
Year	1st	58.251	32.117		108
of	2nd	46.924	25.872		87
Study	3rd	47.464	26.169		88
	Postgraduate				60
	Subtotal	185	102	56	343

The 58.251 arises as the appropriate proportion, $\frac{108}{343}$, of 185, similarly

$$\frac{108}{343} \times 102 = 32.117, \text{ and } \frac{87}{343} \times 185 = 46.924 \text{ etc.}$$

How many postgraduate students are expected to have chosen hatchbacks? The answer is the number that gives the sub-total 185 i.e.

$$185 - (58.251 + 46.924 + 47.464) = 32.361$$

Similarly, the number of postgraduates choosing estates is expected to be 17.942. The number of each year choosing sports cars can be found by making the row sub-totals correct. The result of this process is shown in the table of expected frequencies.

		Expected frequencies		
		Hatchback	Estate	Sports
Year of	1st	58.251	32.117	17.632
Study	2nd	46.924	25.872	14.204
	3rd	47.464	26.169	14.367
	Postgraduate	32.361	17.842	9.797

The actual results of the survey are shown below in the table of observed frequencies.

		Observed frequencies		
		Hatchback	Estate	Sports
Year of	1st	71	26	11
Study	2nd	52	23	12
	3rd	38	32	18
	Postgraduate	24	21	15

Is there evidence of association between year of study and choice of car style? The table of expected frequencies has been derived from the assumption that the factors are independent, hence the appropriate hypotheses are:

H_0: year of study and choice of style are independent;
H_1: year of study and choice of style are associated.

The measure of fit, $\sum \frac{(O-E)^2}{E}$, for these data based on the independence hypothesis is:

$$\frac{(71-58.251)^2}{58.251} + \frac{(26-32.117)^2}{32.117} + \dots + \frac{(15-9.797)^2}{9.797} \approx 17.247$$

This appears to be a large value, however, to decide this you need to sort out the degrees of freedom for this contingency table. What are the degrees of freedom? Reflect on the table of expected car choice, once the model determined the content of the six cells shown, the data imposed constraints on all the other cell frequencies. Hence, there are six degrees of freedom.

The five per cent upper-tail critical value of the χ^2_6 statistic is 12.592. The calculated measure of fit, 17.247, is larger than this, hence there is evidence to reject the null hypothesis.

In other words, these data indicate that there is association between year of study and choice of car style.

Nature of association

We can use a simple process to identify the nature of the association where there is evidence of this existence. We start by identifying the sign of the association – this is the same as the sign (positive or negative) of the differences $(O - E)$ in each frequency cell.

	Sign of $(O - E)$		
	Hatchback	Estate	Sports
1st	+	–	–
2nd	+	–	–
3rd	–	+	+
Postgraduate	–	+	+

The next stage is to identify where the greatest relative difference between the observed and expected frequencies occurs. We do this by expressing the measure of fit $\frac{(O-E)^2}{E}$ for each cell as a proportion or percentage of the overall measure of fit, $\sum \frac{(O-E)^2}{E}$. Combining these percentage differences with the signs leads to this table.

	Hatchback	Estate	Sports
1st	+16.2%	–6.8%	–14.5%
2nd	+3.2%	–1.8%	–2.0%
3rd	–10.9%	+7.5%	+5.3%
Postgraduate	–12.5%	+3.2%	+16.0%

The greatest differences are in first-years choosing hatchbacks and postgraduates choosing sports cars. These show a high positive association which can be interpreted as indicating that first-year students are attracted by hatchback cars and postgraduates prefer sports cars.

Large negative associations indicate that third-year students and postgraduates shun hatchbacks and that first-year students don't like sports cars.

Yates' correction

Critical values of the distribution of the measure of fit, $\sum \frac{(O-E)^2}{E}$, are approximated by the critical values of the chi-squared statistic with the appropriate number of degrees of freedom. When there is only *one degree of freedom* this approximation is considered to be poor. Under these circumstances it is possible to improve the approximation by using a correction to the measure known as **Yates' correction**.

This correction involves replacing $(O - E)^2$ by:

$$\{\,|O-E| - \tfrac{1}{2}\}^2 \quad \text{or} \quad \{\text{ABS}(O - E) - \tfrac{1}{2}\}^2$$

The measure $\sum \dfrac{\left[\text{ABS}(O-E)-\frac{1}{2}\right]^2}{E}$ is approximately a χ_1^2 statistic.

Example 26.4

One hundred primary school children were asked whether they had arrived at school by motorised transport or non-motorised. The results are given in the table. Is there evidence, at the ten per cent level of significance, that there is an association between mode of transport and gender?

	Motorised	Non-motorised
Boy	44	19
Girl	24	13

Solution
The row and column totals for this contingency table are as follows.

	Motorised	Non-motorised	
Boy			63
Girl			37
	68	32	100

The null hypothesis for this test is that the factors are independent. This means that the number of boys expected to have used motorised transport is $\frac{63}{100} \times 68 = 42.84$. Once this cell frequency is entered, all others are constrained by the data. Hence, the number of degrees of freedom for this 2×2 contingency table is 1. This means that Yates' correction should be used.
The expected frequencies are listed here.

	Motorised	Non-motorised
Boy	42.84	20.16
Girl	25.16	11.84

Hence, the measure of fit is:
$$\frac{(\,|44 - 42.84| - \frac{1}{2})^2}{42.84} + \frac{(\,|19 - 20.16| - \frac{1}{2})^2}{20.16} +$$

$$\frac{(\,|24 - 25.16| - \frac{1}{2})^2}{25.16} + \frac{(\,|13 - 11.84| - \frac{1}{2})^2}{11.84} \approx 0.086$$

The ten per cent upper-tail critical value is 2.706, the measure for this data is considerably less than this critical value. There is no reason to reject the independence model. Hence, there is insufficient evidence to support the view that mode of transport and gender are associated.

EXERCISES

26.3 CLASSWORK

1   An audit of a school library revealed the following data concerning the popularity of 'novels' and 'non-fiction' books. The table shows that there were 659 novels which were never borrowed, 101 non-fiction books which were borrowed very often, and so on.

		Popularity			
		Never	Rarely	Often	Very often
Classification	Novel	659	816	343	222
	Non-fiction	628	427	214	101

   a) How many books are accounted for in the table?
   b) What is the ratio of novel to non-fiction, and the ratio of the four popularity categories?
   c) Assume that the book classification and the popularity category are independent.
       How many novels are expected to be in the 'Never' borrowed category? How many novels does the independence model expect to be in the 'Rarely' and in the 'Often' categories?
   d) Find the number of degrees of freedom of a chi-squared test.
   e) Carry out the test and report your findings fully.

2   A publisher of an evening and a morning daily newspaper uses different production teams for the two editions. The publisher wants to establish if the number of reported misprints is independent of the edition. The following data are collected over a ten-week period.

		Misprints				
		0	1	2	3	≥ 4
Edition	Morning	13	17	15	7	8
	Evening	8	11	24	8	9

Use an appropriate chi-squared test to find whether there is evidence of independence or association between the edition and the number of misprints.

3   A survey of attitudes to smoking was conducted at a college. Students, academic staff and support staff were interviewed. Their opinions on the introduction of a designated smoking area are recorded in the table.

		Opinion		
		In favour	Undecided	Against
Interviewee	Academic staff	28	42	10
	Support staff	9	11	40
	Students	26	24	10

   a) Is there evidence of association between interviewee and opinion?
   b) Report your findings fully and identify the nature of association, if any.

4 A washing machine manufacturer uses a four-stage classification of quality of the output. There are three types of machine manufactured which are distinguished by their maximum spin speed. The following data represent one day's production.

		Classification			
		Perfect	Near perfect	Repairable	Reject
Machine type	600 spin	18	7	4	6
	800 spin	30	10	12	8
	1200 spin	37	13	4	1

a) Assume that output quality and machine type are independent and use an appropriate model to determine the number of machines in each cell expected by the independence model.
b) Find the proportion of cells where the expected frequency is less than 5. Do any of the cells have an expected frequency less than 2?
c) Conduct an appropriate test at ten per cent to judge whether there is evidence of independence between quality and machine type.
d) Report your findings fully.

5 A survey conducted of 1250 passengers on long-distance railway journeys revealed the following data.

		Class of ticket held	
		First	Standard
Gender of passenger	Female	95	405
	Male	165	585

Use an appropriate chi-squared test to find out if there is evidence of association between gender of passenger and class of ticket held:
a) with Yates' correction,   b) without Yates' correction.

EXERCISES

26.3 HOMEWORK

1 A group of 450 randomly-selected married couples were questioned about their daily alcohol consumption. The data are recorded below.

		Gender of partner	
		Female	Male
Alcohol consumption relative to maximum recommended	None	46	34
	Lower	264	151
	Equal to	83	202
	Higher	57	63

a) Assume that alcohol consumption and gender are independent. How many female partners does this assumption expect to consume:
i) no alcohol,   ii) some but lower,
iii) an amount equal to the maximum recommended?
b) In using a chi-squared test, how many degrees of freedom does the statistic associated with this 4×2 table have?

c) Find the value of the measure of fit of an 'independence' model for the data and carry out the appropriate test at 0.5 per cent.

d) Report your findings fully, mention the two most deviant cells as far as the model proposed is concerned.

2   A group of 100 A-level students consisted of 55 boys and 45 girls. During one week, when each recorded the time spent watching television, 23 boys and 15 girls watched for more than ten hours. Is there sufficient evidence in these data to support the view that there is no association between gender and time spent watching television? (Make it clear whether you use Yates' correction.)

3   An analysis of the passenger list of the tragic voyage of the *Titanic* revealed the data shown.

		Ticket class		
		First	Second	Third
Outcome	Survived	203	118	178
of tragedy	Perished	122	167	528

Does the data support the view that the class of ticket held by a passenger had a significant effect on the outcome of the tragedy? Identify clearly any association you find.

4   A survey of 192 international companies revealed the following data about their size and profits.

Profitability	No. of employees				
	Under 500	500 to 1000	1000 to 5000	5000 to 10000	≥ 10 000
Increased	2	6	39	17	24
Decreased	4	9	58	14	19

a) Assume that the size of the company and its profitability are independent. Determine how many companies this model expects in each of the ten possible cells.

b) What proportion of cells have an expected frequency of less than 5?

c) Use an appropriate chi-squared test to test the hypothesis that profitability is affected by the size of the company.

d) Report your findings fully.

5   A survey was conducted among 300 randomly-selected people in a town to gauge opinion about diverting traffic from the town. Three options are offered: a tunnel taking traffic under the town, a new surface dual carriageway, to do nothing. The interviewees were also asked where they lived: in the town, on the outskirts, elsewhere. The results are shown in the table.

		Option		
		Tunnel	Surface	No change
Living	In town	31	20	49
	Outskirts	34	34	32
	Elsewhere	72	25	3

Investigate these data to determine if the preferred option is associated with home location. Report your findings fully.

CONSOLIDATION EXERCISES FOR CHAPTER 26

1 A local council has records of the number of children and the number of households in its area. It is therefore known that the average number of children per household is 1.40. It is suggested that the number of children per household can be modelled by the Poisson distribution with parameter 1.40. In order to test this, a random sample of 1000 households is taken, giving the following data.

Number of children	0	1	2	3	4	≥ 5
Number of households	273	361	263	78	21	4

a) Find the corresponding expected frequencies obtained from the Poisson distribution with parameter 1.40.
b) Carry out a χ^2 test, at the five per cent level of significance, to determine whether or not the proposed model should be accepted. State clearly the null and alternative hypothesis being tested and the conclusion which is reached.

(MEI Question 4, Specimen S3, 1994)

2 A charity fund-raiser makes four telephone calls every hour he works. He recorded the number of calls which produced a donation each hour over a period of two months. These are shown in the table.

No. of successful calls	0	1	2	3	4
No. of hours	25	85	97	58	15

a) What modelling assumptions are needed to use a binomial distribution in this situation?
b) Assume that the distribution, B(4, 0.4) is appropriate and obtain expected frequencies to fit the observed frequencies.
c) Conduct a test at the five per cent level to judge how good a fit this model is. Report your findings.
d) Repeat the procedure using the model B(4, 0.5).

3 A wholesale fruit merchant claims that at least 70 per cent of all the satsumas she sells are free from pips. A consignment of 3000 bags each containing five satsumas produces the following data.

Number free of pips	0	1	2	3	4	5
Number of bags	3	64	371	963	1091	508

a) Use an appropriate model to determine the expected frequencies.
b) Test the fit of the model at five per cent level and report your findings.
A consignment of 6000 bags produced the data below.

Number free of pips	0	1	2	3	4	5
Number of bags	6	128	742	1926	2182	1016

c) Are the two observed distributions similar in appearance?
d) Test the fit of the binomial distribution, B(5, 0.7), as a model for these data.
e) Comment on the results of **b)** and **d)**.

4   A student flips a coin and records the number of flips it takes to get a head. He repeats this until he has 100 recordings. The results are shown in the table.

No. of flips to get a head	1	2	3	4	≥ 5
Frequency	48	32	16	4	0

a) Determine an appropriate model to obtain expected frequencies.
b) Conduct a chi-squared test to judge the appropriateness of your model. Report your findings at:
  i) ten per cent   **ii)** five per cent   **iii)** two per cent levels.

5   When recording for a radio play, the probability that an actor will get his lines exactly right on a given 'take' is 0.7. The following data were obtained in the studio during the recording of *King Lear*.

No. of takes needed for a speech	1	2	3	4	≥ 5
Frequency	149	48	29	10	4

a) Set up an appropriate mathematical model for the number of takes required for a speech.
b) Use your model to determine the frequencies expected.
c) Carry out a goodness-of-fit test at the one per cent level. Interpret the outcome carefully.
d) Determine the probability from the data and repeat the test.

6   The data below represent a random sample of hospital patient records.

		Length of hospitalisation	
		Short stay	Long stay
Costs met by:	Private patient	38	27
	National Health	52	133

Use a test based on the chi-squared distribution to find out whether there is evidence of an association between the length of stay in hospital and who met the cost. Report your findings fully.

7   Students studying part-time for a degree were questioned about whether they were self-funded or received support from their employer. The results are shown below.

	Gender		
		Male	Female
Funding	Self	34	67
	Employer	91	14

Conduct an appropriate chi-squared test to find out if gender of student and funding are independent. Make it clear if you use Yates' correction and report your findings fully.

8 A golfer is practising on a putting green. She deduces that the number of strokes required at each hole can be modelled by the discrete random variable X defined as follows.

$$P(X = r) = k \left(\tfrac{2}{3}\right)^r \qquad r = 1, 2, 3, \ldots$$

a) Show that $k = \frac{1}{2}$. In order to test her model, the golfer records the number of strokes required at each of 54 holes. These figures are summarised in the following frequency table.

No. of strokes	1	2	3	4	5	6+
No. of holes	20	16	14	3	1	0

b) Calculate the expected frequencies according to the golfer's proposed model. Carry out a suitable test at the five per cent level to determine whether the model is a good one or not. State your hypothesis and your conclusions carefully.

(MEI Question 1, Paper S3, June 1993)

9 The following table is the result of analysing a random sample of the invoices submitted by branches of a large chain of book shops.

	Novel	**Textbook**	**General interest**
Hardback	24	10	22
Paperback	66	10	18

Using an approximate χ^2 statistic assess, at the five per cent level of significance, find whether or not there is any association between the type of book sold and its cover. State clearly your null and alternative hypothesis.

(ULEAC Question 5, Paper S2, June 1994)

10 All entrants to a particular science course at a university are required to study French or Russian. The numbers of students of each sex choosing each language are shown in the following table.

	French	**Russian**
Male	39	16
Female	21	14

Use a χ^2 test (including Yates' correction) at the five per cent significance level to test whether choice of language is independent of sex.

(AEB Question 3, Specimen paper 2, 1994)

11 A statistics conference, lasting four days, was held at a university. Lunch was provided and on each day a choice of a vegetarian or a meat dish was offered for the main course. Of those taking lunch, the uptake was as follows.

	Tuesday	Wednesday	Thursday	Friday
Vegetarian	17	24	21	16
Meat	62	42	38	22

a) Use the χ^2 distribution at the five per cent significance level to test whether the choice of dish for the main course was independent of the day of the week.

On each day a choice of fruit, ice-cream or apple pie was offered for dessert. A contingency table was formed showing the number making each choice on each day and $\sum \frac{(O-E)^2}{E}$ was calculated to be 3.7. (No classes were grouped together.)

b) Test, at the five per cent significance level, whether the choice of dessert was independent of the day of the week.

c) There was a total of 80 participants at the conference entitled to lunch each day. Test, at the five per cent significance level, whether the number of participants taking lunch was independent of the day of the week.

d) Describe briefly any variations in the choice and attendance at lunch over the four days.

(AEB Question 2, Paper 9, Winter 1994)

12 Basil considers himself generally unlucky when throwing sixes on a die. He counts how many throws (X) it takes him to obtain a six. He repeats his experiment 200 times, obtaining the following data:

Number of throws (X)	1	2	3	4	5	6	more than 6
Frequency	25	24	23	22	15	8	83

A geometric probability model, with $P(6) = \frac{1}{6}$, is to be used as a model for the distribution of X.

Complete the table below and conduct a χ^2 test at the five per cent significance level to decide if the model is appropriate for the data.

Number of throws (X)	1	2	3	4	5	6	more than 6
Frequency	33.3						

(AQA A Question 6, Paper S2, 2000)

13 A survey was made of 50 girls and 40 boys to see if there was any difference in smoking habits between them. The results were as follows:

	Smoked	Did not smoke
Girls	18	32
Boys	10	30

a) On the basis that there is no difference in their tendency to smoke, calculate the expected frequencies, to three significant figures, and insert them in a table.

b) A χ^2 test is to be applied to assess the claim that there is no difference between the tendency to smoke of girls and boys. Explain why Yates' correction should be applied and show how a value of about 0.231 is obtained for the 'Girls Smoked' cell when carrying out the test.

(AQA A Question 1, Paper S2, 2000)

14 The table shows the numbers of men and women recruited into the various UK services in 1987/88.

	Men	Women
Navy	4601	580
Army	19865	1146
Air Force	5728	885

Use a χ^2 test to see whether there is evidence of any association between a person's gender and the service into which they are recruited. State your null hypothesis clearly, and test at the one per cent level.

(Nuffield Question 2, Specimen, 9870/43, 1994)

15 The following data are from the *British Medical Journal*. The table shows whether or not the subjects suffered from heart disease and how their snoring habits were classified by their partners.

	Never snores	Occasionally snores	Snores nearly every night	Snores every night
Heart disease	24	35	21	30
No heart disease	1355	603	192	224

a) Use a χ^2 test, at the five per cent significance level, to investigate whether frequency of snoring is related to heart disease.

b) On the evidence above, do heart disease sufferers tend to snore more or snore less than others? Give a reason for your answer

c) Do these data show that snoring causes heart disease?

(AQA B Question 5, Paper S4, 2000)

Summary

- The chi-squared statistic can be used as a test for goodness of fit.

$$\chi_v^2 = \sum \frac{(O-E)^2}{E}$$

  where v is the number of degrees of freedom.

    $v = n - \text{con}$
    n = number of frequency cells
  con = number of constraints on the model

- In a contingency table, the expected entry in cell (i, j) is:

$$\frac{(\text{sum of row } i) \times (\text{sum in column } j)}{\text{total number}}$$

  For a contingency table with r rows and c columns the number of degrees of freedom is $(r-1)(c-1)$.

- When there is only one degree of freedom the χ_1^2 statistic is:

$$\sum \frac{\left[\text{ABS}(O-E) - \frac{1}{2} \right]^2}{E}$$

This is called **Yates' correction**.

Answers

CHAPTER 1
Differentiation

Exercises 1.1 class (p.4)

1 a) $10(2x - 1)^4$ **b)** $8x(x^2 + 1)^3$

c) $-\dfrac{4}{(4x+1)^2}$ **d)** $-\dfrac{3x^2-2x}{(x^3-x^2)^2}$

e) $\dfrac{1}{2\sqrt{x-2}}$ **f)** $\dfrac{2x}{(x^2-1)}$

g) $2(x+1)e^{x^2+2x}$

h) $\dfrac{1}{2\sqrt{x}}e^{\sqrt{x}}$ **i)** $4(e^x + 1)(e^x + x)^3$

j) $\dfrac{12}{(4x-1)}$

2 $(0, 1)$

3 a) at $(0.5, 6.25)$: -15 decreasing, at $(2, 6.25)$: 3.75 increasing
  b) $(1, 4)$ is a local minimum

4 a) -8 m s^{-2}
  b) 0.88 m s^{-2}
  c) 0.073 m s^{-2}

5 a) 0.0050 m^3 s^{-1}
  b) 0.050 m^2 s^{-1}

6 a) $4.8c$
  b) $0.01c$ (to 2 d.p.)
  c) 0 (actually $6 \times 10^{-173}c$)

7 $\dfrac{5}{4}\sqrt{\dfrac{3}{\pi}} = 1.2215$ mm s^{-1}

Exercises 1.1 home (p.5)

1 a) $12(3x + 2)^3$ **b)** $6t^2(t^3 - 1)$

c) $-\dfrac{1}{(s-7)^2}$ **d)** $\dfrac{-6}{(2t+1)^4}$

e) $\dfrac{-2x(6x+1)}{(4x^3+x^2)^2}$ **f)** $x(3x - 4)e^{x^3-2x^2}$

g) $\dfrac{-1}{\sqrt{x}}e^{-2\sqrt{x}}$ **h)** $\dfrac{(2x-e^x)}{2(e^x-x^2)^{\frac{3}{2}}}$

i) $\dfrac{8}{2s+3}$ **j)** $\dfrac{8x+3}{4x^2+3x}$

2 a) 1.25 increasing
  b) no stationary points
  c) $x < -3$ and $x > 0$
  d) ∞

3 a) $(0, e^{-1})$ is a (local) minimum
  b) $(0, 0)$ is a (local) minimum
  c) $(-1, 0)$ and $(1, 0)$ are (local) minima
  d) $\left(1, \dfrac{1}{\sqrt{3}}\right)$ is a (local) maximum

4 3π cm^2 s^{-1}
5 $\dfrac{1}{16}$ m min^{-1}
6 $-240(5 + 2e^{-3t})e^{-3t}$
7 b) $\dfrac{90}{\pi h^2}$ cm s^{-1}

Exercises 1.2 class (p.7)

1 a) $3x^2 - 2x + 1$ **b)** $\dfrac{3x+1}{2\sqrt{x}}$

c) $2(2x + 1)(4x^2 + x - 2)$

d) $-\dfrac{1}{(x-1)^2}$ **e)** $2(x-1)^2(2x+1)$

f) $t(5t^3 + 6t - 2)$ **g)** $\dfrac{(s-1)(5s+3)}{2\sqrt{s+1}}$

h) $(2u - 3u^2)e^{-3u}$

i) $(x - 1)(1 + x)e^x$

j) $(2 - 6x - 4x^2)e^{-x^2}$

k) $2(1 + \ln(2x + 1))$

l) $\left(\dfrac{1}{x} - \ln x\right)e^{-x}$

2 a) $y = 4x - 2$ increasing
  b) $(-1, -e^2)$ is a local minimum
  $(2, 2e^{-4})$ is a local maximum

3 at $(0, 0)$: $y = 0$ neither increasing nor decreasing
  at $(1, e^1)$: $y = (5x - 4)e^1$ increasing,
  at $(-1, -e^1)$: $y = (5x + 4)e^1$ increasing,
  $(0, 0)$ is a point of inflexion

4 a) $\dfrac{(5-2t)}{4}e^{-0.25t}$
  b) $t < 2.5$, the object is moving towards the origin
  c) $t = 0$, $v = 1.25$ m s^{-1}
  d) $x \to \infty$, $v \to 0$

5 b) 0.32 m^2

Exercises 1.2 home (p.8)

1 a) $4x - 1$ **b)** $2(9t^2 + 9t - 5)$
  c) $4s^3 + 9s^2 - 4s - 10$
  d) $-(4x + 3)x^{-4}$
  e) $\dfrac{2s^2+1}{\sqrt{s^2+1}}$ **f)** $(1 - 2u^2)e^{-u^2}$
  g) $-2(3v^2 - 3v + 1)e^{-2v}$
  h) $\dfrac{(5x+3)}{(1+x)^3}$ **i)** $\dfrac{2-3x}{x-4} - 3\ln(0.5x - 2)$
  j) $(2t^2 - 1 + t^{-2})e^{t^2}$
  k) $\left(3\ln(2x-1) + \dfrac{2}{(2x-1)}\right)e^{3x}$
  l) $\dfrac{1}{3}(25t^7 + 32t - 23)(t^2 + 2t - 1)^{-\frac{7}{3}}$

2 a) $x(12x^4 + 5x^3 - 12x - 3x + 2)$
  b) $-2x(6x^2 - 6x - 1)e^{-2x}$
  c) $2xe^{-3x} - 2(3x^2 + x - 1)e^{-3x}\ln(x + 1)$

3 $(0, 0)$ point of inflexion,
  $(1, 0)$ local minimum,
  $(-1, 0)$ local maximum,
  $\left(-\sqrt{\dfrac{3}{7}}, \dfrac{48}{343}\sqrt{\dfrac{3}{7}}\right)$ and $\left(-\sqrt{\dfrac{3}{7}}, -\dfrac{48}{343}\sqrt{\dfrac{3}{7}}\right)$
  local minimum

4 a) $y = -\dfrac{2}{3}x - \ln 3$, decreasing,
  $y = \left(\dfrac{5}{12} + 3\ln 6\right)x - \left(\dfrac{5}{8} + 3.25\ln 6\right)$, increasing
  b) $(-1, 0)$ is local maximum, $(0.22, -1.18)$ is local maximum

5 a) $t = 3.857$ h, $r = 5.0850$ m
  b) $t = 0$, $r = 1.7$ m and $t = \infty$, $r = 0.6$ m

Exercises 1.3 class (p.10)

1 a) $\dfrac{(x+4)(x-4)}{x^2}$ **b)** $\dfrac{t(t+6)}{(t+3)^2}$

c) $\dfrac{(x-4)}{x^3}$ **d)** $\dfrac{t^{\frac{1}{4}}(4t-15)}{4(4t-3)^2}$

e) $-\dfrac{(10x^2 + 18x + 5)}{(2x^2-1)^2}$ **f)** $-\dfrac{4t}{(t^2-1)^2}$

g) $\dfrac{-e^{-2x}(2x+3)}{(1+x)^2}$ **h)** $\dfrac{-2t\ln(t+1)-(1-t)}{(\ln(t+1))^2}$

i) $\dfrac{(1+2x-2x^2)e^{x^2}}{(1-x)^2}$ **j)** $\dfrac{2(1-\ln(2t-3))}{(2t-3)^2}$

k) $2x$ **l)** $\dfrac{(t^3-2)-3t^3\ln(t)}{t(t^3-2)^2}$

2 a) $(\sqrt{3} - 2, \sqrt{3} - 2)$ is a local minimum $(-\sqrt{3} - 2, -\sqrt{3} - 2)$ is a local maximum

3 $(1, \dfrac{1}{2}e^1)$ is a point of inflexion

4 $v = 2\sqrt{\dfrac{10}{7}}$

Exercises 1.3 home (p.11)

1 a) $-\dfrac{(x+2)(x+6)}{x^2}$ **b)** $\dfrac{5(2u+1)}{(1-u)^4}$

c) $\dfrac{2x(x-4)}{(x-2)^2}$ **d)** $\dfrac{s^{\frac{4}{3}}(12s-7)}{3(3s-1)^2}$

e) $\dfrac{3x^2-2x-3}{(x^2+1)^2}$ **f)** $\dfrac{(s+5)}{(1-s)^3}$

g) $\dfrac{2e^{4x}(7-4x)}{(3-2x)^2}$

h) $\dfrac{x(2x+1)\ln x - (x^2+x+1)}{x(\ln x)^2}$

i) $-e^{-2x^2}\dfrac{(12x^2+8x+3)}{(3x+2)^2}$

j) $\dfrac{1-\ln(x-1)}{(x-1)^2}$ **k)** $\dfrac{e^{-x}(e^{-2x}-1)}{(e^{2x}+1)^2}$

l) $\dfrac{(s-4)}{2\sqrt{1-s}(s+2)^2}$

2 $(0, 0)$ is a (local) minimum

3 a) $(0.28, 8.82)$ is a local minimum, $(-1.78, 0.06)$ is a local maximum
  b) no stationary points

4 a) $v = \dfrac{1-t^2}{(t^2+1)^2}$, $v = 0$ when $t = 1$
  b) 4.5 **c)** 1

5 $x = R$

Exercises 1.4 class (p.12)

1 $\dfrac{dy}{dx} = \dfrac{e^y}{(1-y)}$

2 $\dfrac{dy}{dx} = (1 - y)$ or $\dfrac{dy}{dx} = e^x$

3 $\dfrac{dy}{dx} = 2^x \ln 2$

4 $\dfrac{dy}{dx} = \dfrac{1}{e^y + e^{-y}}$

5 $\dfrac{(3x+4)}{2\sqrt{x+2}}$

6 $24(2x^3 - 3)^3$

7 $\dfrac{x+2}{2(x+1)^{\frac{3}{2}}}$

8 $(8x + 1)e^{4x^2 + x - 1}$
9 $e^{x^2}(2x^3 - 6x^2 + 6x - 3)$
10 $\frac{1}{10}(8-t)e^{-0.1t}$
11 $\frac{-8x^3}{\left(x^4+1\right)^3}$
12 $(t-2)(3t-4)$
13 $\frac{(2t-1)}{2\sqrt{t^2-t+1}}$
14 $\frac{e^t\left(t^3-t^2+t+1\right)}{\left(t^2+1\right)^2}$

Exercises 1.4 home (p.12)
1 $\frac{dy}{dx} = \frac{2y+1}{2}$ or $\frac{dy}{dx} = \frac{1}{2}e^x$
2 $\frac{dy}{dx} = 4\ln3(3)^x$ **3** $\frac{dy}{dx} = \frac{1}{2\left(e^{2y}-e^{-2y}\right)}$
4 $\frac{dy}{dx} = \frac{1}{2y-2}$ **5** $-\frac{\left(x^2+4\right)}{\left(x^2-4\right)^2}$
6 $1 + \ln u$ **7** $4t + \frac{3}{2}\sqrt{t}$
8 $(2t-3)e^{t^2-3t+4}$
9 $2e^{2x-5}(x^2 - 3x - 3)$
10 $\frac{2t}{t^2+3}$ **11** $\frac{(1-x)e^x+(x+1)e^{-x}}{\left(e^x-e^{-x}\right)^2}$
12 $10^x\ln10$ **13** $-\frac{7}{(x-2)^2}$ **14** $\frac{(2-s)^2(1-2s)}{\sqrt{s(2-s)^3}}$

Consolidation Exercises for Chapter 1 (p.14)
1 $\left(\frac{1}{2},-\frac{3}{2}\right),\left(-\frac{1}{2},\frac{3}{2}\right)$
2 a) $x(x^3 + 4)^2(22x^3 - 9x + 16)$
b) $\frac{\left(3x^2-1\right)}{2x^{\frac{3}{2}}}$ **c)** $6x(x^2 + 2)^2$
d) $e^x\ln x + \frac{1}{x}e^x$ **e)** $-\frac{1}{(2x-3)^2}$
f) $\frac{\left(1-x^2\right)}{\left(1+x^2\right)^2}$
3 $\left(\frac{1}{3}, \sqrt{10}\right)$ is a (local) maximum
4 a) $(c, 0)$ is a local minimum $\left(\frac{1}{3}(c+2),\frac{4}{27}(c-1)^3\right)$ is a local maximum, when $c = 1$ then $(1, 0)$ is a point of inflexion
5 0.5π mm^2 s^{-1}
6 a) $r = \sqrt{6}$
7 a) $-\frac{f^2}{(u-f)^2}$
b) $\frac{3}{32}$ cm s^{-1} increasing
8 0.0134 m s^{-1} (to 4 d.p.)
9 a) $\frac{1}{3}$s **b)** 0.28 cm s^{-1}
c) $t \to \infty, r \to 4$ cm
10 b) £127 million, 109 km
11 a) $h = 9$ cm, $V = 5$ cm^3
b) 0.024 cm^3 s^{-1}

CHAPTER 2
Calculus of Trigonometric Functions

Exercises 2.1 class (p.21)
1 a) $3\cos x$ **b)** $-4\sin x$
c) $\frac{1}{2}\sec^2 x$ **d)** $\frac{1}{4}\cos x$
e) $3\cos x - 4\sin x$ **f)** $-\sec^2 x$
g) $2x + 8\cos x$ **h)** $3e^{3x} + \sec^2 x$

2 a) $21\cos 7x$ **b)** $44\sin 11x$
c) $10\sec^2 4x$ **d)** $6\cos(2x - 5)$
e) $2\sec^2\frac{1}{2}x - 2\cos\frac{1}{3}x$
f) $-3\sin\frac{1}{5}x - 3\cos\frac{1}{4}x$
g) $\frac{1}{2x} - \frac{9}{2}\sin(5x + 7)$
h) $4e^{4x} + 4^x\ln 4 + 3\cos(1 - 3x)$
3 a) $2\sin x\cos x$ **b)** $2x\cos x^2$
c) $\frac{1}{x^2}\sin\frac{1}{x}$ **d)** $-\frac{\sin x}{2\sqrt{1+\cos x}}$
e) $6\tan^2 2x\sec^2 2x$
f) $\frac{2\cos 2x}{1+\sin 2x}$ **g)** $e^{\sin x}\cos x$
h) $e^x\cos e^x$ **i)** $-\tan x$
j) $-\frac{\sin\ln x}{x}$
4 a) $x\sec^2 x + \tan x$
b) $\cos x\cos 2x - 2\sin x\sin 2x$
c) $3x^2\cos 2x - 2x^3\sin 2x$
d) $e^x(\cos x - \sin x)$
e) $e^{-\frac{1}{2}x}(2\cos 2x - \frac{1}{2}\sin 2x)$
f) $\sqrt{x}\sec^2 x + \frac{\tan x}{2\sqrt{x}}$
g) $\frac{\sin x}{x} + \cos x\ln x$
h) $e^{\sin x}(x\cos x + 1)$
5 a) $\frac{x\cos x - \sin x}{x^2}$
b) $\frac{\sin^3 x\left(4\cos^2 x + 3\sin^2 x\right)}{\cos^4 x}$
c) $\frac{e^x(\sin x - \cos x)}{\sin^2 x}$ **d)** $\frac{2x\cos x - \sin x}{2\sqrt{x^3}}$
e) $\frac{x(2-x)\cos x + x(2+x)\sin x}{(\sin x + \cos x)^2}$
f) $\frac{(2x+1)\tan x - \left(x^2+x+1\right)\sec^2 x}{\tan^2 x}$
6 $\frac{d}{dx}(\cosec x) = -\cosec x\cot x$
and $\frac{d}{dx}(\cot x) = -\cosec^2 x$
$3\sec(3x - 1)\tan(3x - 1)$,
$-\frac{1}{2}\cosec\frac{1}{2}x\cot\frac{1}{2}x$,
$-\frac{3}{5}\cosec^2(\frac{3}{5}x - \frac{\pi}{4})$
7 Equation of normal is $y = -\pi x + (\pi^2 + \ln 4\pi - 3)$
8 Equation of tangent is $2y = -20x + 5(\pi - \sqrt{3})$
9 tangent: $2y = 8x - (4\pi - 3)$, normal: $8y = -2x + (12 + \pi)$
10 a) maximum $\frac{1}{2}$, minimum $-\frac{1}{2}$
b) maximum 1, minimum $-\sqrt{2}$
c) maximum $\frac{3\sqrt{3}}{16}$, minimum $-\frac{3\sqrt{3}}{16}$
d) maximum 3, minimum -1
11 a) $(0, 1)$ and $\left(\frac{2\pi}{3},1\right)$ max. $\left(\frac{\pi}{3},-1\right)$ and $(\pi, -1)$ min
b) $\left(\frac{\pi}{6},\frac{\pi}{6}-\frac{\sqrt{3}}{2}\right)$ min $\left(\frac{5\pi}{6},\frac{5\pi}{6}+\frac{\sqrt{3}}{2}\right)$ max
c) $\left(\frac{3\pi}{4},\frac{\sqrt{2}}{2}e^{\frac{3\pi}{4}}\right)$ max
d) No stationary points in this domain.
12 a) $a = 0.2, c = 0.5$
c) i) 0, **ii)** -0.2π
d) i) $-0.2\pi^2$, **ii)** 0

Exercises 2.1 home (p.22)
1 a) $7\cos x$ **b)** $\frac{3}{4}\sin x$
c) $-11\sec^2 x$ **d)** $-\frac{\sin x}{5}$
e) $\frac{\cos x + \sin x}{10}$ **f)** $\frac{x^4}{3} - \frac{1}{3x} - \frac{\sin x}{5}$
g) $3\sec^2 x + \frac{1}{x}$ **h)** $\frac{1}{4}e^{\frac{x}{5}} + \frac{1}{10}\sin x$
2 a) $\frac{25}{4}\cos 5x$ **b)** $-\frac{1}{3}\sec^2\frac{4x}{3}$
c) $-\frac{3}{2}\sin 2x$
d) $\frac{66}{7}\sin 11x + \frac{11}{4}\sec^2 11x$
e) $10\cos(4x - 3) - 2\sin(3x - 4)$
f) $-5\cos(\frac{2\pi}{3} - 5x) - 6\sin(\frac{3\pi}{4} + 6x)$
g) $\frac{11}{x} - \frac{5}{4}\sec^2\frac{x}{4} + \frac{1}{\sqrt{x}}$
h) $\frac{\sqrt{x^5}}{6} + 6\sin(\frac{\pi}{9} - 6x) + \frac{5}{x^2}$
3 a) $-3\cos^2 x\sin x$
b) $20\sin^3 5x\cos 5x$
c) $-\frac{\sin\sqrt{x}}{2\sqrt{x}}$ **d)** $\frac{1-\sin x}{2\sqrt{x+\cos x}}$
e) $-3\cos^5\frac{1}{2}x\sin\frac{1}{2}x$
f) $\frac{1+\cos x}{x+\sin x}$ **g)** $-e^{\cos x}\sin x$
h) $-e^x\sin e^x$ **i)** $\frac{3(\cos 3x - \sin 3x)}{\cos 3x + \sin 3x}$
j) $-\frac{2}{x^3}\sec^2\frac{1}{x^2}$
4 a) $2x(x\cos x + \sin x)\sin x$
b) $2\cos x(2\cos x\cos 4x - \sin x\sin 4x)$
c) $4\tan 3x\cos 4x + 3\sec^3 x\ 3x\sin 4x$
d) $4x\cos 4x + \sin 4x$
e) $4\cos(4x + \frac{\pi}{3})\cos(2x - \frac{\pi}{4}) - 2\sin(4x + \frac{\pi}{3})\sin(2x - \frac{\pi}{4})$
f) $e^{-x}(\cos x - \sin x)$
g) $3(1 + x)^2\cos 3x - 3(1 + x)^3\sin 3x$
h) $\frac{\sec x}{x} + \ln x\tan x\sec x$
5 a) $-\frac{x\sin x + \cos x}{x^2}$ **b)** $\frac{\cos x - \sin x - 1}{(1-\cos x)^2}$
c) $\frac{\left(\sec^2 x - \tan x\right)}{e^x}$ **d)** $\frac{1}{x\tan x} - \frac{\ln x\sec^2 x}{\tan^2 x}$
e) $\frac{2\cos x}{(1-\sin x)^2}$ **f)** $\frac{2\sec x\tan x}{(1-\sin x)^2}$
6 $x° = \frac{\pi x}{180}$ radians, $\frac{\pi}{180}\cos x°$, $-\frac{\pi}{180}\sin x°$, $\frac{\pi}{36}\sec^2 x°$, $\frac{\pi}{36}\cos 5x°$, $-\frac{\pi}{360}\sin\frac{1}{2}x°$, $\frac{\pi}{60}\sec^2(3x - 45)°$
7 Equation of normal is $8y = \pi^3 - 2\pi^2 x$
8 tangent: $y = 5x - 5(\pi - 1)$, normal: $5y = -x + (\pi + 25)$
9 tangent: $y = -16x - 4$, normal: $16y = x - 64$
10 a) max: $\sqrt{5}$, min: -1
b) max: 3, min: -5
c) max: $-2\sqrt{2}$, min: $2\sqrt{2}$
d) max: 1, min: -1
11 a) $\left(\frac{\pi}{10},1\right), \left(\frac{\pi}{2},1\right)$ and $\left(\frac{9\pi}{10},1\right)$ max, $\left(\frac{3\pi}{10},-1\right)$ and $\left(\frac{7\pi}{10},-1\right)$ min
b) $\left(\frac{3\pi}{4},\frac{3\pi}{2}+1\right)$ min, $\left(\frac{\pi}{4},\frac{\pi}{2}-1\right)$ max

c) $\left(\frac{3\pi}{4},-1\right)$ min

d) $\left(\frac{\pi}{2},8.5\right)$ max, $\left(\frac{\pi}{6},8\right)$ and $\left(\frac{5\pi}{6},8\right)$ min

12 b) i) $V = 2.26$, $a = 0.186$
ii) $V = -1.17$, $a = 0.234$
d) $t = 5.64$, $h = 9.41$

Exercises 2.2 class *(p.25)*
1 All answers are $+ c$.
a) $-\frac{\cos 3x}{3}$ **b)** $\frac{\sin 6x}{6}$ **c)** $2\sin\frac{x}{2}$
d) $\frac{\sin x}{2}$ **e)** $\frac{2}{3}\sin\frac{3}{2}x$ **f)** $\frac{\tan 4x}{4}$
g) $4\tan x$ **h)** $-3\cos x - 2\sin x$
i) $\frac{1}{2}(\sin x - \cos x)$
j) $-\frac{1}{2}\cos(2x+4)$
k) $-3\tan(\frac{\pi}{3}-x)$ **l)** $\frac{1}{2}\sin(2x+\frac{\pi}{4})$

2 a) 2 **b)** $\frac{1}{2}$ **c)** 2 **d)** $\frac{1}{2}$ **e)** π
f) -3 **g)** 2 **h)** $\frac{\pi}{9}$ **i)** 4

3 $\frac{2\sqrt{2}}{3}+\frac{1}{2} = 1.4428$ to 4 d.p.

4 a) $2 - \sqrt{2} = 0.58578$
b) $\sqrt{2} - 1 = 0.41421$
c) $\sqrt{2} = 1.41421$
5 b) $0.739\,085\,133$
c) $0.400\,488\,612$
d) $0.599\,511\,387$

6 a) $\frac{d}{dx}(\ln\sin x) = \cot x$,
$\int\cot x\,dx = \ln\sin x + c$
b) $\frac{1}{5}\ln\sin x$, $12\ln\sin\frac{1}{4}x$,
$\frac{1}{4}\ln\sin(4x+\pi)$

Exercises 2.2 home *(p.26)*
1 All answers are $+ c$.
a) $\frac{3}{4}\sin 4x$ **b)** $-15\cos\frac{1}{3}x$
c) $-\cos\frac{1}{5}x$ **d)** $-\frac{1}{5}\cos x$
e) $-5\cos\frac{1}{5}x$ **f)** $\frac{2}{3}\tan\frac{3}{2}x$
g) $49\tan\frac{1}{7}x$
h) $-\frac{4}{3}\cos 3x - \frac{5}{7}\sin 7x$
i) $\sin\frac{1}{2}x - \cos\frac{1}{2}x$
j) $-2\cos\left(\frac{x}{2}-1\right)$ **k)** $2\tan(x-\frac{\pi}{2})$
l) $-\frac{1}{3}\sin(\frac{\pi}{4}-3x)$

2 a) 1 **b)** -1 **c)** 0 **d)** $\frac{3}{4}$ **e)** 1
f) 6 **g)** 1.2071 **h)** π **i)** $\frac{1}{2}$

3 a) $\frac{\pi}{4}(9\pi + 8) = 9.0686$ to 4 d.p.

4 a) $x = \frac{2\pi}{3}$ **b)** 0.526 67
c) 0.171 46
5 b) 0.588 532 744 and
3.096 363 932
c) 0.276 614 887
d) 1.320 805 545
6 a) $\frac{d}{dx}(\ln\cos x) = -\tan x$,
$\int\tan x\,dx = -\ln\cos x + c$

b) $-\frac{1}{3}\ln\cos 3x$, $2\ln\cos\frac{1}{2}x$,
$-\frac{1}{2}\ln\cos(\frac{\pi}{4}-2x)$

Exercises 2.3 class *(p.29)*
1 a) $\frac{1}{2}x - \frac{1}{12}\sin 4x + c$
b) $-\frac{1}{2}x - \frac{1}{12}\sin(6x - \frac{2\pi}{3})$

2 a) 3π **b)** 0.129 72
3 a) volume $= \frac{\pi}{4}(3\pi + 8) = 4.3562\pi$
b) volume $= 3\pi$
c) volume $= \pi - \frac{\pi^2}{4}$
4 a) $3\sin^2 x\cos x$
b) $\sin x - \frac{1}{3}\sin^3 x + c$ **c)** $\frac{2\pi}{3}$
5 c) $\frac{3x}{8} - \frac{1}{4}\sin 2x + \frac{1}{32}\sin 4x + c$
d) $\frac{27\pi^2}{16}$
6 b) Both are equal to $2\sec^2 x\tan x$
since $1 + \tan^2 x = \sec^2 x$.
7 b) $\ln(\sec x + \tan x) + c$
c) 2.6339 and 1.7627
8 0.9014

Exercises 2.3 home *(p.30)*
1 a) $\frac{1}{2}x + \frac{1}{2}\sin 10x + c$
b) $\frac{1}{4}x - \frac{1}{2}\sin\frac{1}{2}x + c$
2 a) π **b)** $\frac{\pi}{12}$
3 a) $c - \frac{1}{4}\cos 2x$
b) $\frac{3\pi}{4} + \frac{1}{2} = 2.8562$
4 b) $c - \cos x + \frac{1}{3}\cos^3 x$ **c)** 6
5 a) $2e^x\sin x$ and $2e^x\cos x$
b) $\frac{1}{2}(e^x\sin x - \cos x) + c$
and $\frac{1}{2}(e^x\sin x + \cos x) + c$
c) $\frac{1}{2}(e^\pi + 1) = 12.07$
d) $\frac{\pi}{2}(e^{\frac{\pi}{2}} + e^{-\frac{\pi}{2}}) = 2.5092\pi$

6 b) Both are equal to
$-2\cosec^2 x\cot x$
since $1 + \cot^2 x = \cosec^2 x$.
7 b) $c - \ln(\cosec x + \cot x)$
c) 1.7627 and 2.303
8 -0.6469

Exercises 2.4 class *(p.34)*
1 a) 2.5 **b)** 2 **c)** $\frac{1}{x^2} - \frac{1}{2}$
d) $\frac{2}{3}$ **e)** 2 **f)** $-\frac{x}{2}$
g) $\sqrt{4-x^2}$ **h)** $\frac{9}{16}$ **i)** $\frac{\sqrt{2}}{2}x - \frac{1}{2}x^2$

2 c) estimate is 0.571 45 to 5 d.p.,
both are 0.57 to 2 d.p.
d) cubic approximation is $2x - 3x^3$
e) estimated value = 0.617 to
3 d.p., true value = 0.625
3 a) quadratic approximation is
$f(x) = 3x - 3x^2$ giving integral
$= 0.0140$ exactly
b) cubic approximation is
$f(x) = 3x - 3x^2 + 3x^3$ giving
integral = 0.014 075 to 6 d.p.
(The true value of the integral is
0.014 090 to 6 d.p.)

Exercises 2.4 home *(p.34)*
1 d) $f'(x) = -2\cos x\sin 2x -$
$\sin x\cos 2x = -0.946\,30$ when
$x = 0.2$
e) cubic approx. to $f'(x) = 4x^3 - 5x$
$= -0.968$ when $x = 0.2$
f) Integration involves higher
powers of small numbers and is
hence more accurate.
2 c) true value = 0.049 979 165 to
9 d.p., estimated value =
0.049 979 166 to 9 d.p.
e) estimated value =
0.025 041 666 to 9 d.p. which
compares well with the true
answer of 0.025 041 646 to 9 d.p.
3 a) cubic approximation is $x + 2x^3$
c) approximate value = 0.011 503
to 6 d.p.
e) The approximation for $\sin 4x$
is $4x$ and although the largest
value of x used is 0.15, this
gives $4x = 0.6$ radians, which is
not particularly small.

Consolidation Exercises for Chapter 2 *(p.36)*
1 $y = 2e^{3x} - \frac{3}{2}\cos x + c$
2 a) 0.397 **b)** 0.740
3 b) 2.79
d) 0.146, 3 roots
4 0.035%
5 $e^{2x}(2\cos x - \sin x)$
b) $y = 2x + 1$
6 a) $e^{-x}(\cos x - \sin x)$
b) $(-2.4, -7.5)$, $(0.79, 0.32)$
7 a) $2\cos 2x$
b) $1 - \frac{1}{2}\sin^2 2x$
8 a) 13 cm, $\frac{\pi}{2}$
b) 0.478
c) $v = -12\sin 4t$
$v(2) = -11.87$ m s^{-1} moving up
9 b) $\frac{1}{8}(\sin 4x + 2\sin 2x)$
c) $\frac{\pi}{12} - \frac{\sqrt{3}}{8} (= 0.045\,293)$
10 5.5102, 3.046 38π
11 $\frac{2}{5}\sin^5 x + c$
12 a) $\frac{1}{18}$ **b)** $f(x) \leq 0$ on domain
c) $\frac{1}{6}\ln(2) - \frac{\pi^2}{72} (= -0.021\,553)$

CHAPTER 3
Algebra

Exercises 3.1 class *(p.43)*
1 a) $1 - x + x^2 - x^3 + x^4$
b) $1 + \frac{3}{2}x - \frac{9}{8}x^2 + \frac{27}{16}x^3 - \frac{405}{128}x^4$
c) $1 + \frac{2}{3}x + \frac{1}{9}x^2 + \frac{4}{27}x^3 + \frac{5}{81}x^4$
d) $2\left(1 + \frac{x}{24} - \frac{x^2}{576} + \frac{5x^3}{41472} - \frac{5x^4}{497664}\right)$
e) $1 - x + \frac{3}{2}x^2 - \frac{5}{2}x^3 + \frac{35}{8}x$
f) $1 + \frac{15}{4}x - \frac{75}{32}x^2 + \frac{625}{128}x^3 - \frac{28\,125}{2048}x^4$
2 a) $1 + x - \frac{1}{2}x^2 + \frac{1}{3}x^3$, 1.02
b) 9.80 to 3 s.f. **c)** 2.03

3 $1 - 2x + 2x^2 - 2x^3$
4 $a^{\frac{1}{2}}b^{-\frac{1}{2}}$ 0.816
5 $a = \frac{1}{2}, P = -1, Q = \frac{3}{4}$
6 $n = -\frac{1}{5}, r = \frac{15}{2}, -0.06 < x < 0.06$

Exercises 3.1 home (p.44)
1 a) $1 - 3x + 6x^2 - 10x^3$
b) $1 - 6x + 24x^2 - 80x^3$
c) $1 + 0.2x + 0.04x^2 + 0.008x^3$
d) $3(1 + 0.0123x - 0.000\,152x^2 + 3.14 \times 10^{-6}\, x^3)$
e) $1 + 3.5x - 6.125x^2 + 21.4375x^3$
f) $1 - 3.75x + 1.406\,25x^2 + 1.0547x^3$
2 a) $1 - 2.5x - 3.125x^2 - 7.8125x^3$, 0.975
b) 0.986 c) 2.0037
3 $1 + 1.5x + 0.875x^2 + 0.6875x^3 + 0.5859x^4$
4 $a = 4, b = -\frac{1}{32}$
5 $1 + 0.5x + 0.375x^2 - 0.1875x^3 + 0.023\,437x^4, -0.8 \le x \le 1.1$
6 $1 - \frac{2.667}{x} + \frac{7.111}{x^2} - \frac{31.61}{x^3}$

Exercises 3.2 class (p.51)
1 a) $x = 0$ b) $x = 3$
c) $x = -2$ and $x = 1$
d) $x = 3$ e) none
f) $x = \frac{1}{2}, x = 2$ and $x = 3$
2 a) $y = 1$ b) $y = 0$
c) $y = 1$ d) $y = -1$
e) $y = \frac{1}{4}$ f) $y = 0$
3 a) yes b) no c) yes d) no
6 vertical asymptotes: $x = 2$ and $x = -2$, horizontal asymptotes: $y = 4$ and $y = -4$ domain: $-\infty < x -2, 2 < x < \infty$

Exercises 3.2 home (p.52)
1 a) $x = 0$ b) $x = -4$ c) $x = 5$
d) $x = -\frac{1}{2}$ and $x = \frac{1}{2}$ e) none
f) $x = 1, x = 2$ and $x = 3$
2 a) $y = 1$ b) $y = 0$ c) $y = \frac{1}{3}$
d) $y = \frac{5}{7}$
3 a) yes b) no c) yes d) no

Exercises 3.3 class (p.55)
1 a) and d)
2 29
3 $a = -7, b = -3$

Exercises 3.3 home (p.55)
1 a) 9 b) –4 c) 23 d) 19
2 $a = -2, b = 3, c = 54$
3 $h = 4, g = -1$
$(x - 2)(x + 1)(x + 2)(x + 3)$
6 b) rs

Exercises 3.4 class (p.59)
1 a) $\frac{1}{x-1} - \frac{1}{x+1}$ b) $\frac{1}{x-2} - \frac{1}{x-1}$
c) $\frac{4}{x-1} - \frac{4}{x}$ d) $\frac{1}{2(x+3)} + \frac{1}{2(x-1)}$
e) $\frac{3}{(x-2)} - \frac{1}{(x-1)}$ f) $\frac{1}{3(x-1)} - \frac{1}{3(x+2)}$
g) $x - 1 + \frac{1}{3(x-1)} + \frac{8}{3(x+2)}$

h) $-\frac{3}{x-5} - \frac{2}{(x+5)}$ i) $\frac{1}{x} - \frac{x}{x^2+1}$
j) $\frac{2}{19(4-x)} - \frac{2x+8}{19(x^2+3)}$
k) $\frac{12}{(3x+2)} - \frac{1}{(x+1)^2} - \frac{4}{(x+1)}$
l) $\frac{2}{(x-2)^2} - \frac{1}{(x-2)} + \frac{1}{(x-1)}$
2 $\frac{5}{(x-3)} - \frac{2}{(3x+2)}$, (–4.90625) or $-\frac{157}{32}$
3 $y = \frac{1}{(x-3)} - \frac{1}{(x-1)}$
$\frac{dy}{dx} = -\frac{1}{(x-3)^2} + \frac{1}{(x-1)^2}$
$\frac{d^2y}{dx^2} = \frac{2}{(x-3)^3} - \frac{2}{(x-1)^3}$
(2, –2) is a local maximum

Exercises 3.4 home (p.60)
1 a) $\frac{1}{3(x-3)} - \frac{1}{3x}$ b) $\frac{1}{(x+1)} - \frac{1}{(x+2)}$
c) $\frac{17}{10(x-10)} + \frac{3}{10x}$
d) $\frac{5}{3(2x-1)} - \frac{4}{3(x+1)}$
e) $\frac{1}{6(2x-1)} - \frac{1}{6(2x+3)}$
f) $\frac{1}{x+3}$ g) $\frac{2}{(x-1)} - \frac{1}{(x-1)^2}$
h) $\frac{9}{(3x-1)^2} - \frac{9}{(3x-1)} - \frac{3}{10x}$
i) $\frac{3x}{10(x^2+10)} - \frac{2}{(x^2+10)} - \frac{3}{10x}$
j) $\frac{1}{2(x-1)} - \frac{1}{2(x+1)} + 1$
k) $\frac{1}{(x+2)} + \frac{1}{(x-1)} + x - 1$
l) $-\frac{x}{(x^2+2)} - \frac{31}{(x^2+2)} + \frac{x}{(x^2+1)} + \frac{3}{(x^2+1)}$
2 $y = -\frac{4}{(x+6)^2} - \frac{1}{(x-2)}$,
$\frac{dy}{dx} = -\frac{4}{(x+6)^2} + \frac{1}{(x-2)^2}$,
$\frac{d^2y}{dx^2} = -\frac{84}{(x+6)^3} + \frac{2}{(x-2)^3}$
3 $y = 1 - \frac{5}{4(x-2)} + \frac{5}{4(x+2)}$,
$\frac{dy}{dx} = 1 - \frac{5}{4(x-2)^2} - \frac{5}{4(x+2)^2}$,
$\frac{d^2y}{dx^2} = -\frac{5}{2(x-2)^3} + \frac{5}{2(x+2)^3}$

Exercises 3.5 class (p.62)
1 a) $2 + 3x + 3x^2 + 3x^3$ $\quad|x| < 1$
b) $\frac{1}{2} + \frac{x}{4} - \frac{x^2}{8} + \frac{x^3}{16}$ $\quad|x| < 1$
c) $-\frac{1}{3} + \frac{x}{9} - \frac{8x^2}{27} - \frac{8x^3}{81}$ $\quad|x| < 2$
d) $1 - \frac{3x}{2} + \frac{11x^2}{8} - \frac{23x^3}{16}$ $\quad|x| < 3$
e) $\frac{1}{2} - \frac{3x}{2} + \frac{13x^2}{8} - \frac{51x^3}{16}$ $\quad|x| < \frac{1}{2}$
f) $\frac{1}{2} + \frac{3x}{4} + \frac{7x^2}{8} + \frac{15x^3}{16}$ $\quad|x| < 1$
g) $5 + 5x + 35x^2 + 65x^3$ $\quad|x| < \frac{1}{3}$
h) $\frac{1}{3} + \frac{5x}{9} + \frac{13x^2}{27} + \frac{41x^3}{81}$ $\quad|x| < 1$
2 $\frac{1}{2} + \frac{3x}{3}$ $\quad|x| < 1$
3 $4 + \frac{20x}{3} + \frac{88x^2}{9}$

Exercises 3.5 home (p.62)
1 a) $-2 + 4x - 4x^2 + 4x^3$ $\quad|x| < 1$
b) $x + 2x^2 + 4x^3$ $\quad|x| < \frac{1}{2}$
c) $1 + x + 3x^2 + 3x^3$ $\quad|x| < 1$
d) $\frac{1}{2} - \frac{x}{4} + \frac{3x^2}{8} - \frac{5x^3}{16}$ $\quad|x| < 1$
e) $2 + \frac{23x}{4} + \frac{1103x^2}{64} + \frac{2647x^3}{512}$ $\quad|x| < \frac{1}{3}$
f) $-\frac{1}{2} + \frac{x}{4} + \frac{5x^2}{8} + \frac{17x^3}{8}$ $\quad|x| < \frac{2}{3}$
g) $\frac{x}{2} - \frac{5x^2}{4} + \frac{17x^3}{8}$ $\quad|x| < 1$
h) $-\frac{1}{4} - \frac{3x}{16} - \frac{29x^2}{64} - \frac{99x^2}{256}$ $\quad|x| < \frac{1}{3}$
2 $\frac{1}{2} + \frac{x}{4} - \frac{9x^2}{8} + \frac{9x^3}{16}$
3 $p_0 = 2$
$p_1 = 2 + 3x$
$p_2 = 2 + 3x + 3x^2$
$p_3 = 2 + 3x + 3x^2 + 3x^3$
$p_4 = 2 + 3x + 3x^2 + 3x^3 + 3x^4$

Consolidation Exercises for Chapter 3 (p.62)
1 a) $1 + 0.5x^2 + 0.375x^4 + 0.3125x^6$
c) 1.4141
2 a) $d^2 = 25 - 24x$
b) $p = 5, q = -2.25, r = 0.506\,25$
c) $d = 4.988$
3 a) $16 - 32x + 24x^2 - 8x^3 + x^4$
b) $1 - 6x + 24x^2 - 80x^3$, converge for $-0.12 \le x \le 0.12$
c) $a = -128$ $b = 600$
4 a) $1 + 3x + 3x^2 + x^3$
b) $1 + 4x + 10x^2 + 20x^3$ valid for $x : -0.17 \le x \le 0.17$
c) $a = 25, b = 63$
5 a) $x = -\frac{1}{2} + \frac{1}{2}\sqrt{1-4p}$
or $x = -\frac{1}{2} - \frac{1}{2}\sqrt{1-4p}$
b) $A = -2$ $B = -2$ $C = -4$, valid for $p : -0.30 \le p \le 0.23$
c) $x = -(2p^3 + p^2 + p)$ (1)
$x = 2p^3 + p^2 + p - 1$ (2)
d) $x = -0.112, x = -0.888$
6 a) $a = 6, 10$ b) 810
7 a) $a = -7$ b) 6 c) –3
8 a) $\frac{1}{1-2x} + \frac{1}{x-1} + \frac{1}{(x-1)^2}$
b) $1 + 3x + 6x^2 + 11x^3$
c) $|x| < \frac{1}{2}$
9 a) $x = -1$ and $x = 5$ and $y = 0$
b) $\frac{1}{6(x-5)} - \frac{1}{6(x+1)}$
c) $\left(2, -\frac{1}{9}\right)$ is a local maximum
10 a) $x = -2$ and $x = 1$
b) $2x - 1 + \frac{1}{(x-1)} - \frac{3}{(x+2)}$
c) slant asymptote $y = 2x - 1$
11 $-\frac{8}{9(x-2)} - \frac{4}{3(x+1)^2} + \frac{8}{9(x+1)}$,
$y = -x + 2$
12 $-\frac{4}{3(2x-1)} - \frac{4}{3(x+1)}$,
$1 + 3x + 5x^2 + 11x^3$ for $|x| < \frac{1}{2}$
13 $f(x) \cong \frac{2}{(x-2)} - \frac{3}{(x-1)}$
$f(x) \cong 2 + 2.5x + 2.75x^2 + 2.875x^3$
14 a) $A = 6, B = 2, C = 5$
b) $9 - 12x + 18x^2 - 42x^3$

c) $f'(0) = -12$

15 a) $\frac{14}{9(2x+1)} + \frac{5}{3(x-1)^2} - \frac{7}{9(x-1)}$

b) $4 + x + 12x^2 - 5x^3$

16 a) $A = 3, B = 1, C = -2$

b) $\frac{dy}{dx} = 3$ when $x = 0$

17 $f'(x) = -\frac{1}{(x+3)^2} < 0$ for all x

Range of $f'(x)$: $y \in \Re, y \neq 2$,

$f'(x) = 2 + \frac{1}{x+3}$, translation -2 units // y-axis followed by translation 3 units // x-axis

18 $\frac{1}{(x-1)} + \frac{1}{(x-1)^2} - \frac{7}{(2x-1)}$

$1 + 3x + 6x^2 + 11x^3$

19 $x = -1$ is vertical asymptote, $y = x - 1$ is a slant asymptote

CHAPTER 4
Integration 3

Exercises 4.1 class (p.71)

1 a) $\frac{1}{5}(x+4)^5 + c$

b) $\frac{1}{12}(2x-3)^6 + c$

c) $\frac{14}{3}$ **d)** $\frac{2}{27}(3x^2+2)^{\frac{9}{4}} + c$

e) $\frac{1}{4}(e^7 - e^3)$ **f)** $e^4 - 1$

g) $\frac{1}{2}(x^2 + 3x + 7)^2 + c$ **h)** 114

2 a) $\frac{1}{7}(x-5)^7 + c$ **b)** 10

c) $\frac{2}{9}(3x-1)^{\frac{3}{2}} + c$

d) $\frac{1}{6}(x^2-1)^3 + c$

e) $2(x^2 - x + 3)^{\frac{1}{2}} + c$

f) $\frac{1}{6}(6^6 - 4^6) = \frac{21280}{3}$

g) $\frac{1}{2}e^{2x+5} + c$ **h)** $e^{x^2-3x+1} + c$

3 $\frac{256}{5}$ **4** $\frac{1}{3}(e^2 - e^{-1})$ **5** $\frac{64\pi}{3}$

6 $\frac{4\pi}{3}$ **7** $\frac{9\sqrt{30} - \sqrt{10}}{125}$ (= 0.369 062)

8 $\frac{80\sqrt{10} - 13\sqrt{13}}{27}$ (= 7.633 70)

Exercises 4.1 home (p.72)

1 a) $\frac{1}{12}(3x+4)^4 + c$

b) $-\frac{2}{3}(x-3)^{-3} + c$

c) $\frac{1}{3}(2x-1)^{\frac{3}{2}} + c$

d) $\frac{125\sqrt{5}-1}{7}$ (= 39.7869)

e) $\frac{1}{5}$ **f)** $e^{x-1} + c$

g) $\frac{1}{2}(x^3-3)^5 + c$ **h)** $e^{2x^2+x-2} + c$

2 a) $\frac{1}{5}(x+3)^5 + c$ **b)** $\frac{247}{3}$

c) $\frac{1}{3}(2x+3)^{\frac{3}{2}} + c$

d) $\frac{1}{3}(x^2 - 2x + 3)^{\frac{3}{2}} + c$

e) $\frac{-1}{8(4x+2)^2} + c$ **f)** $\frac{1}{3}e^{3x-1} + c$

g) $e^{x^2+x+4} + c$ **h)** $\frac{1-e^{-4}}{2}$

3 $\frac{8}{3}$ **4** $2(1 - e^{-0.25})$

5 $\frac{8\pi}{3}$ **6** $\frac{2\pi}{5}$

7 $\bar{x} = \frac{185}{336}(\approx 0.55)$ **8** $\frac{1-e^{-0.25}}{2}$

Exercises 4.2 class (p.75)

1 a) $\frac{3}{2}\ln|1 + 2x| + c$

b) $2\ln|2 + 3x| + c$

c) $\frac{3}{2}\ln\frac{11}{3}$

d) $\ln|1 - 2x + x^3| + c$

e) $\frac{3}{2}(\sqrt{6} - \sqrt{5})$

f) $\frac{1}{2}\ln|1 - e^{-2x}| + c$

2 a) $-\frac{1}{3}\ln|2 - 3x| + c$

b) $\ln 5$ **c)** $\sqrt{x^2+2x+2} + c$

d) $\ln|\ln x| + c$ **e)** $\ln|e^x + e^{-x}| + c$

f) $\frac{1}{3}\ln|x^3 + 3x^2 + 1| + c$

g) $\frac{1}{2}\ln 13$ **h)** $\ln|xe^x - 1| + c$

3 $10\ln 3 - 5\ln 5 = 5$

4 1

5 a) $s = -\frac{5}{4}\ln(10 - 0.4u^2) + \frac{5}{4}\ln(10)$

b) $\frac{5}{2}\ln\frac{5}{3}$

c) $u = 5\sqrt{1 - e^{-0.8t}}$

d) $u \to 5$ as $s \to \infty$

6 a) $t = -2\ln(X - 40) + 2\ln 40$

b) $2\ln 2 \approx 1.386$ minutes

c) $X = 40(1 + e^{-\frac{1}{2}t})$

d) $X \to 40°C$ as $t \to \infty$
The object cools to 40°C.

Exercises 4.2 home (p.76)

1 a) $\frac{5}{4}\ln|1 + 4x| + c$

b) $-\frac{3}{2}\ln|0.5 - 2x| + c$

c) $\frac{1}{4}\ln\frac{5}{3}$

d) $-\ln 3$

e) $2\sqrt{t^4 - 3t} + c$

f) $\frac{5}{3}\ln|2 + e^{3x}| + c$

2 a) $\frac{1}{7}\ln|2 + 7x| + c$

b) $\ln 2 - \frac{1}{2}\ln 3 = \frac{1}{2}\ln\frac{4}{3}$

c) $\sqrt{v^2 + v - 1} + c$

d) 2

e) $\frac{1}{6}\ln|2x^3 - 3x^2 + 6x + 1| + c$

f) $1 - \frac{1}{\sqrt{22}}$

g) $\ln|e^{2x} - x| + c$

h) $\left(\frac{1}{1-e^5}\right) - \left(\frac{1}{1-e^1}\right) \approx 0.575193$

3 $\frac{\pi}{8}$ **4** $\frac{5}{2}\ln 3$

5 a) $s = -\frac{5}{2}\ln(10 + 0.2u^2) + \frac{5}{2}\ln 30$

$= \frac{5}{2}\ln\frac{30}{10 + 0.2u^2}$

b) maximum height $= \frac{5}{2}\ln 3$
$= 2.7465$ metres

6 a) $t = -\frac{10}{3}\ln(10 - 0.3u) + \frac{10}{3}\ln 10$

b) $u = \frac{100}{3}(1 - e^{-0.3t})$

c) $u \to \frac{100}{3}$ as $t \to \infty$

$u = \frac{100}{3}$ m s^{-1} is the terminal speed.

Exercises 4.3 class (p.80)

1 a) $-\frac{1}{9}(1 + 3x)e^{-3x} + c$

b) $\frac{1}{4}(1 + e^2)$

c) $\frac{x^5}{25}(5\ln x - 1) + c$

d) $\frac{1}{27}(17e^{-3} - 50e^{-6})$

e) $(x + 2)e^x + c$

f) $\frac{1}{9}(\sin 3x - 3x \cos 3x) + c$

g) $\frac{\pi^2}{4} - 2$ **h)** $8\ln 2 - 3$

i) $\frac{1}{2}(2x + 3)\ln(2x + 3) - x + c$

j) $e^x(x^2 - x + 3) + c$

k) $\frac{2^{n+1}((n+1)\ln 2 - 1) + 1}{(n+1)^2}$

l) $\frac{1}{30}(x - 1)^5(5x + 1) + c$

m) $\frac{1663}{14}$

n) $\frac{1}{13}e^{2x}(2\sin 3x - 3\cos 3x) + c$

2 c) $2(\ln 2)^4 - 8(\ln 2)^3 + 24(\ln 2)^2 - 48\ln 2 + 24$

3 b) $\int x^2 e^{-x^2}\, dx = I_2 = -\frac{1}{2}xe^{-x^2}$

$+ \frac{1}{2}I_0$

$\int x^4 e^{-x^2}\, dx = I_4 = -\frac{1}{2}x^3 e^{-x^2}$

$+ \frac{3}{4}I_0$

$\int x^6 e^{-x^2}\, dx = I_6 = -\frac{1}{2}x^5 e^{-x^2}$

$- \frac{5}{4}x^3 e^{-x^2} - \frac{15}{8}xe^{-x^2} + \frac{15}{8}I_0$

4 c) $I_0 = \sin x$
$\int x^4 \cos x\, dx = I_4 = x^4 \sin x +$
$4x^3 \cos x - 12x^2\sin x - 24x \cos x$
$+ 24 \sin x$

$\int x^6 \cos x\, dx = I_6$
$= x^6 \sin x - 6x^5 \cos x - 30I_4$
$= \sin x(x^6 - 30x^4 + 360x^2 - 720)$
$+ \cos(6x^5 - 120x^3 + 720x)$

Exercises 4.3 home (p.81)

1 a) $\frac{1}{25}(5x - 1)e^{5x} + c$

b) $4 - 6e^{-0.5}$

c) $\frac{1}{4}(2x^2 - 2x + 1)e^{2x} + c$

d) $\frac{32}{3}\ln 2 - \frac{7}{4}$ **e)** $\frac{1}{660}$

f) $\frac{1}{2}(x + 1)^2 \ln(x + 1)$
$- \frac{1}{4}x(x + 2) + c$

g) $-(2x^2 + x + 2)e^{-x} + c$

h) $\frac{1}{16}(\sin 4x - 4x \cos 4x) + c$

i) $\frac{\pi^3}{128} - \frac{3\pi}{16} + \frac{3}{8}$

j) $\frac{1}{2}(x^2 - 1)e^{x^2} + c$

k) $\frac{1}{27}(2e^3 - 101e^6)$

l) $\frac{448}{45}$

m) $\frac{2}{3}(x - 2)\sqrt{x + 1} + c$

n) $-\frac{1}{5}(2 \cos 2x + \sin 2x)e^{-x}$

2 a) $I_n = \frac{x^{n+1}((n+1)\ln x - 1) + 1}{(n+1)^2}$

3 b) $\frac{5\pi}{32}$

4 $I_n = -x^n \cos x + nx^{n-1}\sin x -$
$n(n - 1)I_{n-2}$
$I_1 = \sin x - x \cos x$
$I_5 = x^5 \sin x\, dx$
$= (5x^4 - 60x^2 + 120) \sin x$
$- (x^5 - 20x^3 + 120x)\cos x$

Exercises 4.4 class *(p.84)*

1. a) $\frac{1}{2}\ln|x| - \frac{1}{2}\ln|x+2| + c$
   b) $2\ln 2 - \ln 3$
   c) $\frac{1}{2}\ln|x+2| - \frac{1}{2}\ln|x-2| + c$
   d) $\frac{1}{2}\ln|x-1| + \frac{1}{2}\ln|x+1| + c$
   e) $5\ln 2 - 3\ln 3$
   f) $\ln 3 - 2\ln 2 + \frac{1}{2}$
   g) $\ln|x-2| - \ln|x+3| + c$
   h) $\frac{3}{2}(\ln|x-1| - \ln|x+1|) + c$
   i) $\frac{1}{5}(\ln|x+3| + 4\ln|x-2|) + c$
   j) $\frac{1}{2}\ln 5 - \ln 2$
   k) $x + 4\ln|x| - 3\ln|x-1| + c$
   l) $\frac{1}{2}x^2 - x + 2\ln|x| - \ln|x+1| + c$

2. $2\ln 15 + 4$

3. $2\ln 2 - \ln 3$

4. $\frac{4}{5}\pi\ln 2$

5. a) $t = 10\ln|H| - 10\ln|5 - 2H| + 10\ln 23$
   b) i) $10\ln\frac{23}{3}(\approx 20.37)$,
      ii) $10\ln 46\ (\approx 38.29)$
   c) $H = \frac{5e^{0.4t}}{23 + 2e^{0.4t}}$
   d) $H_{\max} = 2.5$

6. a) $kt = \frac{1}{2a}\left|\ln|a-x| - \ln|a+3x|\right|$
   b) $x = \frac{a(e^{2akt} - 1)}{(3e^{2akt} - 1)}$
   c) $x \to \frac{a}{3}$ as $t \to \infty$

7. $y = \frac{1}{2}\ln\left(\frac{x+1}{x+3}\right) + \frac{1}{2}\ln 3$

Exercises 4.4 home *(p.85)*

1. a) $\ln|x| - \ln|x+1| + c$
   b) $\ln\frac{2}{3}$
   c) $\frac{3}{5}(\ln|x-2| - \ln|x+2|) + c$
   d) $2\ln|x-2| - \ln|x-1| + c$
   e) $\frac{1}{3}\ln(x+2) + \frac{2}{3}\ln|x-1| + c$
   f) $\frac{1}{2}(5\ln(x-1) - \ln(x+1) + c)$
   g) $\frac{1}{10}(\ln|t-5| - \ln|t+5|) + c$
   h) $\ln\frac{5}{3}$
   i) $\frac{1}{6}(2\ln|x+2| + \ln|x-1| - 3\ln|x+1|) + c$
   j) $-2\ln|x| + \frac{1}{4}(5\ln|x+2| + 3\ln|x-2|) + c$
   k) $\frac{1}{2}(9\ln 2 - 5\ln 5)$
   l) $\ln 2 - \frac{1}{2}$

2. $20 - 20\ln 2$

3. $7\ln 3 - 14\ln 2 + \frac{14}{3}$

4. $\frac{\pi}{3}\ln 2$

5. a) $kt = \frac{1}{M}(\ln x - \ln(M - x))$
   b) $x = \frac{Me^{KMt}}{1 + e^{KMt}}$
   c) $x \to M$ as $t \to \infty$

6. a) $t = 2\ln\left(\frac{2(u+5)}{3u}\right)$
   b) $4\ln 2 - 2\ln 3 (\approx 0.5754)$ s
   c) $u = \frac{10}{3e^{0.5t} - 2}$
   d) $u \to 0$ as $t \to \infty$

7. a) $t = \frac{\sqrt{2}}{4}(\ln(5\sqrt{2} + u) - \ln(5\sqrt{2} - u))$
   b) $u = 5\sqrt{2}\,\dfrac{e^{2\sqrt{2}t} - 1}{e^{2\sqrt{2}t} + 1}$

c) $u \to 5\sqrt{2}$ as $t \to \infty$
$u = 5\sqrt{2}$ m s^{-1} is called the terminal speed.
The parachute will eventually travel with this constant speed.

Consolidation Exercises for Chapter 4 *(p.86)*

1. a) $2\ln(2) - \frac{1}{2}\ln(7)$
   b) $-\frac{1}{4}(2x + 1)e^{-2x} + c$
   c) $-\frac{1}{6}e^{-3x^2} + c$ d) $\ln\frac{3}{2}$
   e) 2   f) $\frac{1}{3}\ln(t^2 + 7)^{\frac{3}{2}} + c$
   g) $\frac{1}{9}(3x^2\ln(x) - x^3 + c)$
   h) $\frac{1}{2}(45\sqrt{5} - \sqrt{3})$
   i) $\frac{1}{3}\ln|3x + 5| + c$
   j) $-\frac{1}{12(t3+9)4} + c$
   k) $\frac{1}{32}((1 - 8x^2)\cos 4x + 4x\sin x) + c$
   l) $\frac{1}{13}(3\sin 3x - 2\cos x)e^{-2x} + c$

2. a) $T = 90 + \frac{40}{2t+1}$
   b) $T \to 90$ as $t \to \infty$

3. $\frac{1}{243}(85\sqrt{85} - 8) \approx 3.192$

4. $24\pi\ln\frac{3}{2}$

5. a) $kt = -\ln(a + x) + \ln(a)$ $T = \frac{1}{k}\ln 2$
   b) $kt = \frac{1}{(n-1)(a-x)^{n-1}} - \frac{1}{(n-1)a^{n-1}}$,
      $T = \frac{(2^{n-1} - 1)}{(n-1)a^{n-1}}$

6. a) $kt = \frac{1}{2}(2\ln(2 - x) - \ln(1 - x) - \ln(3 - x)) + \frac{1}{2}\ln\frac{3}{4}$
   b) $x = \dfrac{2\left(\sqrt{4e^{2kt} - 3} - \sqrt{e^{2kt}}\right)}{\sqrt{4e^{2kt} - 3}}$

7. a) $t = \ln(1 + 0.1u) - \ln(u) + \ln\frac{100}{11}$
   b) $2\ln 2 - \ln\frac{11}{3}$
   c) $u = \frac{100}{11e^t - 100}$
   d) $u \to -10$ as $t \to \infty$

8. a) $A = 1, B = -1, C = 2$

9. a) A is point $(-\frac{1}{2}, 0)$, asymptote is $x = 1$
   b) $y = 4x + 1$, tangent cuts curve at $\left(\frac{7}{4}, 8\right)$

10. a) $\frac{3x}{(x+1)} - \frac{1}{(x^2+1)} - \frac{4}{(x-2)}$

11. a) $\frac{3}{2}x^2(1 + x^3)^{-\frac{1}{2}}$ b) $\frac{4}{3}$

12. a) A is point $(1, 0)$, gradient at A is 1
    b) B is point $(e^{-0.5}, -\frac{1}{2}e^{-1})$
    $\frac{d^2y}{dx^2} = 2$ at B

13. $v = \frac{1}{(1+t)} - 1$, 2.1, 2.13, 2.14, 2.145, 2.146, 2.146, 2.146

14. $\frac{\pi}{12}$

15. $A = -2, B = 6, C = 2,$

16. a) $A = 3, B = -2, C = 2$
    b) $-\frac{17}{36}$
    c) $\frac{9}{4} + \ln\left(\frac{25}{64}\right)$

17. $\frac{1}{1-x} + \frac{2}{(1-x)^2} + \frac{3}{(4-x)}$

18. $\frac{2}{5}\sin^5 x + c$

19. a) $\frac{1}{2}\ln(x^2 + 4) + c$
    c) $f'(0) = -\frac{17}{4}$, $f'(8) = -\frac{1}{1156}$
    d) $\frac{8-x}{(x^2+4)(2x+1)}$

21. b) $\frac{25}{2}\ln 5 - 6$, trapezium rule gives 14.25
    c) percentage error is 0.94%

22. a) i) $(x - 1)(x + 2)(2x - 3)$
       ii) $-2 < x < 1$ and $x > 1.5$
    b) $A = 1, B = 0, C = 1$
       ii) $\frac{1}{2}\ln(2x + 3) + \frac{1}{2}\arctan\left(\frac{x}{2}\right)$

CHAPTER 5
Vectors

Exercises 5.1 class *(p.94)*

1. $\overrightarrow{CF}, \overrightarrow{AD}, \overrightarrow{BE}$, are three possible vectors.
   $\begin{pmatrix} 5 \\ 2 \end{pmatrix}$ or (5.39, 21.80°)

2. Birmingham from Bristol 128 km, 29° (bearing from north)
   Dover from London 102.7 km, 245° (bearing from north)

3.

Vector	Components	Magnitude	Direction
a	$\begin{pmatrix} 0 \\ 3 \end{pmatrix}$	3	90°
b	$\begin{pmatrix} -2 \\ 0 \end{pmatrix}$	2	180°
c	$\begin{pmatrix} 2 \\ -1 \end{pmatrix}$	2.24	333.43°
d	$\begin{pmatrix} 2 \\ 0 \end{pmatrix}$	2	0°
e	$\begin{pmatrix} 4 \\ 2 \end{pmatrix}$	4.47	26.57°

4.

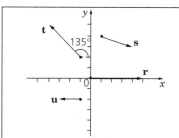

5. a) $\mathbf{a} = \begin{pmatrix} 4.32 \\ 1.57 \end{pmatrix}$, $\theta = 20°$
   b) $\mathbf{b} = \begin{pmatrix} 2.54 \\ -1.78 \end{pmatrix}$, $\theta = 325°$
   c) $\mathbf{c} = \begin{pmatrix} -2.60 \\ -4.50 \end{pmatrix}$, $\theta = 240°$

d) $\mathbf{d} = \begin{pmatrix} -5.36 \\ 4.50 \end{pmatrix}$, $\theta = 140°$

6 a) $\begin{pmatrix} 2 \\ 1 \end{pmatrix}$ **b)** $\begin{pmatrix} -4 \\ 6 \end{pmatrix}$ **c)** $\begin{pmatrix} -1 \\ 1 \end{pmatrix}$

d) $\begin{pmatrix} 2 \\ 2 \end{pmatrix}$ **e)** $\begin{pmatrix} 1 \\ 2 \end{pmatrix}$ **f)** $\begin{pmatrix} -7 \\ -4 \end{pmatrix}$

g) $\begin{pmatrix} -8 \\ -1 \end{pmatrix}$ **h)** $\begin{pmatrix} 7 \\ 7 \end{pmatrix}$

Exercises 5.1 home (p.95)

1 $\overrightarrow{AE}, \overrightarrow{BF}, \overrightarrow{CG}, \overrightarrow{DH}$ are possible displacements, $\begin{pmatrix} -5 \\ 3 \end{pmatrix}$ or (5.83, 149.04°)

2

Vector	Component form	Magnitude	Direction
$\overrightarrow{AB}$	$\begin{pmatrix} 8 \\ 0 \end{pmatrix}$	8	0°
$\overrightarrow{BD}$	$\begin{pmatrix} -7 \\ -4 \end{pmatrix}$	8.06	209.74°
$\overrightarrow{CA}$	$\begin{pmatrix} -7 \\ 5 \end{pmatrix}$	8.60	144.46°
$\overrightarrow{AD}$	$\begin{pmatrix} 1 \\ -4 \end{pmatrix}$	4.12	284.04°

3

4 a) 2.24, 26.57°
b) 5, 306.87°
c) $\sqrt{2} = 1.41$, 135°
d) 3.61, 326.31°
e) 4.47, 243.43°
f) 3.49, 62.70°

5 a) $\mathbf{a} = \begin{pmatrix} 2.75 \\ 2.48 \end{pmatrix}$ **b)** $\mathbf{b} = \begin{pmatrix} -2.64 \\ 3.14 \end{pmatrix}$

c) $\mathbf{c} = \begin{pmatrix} -4.50 \\ 2.60 \end{pmatrix}$ **d)** $\mathbf{d} = \begin{pmatrix} 1.79 \\ -0.65 \end{pmatrix}$

6 a) 4, 0° **b)** 2.83, 45°
c) 3.61, 213.69°
d) 5.10, 101.31°
e) 8, 180° **f)** 6.40, 218.66°
g) 6.40, 308.66°
h) 7.07, 225°

Exercises 5.2 class (p.100)

1 a) $\mathbf{d}$ **b)** $\mathbf{f}$
c) $\mathbf{e} = -\mathbf{a}$ **d)** $\mathbf{g} = 2\mathbf{a}$

2 a) i) $\overrightarrow{CD} = -\mathbf{a}$ **ii)** $\overrightarrow{AD} = \mathbf{b}$
iii) $\overrightarrow{AC} = \mathbf{a} + \mathbf{b}$

b) i) $\overrightarrow{AM} = \mathbf{a} + \frac{1}{2}\mathbf{b}$
ii) $\overrightarrow{MD} = \frac{1}{2}\mathbf{b} - \mathbf{a}$

3

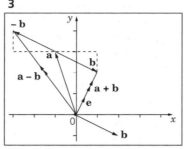

Unit vector in direction of

$\mathbf{a} + \mathbf{b}$ is $\begin{pmatrix} \frac{1}{\sqrt{5}} \\ \frac{2}{\sqrt{5}} \end{pmatrix} = \mathbf{e}$

4 $\mathbf{a} = -2\mathbf{i} + 2\mathbf{j}$, $\mathbf{b} = \mathbf{i} + 2\mathbf{j}$, $\mathbf{c} = 2\mathbf{i} + 3\mathbf{j}$, $\mathbf{d} = 3\mathbf{i} - 2\mathbf{j}$

5 a) $\begin{pmatrix} 1 \\ 1 \end{pmatrix}$ **b)** $\begin{pmatrix} 4 \\ 4 \end{pmatrix}$ **c)** $\begin{pmatrix} 0 \\ -5 \end{pmatrix}$ **d)** $\begin{pmatrix} 3 \\ 2 \end{pmatrix}$
e) $\begin{pmatrix} 7 \\ -3 \end{pmatrix}$ **f)** $\begin{pmatrix} -3 \\ -5 \end{pmatrix}$ **g)** $\begin{pmatrix} 5 \\ 6 \end{pmatrix}$

6 a) $2\mathbf{j}$ **b)** $\mathbf{i} - 2\mathbf{j}$
c) $2\mathbf{i} - \mathbf{j}$ **d)** $-\mathbf{i} + 4\mathbf{j}$
e) $5\mathbf{i} - \mathbf{j}$ **f)** $8\mathbf{i} - 4\mathbf{j}$

7 a) $4\mathbf{i} + \mathbf{j}$, $-3\mathbf{i} - 2\mathbf{j}$
b) $\overrightarrow{PQ} = -7\mathbf{i} - 3\mathbf{j}$

or **a)** $\begin{pmatrix} 4 \\ 1 \end{pmatrix}$, $\begin{pmatrix} -3 \\ -2 \end{pmatrix}$ **b)** $\begin{pmatrix} -7 \\ -3 \end{pmatrix}$

8 a) $\begin{pmatrix} \frac{3}{5} \\ \frac{4}{5} \end{pmatrix}$ **b)** $\frac{5}{13}\mathbf{i} + \frac{12}{13}\mathbf{j}$

c) $\frac{4}{5}\mathbf{i} - \frac{3}{5}\mathbf{j}$ **d)** $\begin{pmatrix} -\frac{1}{\sqrt{2}} \\ -\frac{1}{\sqrt{2}} \end{pmatrix}$ **e)** $-\mathbf{i}$

f) $\begin{pmatrix} 0 \\ 1 \end{pmatrix}$ **g)** $\begin{pmatrix} \cos\theta \\ \sin\theta \end{pmatrix}$

h) $\dfrac{a}{\sqrt{a^2+b^2}}\mathbf{i} + \dfrac{b}{\sqrt{a^2+b^2}}\mathbf{j}$

9 a) $\overrightarrow{AP} = \frac{1}{2}\mathbf{a}$, $\overrightarrow{AQ} = \frac{1}{2}\mathbf{b}$,

$\overrightarrow{PQ} = \frac{1}{2}(\mathbf{b} - \mathbf{a})$, $\overrightarrow{BC} = \mathbf{b} - \mathbf{a}$
b) PQ and BC are parallel and length of PQ = $\frac{1}{2}$ length of BC.

10 a) $k = 1$ **b)** $k = \frac{1}{2}$
c) $k = \frac{1}{3}$

Exercises 5.2 home (p.101)

1 a) $\mathbf{b}, \mathbf{c}, \mathbf{f}$ **b)** $\mathbf{c}$ **c)** $\mathbf{a}, \mathbf{e}$

2 b) $\overrightarrow{DE} = -\mathbf{a}$, $\overrightarrow{BD} = 2\mathbf{b} - \mathbf{a}$,
$\overrightarrow{BF} = \mathbf{b} - 2\mathbf{a}$

3 a) $\mathbf{c}$ has magnitude 49 mm and direction 39°, $\mathbf{d}$ has magnitude 12 mm and direction 250°
b) $\mathbf{e}$ has magnitude 147 mm and direction 39°, $\mathbf{e} = 3\mathbf{c}$

4 a) $\begin{pmatrix} -2 \\ 1 \end{pmatrix}$ **b)** $\begin{pmatrix} -2 \\ 0 \end{pmatrix}$ **c)** $\begin{pmatrix} -6 \\ -3 \end{pmatrix}$

d) $\begin{pmatrix} 12 \\ 11 \end{pmatrix}$ **e)** $\begin{pmatrix} 12 \\ 8 \end{pmatrix}$ **f)** $\begin{pmatrix} 6 \\ 9 \end{pmatrix}$

5 a) $-\mathbf{i} + 3\mathbf{j}$ **b)** $\mathbf{i}$ **c)** $-2\mathbf{i} + 3\mathbf{j}$ **d)** $8\mathbf{i} + \mathbf{j}$
e) $-4\mathbf{i} + 4\mathbf{j}$ **f)** $7\mathbf{i} - 4\mathbf{j}$

6 a) $\begin{pmatrix} \frac{4}{5} \\ \frac{3}{5} \end{pmatrix}$ **b)** $\begin{pmatrix} -1 \\ 0 \end{pmatrix}$

c) $\frac{1}{\sqrt{2}}\mathbf{i} + \frac{1}{\sqrt{2}}\mathbf{j}$ **d)** $\frac{12}{13}\mathbf{i} - \frac{5}{13}\mathbf{j}$

e) $\begin{pmatrix} -\frac{1}{\sqrt{2}} \\ \frac{1}{\sqrt{2}} \end{pmatrix}$ **f)** $\begin{pmatrix} 0 \\ 1 \end{pmatrix}$

g) $-\frac{2}{\sqrt{13}}\mathbf{i} - \frac{3}{\sqrt{13}}\mathbf{j}$

h) $\begin{pmatrix} \dfrac{r}{\sqrt{r^2+s^2}} \\ \dfrac{s}{\sqrt{r^2+s^2}} \end{pmatrix}$

7 a) $\begin{pmatrix} -2 \\ -3 \end{pmatrix}, \begin{pmatrix} -1 \\ 4 \end{pmatrix}, \begin{pmatrix} 4 \\ 3 \end{pmatrix}, \begin{pmatrix} 3 \\ -4 \end{pmatrix}$

b) $\overrightarrow{AB} = \begin{pmatrix} 1 \\ 7 \end{pmatrix}, \overrightarrow{BC} = \begin{pmatrix} 5 \\ -1 \end{pmatrix}$,
$\overrightarrow{DC} = \begin{pmatrix} 1 \\ 7 \end{pmatrix}, \overrightarrow{AD} = \begin{pmatrix} 5 \\ -1 \end{pmatrix}$

c) ABCD is a parallelogram

8 $\begin{pmatrix} -3 \\ -2 \end{pmatrix}$

9 $\overrightarrow{OD} = \frac{1}{2}\mathbf{b} + \frac{1}{2}\mathbf{c}$, $\overrightarrow{OG} = \frac{1}{3}(\mathbf{a}+\mathbf{b}+\mathbf{c})$

Exercises 5.3 class (p.103)

1 a) -2 **b)** -1
c) -3 **d)** 0
e) 1 **f)** -1

2 a) 26.57° **b)** 78.69°
c) 30.96° **d)** 90°
e) 94.64° **f)** 101.31°

3 a) $m = -\frac{1}{2}$ **b)** $m = 2$
c) $m = 0.66$

4 a) $\overrightarrow{AC} = \begin{pmatrix} 3 \\ 3 \end{pmatrix}, \overrightarrow{BD} = \begin{pmatrix} -3 \\ 3 \end{pmatrix}$

5 a) $x \bullet y = -78$ **b)** $m = -\frac{3}{4}$

Exercises 5.3 home (p.104)

1 a) -16 **b)** -7
c) 3 **d)** 0
e) 1 **f)** 0

2 a) 74.74° **b)** 26.57°
c) 42.27° **d)** 171.87°
e) 0 **f)** 98.13°

3 a) $k = -3$ **b)** $k = \frac{4}{3}$
c) $k = \frac{2}{5}$

4 a) $2 - m$ **b)** $m = 1$

5 a) -132 **b)** $m = -\frac{27}{2}$

Exercises 5.4 class (p.107)

2 a) $\mathbf{r} = \begin{pmatrix} 0 \\ 1 \end{pmatrix} + t\begin{pmatrix} 1 \\ 1 \end{pmatrix}$

b) $\mathbf{r} = \begin{pmatrix} 2 \\ 3 \end{pmatrix} + t\begin{pmatrix} -3 \\ -6 \end{pmatrix}$

c) $\mathbf{r} = \begin{pmatrix} -2 \\ 1 \end{pmatrix} + t\begin{pmatrix} -1 \\ 3 \end{pmatrix}$

3 a) $\mathbf{r} = (-\mathbf{i} + \mathbf{j}) + t(2\mathbf{i} + \mathbf{j})$

b) $\mathbf{r} = \begin{pmatrix} 3 \\ -1 \end{pmatrix} + t\begin{pmatrix} 6 \\ 1 \end{pmatrix}$

c) $\mathbf{r} = (3\mathbf{i} + 4\mathbf{j}) + t(-2\mathbf{i} - 3\mathbf{j})$

4 b) $\mathbf{r} = \begin{pmatrix} x \\ 3x+1 \end{pmatrix} + t\begin{pmatrix} 1 \\ 3 \end{pmatrix}$
for any choice of x

5 a) $\mathbf{r} = \begin{pmatrix} 0 \\ 5 \end{pmatrix} + t\begin{pmatrix} 1 \\ -2 \end{pmatrix}$

b) $\mathbf{r} = \begin{pmatrix} 0 \\ -2 \end{pmatrix} + t\begin{pmatrix} 1 \\ 3 \end{pmatrix}$

6 b) $6y = x - 9$

7 a) $3y = x + 7$ **b)** $2y = 3x - 1$

8 a) $\begin{pmatrix} 2 \\ 3 \end{pmatrix}$ **b)** $\begin{pmatrix} -5 \\ 3 \end{pmatrix}$

c) $\begin{pmatrix} -8 \\ 14 \end{pmatrix}$ **d)** $\begin{pmatrix} -1 \\ 1 \end{pmatrix}$

9 a) $\mathbf{r} = \begin{pmatrix} -2 \\ 3 \end{pmatrix} + t\begin{pmatrix} 6 \\ -6 \end{pmatrix}$

b) $\mathbf{r} = \begin{pmatrix} -3 \\ -1 \end{pmatrix} + s\begin{pmatrix} 8 \\ 4 \end{pmatrix}$

c) $\begin{pmatrix} 1 \\ 0 \end{pmatrix}, \begin{pmatrix} 1 \\ 1 \end{pmatrix}$ **d)** 71.57°

e) $\begin{pmatrix} \frac{1}{3} \\ \frac{2}{3} \end{pmatrix}$

Exercises 5.4 home (p.108)

2 a) $\mathbf{r} = \begin{pmatrix} -1 \\ 0 \end{pmatrix} + t\begin{pmatrix} 4 \\ 4 \end{pmatrix}$

b) $\mathbf{r} = \begin{pmatrix} 5 \\ 12 \end{pmatrix} + t\begin{pmatrix} -5 \\ -13 \end{pmatrix}$

c) $\mathbf{r} = \begin{pmatrix} 2 \\ 1 \end{pmatrix} + t\begin{pmatrix} -3 \\ 2 \end{pmatrix}$

3 a) $\mathbf{r} = \begin{pmatrix} 2 \\ 3 \end{pmatrix} + t\begin{pmatrix} -2 \\ 4 \end{pmatrix}$

b) $\mathbf{r} = 5\mathbf{i} + t(-\mathbf{i} + \mathbf{j})$

c) $\mathbf{r} = 3\mathbf{j} + 3t\mathbf{i}$

4 a) $\mathbf{r} = \begin{pmatrix} 0 \\ -1 \end{pmatrix} + t\begin{pmatrix} 1 \\ 4 \end{pmatrix}$

b) $\mathbf{r} = \begin{pmatrix} 0 \\ 4 \end{pmatrix} + t\begin{pmatrix} 1 \\ -1 \end{pmatrix}$

c) $\mathbf{r} = \begin{pmatrix} 0 \\ -\frac{1}{3} \end{pmatrix} + t\begin{pmatrix} 3 \\ 2 \end{pmatrix}$

5 a) $y = x + 3$ **b)** $2y = -x + 5$
c) $y = -x - 3$

6 a) $\begin{pmatrix} 8 \\ 8 \end{pmatrix}$ **b)** $\begin{pmatrix} -2 \\ -2 \end{pmatrix}$ **c)** $\begin{pmatrix} 3 \\ 4 \end{pmatrix}$

8 a) $\mathbf{r} = 6\mathbf{i} + 8\mathbf{j} + t(4\mathbf{i} - 3\mathbf{j})$,
$\mathbf{r} = 9\mathbf{i} + 12\mathbf{j} + s(-3\mathbf{i} - 9\mathbf{j})$
b) 71.57°   **c)** $\left(\frac{22}{3}, 7\right)$

9 a) $\mathbf{r} = \begin{pmatrix} 1 \\ 3 \end{pmatrix} + t\begin{pmatrix} -2 \\ 4 \end{pmatrix}$

b) $(0,5), \left(\frac{5}{2}, 0\right)$

Exercises 5.5 class (p.111)

1 a) $\begin{pmatrix} 1 \\ -1 \\ 2 \end{pmatrix} + t\begin{pmatrix} 1 \\ 0 \\ -1 \end{pmatrix}$

b) $\begin{pmatrix} -1 \\ -2 \\ -1 \end{pmatrix} + t\begin{pmatrix} 4 \\ 3 \\ -1 \end{pmatrix}$

c) $\begin{pmatrix} 2 \\ 1 \\ 1 \end{pmatrix} + t\begin{pmatrix} -1 \\ 0 \\ 2 \end{pmatrix}$

d) $\mathbf{i} - \mathbf{k} + t(2\mathbf{i} + \mathbf{j} - 3\mathbf{k})$

2 a) 61.9°   **b)** 50.8°
c) 90°   **d)** 83.5°

3 a) 47.6°   **b)** 66.4°
c) 35.3°

4 a) intersect at $(-1, -6, -9)$
b) skew lines   **c)** skew lines
d) intersect at $(-1, 6, -4)$

5 $\mathbf{r} = \frac{13}{8}\mathbf{i} - \frac{1}{4}\mathbf{j} + \frac{21}{8}\mathbf{k}$

6 b) $2\mathbf{i} + \mathbf{j} + 6\mathbf{k} + t(\mathbf{i} + 2\mathbf{j} + 3\mathbf{k})$
c) $(0, -3, 0)$ **d)** 18°
e) $3\mathbf{i} - \mathbf{j} + 7\mathbf{k}$

Exercises 5.5 home (p.112)

1 a) $\begin{pmatrix} 0 \\ 1 \\ 0 \end{pmatrix} + t\begin{pmatrix} 2 \\ -2 \\ 3 \end{pmatrix}$ **b)** $\begin{pmatrix} 2 \\ 0 \\ 1 \end{pmatrix} + t\begin{pmatrix} -3 \\ 2 \\ 3 \end{pmatrix}$

c) $3\mathbf{i} + 4\mathbf{j} + \mathbf{k} + t(\mathbf{i} + \mathbf{j} + \mathbf{k})$

d) $\begin{pmatrix} -1 \\ -1 \\ 2 \end{pmatrix} + t\begin{pmatrix} 5 \\ 0 \\ -1 \end{pmatrix}$

2 a) 56.9°   **b)** 29°
c) 90°   **d)** 76.2°

3 a) $(2, 1, 2)$, 59.8°
b) $(1, 0, -1)$, 45°   **c)** skew lines
d) $(4, 7, -5)$, 7.4°

4 $\overrightarrow{OP} = 15\mathbf{i} + 9\mathbf{k}$, $\overrightarrow{OQ} = -8\mathbf{j} + 16\mathbf{k}$

5 a) $a = 7, b = 6$
b) 68.5°
c) $\mathbf{i} + 2\mathbf{j} - \mathbf{k} + t(3\mathbf{i} + 9\mathbf{k})$
point of intersection $-\mathbf{i} + 2\mathbf{j} - 7\mathbf{k}$

6 a) 17, 40.2°
b) $\mathbf{d} = 4\mathbf{i} - 4\mathbf{j} + 3\mathbf{k}$
c) $\mathbf{e} = -5\mathbf{j} + \mathbf{k}$

Consolidation exercises for chapter 5 (p.115)

1 a) 5.12 m
b) Collide after $4\frac{2}{3}$ s unless avoiding action is taken

2 a) $\overrightarrow{AB} = \mathbf{i} - \mathbf{j} + \mathbf{k}$, 28.4°
b) $\mathbf{r} = 2\mathbf{i} - \mathbf{j} + 6\mathbf{k} + t(\mathbf{i} - \mathbf{j} + \mathbf{k})$
c) $\mathbf{r} = -\mathbf{i} + 2\mathbf{j} + 3\mathbf{k}$

3 a) AB: $\mathbf{r} = \mathbf{i} + 11\mathbf{j} + t(\mathbf{i} - 3\mathbf{j})$
DC: $\mathbf{r} = -2\mathbf{i} + 8\mathbf{j} + s(\mathbf{i} - \mathbf{j})$
b) $4\mathbf{i} + 2\mathbf{j}$ **c)** $4\mathbf{j}$

4 a) $3\mathbf{j} + 4\mathbf{k}$ **b)** $\mathbf{r} \bullet (3\mathbf{j} + 4\mathbf{k}) = 0$
c) 78.69°

5 b) $\mathbf{r} = (3\mathbf{i} - \mathbf{j} + \mathbf{k}) + t(-4\mathbf{i} + 2\mathbf{j} - 7\mathbf{k})$
c) $11\mathbf{i} - 5\mathbf{j} - 12\mathbf{k}$ **d)** 28.0°

6 a) $\mathbf{r} = 4\mathbf{i} + 5\mathbf{j} + 6\mathbf{k} + t(\mathbf{j} - 4\mathbf{k})$
b) $4\mathbf{i} + 8\mathbf{j} - 6\mathbf{k}$ **d)** 45.6°

7 $\begin{pmatrix} -2 \\ 1 \\ 3 \end{pmatrix}$

8 b) $\begin{pmatrix} 5 \\ 8 \\ -6 \end{pmatrix}$ **c)** 32°   **d)** $2x - z = 16$

CHAPTER 6
Proof
For the answers to the Exercises in this chapter we provide the starting points for most of the proofs.

Exercises 6.1 class (p.122)

1 a) $\Rightarrow$
b) $\Leftrightarrow$
c) $\Leftarrow$
d) $\Leftrightarrow$
e) $\Leftarrow$
f) $\Rightarrow$

2 a) false: e.g. $n = 6$
b) true
c) false; $P \times S$ e.g. $n = 6, 12$
d) true
e) false; e.g. $n = 12$
f) true

3 a) always true
b) never true; however $-x < -7$ is always true
c) always true;
d) sometimes true; for $x \geq 2$ always true
e) never true; To multiply an integer by 10 you add a nought to the right hand end of the number.

4 a) if 4 divides n^2 then 4 divides n false; consider $n = 36$
b) if $(x - a)$ is a factor of $\mathrm{P}(x)$ then $\mathrm{P}(a) = 0$ true
c) if $\frac{dy}{dx} = \cos x$ then $y = \sin x$ false; $y = \sin x + c$ where c is a constant
d) every number of the form $6n \pm 1$ is a prime greater than 3 false; consider $n = 4$

Exercises 6.1 home (p.123)

1 a) $\Leftrightarrow$
b) $\Rightarrow$
c) $\Rightarrow$
d) $\Rightarrow$
e) $\Leftrightarrow$
f) $\Leftrightarrow$

2 a) if $a^2 = b^2 + c^2$ then triangle ABC has a right angle at A true
b) if $x^2 - 2 = 0$ then $x = \sqrt{2}$ false; $x = +\sqrt{2}$ or $x = -\sqrt{2}$
c) if n^3 is an even integer then n is an even integer true
d) if $p^2 - 1$ is divisible by 24 then p is a prime number greater than 3 false; consider $p^2 - 1 = 72$

3 a) sufficient
b) neither
c) necessary and sufficient
d) necessary
e) sufficient but not necessary

4 a) false; consider $n = 3$
b) false; consider $\mathrm{f}(n) = 41$

Exercises 6.2 class (p.125)

1 Let n be any even integer then $n = 2k$ consider n^2

2 Assume $\mathrm{f}(a) = \mathrm{f}(b)$ for two elements a and b in the domain of f. Show that $a = b$

3 Use arithmetic progression formula to find the sum. Hence the result follows.

4 Show that all integers can be written in the form $6n + 1$, $6n + 2$, $6n + 3$ but that only $6n + 1$ can be possible primes. Consider $p^2 - 1$ using $p = 6n + 1$

5 Follow Example 6.3 but remember that a and b are negative.

6 $n^2 + n = n(n + 1)$ is product of consecutive integers, one even and one odd. Consider the product $2k(2k + 1)$

7 $a < b \Rightarrow a \neq b \Rightarrow a - b \neq 0 \Rightarrow 0 < (a - b)^2$ continue from here The condition is not necessary because $4ab < (a + b)^2$ for $a > b$ as well as for $a < b$. A necessary and sufficient condition requires $a \neq b \Leftrightarrow 4ab < (a + b)^2$

8 Use the cosine rule for triangles

Exercises **6.2 home** *(p.125)*

1 Investigate 'the formula' for solving quadratic equations.

2 Start with $a = 2k + 1$, $b = 2m + 1$, $c = 2n + 1$ and show that $a + b + c$ can be written as $2p + 1$ for some integer p.

3 If n is a factor of a and b then $a = i \times n$ for some integer i and $b = j \times n$ for some integer j. Show that $ax + by$ can be written as $k \times n$ for some integer k.

4 Every positive integer n can be written as $10m + k$ where m is an integer and k has values 0, 1, 2, ..., 9 is the units of n. Show that n^5 can be written as $10 + k^5$ for some integer p. Show, by trying each possible value of k that $k^5 = 10r + k$. and hence deduce the result. Consider $n^5 - n$

5 Start with $b = a \times n$ and $c = m \times b$

6 The result is a perfect square. Consider $n(n + 4) + 4$

7 Assume that $f(a) = f(b)$ for two elements a and b in the domain for f. Show that $a = b$

8 The remainder is 1. Consider $(4k + 1)^2$. Why choose $4k + 1$ for the odd integers?

Exercises **6.3 class** *(p.128)*

1 Assume that m is even, i.e. $m = 2k$ for some integer k. Show that $m \times n$ must be even.

2 Suppose that 101 is even, i.e. $101 = 2k$ for some integer k. Show that $1 = 2(k - 50)$ and hence that $1 \geq 2$

3 Follow Example 6.4

4 Assume that n^3 is even but that n is odd i.e. $n = 2k + 1$ for some integer k. Show that this leads to a contradiction.

5 Follow Example 6.5 and use the result of Problem 4 to get a contradiction.

6 Let p be the largest integer; $p \geq 1$. Consider p^2. If p is the largest integer what can you say about p^2? Show that this leads to a contradiction.

7 a) Assume that $a = 2k + 1$, $b = 2m + 1$, $c = 2n + 1$ leads to a contradiction.
b) Assume a odd, b odd and show that c must be even Assume a even, b odd, v even leads to a contradiction,

Exercises **6.3 home** *(p.128)*

1 Follow Example 6.4

2 Assume that $n^2 = 3k$ but that $n \neq 3p$. Show that all such numbers n can be written as $3p + 1$, $3n + 2$. Consider n^2 and show that this leads to a contradiction.

3 Follow Example 6.5

4 Similar approach to Problem 6 of 6.3 class with $0 < p \leq 1$.

5 Suppose that $\frac{x}{y}, \frac{y}{z}, \frac{z}{x}$ are equal to each other, call the value of each ratio r. Show that their product is 1. What can you deduce about r from this? Use an argument that involves contradiction to prove the result.

6 a) For any non-zero real number a, $a > 0$ or $a < 0$ hence deduce $a^2 > 0$.
b) Assume that 1 is a negative number, a is a positive number. Show that $a \times 1$ leads to a contradiction.

7 Assume that $ac \leq bc$ but that $c > 0$. Show that this leads to a contradiction.

Exercises **6.4 class** *(p.129)*

In each of Problems **1 – 6** there are many counter-examples, you only need to find one.

7 Try all integers n as factors for which $n < \sqrt{163}$

8 Use the method of exhaustion starting with $n = 10k + r$ where $r = 0, 1, 2, ..., 9$.

Exercises **6.4 home** *(p.130)*

In each of problems **1a) – e)** there are many counter-examples, you only need to find one.

2 Try all integers n as factors for which $n < \sqrt{199}$

3 Try all integers between –2 and 2.

4 Try all integers n, m in the range $0 \leq n < m \leq 5$

Consolidation Exercises for Chapter 6 *(p.130)*

1 a) true; use the method of exhaustion and consider the squares of numbers 1 to 9
b) false; e.g. $n = 7$
c) true; consider $m = 2k + 1$ and $n = 2p + 1$ and show that $m^2 + n^2 = 4q + 2$ for some integer q.
d) false; use counter-example
e) false; (you might have to try many values of n to find a counter-example!)
f) true; use exhaustion.

2 No integer can be more than 3 away from a multiple of 6 so every positive integer can be written as $6n$, $6n + 1$, $6n + 2$, $6n + 3$ and only $6n + 1$ could be prime. (Explain why.)

3 In line 4 of the proposed proof, each side is divided by $(y - x)$. Since $x = y$, we are dividing by zero which is not allowed.

4 a) i) true, ii) true, iii) false, iv) false
b) i) true, ii) false, iii) true, iv) false

6 Let $a = 2n$, $b = n^2 - 1$ and $c = n^2 + 1$ then show that $a^2 + b^2 = c^2$ As a counter-example, 5, 12, 13 form the sides of a right-angle triangle but cannot be written in the given form.

7 a) Direct proof: $n^2 - n = n(n - 1)$ which is the product of consecutive integers.
b) Proof by exhaustion: all numbers can be written as $2k$, $2k + 1$. Consider $n^2 - n$ for each case.

8 Proof by exhaustion.

10 a) $(b - c)^2 > 0 \Rightarrow b^2 + c^2 > 2bc$ Also $c^2 + a^2 > 2ac$, $a^2 + b^2 > 2ab$ Adding the inequalities gives the required results
b) $(b - c)^2 > 0 \Rightarrow b^2 - 2bc + c^2 > 0$ $b^2 - bc + c^2 > bc$. Multiplying by $(b + c)$ gives $b^3 + c^3 > bc(b + c)$ Repeat for a, b and for a, c. Add the inequalities for the required result.

CHAPTER 7
Curves

Exercises **7.1 class** *(p.135)*

1 a) $x^2 + y^2 = 49$
b) $(x - 4)^2 + y^2 = 16$ or $x^2 + y^2 - 8x = 0$
c) $(x - 2)^2 + (y - 1)^2 = 25$

or $x^2 + y^2 - 4x - 2y - 20 = 0$
d) $(x + 3)^2 + (y - 2)^2 = 9$
or $x^2 + y^2 + 6x - 4y + 4 = 0$
e) $x^2 + (y + 5)^2 = 6.25$
or $x^2 + y^2 + 10y + 18.75 = 0$
f) $(x + 1)^2 + (y + 1)^2 = 36$
or $x^2 + y^2 + 2x + 2y - 34 = 0$
2 a) centre $(0, 0)$, radius 11
b) centre $(0, 5)$, radius 9
c) centre $(3, 4)$, radius 5
d) centre $(2, -3)$, radius 4
e) centre $(-4, 0)$, radius 7
f) centre $(0, 1)$, radius 6
g) centre $(2, 0)$, radius 8
h) centre $(-1.5, 2.5)$, radius $\frac{1}{2}\sqrt{298}$
i) centre $(1, 2)$, radius $2\sqrt{34}$
j) centre $(3.5, 2)$, radius 5
3 (a), (c), (f) are circles
4 a) $(x - 5)^2 + (y - 4)^2 = 25$
or $x^2 + y^2 - 10x - 8y + 16 = 0$
b) $(x + 0.5)^2 + (y - 1.5)^2 = 0.5$
or $x^2 + y^2 + x - 3y + 2 = 0$
c) $(x + 0.5)^2 + (y + 0.5)^2 = 8.5$
or $x^2 + y^2 + x + y - 8 = 0$
5 $(3, 0)$, $(27, 0)$
6 $(1 - 2\sqrt{33}, 0)$, $(1 + 2\sqrt{33}, 0)$,
$(0, 1.5 + \sqrt{133.25})$,
$(0, 1.5 - \sqrt{133.25})$
or $(-10.49, 0)$, $(12.49, 0)$,
$(0, 13.04)$, $(0, -10.04)$

Exercises 7.1 home (p.136)
1 a) $x^2 + y^2 = 36$
b) $(x - 3)^2 + y^2 = 1$
or $x^2 + y^2 - 6x + 8 = 0$
c) $x^2 + (y + 2)^2 = 0.25$
or $4x^2 + 4y^2 + 16y + 15 = 0$
d) $(x - 3)^2 + (y + 2)^2 = 16$
or $x^2 + y^2 - 6x + 4y - 3 = 0$
e) $(x + 4)^2 + (y + 5)^2 = 2.25$
or $4x^2 + 4y^2 + 32x + 40y + 155 = 0$
f) $(x - 0.5)^2 + (y - 0.25)^2 = 4$
or $16x^2 + 16y^2 - 16x - 8y - 59 = 0$
2 a) centre $(0, 0)$, radius 9
b) centre $(1, 0)$, radius 7
c) centre $(0, -2)$, radius 10
d) centre $(1, -2)$, radius 2
e) centre $(-3, 1)$, radius 4
f) centre $(3, -1)$, radius 3
g) centre $(6, 0)$, radius $2\sqrt{22}$
h) centre $(0, 2.5)$, radius $\sqrt{6}$
i) centre $(\frac{3}{4}, \frac{5}{4})$, radius $\frac{1}{2}\sqrt{34}$
j) centre $(1, -2)$, radius $4\sqrt{\frac{2}{3}}$
3 (b), (d), (e) are circles.
4 $(0, 1)$, $(0, 15)$, $(6 + \sqrt{21}, 0)$,
$(6 - \sqrt{21}, 0)$
PQ is not a diameter.
5 a) $(x - 1)^2 + (y - 1)^2 = 2$
or $x^2 + y^2 - 2x - 2y = 0$

b) $(x - 0.5)^2 + (y - 1)^2 = 6.25$
or $x^2 + y^2 - x - 2y - 5 = 0$
c) $(x - 2.5)^2 + (y - 6)^2 = 42.25$
or $x^2 + y^2 - 5x - 12y = 0$
6 A: $(-2, -3)$, B: $(6, -3)$

Exercises 7.2 class (p.140)
1 a) ellipse **b)** ellipse **c)** hyperbola
d) parabola **e)** rectangular hyperbola **f)** hyperbola
2 a) $\frac{x^2}{4} + \frac{y^2}{9} = 1$
b) $\frac{1}{4}(x - 1)^2 + \frac{4}{9}(y - 2)^2 = 1$
or $9x^2 + 16y^2 - 18x - 64y - 37 = 0$
c) $\frac{4(x+2)^2}{25} + \frac{(y+1)^2}{4} = 1$
or $16x^2 + 25y^2 + 64x + 50y - 11 = 0$
3 a) $x^2 - y^2 = 9$
b) $(x - 1)^2 - y^2 = 9$
or $x^2 - 2x - y^2 - 8 = 0$
c) $y^2 - x^2 = 4$
4 a) $\frac{(x+1)^2}{5^2} + \frac{(y-3)^2}{\left(\frac{5}{\sqrt{2}}\right)^2}$
ellipse, centre $(-1, 3)$, major axis 10, minor axis $\frac{10}{\sqrt{2}}$
b) $\frac{(x+1)^2}{3^2} + \frac{y^2}{\left(\frac{5}{\sqrt{2}}\right)^2} = 1$
hyperbola, centre $(-1, 0)$, with asymptotes $y = \pm\frac{1}{\sqrt{2}}(x + 1)$
c) $\frac{(x-1.5)^2}{4^2} - \frac{(y-2.5)^2}{4^2} = 1$
rectangular hyperbola, centre $(1.5, 2.5)$, with asymptote $y - 2.5 = \pm(x - 1.5)$.

Exercises 7.2 home (p.141)
1 a) ellipse **b)** hyperbola
c) hyperbola **d)** circle
e) ellipse **f)** parabola
3 a) $\frac{x^2}{4^2} + y^2 = 1$ or $x^2 + 16y^2 = 16$
b) $\frac{(x+1)^2}{\left(\frac{1}{2}\right)^2} + \frac{(y-3)^2}{\left(\frac{3}{2}\right)^2} = 1$
or $36(x + 1)^2 + 4(y - 3)^2 = 9$
c) $\frac{(x-0.5)^2}{\left(\frac{3}{2}\right)^2} + \frac{(y-2.5)^2}{2^2} = 1$
or $16(x - 0.5)^2 + 9(y - 2.5)^2 = 36$
4 a) $\frac{x^2}{16} - \frac{y^2}{64} = 1$ or $4x^2 - y^2 = 64$
b) $x^2 - y^2 = 1$ **c)** $\frac{x^2}{4} - \frac{y^2}{24} = 1$

Exercises 7.3 class (p.143)
1 a) $(0, -3)$, $(3, 0)$
b) $\left(\frac{\sqrt{19} - 2}{5}, \frac{2\sqrt{19} - 9}{5}\right)$
$\left(-\frac{\sqrt{19} - 2}{5}, -\frac{2\sqrt{19} - 9}{5}\right)$
c) $(-1, 4)$, $\left(\frac{4}{5}, \frac{-7}{5}\right)$
d) $(-1, 1)$, $(6, -6)$
e) $(-2, 0)$, $\left(\frac{10}{13}, \frac{36}{13}\right)$
2 $m = -3$, $(2, -6)$
$m = \frac{13}{9}$, $\left(\frac{-18}{5}, -\frac{26}{5}\right)$

3 $m = 3$, $(2, 7)$,
$m = \frac{1}{3}$, $(6, 3)$
4 a) $2\sqrt{3}$ **b)** $2\sqrt{3}$ **c)** $4\sqrt{2}$
5 a) $4y = -3x + 25$ **b)** $3y = x + 3$
c) $3y = 4x - 34$
7 a) $c = \sqrt{5} - 2$ and $c = -\sqrt{5} - 2$
b) $-\sqrt{5} - 2 < c < \sqrt{5} - 2$
c) $c < -\sqrt{5} - 2$ or $c > \sqrt{5} - 2$
8 $(1, 1)$, $(\sqrt{3} - 2, -\sqrt{3} - 2)$, $(-2 - \sqrt{3}, -2 + \sqrt{3})$
9 $(2\sqrt{2}, \pm 1)$, $(-2\sqrt{2}, \pm 1)$
10 $(1, 1)$
11 $7\pi + 4\sqrt{3}$

Exercises 7.3 home (p.144)
1 a) $(1, -1)$, $\left(-\frac{1}{5}, \frac{7}{5}\right)$
b) $(1, 2)$, $\left(-\frac{1}{2}, \frac{1}{2}\right)$
c) no points of intersection
d) $(-1, -5)$, $(5, 1)$
e) $\left(\frac{6}{\sqrt{37}}, \frac{3}{\sqrt{37}}\right)$, $\left(\frac{-6}{\sqrt{37}}, -\frac{2}{\sqrt{37}}\right)$
2 $m = 1$, $(-1, -1)$
$m = -\frac{1}{7}$, $\left(\frac{7}{5}, -\frac{1}{5}\right)$
3 $m = \frac{12}{5}$, $\left(\frac{-10}{13}, \frac{15}{13}\right)$
$m = 0$, $(2, 3)$
4 a) $m = -\sqrt{3}$ and $m = \sqrt{3}$
b) $m < -\sqrt{3}$ or $m > \sqrt{3}$
c) $-\sqrt{3} < m < \sqrt{3}$
6 a) 4 **b)** $2\sqrt{10}$ **c)** $\sqrt{23}$
7 For $(-2, -4)$, $y = -\frac{3}{2}x - 7$
For $(3, 1)$, $y = -\frac{2}{3}x + 3$
For $(-2, 0)$, $y = \frac{3}{2}x + 3$
8 $(2\sqrt{2}, \sqrt{2})$, $(-2\sqrt{2}, -\sqrt{2})$
9 $(1, 2)$, $(1, -2)$
10 $\frac{25\sqrt{3}}{2}$
11 $(x - 5)^2 + (y - 13)^2 = 9$
or $x^2 + y^2 - 10x - 26y + 185 = 0$

Exercises 7.4 class (p.147)
1 $\frac{dy}{dx} = -\frac{x}{y}$ **2** $\frac{dy}{dx} = \frac{x}{y}$

3 $\frac{dy}{dx} = \frac{1-x}{2+y}$ **4** $\frac{dy}{dx} = \frac{(x-1)}{2(y+1)}$

5 $\frac{dy}{dx} = \frac{3x^2-y}{x-2y}$ **6** $\frac{dy}{dx} = \frac{2(5y-2x)}{(8y-5x)}$

7 $\frac{dy}{dx} = \frac{5\cos 5x}{2\sin 5x}$ **8** $\frac{dy}{dx} = \frac{\cos x}{\sin x}$

9 $\frac{dy}{dx} = \frac{-y\sin(xy)}{1+x\sin(xy)}$ **10** $\frac{dy}{dx} = \frac{2x-y}{x+3e^{3y}}$

11 -0.75 **12** -2
13 0.2 **14** 1.4
15 -1 **16** $-\frac{3}{2}$
17 0 **18** $-\frac{\sqrt{3}}{6}$

	tangent	normal
21	$y = -\frac{1}{\sqrt{3}}x + \frac{8}{\sqrt{3}}$	$y = \sqrt{3}x$
22	$y = -\frac{4}{3}x + \frac{23}{3}$	$y = \frac{3}{4}x - \frac{11}{4}$
23	$y = \frac{2}{3}x - \frac{4}{3}$	$y = -\frac{3}{2}x - \frac{7}{2}$
24	$y = -3x + 7$	$y = \frac{1}{3}x + \frac{11}{3}$

25 $y = \frac{1}{2}x + 2$ $y = -2x + 7$
26 $y = 2x - 7$ $2y = 1 - x$

Exercises 7.4 home (p.148)

1 $\frac{dy}{dx} = -\frac{x}{y}$ **2** $\frac{dy}{dx} = \frac{x}{y}$

3 $\frac{dy}{dx} = -\frac{2x}{3y}$ **4** $\frac{dy}{dx} = \frac{3}{2(y-2)}$

5 $\frac{dy}{dx} = \frac{4-x}{3+y}$ **6** $\frac{dy}{dx} = \frac{2x+3}{4y-5}$

7 $\frac{dy}{dx} = \frac{y\sin x + \sin y}{\cos x - x\cos y}$ **8** $\frac{dy}{dx} = \frac{2x - ye^y}{x(x+e^y)}$

9 $\frac{dy}{dx} = \frac{1}{\cos(x+y)} - 1$ **10** $\frac{dy}{dx} = \frac{y\cos xy}{1 - x\cos xy}$

11 $-\frac{1}{2}$ **12** $\frac{1}{6}$ **13** $-\frac{7}{9}$ **14** $-\frac{4}{15}$

15 2 **16** $\sqrt{\frac{2}{3}}$ **17** 0 **18** $\frac{9}{16}$

    tangent   normal

21 $\sqrt{5}\,y - 2x = 18$ $2y + \sqrt{5}\,x = 0$
22 $y = x - 3$ $y = -x - 1$
23 $y = -\frac{1}{4}x + \frac{11}{4}$ $y = 4x - 10$
24 $y = -8x + 21$ $y = \frac{1}{8}x + \frac{19}{4}$
25 $y = 2x + 4$ $y = -\frac{1}{2}x + \frac{3}{2}$
26 $y = -\frac{10}{3}x + \frac{37}{3}$ $10y = 3x - 22$

Consolidation Exercises for Chapter 7 (p.149)

1 hyperbola, centre (0,0), asymptotes $y = \pm x$
2 circle, centre (2, −3), radius 10
3 ellipse, centre (2, 3), major axis $5\sqrt{2}$, minor axis 10
4 parabola, $x \geq -2$, axis $y = 1$
5 tangent $y = \frac{1}{3}x + 1$, normal $y = -3x + 21$
6 a) $\frac{6-\sqrt{6}}{4} < m < \frac{6+\sqrt{6}}{4}$
   b) $m = \frac{6\pm\sqrt{6}}{4}$
   c) $m < \frac{6-\sqrt{6}}{4}$ or $m > \frac{6+\sqrt{6}}{4}$
8 a) $3y = 4x - 150$
   b) $x^2 + y^2 = 900$
   c) $(24, -18)$
9 a) i) $7\sqrt{5}$ ii) $7\sqrt{5} - 13 = 133$ mm
   b) i) 1
   ii) AC has equation $y = -x + 10$
10 A: (1, 2)
    P: (5, −1), Q : (6, 2)
11 Centre (3, 0), radius = 3, $k = 3 \pm 3\sqrt{2}$
12 a) $x^2 + y^2 - 2x - 8y + 8 = 0$
    b) inside
13 -1
14 Distance of P to centre = $\sqrt{20}$
    Length of tangent = 2

CHAPTER 8
Curves 2

Exercises 8.1 class (p.155)

1 a) $x^2 + y^2 = 4$, circle, centre (0, 0), radius 2
   b) $\frac{x^2}{16} + \frac{y^2}{9} = 1$

    ellipse: centre (0,0), major axis 8, minor axis 6
   c) $y = \frac{2}{x}$, rectangular hyperbola
   d) $y = x^2 + 2x + 2$, parabola with $x = -1$ as axis of symmetry
   e) $(x - 1)^2 + (y - 2)^2 = 9$, circle, centre (1, 2), radius 3
2 b) $\frac{x^2}{4} - \frac{y^2}{9} = 1$ c) hyperbola
3 $2y = x + 2$
   a) $a = 2$ b) $T = \frac{3}{2}$
4 $y^2 = 1 - \frac{1}{5}x$, parabola with x–axis as axis symmetry of symmetry, $x \leq 5$
7 (3, −1), (7, 5)
8 (4, 3), (7, −3)

Exercises 8.1 home (p.155)

1 a) $x^2 + y^2 = 25$, circle; centre (0, 0), radius 5
   b) $y = \frac{10}{x}$, rectangular hyperbola, asymptotes $y = 0$ and $x = 0$
   c) $2(y - 1)^2 = 9(1+ x)$, parabola with $y = 1$ as axis of symmetry
   d) $\frac{(x+3)^2}{4} + \frac{(y-1)^2}{25} = 1$, ellipse, centre (−3, 1), major axis 4, minor axis 10
   e) $y = x - 2$, straight line, slope 1, y–intercept (0, −2)
2 a) $x^2 - y^2 = 4$
   b) hyperbola, asymptotes $y = x$ and $y = -x$
3 $(1 - y)^2 - (x - 1)^2 = 1$, hyperbola, asymptotes $y = 2 - x$, $y = x$
4 a) $2x + y = 5\cos\theta$, $x - 2y = 5\sin\theta$
   b) $(2x + y)^2 + (x - 2y)^2 = 25$ or $x^2 + y^2 = 5$
   c) circle, centre (0, 0), radius $\sqrt{5}$
7 (3, 1), (6, −5)
8 b) $y = 3$

Exercises 8.2 class (p.158)

1 tangent $y = \frac{3}{2}x + 2$
   normal $y = -\frac{2}{3}x + 2$
2 tangent $y = -\frac{31}{\sqrt{3}}x + \frac{7\sqrt{3}}{3} - 1$
   normal $y = \sqrt{3}\,x - 1 - \sqrt{3}$
3 tangent $y = -3x + 11$
   normal $y = \frac{1}{3}x + \frac{13}{3}$
4 tangent $y = 2$, normal $x = 0$
5 tangent $y = -\frac{x}{\sqrt{2}} + 1$
   normal $y = \sqrt{2}\,x + 1 - 3\sqrt{2}$
6 tangent $y = \frac{9}{4}x - 1$
   normal $y = -\frac{4}{9}x + \frac{43}{54}$
7 (−2, 0) is a local minimum for $t = -1$ area = 2.568
8 $\left(-\frac{1}{\sqrt{3}}, \frac{2\sqrt{3}}{9}\right)$ is a local maximum for $t = -\frac{1}{\sqrt{3}}$
   $\left(\frac{1}{\sqrt{3}}, -\frac{2\sqrt{3}}{9}\right)$ is a local minimum for $t = \frac{1}{\sqrt{3}}$ area = 18

Exercises 8.2 home (p.158)

1 tangent $y = -2x - 2$
   normal $y = \frac{1}{2}x - \frac{9}{2}$
2 tangent $y = -\frac{x}{\sqrt{3}} + 1 + 3\sqrt{3}$
   normal $y = \sqrt{3}\,x + 1 + \sqrt{3}$
3 tangent $y = -\frac{2x}{3\sqrt{3}} + 3 - \frac{16\sqrt{3}}{9}$
   normal $y = \frac{3\sqrt{3}\,x}{2} + 3 + \frac{17}{4}\sqrt{3}$
4 tangent $y = 2x - 1$
   normal $y = -\frac{1}{2}x + \frac{3}{2}$
5 tangent $y = x - 1$
   normal $y = -x + 1$
6 tangent $y = \left(\sqrt{2}-1\right)x +1+ \frac{\pi}{4}\left(1-\sqrt{2}\right)$
   normal $y = \frac{1}{1-\sqrt{2}}x - 1 + \frac{\pi}{4}\left(1+\sqrt{2}\right)$
7 $\frac{dy}{dx} = -4x$
8 a) $\frac{dy}{dx} = -\frac{1}{2}$ tangent $y = -\frac{1}{2}x + \frac{7}{2}$
   normal $y = 2x + 1$
   b) Tangent intersects again at point (16, −4.5). Normal does not intersect again.
9 $16 \ln 4$
10 $\frac{3\pi}{2}$

Consolidation Exercises for Chapter 8 (p.159)

1 a) position $(1, \sqrt{3})$ speed 2
   b) direction of travel is $\frac{\pi}{6}$ above negative x-direction
   c) $x^2 + y^2 = 4$
2 c) $y = -\frac{x}{t^2} + \frac{4}{t}$
   d) area of triangle = 8
3 a) $\left(2(t_1+t_2), 2\left(\frac{1}{t_1} + \frac{1}{t_2}\right)\right)$
   c) $y = -2x + 8t$
   d) $(2\sqrt{2}, 4\sqrt{2})$, $(-2\sqrt{2}, -4\sqrt{2})$
4 c) $y = tx - 2t^2$
   d) $(2(t_1 + t_2), 2t_1\, t_2)$
   e) $y = \frac{1}{2}x$
5 a) $t = 1$
   c) $y = -x + 3$
   e) (−8, −5)
7 a) $\frac{dy}{dx} = \frac{t^2+1}{t^2-1}$
   c) $\frac{29}{12}\pi = 2.417\pi$
8 a) $y = -\frac{2}{3}x + \frac{5}{3}$ b) $\frac{23}{20}$
10 $p^2 = b - 2$ $s = -\frac{2+r^2}{r}$
11 $\frac{dy}{dx} = \frac{\cos\theta - \theta\sin\theta}{\cos\theta}$

   Root > $\frac{\pi}{4}$ since $\frac{1}{(\pi/4)} > \tan\left(\frac{\pi}{4}\right)$
12 b) $4y - 6x = -1$
13 a) $x = 3a\cos\theta, y = 2a\sin\theta$
   b) $0 \leq \theta \leq 2\pi$
14 a) $\frac{dy}{dx} = \frac{3t^2}{2}$ gradient at $P = 6$
   b) $\frac{d^2y}{dx^2} = \frac{3t}{2}$
   c) $y = \frac{1}{8}(x+1)^2$
   d) x-intercept = −1, y-intercept = $\frac{1}{8}$

CHAPTER 9
Differential equations

Exercises 9.1 class *(p.165)*

1 $\frac{dy}{dx} = x + y$, $y = 1$ when $x = 0$

2 $\frac{dx}{dt} = k\sqrt{1-x^2}$, k is constant,
$x = 0$ when $t = 0$

3 h is height in cm, t is time in days
$\frac{dh}{dt} = 0.25h$, $h = 2$ when $t = 0$

4 P is the population, t is time
in years, $\frac{dP}{dt} = 0.02P$

5 $\frac{dT}{dt} = -\frac{0.4}{70}(T - 20)$,
$T = 90$ when $t = 0$

6 a) $\frac{dA}{dt} = kr$, k is constant

  b) $\frac{dA}{dr} = 2\pi r$ c) $\frac{dr}{dt} = \frac{k}{2\pi}$

7 r is radius in cm, t is time in s
$\frac{dr}{dt} = -\frac{2.5}{144\pi}$

8 h is height in m, t is time in hours,
$\frac{dh}{dt} = -\frac{(1+2h)}{35}$

9 c is concentration in $g\ cm^{-3}$,
t is time in s, $\frac{dc}{dt} = -0.2c$

10 h is height in m, t is time in s,
$\frac{dh}{dt} = 0.004 - 0.0008h$,
$h = 0.5$ when $t = 0$. Tank fills.

Exercises 9.1 home *(p.167)*

1 m is mass and t is time.
$\frac{dm}{dt} = -km$, k is constant

2 P is number of rabbits, t is time in
months
$\frac{dP}{dt} = 0.07P$ $P = 10$ when $t = 0$

3 $\frac{dy}{dx} = x^2 - y^2$ $y = 1$ when $x = 1$

4 T is temperature in °C, t is time in
minutes
$\frac{dT}{dt} = -0.3(T - 20)$
$T = 2$ when $t = 0$

5 r is radius in cm, t is time in s
  a) $\frac{dV}{dt} = -\frac{V}{450\pi}$ b) $\frac{dr}{dt} = -\frac{r}{1350\pi}$
$r = 20$ when $t = 0$

6 r is radius in cm, t is time in s,
$\frac{dr}{dt} = \frac{5}{\pi r^2}$

7 m is mass of carbon–14 in grams, t
is time in years,
$\frac{dm}{dt} = -km$, k is a constant
$m = 10^{-22}$ when $t = 0$

8 i is current in mA, t is time in s,
$\frac{di}{dt} = -\frac{1}{80}i$

9 h is depth of water in cm, t is time
in s, $\frac{dh}{dt} = \frac{8}{\pi h^2}(60 - h)$
$h = 50$ when $t = 0$.
Cone initially fills. Depth is
constant when $t = 60$.

10 $\frac{dP}{dt} = kP(1500 - P)$,
k is a constant
$P = 1$ when $t = 0$

Exercises 9.2 class *(p.172)*

1 a) $y = \frac{1}{3}x^3 + c$ b) $y = -\cos x + c$

 c) $y = -\frac{1}{2}e^{-2x} + c$

 d) $y = \ln\frac{x}{x+1} + c$ e) $y = \frac{2}{3}t^{\frac{3}{2}} + c$

 f) $s = \frac{8}{5}t^{\frac{5}{2}} + c$

2 a) $y = \sqrt{c + x^2}$ b) $y = -\frac{1}{(c + \frac{1}{2}x^2)}$

 c) $y = \sqrt{c - 2\cos x}$

 d) $y = \frac{1}{4}\ln(2x^2 + c)$

 e) $y = e^{\sin x} + c$ or $y = Ae^{\sin x}$

 f) $\ln\frac{1+y}{1-y} = 2x + c$ or $y = \frac{Ae^{2x} - 1}{Ae^{2x} + 1}$

3 a) $y = \frac{1}{3}x^3 + x - 8$

 b) $\ln y = (1 + x)^2 - 1$ or $y = e^{(1+x)^2 - 1}$

 c) $y = \frac{1}{\cos x}$

 d) $\ln\frac{x-1}{x+1} = 2t^2 - 2 + \ln\frac{1}{3}$
 or $x = \frac{e^{2t^2 - 2} + 3}{3 - e^{2t^2 - 2}}$

 e) $\ln\frac{P}{1-P} = 3t$ or $P = \frac{e^{3t}}{1 + e^{3t}}$

 f) $e^{2x} = \frac{5}{3} - \frac{2}{3}\cos 3t$
 or $x = \frac{1}{2}(\frac{5}{3} - \frac{2}{3}\cos 3t)$

 g) $y^2 = 4\frac{(1+x)^2}{(1-x)^4} - 1$

 h) $y^2 = 1 + \frac{8}{3}(x^2 - 1)$

4 $y = \frac{1}{2} + \frac{3}{2}e^{2x}$

5 $y = \sqrt{\frac{x-1}{x+1}} - 1$

6 $y = 5 - \frac{4}{x}$

7 (3) $h = 2e^{0.25t}$ (4) $P = P_0 e^{0.02t}$
 (5) $T = 20 + 70\,e^{-0.4t/70}$
 Time to reach 30 °C is 340.5 s.
 (6) $r = \frac{kt}{2\pi} + r_0$
 (7) $r = -\frac{2.5t}{144\pi} + r_0$
 (8) $h = Ae^{-\frac{2t}{35}} - \frac{1}{2}$
 $h = \frac{9}{2}e^{-\frac{2t}{35}} - \frac{1}{2}$
 Time to half empty is 10.3 hours.
 (9) $c = Ae^{-0.2t}$
 Time to decay to 25% of initial
 dose is 6.93 s.
 (10) $h = 5 - 4.5\,e^{-0.0008t}$
 Time to overflow is 147 s.

Exercises 9.2 home *(p.173)*

1 a) $y = \frac{1}{4}x^4 + c$

 b) $y = \sin x - x + c$

 c) $y = \frac{1}{4}e^{4x} + c$

 d) $s = \ln\frac{t+1}{t+2} + c$

 e) $P = (t - 1)e^t + c$

 f) $v = -\frac{16}{9}s^{\frac{9}{4}} + c$

2 a) $y = Ae^{-\frac{1}{x}}$

 b) $\ln\frac{P}{3-P} = 6t + c$

 or $P = \frac{3Ae^{6t}}{1 + Ae^{6t}}$

 c) $y = \sqrt{(c + (x+2)^2)}$

 d) $r^2 = \theta - \frac{1}{2}\sin 2\theta + c$

 e) $\frac{1+y}{3+2y} = \frac{A}{1-x}$ or $y = \frac{1-x-3A}{2A-1+x}$

 f) $v^2 = \frac{1}{2}(3 - Ae^{-4s})$

3 a) $y = x^3 - x^2 + x + 1$

 b) $\ln y = 1 - \cos x$ or $y = e^{1-\cos x}$

 c) $y = (\frac{5}{2} - \frac{1}{2}e^{-x})^2$

 d) $y = \frac{1+x}{3-x}$ e) $T = 20 - 15e^{-2t}$

 f) $v + \frac{10}{3}\ln\frac{10-3v}{7} = 1 - 3s$

 g) $s = \frac{1}{2}\ln\frac{5-2\cos 3t}{3}$

 h) $v = \frac{40e^{-0.2t}}{41 - 40e^{-0.2t}}$

4 a) $h = \frac{1}{1 + \frac{3}{4}t}$

 b) Time to 10 cm is 12 minutes.

5 $y = 4x - 10$

6 $y = \frac{1}{4}(x+4)^2$

7 (2) $P = 10e^{0.07t}$
 (4) $T = 20 - 18e^{-0.3t}$
 Time to reach 10°C is
 1.96 minutes ($\approx$ 2 minutes).
 (5) $r = 20e^{\frac{-t}{1350\pi}}$
 Time to become 10 cm is
 2940 seconds.
 (6) $r = \sqrt[3]{\frac{15t}{\pi} + c}$
 (7) $m = 10^{-22}e^{-kt}$
 Time for mass to be 3.5×10^{-23} g is
 $1.05/k$ years.
 (8) $i = Ae^{-\frac{t}{80}t}$
 (9) $h^2 + 120h + 7200\ln\frac{60-h}{10} = 8500 - \frac{16t}{\pi}$
 (10) $P = \frac{1500}{1 + 1499e^{-1500kt}}$

Exercises 9.3 class *(p.178)*

1 $y(1.2) \approx 0.22$

2 $y(0.5) \approx 0.704867$

3 $v(0.5) \approx 6.26597$

4 1.56623

5 2.23106 (neglect value for $h = 1$)

6 a)

h	$y(2)$
0.02	0.214452
0.05	0.214688
0.1	0.215041
0.20	215 5555

 b) 0.214374

 c) $y = \frac{1}{2 + \frac{1}{3}x^3}$, 0.214285

Exercises 9.3 home *(p. 179)*

1 $y(0.5) \approx 0.818706$ (6 s.f.)

2 $y(0.5) \approx 1.07284$ (6 s.f.)

3 $v(2) \approx 10.0207$ (6 s.f.)

4 1.8412

5 1.9593

6

x	2	3	4	5
y	2.9	6.7	11.5	17.4

Consolidation Exercises for Chapter 9 *(p.183)*

1 a) $\frac{dT}{dt} = -k(T - 32.2)$

$T(0) = 34.8$, $T(1) = 34.1$
T is temperature in °C, t is time in hours after 2.30 a.m. and k is constant. Assume rate of temperature change is proportional to difference between body temperature and room temperature. Assume room temperature is constant.

b) $T = 32.2 + 2.6\,e^{-0.314t}$

c) Time of death was about 0.33 a.m. ($t = -117$ minutes)

2 a) $\frac{dy}{dx} = x + y^2$,
$y = 1$ when $x = 0$

b) $Y_{n+1} = Y_n + h(x_n + Y_n^2)$
$Y_0 = 1$

3 a) $R = 10e^{-kt}$

c) 9.58 grams

4 a) $\cos x + x\sin x + c$

b) $\frac{1}{2}y + \frac{1}{4}\sin 2y + c$

c) $\frac{1}{2}y + \frac{1}{8}\sin 4y = \cos x + x\sin x + c$

5 a) $\frac{1}{3}\left(\frac{1}{y} + \frac{1}{3-y}\right)$

b) $\frac{1}{3}\ln\frac{y}{3-y} + c$

c) $y = \frac{3x^3}{4+x^3}$

6 a) 947, 890

b) Critical value of P is 1600 mice.

c) $P > 1600$ then $\frac{dP}{dt} > 0$ so P increases.
$P < 1600$ then $\frac{dP}{dt} < 0$ so P decreases.

7 b) $2\sqrt{x} = -kt + c$

c) 22 minutes

8 b) $t = -\frac{1}{k}\ln\frac{2.5-h}{2.5}$

c) an infinite time to fill

d) 7.43 min

9 $\frac{dx}{dt} = -0.1\sqrt{x}$; $x = 200$ at $t = 0$
Leaking for ~ 82.8 minutes

10 a) $h = 10 - \frac{1}{8}t$

b) $\frac{dh}{dt} = -kh$, $h = 10e^{-0.017t}$

c) Alan $h(0) = 10$
Bhavana $h(0) = 10$

d) Bhavana's model – as rate of leaking is likely to depend on pressure which depends on depth h.

11 a)

n	t	$\frac{dn}{dt}$	dt	dn
10	0	9.98	5	49.9
59.9	5	59.182	5	295.9
355.8	10			

b) reduce the time step dt

12 b) $0.15\,\text{cm s}^{-1}$

13 $y = (1 + \frac{1}{6}\tan(3x))^2$.

CHAPTER 10
Projectiles

Exercises **10.1 class** *(p.193)*

1 a) $3.76\mathbf{i} + 1.37\mathbf{j}$ **b)** $-9.8\mathbf{j}$
c) $\mathbf{v} = 3.76\mathbf{i} + (1.37 - 9.8t)\mathbf{j}$
d) $\mathbf{r} = 3.76t\mathbf{i} + (1.37t - 4.9t^2)\mathbf{j}$

2 a) $4.83\mathbf{i} + 1.29\mathbf{j}$
b) $\mathbf{r} = 4.83t\mathbf{i} + (1.29t - 4.9t^2)\mathbf{j}$
c) 0.264 s **d)** 1.28 m **e)** 0.09 m

3 a) 7.8 m **b)** No, this is probably the speed for a top athlete.

4 a) 22.46 m **b)** No
c) The lighter ball.

5 a) 48.85 m **c)** $25\,\text{ms}^{-1}$
d) Lower one less likely to be affected by air resistance due to shorter time of flight.

6 a) $5.48\,\text{m s}^{-1}$ **b)** 45°
c) Minimum speed at 45°, $4.2\,\text{m s}^{-1}$

7 a) 24° or 66° **b)** difference
c) More difficult to give a heavier one the same initial velocity.

8 b) $\mathbf{r} = 75t\mathbf{i} - 4.9t^2\mathbf{j}$
c) $225\mathbf{i} - 44.1\mathbf{j}$ **d)** $80.6\,\text{m s}^{-1}$

9 a) $\mathbf{r} = 2.05t\mathbf{i} + (2 + 5.64t - 4.9t^2)\mathbf{j}$ **b)** 3.62 m
c) 1.44 s, 2.94 m

10 a) $\mathbf{r} = 6.30t\mathbf{i} + (1.8 + 4.93t - 4.9t^2)\mathbf{j}$ **b)** 0.63 s **c)** 2.95 m
d) Increase the angle of projection a little.

Exercises **10.1 home** *(p.195)*

1 a) $6.06\mathbf{i} + 3.5\mathbf{j}$ **b)** $-9.8\mathbf{j}$
c) $\mathbf{v} = 6.06\mathbf{i} + (3.5 - 9.8t)\mathbf{j}$
d) $\mathbf{r} = 6.06t\mathbf{i} + (3.5t - 4.9t^2)\mathbf{j}$

2 a) $1.88\mathbf{i} + 0.68\mathbf{j}$
b) $\mathbf{r} = 1.88t\mathbf{i} + (0.68t - 4.9t^2)\mathbf{j}$
c) 0.14 s **d)** 0.262 m **e)** 0.024 m

3 a) 13.8 m **b)** Yes

4 a) 19.89 m **b)** Not unless air resistance is considered
c) Range reduced as air resistance has a greater effect on a lighter ball.

5 a) 2.23 m **c)** $8\,\text{m s}^{-1}$
d) Lower angle, less time of flight for resistance, etc. to deflect dart.

6 a) $19.13\,\text{m s}^{-1}$ **b)** 45°
c) $15.3\,\text{m s}^{-1}$

7 a) 0.102 m **b)** 10.5 cm
c) 6.4 cm

8 a) Both have some horizontal component of velocity, if the air resistance is negligible.
b) $Vt\mathbf{i} - 4.9t^2\mathbf{j}$ **c)** $20.85\,\text{m s}^{-1}$

9 a) $\mathbf{r} = 4.91t\mathbf{i} + (1.7 + 3.44t - 4.9t^2)\mathbf{j}$ **b)** 1.04 s, 5.10 m
d) A large force would be needed to alter the path of a heavy object significantly.

10 a) $42.3\,\text{m s}^{-1}$ **b)** 1102.5 m
c) Lengths of holes need to be increased by a factor 6.125.

Exercises **10.2 class** *(p.199)*

1 a) $y = x - 0.00306x^2$, 326.5 m
b) $y = 2x - 0.049x^2$, 40.82 m
c) $y = 1.5x - 0.034x^2$, 44.1 m
d) $y = 3 + \frac{2}{3}x - 0.136x^2$, 7.74 m

2 $y = 0.5x - 0.05x^2$

3 a) $\mathbf{r} = 39.0t\mathbf{i} + (22.5t - 4.9t^2)\mathbf{j}$
b) $y = 0.577x - 0.003\,23x^2$
c) 10.26 m

4 a) $\mathbf{r} = 15.59t\mathbf{i} + (9t - 4.9t^2)\mathbf{j}$
b) $y = 0.577x - 0.0202x^2$
c) 1.55 m **d)** Very unlikely.

5 a) $\mathbf{r} = v\cos70°t\mathbf{i} + (1 + v\sin70°t - 4.9t^2)\mathbf{j}$
b) $y = 1 - \tan 70°x - \frac{4.9x^2}{V^2\cos^2 70°}$
c) $8.48\,\text{m s}^{-1}$

6 a) $y = 1.732x - \frac{19.6x^2}{v^2}$
b) $v > 7.27\,\text{m s}^{-1}$
c) No. Air resistance very significant. Also size important when near to net.

7 a) $y = 2.747x - 0.0465x^2$
b) $y = 0.0875x$ **c)** $x = 57.15$, $y = 5.00$ **d)** 57.37 m

8 a) $y = 1 - 0.196x^2$
b) $y = -0.577x$
c) $(4.17, -2.41)$, when $t = 0.834$ s.

9 a) $y = x\tan\alpha - \frac{4.9x^2}{30^2\cos^2\alpha}$
b) $49\tan^2\alpha - 1500\tan\alpha + 549 = 0$
c) $\alpha = 20.3°$ or 88.1°
d) 20.3° as he is unlikely to get up the ramp at 88°.

10 a) $y = 2x\tan\alpha - \frac{4.9x^2}{20^2\cos^2\alpha}$
b) $\alpha = 3.2°$ or 81.6°
c) $\alpha = 3.2°$ because the time of flight will be less and the ball will land in the required area.

Exercises **10.2 home** *(p.201)*

1 a) $y = x - 0.0111x^2$, 90 m
b) $y = 1.3333x - 0.0014x^2$, 979.6 m **c)** $y = 3x - 10x^2$, 3.33 m **d)** $y = x\tan\beta - \frac{4.9x^2}{u^2\cos^2(\beta)}$, $\frac{u^2\sin\beta\cos\beta}{4.9}$ m

2 $y = \frac{x}{\sqrt{3}} - \frac{4x^2}{375}$

3 a) $\mathbf{r} = 12.02t\mathbf{i} + (12.02t - 4.9t^2)\mathbf{j}$
b) $y = x - 0.0339x^2$ **c)** 3.08 m

4 a) $\mathbf{r} = 8.66t\mathbf{i} + (5t - 4.9t^2)\mathbf{j}$
b) $y = 0.577x - 0.065x^2$
c) 25.3 cm **d)** Yes

5 a) $\mathbf{r} = V\cos60°t\mathbf{i} + (2 + V\sin60°t - 4.9t^2)\mathbf{j}$
b) $y = 2 + 1.732x - \frac{19.6x^2}{v^2}$
c) $7.98\,\text{m s}^{-1}$

6 a) $y = 1.19x - \frac{11.859x^2}{v^2}$

b) $v \geq 5.86$ m s^{-1} **c)** No, air resistance will be significant.

7 a) $y = 1.732x - 0.049x^2$
b) $y = 0.466x$ **c)** $25.8\mathbf{i} + 12.0\mathbf{j}$
d) 28.5 m

8 a) $y = -0.0054x^2$
b) $y = -0.2679x - 0.536$
c) $x = 51.1$, $y = -14.2$

9 a) $y = x \tan\alpha - \dfrac{0.00162x^2}{\cos^2\alpha}$
b) $196\tan^2\alpha - 3025\tan^2\alpha + 196 = 0$ **c)** 3.72° or 86.3°
d) 3.72°

10 a) $y = x \tan\alpha - \dfrac{5x^2}{V^2\cos^2\alpha}$
b) $0 = 10\tan\alpha - \dfrac{500\tan^2\alpha}{V^2} - \dfrac{500}{V^2} + 1$

Consolidation Exercises for Chapter 10 (p.203)

1 a) 5.9 m **b)** 4.8 m **c)** air resistance
2 a) Gravity is the only force acting **b)** $63.4 \leq \theta \leq 80.5$
c) $80 \sin 2\theta$ **d) i)** 63.4°
ii) 63.4°
3 a) i) 0.75 s **b) i)** 8.47 m s^{-1}
4 a) 29.9 s, 6776 m **b)** 8.9°
5 b) 4 m
6 a) $20\cos\alpha$, $20\sin\alpha$
b) $x = 20t\cos\alpha$ **e)** No.

CHAPTER 11
Kinematics with calculus

Exercises 11.1 class (p.211)
1 $2t - 10$ m s^{-2}
2 b) 80 s **c)** 4270 m, 80 m s^{-1}
3 a) $v = 16 - 9.8t$ **b)** 15.1 m
c) -9.8 m s^{-2}
4 a) 20 s **b)** 80 m s^{-1}, 1070 m
5 a) $v = \dfrac{200t - t^3}{100}$, $a = 2 - \dfrac{3t^2}{100}$
b) 10.9 m s^{-1}
6 a) 20 m s^{-1}
b) $a = \dfrac{1}{\sqrt{t}}$
c) 0.1 m s^{-2}
7 a) $v = 20t - 5t^2$, $a = 20 - 10t$
b) $t = 2$ s, 20 m s^{-1}, 26.7 m
c) 46.7 m
8 b) 6.95 m s^{-1} **c)** $9.8e^{-1.4t}$
9 a) $v = \dfrac{1}{8\pi}\cos\left(\dfrac{t}{40\pi}\right)$, $a = -\dfrac{1}{320\pi}\sin\left(\dfrac{t}{40\pi}\right)$
b) $\dfrac{1}{8\pi} = 0.0398$ m s^{-1}
c) $k = \dfrac{1}{1600\pi^2}$
10 a) 4.41 m
b) Decreases in magnitude.

Exercises 11.1 home (p.213)
1 a) $a = 2 - t$ **b)** 2 m s^{-1}
2 a) $v = 3t^2 - 8t + 4$
b) 1.19 m **c)** 2.37 m s^{-1}

e) The original is more realistic. In the second the diver may leave the water.
3 a) $v = 1.6t$, $a = 1.6$
b) Velocity becomes constant and acceleration zero.
c) with constant velocity.
4 0.0001 m s^{-6}
5 a) $t = 5$, $t = 15$
b) 225 m s^{-1}
6 a) 3.85 m s^{-1} **b)** 0 and 0 m s^{-1}
c) 1 m s^{-2} and -2 m s^{-2}
7 a) $v = 0.66 + 1.04t$, $a = 1.04$ m s^{-2}
b) Initially moves at 0.66 m s^{-1}
c) $\mu = 0.85$
8 a) 4.8 m s^{-1} **c)** 20.0 m s^{-1}
d) $-9.92e^{-0.4t}$ reasonable since both gravity and air resistance initially oppose motion
9 a) 7.54 m s^{-1} **b)** 1890 m s^{-2}
10 $A = B = 62.5$, $C = 5$

Exercises 11.2 class (p.217)
1 a) $v = t - \dfrac{t^2}{80}$ **b)** $s = \dfrac{t^2}{2} - \dfrac{t^3}{240}$
c) $t = 40$ **d)** 533 m
2 a) $a = 0.5 - \dfrac{t}{60}$
b) $v = \dfrac{t}{2} - \dfrac{t^2}{120} + c$, 7.5 m s^{-1}
c) $s = \dfrac{t^2}{4} - \dfrac{t^3}{360}$, 150 m
3 a) $a = 0.4 - \dfrac{t}{50}$
b) 4 m s^{-1} **c)** 53.3 m
4 a) $s = \dfrac{15t^2}{2} - \dfrac{t^3}{3}$
b) 563 m
5 400 m
6 16.3 m s^{-1}, 203 m
7 a) 2 s **c)** $0 \leq t \leq 4$
d) Use a trigonometric function
8 a) 5.09 m s^{-1} **b)** 25.9 m
9 a) 8.33 **b)** 4.17 m s^{-2}
10 a) Opposite to motion
b) 20 m s^{-1} **c)** 20 m s^{-1}
e) 12 m s^{-1}
f) Braking force increased and then relaxed, driver may have felt able to stop comfortably.

Exercises 11.2 home (p.218)
1 b) 12 m
2 a) 50 m s^{-1} **b)** 333 m
3 a) 10 m s^{-1} **b)** 133 m
4 36 s, 1037 m
5 $\alpha = \dfrac{1}{10}$ **b)** 92 m
6 $\alpha = 2$, $\beta = \dfrac{1}{20}$
7 a) $s = 2t - \dfrac{t^3}{12}$ **b)** 2.83 s

c) $0 \leq t \leq \sqrt{24}$
d) Use a trigonometric function.
8 a) $A = 55.0$ **b)** 50 m
9 $v = t + \dfrac{20}{\pi}\cos\left(\dfrac{\pi t}{10}\right) - \dfrac{20}{\pi}$,
$s = \dfrac{t^2}{2} + \dfrac{200}{\pi^2}\sin\left(\dfrac{\pi t}{10}\right) - \dfrac{20t}{\pi}$
10 a) -9 **c)** 4 m s^{-1}

Exercises 11.3 class (p.217)
1 a) $\mathbf{v} = 5\mathbf{i} + (6 - 9.8t)\mathbf{j}$
b) 9.8 m s^{-2}, vertically downwards.
2 a) $\mathbf{v} = \dfrac{t^2}{10}\mathbf{i} + \dfrac{t^3}{30}\mathbf{j} + 5\mathbf{k}$,
$\mathbf{a} = \dfrac{t}{5}\mathbf{i} + \dfrac{t^2}{10}\mathbf{j}$
b) 5 m s^{-1} **c)** horizontal
3 26.9 m, $\mathbf{v} = 0.84\mathbf{i} - 14.03\mathbf{j}$
4 a) $\mathbf{v} = 5\mathbf{i} + \dfrac{t}{3}\mathbf{j}$, $\mathbf{a} = \dfrac{1}{3}\mathbf{j}$
b) 5 m s^{-1}, 5.17 m s^{-1}
c) It is constant at 90° to original motion.
5 a) $\mathbf{v} = 2\cos t\mathbf{i} - 2\sin t\mathbf{j} - 0.5\mathbf{k}$,
$\mathbf{a} = -2\sin t\mathbf{i} - 2\cos t\mathbf{j}$
b) 2.06 m s^{-1}
c) towards the centre of the helter skelter
6 a) $\mathbf{v} = 10\mathbf{i} + (6t^2 - 36t + 54)\mathbf{j}$
b) $\mathbf{a} = (12t - 36)\mathbf{j}$
c) $(10\mathbf{i} + 0\mathbf{j})$ m s^{-1}, $(30\mathbf{i} + 54\mathbf{j})$ m
d) $\mathbf{v} = 10\mathbf{i} - 9.8t\mathbf{j}$,
$\mathbf{r} = (30 + 10t)\mathbf{i} + (54 - 4.9t^2)\mathbf{j}$
e) 63.2 m
7 a) $\mathbf{a} = 12\mathbf{i} + 10\mathbf{j}$
b) $(36\mathbf{i} + 27\mathbf{j})$ m s^{-1}, 45 m s^{-1}
c) $t = 5$
8 a) $\mathbf{r} = 4t\mathbf{i} + (2 + 2t - 5t^2)\mathbf{j}$
b) $\mathbf{r} = (3t + 2t^2)\mathbf{i} + \left(-2t + \dfrac{t^3}{6}\right)\mathbf{j}$
c) $\mathbf{r} = \left(10t + \dfrac{t^4}{12}\right)\mathbf{i} + \left(-20t - \dfrac{t^5}{20}\right)\mathbf{j}$
9 a) $\mathbf{v} = \left(30 + \dfrac{1}{5}t\right)\mathbf{i} + \dfrac{1}{20}t^2\mathbf{j}$,
$\mathbf{r} = \left(30t + \dfrac{1}{10}t^2\right)\mathbf{i} + \dfrac{1}{60}t^3\mathbf{j}$

Exercises 11.3 home (p.217)
1 9.8 m s^{-1} vertically downwards
2 a) $\mathbf{v} = 5\mathbf{i} + (12 - 0.3t^2)\mathbf{j}$,
$\mathbf{a} = -0.6t\mathbf{j}$
c) Parallel to $\mathbf{j}$
3 a) $0 \leq t \leq 2$
b) $\mathbf{v} = 6.4\mathbf{i} - 8\mathbf{j}$ $\mathbf{a} = 9.6\mathbf{i} - 4\mathbf{j}$
4 $\mathbf{v} = \dfrac{1}{4}\mathbf{i} - \dfrac{1}{16}\mathbf{j}$,
$\mathbf{a} = -\dfrac{1}{32}\mathbf{i} + \dfrac{3}{128}\mathbf{j}$
5 a) In $\mathbf{j}$ direction

b) $4\,\text{m s}^{-1}$, $15.5\,\text{m s}^{-1}$
c) $40\mathbf{i} + 100\mathbf{j}$

6 a) $\mathbf{r} = \left(\dfrac{t^3}{12} + 4t\right)\mathbf{i} + \dfrac{t^3}{18}\mathbf{j}$

b) $\mathbf{r} = \left(\dfrac{t^3}{2} + 20t\right)\mathbf{i} + \left(-\dfrac{t^3}{3} - 18t\right)\mathbf{j}$

c) $\mathbf{r} = \left(\dfrac{4t^{\frac{5}{2}}}{15} + 10t\right)\mathbf{i} + \left(\dfrac{8t^{\frac{5}{2}}}{15} - 2t\right)\mathbf{j}$

7 a) $\mathbf{v} = \left(4t - \dfrac{t^2}{10}\right)\mathbf{i} + \left(2t - \dfrac{t^2}{20}\right)\mathbf{j}$

c) $t = 40$ **d)** $\dfrac{3200}{3}\mathbf{i} + \dfrac{1600}{3}\mathbf{j}$

8 a) $\mathbf{v} = \left(8 - \dfrac{t^2}{40}\right)\mathbf{i} + (2 - 10t)\mathbf{j}$

b) $\mathbf{r} = \left(8t - \dfrac{t^3}{120}\right)\mathbf{i} + (2t - 5t^2)\mathbf{j}$

c) $3.20\mathbf{i}$
9 a) $136.5\mathbf{i} - 68.3\mathbf{j}$
10 a) $\mathbf{v} = \dfrac{t}{2}\mathbf{i} - \dfrac{(t-4)^3}{6}\mathbf{j}$,

$\mathbf{r} = \dfrac{t^2}{4}\mathbf{i} + \left(\dfrac{32}{3} - \dfrac{(t-4)^4}{24}\right)\mathbf{j}$

b) $t = 4$ **c)** $0.4\,\text{m}$

Consolidation Exercises for Chapter 11 *(p.225)*
1 $t = 6$, $108\,\text{m}$
2 a) $\mathbf{v} = (3t^2 - 3)\mathbf{i} + 8t\mathbf{j}$
b) $t = 3$
3 a) $\mathbf{a} = 2t\mathbf{i} - 4\mathbf{j}$ **b)** $t = 1.25$
c) $6.71\,\text{m}$
4 a) $\mathbf{v} = 25\mathbf{i} + 5\sin\left(\dfrac{\pi t}{10}\right)\mathbf{j}$

b) $\mathbf{v} = \sqrt{625 + 25\left[\sin\left(\dfrac{\pi t}{10}\right)\right]^2}$

c) Min speeds $t = 0$, 10, 20
Maximum Speeds $t = 5$, 15
Increases, Decreases, Increases, Decreases
d) Expect to decrease uphill and increase downhill.
5 a) $150\,\text{m}$ **d)** $4.5\,\text{m s}^{-2}$

CHAPTER 12
Energy, work and power

Exercises 12.1 class *(p.230)*
1 a) Electric motor in a washing machine. Dynamo on a bicycle.
b) Pinball machine.
2 In a power station. From brakes on a car.
3 Chemical to mechanical during run up. Mechanical to potential going up during jump. Potential to mechanical going down during jump.
4 Potential converted to mechanical.

5 Potential energy is converted to mechanical energy, which then is converted to potential energy stored in the elastic.

Exercises 12.1 home *(p.230)*
1 a) When a ball goes up in the air.
b) When a person walks or runs.
2 At extremities maximum potential and zero kinetic. At lowest point minimum potential and maximum kinetic.
3 Chemical to kinetic during run. Kinetic to potential during vault. Also some to elastic energy in pole as it bends, and then back to kinetic.
4 The kinetic energy of the wind is transferred to the kinetic energy of the sails, which is then transferred to electrical energy.
5 Kinetic energy is converted to elastic potential energy and heat. The elastic potential energy is then returned to kinetic energy.

Exercises 12.2 class *(p.231)*
1 a) $405\,000\,\text{J}$ **b)** $0.375\,\text{J}$
c) $0.3\,\text{J}$ **d)** $20.48\,\text{J}$
2 $1575\,\text{J}$
3 a) $250\,\text{J}$ **b)** $250\,\text{J}$ **c)** $0.0922\,\text{m s}^{-1}$
4 a) $0.192\,\text{J}$ **b)** $3.58\,\text{m s}^{-1}$
c) Heat. Squash balls warm up during games.
5 a) $56.6\,\text{m s}^{-1}$ **b)** $36.5\,\text{m s}^{-1}$
c) $2.5\,\text{kg}$
6 $12.4\,\text{m s}^{-1}$
7 a) $0.8\,\text{J}$ **b)** $0.8\,\text{J}$
8 a) $2.24\,\text{m s}^{-1}$, $3.16\,\text{m s}^{-1}$
b) $145\,\text{J}$, $290\,\text{J}$ **c)** $580\,\text{J}$
9 a) $6.26\,\text{m s}^{-1}$ **b)** $2.94\,\text{J}$
c) All the potential energy is converted to kinetic energy.
10 a) $0.784\,\text{J}$ **b)** $0.627\,\text{J}$ **c)** 20%
d) 20% loss of energy results in a 20% change in height.

Exercises 12.2 home *(p.232)*
1 a) $562.5\,\text{J}$ **b)** $2.5 \times 10^6\,\text{J}$
c) $0.005\,76\,\text{J}$ **d)** $3.2 \times 10^5\,\text{J}$
2 $1.8 \times 10^6\,\text{J}$
3 a) $0.768\,\text{J}$ **b)** $7.155\,\text{m s}^{-1}$
4 a) $0.9\,\text{J}$ **b)** $0.9\,\text{J}$ **c)** $6.708\,\text{m s}^{-1}$
5 a) $126\,\text{m s}^{-1}$ **b)** $89\,\text{m s}^{-1}$
c) 5 grams
6 a) $3.16\,\text{m s}^{-1}$. **b)** Some energy lost due to air resistance.
7 a) $12\,500\,\text{J}$ **b)** $12\,500\,\text{J}$
c) Some energy will be lost due to air resistance.
8 a) $6.93\,\text{m s}^{-1}$, $9.80\,\text{m s}^{-1}$
b) $28\,800\,\text{J}$, $57\,600\,\text{J}$
c) $115\,200\,\text{J}$
9 a) $24.25\,\text{m s}^{-1}$, $20\,580\,\text{J}$
b) $20\,580\,\text{J}$ **c)** $17\,080\,\text{J}$
10 a) $0.8\,\text{m}$, $0.45\,\text{m}$ **b)** 0.8J, 0.45J

Exercises 12.3 class *(p.236)*
1 a) $2400\,\text{J}$ **b)** $1.85\,\text{m s}^{-1}$
2 a) $4000\,\text{J}$ **b)** $9.88\,\text{m s}^{-1}$
c) No resistance factors have been considered.
3 a) $0.960\,\text{J}$ **b)** $5.24\,\text{m s}^{-1}$
c) $12.7\,\text{N}$
4 a) $75\,000\,\text{J}$ **b)** $5.25 \times 10^7\,\text{J}$
c) $2.1\,\text{J}$
5 a) $6.32\,\text{m s}^{-1}$ **b)** $0.569\,\text{m s}^{-1}$
c) $5\,\text{m s}^{-1}$
6 a) $12\,618\,\text{J}$ **b)** $12\,348\,\text{J}$ **c)** $270\,\text{J}$
d) $0.88\,\text{m s}^{-1}$
7 a) $25\,\text{J}$ **b)** $9.8\,\text{J}$ **c)** $15.2\,\text{J}$
d) $3.9\,\text{m s}^{-1}$
8 a) $4000\,\text{J}$ **b)** $3000\,\text{J}$
9 a) $7056\,\text{J}$, $14\,\text{m s}^{-1}$ **b)** $12\,700\,\text{J}$
10 $137\,\text{m s}^{-1}$ The force has been assumed to be constant and both the doorpost and the barrier assumed to have the same constitution.

Exercises 12.3 home *(p.238)*
1 a) $150\,\text{J}$ **b)** $6.12\,\text{m s}^{-1}$
c) No, speed reached is excessive.
2 a) $4.8 \times 10^5\,\text{J}$ **b)** $15.5\,\text{m s}^{-1}$
c) $3.52 \times 10^5\,\text{J}$
3 a) $729\,\text{J}$ **b)** $4.85\,\text{m s}^{-1}$
c) $73\,520\,\text{N}$
4 a) $1423.5\,\text{J}$ **b)** $456\,\text{J}$ **c)** $243\,\text{J}$
5 a) $96\,000\,\text{J}$, $12.73\,\text{m s}^{-1}$
b) $1 \times 10^5\,\text{J}$, $20.25\,\text{m s}^{-1}$
c) $6\,\text{J}$, $15.49\,\text{m s}^{-1}$
6 a) $7.4 \times 10^4\,\text{J}$ **b)** $7.35 \times 10^4\,\text{J}$
c) $500\,\text{J}$ **d)** $1.15\,\text{m s}^{-1}$
7 a) $2940\,\text{J}$ **b)** $3020\,\text{J}$ **c)** $5390\,\text{J}$
8 a) $1 \times 10^5\,\text{J}$ **b)** $4.0 \times 10^4\,\text{J}$
c) $20.86\,\text{m s}^{-1}$
d) The resistance forces will probably increase as the speed increases, so the solution will be an over-estimate.
9 a) $729\,\text{J}$, $4.85\,\text{m s}^{-1}$ **b)** $1033\,\text{J}$
10 a) Constant force of $83\,\text{N}$
b) $129\,\text{m s}^{-1}$
c) It is likely that the force exerted by the sand will depend on the speed of the bullet. This may allow a greater speed to be used.

Exercises 12.4 class *(p.241)*
1 a) $130\,\text{J}$ **b)** $22.6\,\text{J}$ **c)** $453\,\text{J}$
d) $4290\,\text{J}$
2 a) $256\,238\,\text{J}$ **b)** $2.7 \times 10^6\,\text{J}$
c) $70\,\text{m s}^{-1}$ **d)** $67\,\text{m s}^{-1}$
3 a) $85.1\,\text{J}$ **b)** $22.5\,\text{J}$ **c)** $62.6\,\text{J}$
4 a) $6938\,\text{J}$, $2400\,\text{J}$ **b)** $11.5\,\text{m s}^{-1}$
5 a) $68\,400\,\text{J}$
b) $97\,714\,\text{J}$, $29\,314\,\text{J}$ **c)** $1300\,\text{N}$
d) The road is horizontal.
6 a) $3688\,\text{J}$ **b)** $10.12\,\text{m s}^{-1}$
c) $2788\,\text{J}$ **d)** $16.1\,\text{m}$
7 a) $1\,237\,500\,\text{J}$ **b)** $433T$
c) $2858\,\text{N}$

8 a) 37.5 J **b)** 100 J, 2011 J
  c) 2149 J **d)** 1091 N
9 a) 42 690 J **b)** 13.1 m s⁻¹
  c) 8111 J
10 a) The normal reaction is greater.
  b) Gravity: Slope $4mg\cos 50°$ J
    Level 0 J
    Friction: Slope $1.6mg\cos 40°$ J
    Level $7.84m$ J
  c) 3.27 m s⁻¹ **d)** 5.14 m s⁻¹

Exercises 12.4 home (p.243)
1 a) 0 J **b)** 61.7 J **c)** 1015 J
  d) 752 J
2 a) 31 653 J **b)** 251 m, 270 m
3 a) 150 J **b)** 1334 J **c)** 1184 J
4 a) 46 620 J **b)** 75 881 J
  c) 292.6 N **d)** 23.8 m s⁻¹, a
  constant resistance force and
  no driving force.
5 a) 25.6 J **b)** 360 J **c)** 74.2 N
  d) The rotation. Yes, as a
  rotating object must have
  kinetic energy.
6 a) 1534 J **b)** 597 J
  c) 39.8 N **d)** 23.6 m
7 a) 28 129 J
  b) 1276 m from first position.
  c) 68 129 J, 1276 m
8 a) 8.32 m s⁻¹ **b)** 5.27°
9 a) 278 J **b)** 72.6 N
10 Constant resistance of $2.13m$ N
  parallel to the slope, 1.78 m.

Exercises 12.5 class (p.246)
1 a) 1960 J **b)** 0.0196 J
  c) 735 J **d)** 0.49 J
2 a) 14 m s⁻¹ **b)** 1.4 m s⁻¹
  c) 17.1 m s⁻¹ **d)** 3.1 m s⁻¹
3 a) 2430 J **b)** 7.67 m s⁻¹
  c) 8.85 m s⁻¹ **d)** No loss of
  energy, due to air resistance or
  the jerk.
4 a) 7.46 m s⁻¹ **b)** 13 400 J
  c) 6.84 m
5 a) 9.8 J **b)** 19.8 m s⁻¹ **c)** 16.7 m
6 a) 695 800 J **b)** 694 913 J
7 5.58 J, 14.23 m
8 a) 98 J **b)** 48.7 m **c)** 98 J
9 a) $0.2 \times 9.8(8t - 4.9t^2)$
  b) $8 - 15.68t + 9.604t^2$ **c)** 8 J
10 a) $5Mg$ **b)** $\sqrt{2gx}$ **c)** $x = 5 - \dfrac{5M}{m}$

Exercises 12.5 home (p.248)
1 a) 196 J **b)** 14 m s⁻¹
2 a) 448.8 J **b)** 17.3 m s⁻¹
3 a) 2940 J **b)** 7.67 m s⁻¹
4 a) 24 500 J, 14 m s⁻¹
  b) 9.90 m s⁻¹ **c)** The same.
5 a) 78.4 J **b)** 12.52 m s⁻¹
  c) 13.28 m s⁻¹
6 a) 40.8 J **b)** 40.8 J, 10.1 m s⁻¹
7 a) 156 800 J **b)** 250 m
  c) 282 240 J
8 6.56 m s⁻¹ **a)** 9.28 m s⁻¹
  b) Identical
9 a) 30.6 m, 20 m s⁻¹

b) $a = 20$, $b = 24.5$
10 a) $v = \sqrt{2gx}$ **b)** $980m$ J

Exercises 12.6 class (p.251)
1 a) 51 000 W **b)** 250 W
  c) 541 W
2 $R = 1250$ N
3 $3\frac{1}{3}$ m s⁻¹
4 a) 36 N **b)** 432 W **c)** 12.75 m s⁻¹
5 a) 0.125 m s⁻² **b)** 187 500 W
  c) Acceleration assumed
  constant. No account taken of
  working against resistances.
6 a) 22 050 J **b)** 19.6 m s⁻²
  c) $a = \dfrac{29.4}{v} - 9.8$
7 a) 25.9 **b)** 32.9 m s⁻¹
8 0.56 m s⁻¹
9 a) 25.65 N **b)** 25.65 N
  c) 76.95 J **d)** 7.695 N
  e) No, this would reduce the
  forward force by a significant
  proportion.
10 a) 20 **b)** 854 N
  c) 33 m s⁻¹ **d)** 76 m s⁻¹

Exercises 12.6 home (p.253)
1 a) 250 000 W **b)** 72 W
  c) 3136 W
2 a) 511.6 N **b)** 40.95 m s⁻¹
3 a) 50 W **b)** Double to 100 W
  c) Person can work at 100 W,
  and exert force of 40 N.
4 a) 39.0625 kg s⁻¹
  b) 33.56 increase of 4.8%
5 a) 113.4 N **b)** 453.6 W
6 a) 20.5 N **b)** 41 W
7 a) 23 520 W **b)** 3.8 m s⁻¹
8 a) 37.5, 1.875
  b) 40 m s⁻¹, 31.75 m s⁻¹
  c) Proportional to speed squared.
9 a) 1285.7 N **b)** Up, 33.2 m s⁻¹,
  Down, 57.2 m s⁻¹ **c)** No as not
  travelling close to 42 m s⁻¹.
10 a) 3.7 **b)** Up, 7.2 m s⁻¹

Consolidation Exercises for Chapter 12 (p.254)
1 14 600 N
2 a) 1728 J, 6.57 m s⁻¹ **b)** 2.20 m
3 a) 36.1 J, 11.42 m s⁻¹ **b)** 54 W
  c) 0.84
4 a) 52.2 kW **b)** 0.49 m s⁻²
  c) 26.1 m s⁻¹
5 a) $30v$ N **b)** 19% **d)** 28.6 m s⁻¹
6 a) 257 N **c)** 0.707 m s⁻²

CHAPTER 13
Momentum and collisions

Exercises 13.1 class (p.259)
1 Constant magnitude, variable
  direction.
2 a) $2724\mathbf{i} + 5346\mathbf{j}$
  b) $-57851\mathbf{i} - 68944\mathbf{j}$
  c) $72.4\mathbf{i} - 26.3\mathbf{j}$
3 a) $1.046\mathbf{i} - 0.092\mathbf{j}$

b) $48.3\mathbf{i} + 43.5\mathbf{j}$ **c)** $672\mathbf{i} - 106\mathbf{j}$
4 a) $\mathbf{u} = 1.8\cos 40°\mathbf{i} - 1.8\cos 50°\mathbf{j}$,
  $\mathbf{v} = 1.73\cos 30°\mathbf{i} + 1.73\cos 60°\mathbf{j}$
  b) $0.0239\mathbf{i} + 0.4044\mathbf{j}$
  c) 0.045 s
5 a) $-55.2\mathbf{i} + 89.3\mathbf{j}$
6 b) $459\mathbf{i} - 321\mathbf{j}$
  d) If change takes 0.5 s,
  then $T = 1120$ N
7 a) $\mathbf{u} = 3.60\mathbf{i} + 3.02\mathbf{j} - 1.71\mathbf{k}$,
  $\mathbf{v} = -520\mathbf{j} + 3\mathbf{k}$
  b) $\mathbf{I} = -0.108\mathbf{i} - 0.246\mathbf{j} + 0.141\mathbf{k}$
  c) 0.608 N
8 a) $\mathbf{u} = 0.616\mathbf{i} + 1.69\mathbf{j}$,
  $\mathbf{v} = -0.5\mathbf{i} + 0.866\mathbf{j}$
  b) $-357\mathbf{i} - 264\mathbf{j}$ **c)** $1.23\mathbf{i} + 2.91\mathbf{j}$

Exercises 13.1 home (p.261)
1 No, it may have constant
  magnitude, but it will vary in
  direction.
2 a) $592\mathbf{i} + 245\mathbf{j}$
  b) $-3420201\mathbf{i} - 9396926\mathbf{j}$
  c) $-44.8\mathbf{i} - 254.1\mathbf{j}$
3 a) $3.45\mathbf{i} + 2.89\mathbf{j}$
  b) $0.434\mathbf{i} + 0.517\mathbf{j}$
  c) $70.1\mathbf{i} + 40.5\mathbf{j}$
4 a) $\mathbf{u} = 0.410\mathbf{i} - 1.128\mathbf{j}$,
  $\mathbf{v} = 0.401\mathbf{i} + 0.801\mathbf{j}$
  b) $\mathbf{I} = 0.00005\mathbf{i} + 0.231\mathbf{j}$
  c) 0.289 N **d)** Increase and
  then decrease.
5 a) $4.70\mathbf{i} - 1.71\mathbf{j}$, $4.70\mathbf{i} + 1.71\mathbf{j}$
  b) $0.2736\mathbf{j}$, $-0.2736\mathbf{j}$ **c)** $0.4\mathbf{j}$
  d) 7.3 m s⁻¹
6 a) 8.85 m s⁻¹ **b)** $-8.85\mathbf{j}$, $7.97\mathbf{i}$
  c) $398\mathbf{i} + 442\mathbf{j}$ **d)** $498\mathbf{i} + 553\mathbf{j}$
7 a) $-159\mathbf{i} + 903\mathbf{j}$
  b) 305.6 N, 4.63 m s⁻²
8 a) $m(-1.179\mathbf{i} - 0.103\mathbf{j})$
  b) $1.179\mathbf{i} + 0.103\mathbf{j}$
  c) 1.18 m s⁻¹, at 5.0° to $\mathbf{i}$

Exercises 13.2 class (p.265)
1 a) $124\mathbf{i}$, $194\mathbf{i} - 112\mathbf{j}$ **b)** $318\mathbf{i} - 112\mathbf{j}$ **c)** 2.86 m s⁻¹, 19.4° to $\mathbf{i}$
2 a) $4\mathbf{i}$, $20\mathbf{i} - 34.6\mathbf{j}$ **b)** 17.6 m s⁻¹
  c) Due to the effects of external
  forces/to movement of wings.
3 a) $2.5\mathbf{i} + 33.8\mathbf{j}$ **b)** $0.035\mathbf{i} + 0.470\mathbf{j}$ **c)** At an angle of 86°
  above horizontal.
4 a) Final velocities are easy to
  express. They are at 90° to each
  other.
  b) 3.06 m s⁻¹, 2.57 m s⁻¹
5 a) $-23142\mathbf{i} + 1446\mathbf{j}$
  b) 19.3 m s⁻¹ **c)** The handbrake
  is on and it may hit the kerb, so
  its speed is lost quickly.
6 a) $0.421\mathbf{i} + 0.145\mathbf{j}$
  b) $5.27\mathbf{i} + 1.81\mathbf{j}$
7 $v = \dfrac{\sqrt{10}u}{4}$ car 18.4°,
  motorbike 71.6°.

8 a) $(1.085 \times 10^6 m + 7.231 \times 10^{-21})\mathbf{i} + (1.879 \times 10^6 m - 4.175 \times 10^{-21})\mathbf{j}$
 b) $m = 2.22 \times 10^{-27}$ kg
9 a) 88.9 Ns   **b)** 4.85 m s^{-1}
10 5.74 m s^{-1} is the speed at which the gun moves backwards. There is an upward impulse of 19 284 Ns on the gun.

Exercises **13.2 home** (p.267)

1 a) 15 400$\mathbf{i}$, 24 513$\mathbf{i}$ + 20 569$\mathbf{j}$
 b) 8.8 m s^{-1}, at 27° to $\mathbf{i}$
 c) Decrease as they skid.
2 a) $1.99 \times 10^6 \mathbf{i} - 5.91 \times 10^4 \mathbf{j}$
 b) 383 m s^{-1} **c)** 1.7°
3 a) 1.73$\mathbf{i}$ + 133$\mathbf{j}$
 b) 2 m s^{-1}, 0.75° to $\mathbf{j}$ **c)** No
4 a) $m(3.46 \times 10^6 \mathbf{i} + 2.00 \times 10^6 \mathbf{j})$
 b) 3.46×10^6, 1.00×10^6
5 a) $2m\mathbf{i}$ **b)** 1.03 m s^{-1}, 46.9° to $\mathbf{i}$ **c)** Momentum conserved, no effects due to rotation of balls.
6 a) 3.24$\mathbf{i}$ + 0.94$\mathbf{j}$
 b) 3.24$\mathbf{i}$ + 0.94$\mathbf{j}$
7 a) $\sqrt{37}mu$ **b)** $\dfrac{\sqrt{37}u}{4}$
 c) 80.5°, 9.5°
8 a) $(0.684m + 1.928M)\mathbf{i} + (1.879m - 2.298M)\mathbf{j}$
 b) $M = 0.818\,m$
 c) $v = 2.76$ m s^{-1}
9 a) 68.4 Ns **b)** 4.18 m s^{-1}
10 Speed reduced to 2.91 m s^{-1}.

Exercises **13.3 class** (p.272)

1 a) 0.5 **b)** 6 m s^{-1} **c)** 0.75
 d) $10\frac{2}{3}$ m s^{-1}
2 a) 6.26 m s^{-1} **b)** 4.85 m s^{-1}
 c) 0.775
3 a) 0.16 m **b)** 2.78 m **c)** 0.632
 d) 0.730
4 a) 9.5 m s^{-1}, − 9.5 m s^{-1}
 b) 1 m s^{-1}, −1 m s^{-1}
5 a) 3.625 m s^{-1}, 5.625 m s^{-1}
 b) The rotation of the balls.
6 a) Moves at 0.05 m s^{-1}.
 b) 0.975
7 a) 0, v **b)** $\dfrac{v}{4}, \dfrac{3v}{4}$ **c)** $\dfrac{v}{2}, \dfrac{v}{2}$
8 a) $v_A = 2.25$, $v_B = 2.75$
 b) $v_B = 1.4375$, $v_C = 2.3125$
 c) Between A and B.
9 a) $v_A = \dfrac{u(1-e)}{2}$, $v_B = \dfrac{u(1+e)}{2}$.
 b) $v_B = \dfrac{u(1-e)(1+e)}{4}$, $v_C = \dfrac{u(1+e)^2}{4}$
10 $\dfrac{h(1+e^2)}{1-e^2}$

Exercises **13.3 home** (p.274)

1 a) $\frac{2}{3}$ **b)** 0.95 **c)** 5.6 m s^{-1}
 d) 23.3 m s^{-1}

2 a) 9.90 m s^{-1} **b)** 3.96 m s^{-1}
 c) 0.8 m
3 a) 1.96 m **b)** 0.837 **c)** 0.775
 d) 0.55 m
4 a) 5.5 m s^{-1}, 9.5 m s^{-1}
 b) 6.5 m s^{-1}, 8.5 m s^{-1}
5 1.2 m s^{-1}, 2.6 m s^{-1}
6 a) $-\frac{2}{3}$ m s^{-1}, $1\frac{1}{3}$ m s^{-1}
 b) 0.4 m s^{-1}, 0.8 m s^{-1}
7 a) 10 m s^{-1} **b)** $\frac{1}{18}$
8 a) $v_A = 2.6$, $v_B = 3.4$
 b) $v_B = 2.42$, $v_C = 2.98$
 c) A and B
9 a) $v_A = 1.3u$, $v_B = 1.7u$
 b) $v_B = 0.51u$, $v_C = 1.19u$
 c) Next A hits, $v_A = 0.747u$, $v_B = 1.063u$, $v_C = 1.19u$
10 a) $\dfrac{V(e+1) - V(e-1)}{2}$,
 $\dfrac{V(e+1) - v(e-1)}{2}$

Exercises **13.4 class** (p.276)

1 a) 19.1°, 5.29 m s^{-1} **b)** 9.35 Ns
2 a) 1 **b)** 0.685
3 a) 5.09 m s^{-1} at 75.2° to surface
 b) 3.75 Ns, 3.69 Ns
4 a) 6.84 m s^{-1} at 54.2°
 b) 5.97 m s^{-1}

Exercises **13.4 home** (p.276)

1 a) 3.16 m s^{-1}, 0.210 **b)** 36.4 Ns
2 a) 73.4°, 1.86 m s^{-1}
 b) 59.2°, 3.34 m s^{-1}
3 a) smooth wall **b)** 3.30 m s^{-1}
 c) 1.13 Ns
4 14.6 m s^{-1}

Exercises **13.5 class** (p.279)

1 a) 0.252 Ns **b)** 2.52 N **c)** 2.52 N
2 a) 5437.5 Ns **b)** 2.03 m s^{-1}
3 a) 0.318 Ns **b)** 7.26 m s^{-1}
 c) 7.02 m s^{-1}
4 a) 667 Ns **b)** 13.3 m s^{-1}
 c) $w = \dfrac{\pi}{2}$, $A = \dfrac{500\pi}{3}$
5 a) $0 \le t \le \dfrac{1}{15}, \dfrac{1}{15}$ s
 b) 1.24 m s^{-1}
 c) $25\sin(15\pi t) - 1.67$
 d) 0.59 m s^{-1}

Exercises **13.5 home** (p.280)

1 a) 1.2 Ns **b)** $3T$ **c)** 0.4 s
 d) Probably more curved.
2 a) 800 **b)** $3\frac{1}{3}$ m s^{-1}
3 a) 100 000 Ns **b)** 67 m s^{-1}
4 b) $\dfrac{A}{5\pi}$ **c)** $A = 8.64$ **d)** 4 m s^{-1}
5 a) $t = 0.3$ s **b)** 8 m s^{-1}
 c) 5.06 m s^{-1}

Consolidation Exercises for Chapter 13 (p.281)

1 22.4 m s^{-1}
2 c) $I = \dfrac{u(M - 7m)}{4}$

CHAPTER 14
Frameworks

Exercises **14.1 class** (p.286)

1 a) 48 Nm **b)** −1200 Nm
 c) −360 Nm **d)** −30 Nm
2 b) −46.0 N **c)** No
3 a) −96.4 Nm **b)** 90.0 Nm
 c) 13.0 Nm **d)** 16.0 Nm
4 −233 Nm
5 a) 3 m **b)** 1.75 m
 c) 0.58 m **d)** 2 m
6 a) 60° **b)** 70.5°

Exercises **14.1 home** (p.286)

1 a) 120 Nm **b)** 16 Nm
 c) −48 Nm **d)** 0 Nm
2 a) 1.2 Nm **b)** Only if the force continues to act along a tangent.
3 a) 36.7 Nm **b)** 2.21 Nm
 c) 41.1 Nm **d)** −120 Nm
4 a) 2.83 m **b)** 1.79 m
5 a) 33.3° **b)** 152.5°

Exercises **14.2 class** (p.289)

1 a) 58.8 N **b)** 0.5
2 a) 1120 N **b)** Tension increases
3 a) 56.4 N **b)** 41.7 N
4 245 N **b)** 122.5 N
5 a) 539 N, 762 N
 b) 539$\mathbf{i}$ + 0$\mathbf{j}$, −539$\mathbf{i}$ +539$\mathbf{j}$
6 b) 318.5 N **c)** 1443 N
 d) 721 N **e)** 0.442
7 a) 90.8 N **b)** 112 N, 34.1 N
 c) 0.305
8 a) 686 N, $\dfrac{5g(6x+1)}{\tan 50°}$ N
 b) 1.08 m

Exercises **14.2 home** (p.290)

1 b) 78.4 N, 6.91 N, 6.91 N
2 a) 103 N **b)** 453 N
3 a) 39.2 N, 19.3 N, 19.3 N, 6.81 N
 b) 0.353
4 a) 588 N **b)** 1568 N **c)** 509 N
 d) 1444 N at 79.8° to the horizontal
5 b) 349 N **c)** 349 N, 376 N
6 a) 48 N **b)** 31 N, 110 N
 c) 114 N, 74.4° above horizontal
7 a) 196 N **b)** 339.5 N **c)** 0.58
8 0.5

Exercises **14.3 class** (p.294)

1 b) 2.5 m **c)** 3750 N
 d) 1250 N **e)** $T_{AC} = -2500$ N, $T_{AB} = 2165$ N **f)** $T_{BC} = -4330$ N
2 a) 2347 N **b)** 347 N
 c) $T_{AC} = 540$ N, $T_{AB} = -414$ N
 d) $T_{BC} = -2383$ N
 e) AB: compression
  BC: compression
  AC: tension
3 a) To give a zero vertical resultant
 b) $Q = 400$ N
 c) $T_{AB} = 231$ N, compression,
  $T_{AC} = 305$ N, compression,
  $T_{BC} = 231$ N, tension

4 a) Horizontal bar in tension, others exert thrusts.
b) 1800 N in angled bars, 3118 N in horizontal bar.
5 a) A 1825 N downwards. B 6825 N upwards
b) T_{AB} = 1825 N, thrust
T_{BC} = 7066 N, thrust
T_{BD} = 0 N
T_{AD} = 2581 N, tension
T_{CD} = 2581 N, tension
6 a) $R = S = 100$ N
b) $T_{AB} = T_{CD}$ etc.
c) $T_{AB} = T_{CD} = -115$ N
$T_{AE} = T_{DE} = 58$ N
$T_{BE} = T_{CE} = 0$
$T_{BC} = -58$ N
7 AB 462 N, tension
AF 462 N, tension
BF 462 N, thrust
BC 0 N
BD 462 N, tension
DF 462 N, tension
DC 50 N, tension
DE 50 N, tension
EF 0 N
8 Q = 1500 N, vertical force at E of 2500 N
AB 5196 N, tension
AE 3000 N, thrust
BC 1732 N, tension
BD 2000 N, thrust
BE 2000 N, thrust
CD 2000 N, thrust
DE 3464 N, thrust
AF 3000 N, tension
EF 2598 N, thrust

Exercises 14.3 home (p.295)
1 a) 800 N **b)** 400 N
c) T_{CA} = 1170 N, tension
T_{BC} = 1099 N, compression
d) T_{AB} = 1170 N, tension
2 a) Light rods and pin-joints
b) R = 283 N P = 217 N
c) AB, 596 N, tension AC, 634 N, thrust BC, 778 N, tension
3 a) 2500 N
b) AD, 1443 N, compression
AC, 2887 N, tension
BC, 2887 N, tension
BD, 1443 N, compression
CD, 0 N
c) The member CD is redundant.
4 b) 8052 N upward at B, 2052 N down at A.
c) AB, 2931 N, compression
BC, 8569 N, compression
AC, 3578 N, tension
5 a) P = 4000 N, Q = 2000 N, R = 2000 N
b) AB, 2828 N, compression
BC, 2828 N, compression
BD, 4000 N, tension
CD, 2828 N, compression
AD, 2000 N, compression

6 $R = S = 25$ N
AB, 25.9 N, compression
AE, 6.7 N, tension
BC, 13.4 N, compression
BE, 25.9 N, tension
CD, 25.9 N, compression
CE, 25.9 N, tension
DE, 6.7 N, tension
7 245 N
AB 0 N
AC 245 N
AD 0 N
BC 0 N
CD −160 N
8 a) $R = \dfrac{4P}{3}$

b) AB, 127 N, tension
AF, 90 N, compression
BC, 42.4 N, tension
BF, 84.9 N, tension
CD, 42.4 N, tension
CF, 60 N, compression
DE, 42.4 N, tension
DF, 0 N
EF, 30 N, compression

Consolidation Exercises for Chapter 14 (p.297)
2 $\dfrac{W}{\sqrt{3}}$

3 a) $\dfrac{W}{8}\left(4\cot\theta - 1\right)$

CHAPTER 15
Centre of mass
Exercises 15.1 class (p.304)
1 a) $\dfrac{28}{17}\mathbf{i} + \dfrac{11}{17}\mathbf{j}$ **b)** $\dfrac{1}{4}\mathbf{i} - \dfrac{4}{15}\mathbf{j}$
c) $-0.055\mathbf{i} + 0.049\mathbf{j}$
d) $-0.762\mathbf{i} - 1.015\mathbf{j}$
2 a) $0.0643\mathbf{i} - 0.0214\mathbf{j}$
b) Circle of radius 6.78 cm.
3 a) 4.43 cm
b) 3.09 cm from the centre.
4 a) 0.4 m from 500 g mass.
b) 120 grams
5 a) $\dfrac{(0.4m + 1.6)\,\mathbf{i} + (0.4m + 1.6)\,\mathbf{j}}{13 + m}$
b) 922 grams
6 a) 0.312 m
b) Move closer to the centre.
c) Place point mass at centre.
d) 0.118 m from the centre.
7 a) 0.91 m and 7.09 m
b) 1.41 m from bottom
8 a) $m = \frac{2}{3}$ kg, $M = \frac{5}{3}$ kg
b) No, as this would require a zero mass at O.

Exercises 15.1 home (p.305)
1 a) $2.5\mathbf{i} + \mathbf{j}$ **b)** $-0.357\mathbf{i} - \mathbf{j}$
c) $0.25\mathbf{i} + 0.286\mathbf{j}$
d) $0.3125\mathbf{i} + 0.3125\mathbf{j}$
2 a) $0.2\mathbf{i} + 0.267\mathbf{j}$ **b)** 53.1°

3 a) 1.66 cm **b)** 2.07 cm
4 a) $0.12\mathbf{i} + 0.08\mathbf{j}$ **b)** $1\frac{1}{3}$ kg
5 a) $\dfrac{(3.5 + m)\,\mathbf{i} + \sqrt{3}(9.5 + m)\,\mathbf{j}}{17 + m}$
b) 5.5 kg **c)** 1.15 m
6 a) 3.28 cm
b) Moves towards centre.
c) Yes as the centre of mass is so close to the centre already.
7 10 kg
8 a) 0 kg **b)** $0.0267\mathbf{i} + 0.02\mathbf{j}$, with $\mathbf{i}$ along AC and $\mathbf{j}$ along AB.

Exercises 15.2 class (p.308)
1 $1\frac{2}{3}$ cm
2 37.7 cm
3 a) $0\mathbf{i} + 0\mathbf{j}$, $0.0146\mathbf{i} + 0.0354\mathbf{j}$, $0.05\mathbf{i} + 0.05\mathbf{j}$, $0.0854\mathbf{i} + 0.0354\mathbf{j}$, $0.1\mathbf{i}$
4 15.4 cm from front.
5 a) $0.796\mathbf{i} + 0.499\mathbf{j}$
b) $0.719\mathbf{i} + 0.793\mathbf{j}$
6 a) 21.4 cm **b)** 26.6 cm, 6.4 cm
7 a) $0.844\mathbf{i} + 0.247\mathbf{j}$, $0.877\mathbf{i} + 0.110\mathbf{j}$ **b)** 0.137 m **c)** 97 J
d) Probably not perpendicular in both positions.
8 a) 0.193 m **b)** $0.193\mathbf{i} + 2.895\mathbf{j}$
9 a) 0.18 kg **b)** 8.74 cm
c) 5.11 cm **d)** 59.7°
10 $0.29H$

Exercises 15.2 home (p.309)
1 5.2 cm
2 9.3 cm
3 a) i) $0.225\mathbf{i} + 1.065\mathbf{j}$
ii) $0.915\mathbf{i} + 0.706\mathbf{j}$
iii) $1.25\mathbf{i} + 0.126\mathbf{j}$
4 a) $0.1\mathbf{i} + 0.075\mathbf{j}$ **b)** 36.9°
5 a) 1.75 m **b)** 269.5 N
6 a) 60.8 cm
b) i) 65.2 cm **ii)** 67.2 cm
7 a) 1.12 cm, 1.62 m
b) 0.5 m **c)** 980 J
8 9.46°
9 $0.158\mathbf{i} + 0.07\mathbf{j}$ with $\mathbf{i}$ along DC and $\mathbf{j}$ along DA.
10 $\dfrac{1}{(t+16)}\left(\dfrac{5t^2}{64\pi} + 960\right)$ cm

Exercises 15.3 class (p.313)
1 a) 294 N **b)** 285.8 N **c)** Topples
2 b) 490 N **c)** Topples first because 490 < 693. **d)** μ < 0.5
3 a) Slides $\alpha = 21.8°$
Topples $\alpha = 45°$ *Slides*
b) Slides $\alpha = 11.3°$
Topples $\alpha = 78.7°$ *Slides*
c) Slides $\alpha = 45°$
Topples $\alpha = 63.4°$ *Slides*
d) Slides $\alpha = 42°$
Topples $\alpha = 14°$ *Topples*
4 b) $\dfrac{mgd}{6h}$ **d)** $\mu < \dfrac{d}{2h}$

e) Results suggest full can should be used. However, ability of cans to recover once hit could be important.

5 Slides when $\alpha = 38.7°$.

6 a) $\alpha = 30°$ **b)** $\mu > \tan 30°$
c) $\alpha = 22.5°$, $\mu > \tan 22.5°$

7 $F = \dfrac{mg}{\sqrt{2}}$, $\mu > 1$

Exercises **15.3 home** (p.315)

1 a) 274.4 N **b)** 130.7 N
c) Topples
2 b) 1176 N **c)** Topple
3 a) Slides $\alpha = 21.8°$
Topples $\alpha = 26.6°$ Slides
b) Slides $\alpha = 16.7°$
Topples $\alpha = 56.3°$ Slides
c) Slides $\alpha = 50.2°$
Topples $\alpha = 45°$ Topples
d) Slides $\alpha = 38.7°$
Topples $\alpha = 69.4°$ Slides
4 a) 25.68 N **b)** 13.07 N
c) Topples **d)** No
5 a) $\tan 40° = 0.84 > 0.2$ so boxes can slide. **b)** $b = a \tan 50°$
6 $P - \dfrac{2mg}{5}$, $\mu \geq \dfrac{8}{31}$
7 $\mu < \dfrac{b}{2a + b\tan\alpha}$

Exercises **15.4 class** (p.319)

1 $\left(\frac{14}{15}, 0\right)$
2 $\left(\frac{3}{4}, \frac{3}{10}\right)$
3 8.89 cm from the longer side.
4 $\left(\frac{12}{5}, \frac{3}{4}\right)$ or $\left(\frac{12}{5}, -\frac{3}{4}\right)$
5 b) 13.8 cm from base
6 a) $\dfrac{3h}{8}$
7 a) $\left(\frac{5}{3}, 0\right)$ **b)** $\left(\frac{105}{62}, 0\right)$ **c)** $\left(\frac{5a}{6}, 0\right)$
8 $(1, 0)$
9 $\dfrac{27a}{40}$ from base
10 $(8, 0)$

Exercises **15.4 home** (p.320)

1 $\left(\frac{7}{9}, 0\right)$
2 $\left(\frac{4}{5}, \frac{2}{7}\right)$
3 3.85 cm from base
4 a) $\left(\frac{10}{7}, \frac{64}{35}\right)$ **b)** $\left(\frac{32}{11}, \frac{332}{55}\right)$
5 4.89 cm from base
6 b) $\dfrac{h}{4}$ **c)** $\dfrac{10h}{13}$
7 b) $\dfrac{a\left(b - a + b\ln\left(\frac{b}{a}\right)\right)}{a - b}$
8 0.923
9 b) 4.95
10 $\left(\frac{22}{9}, 0\right)$

Consolidation Exercises for Chapter 15 (p.321)

2 43.3°
3 a) 12.25 cm **b)** 32.6°
4 b) $\dfrac{7W}{18}$, $\dfrac{11W}{18}$

CHAPTER 16
Circular motion at constant speed

Exercises **16.1 class** (p.329)

1 a) 7.27×10^{-5} rad s^{-1}
b) 465 m s^{-1}
2 a) 0.157 s **b)** 40 rad s^{-1}
3

Engine flywheel	52.36	0.12	–
Record	4.71	1.33	–
Fairground ride	–	6	10
Planet	8.73×10^{-5}	–	8.3×10^{-4}

4 80 rad s^{-1}, 100 rad s^{-1}
5 a) 12 m s^{-1} **b)** 3 rad s^{-1}
c) 2.09 s **d)** 28.65 revolutions
6 8 rad s^{-1}
7 a) $\mathbf{r} = 5\sin\left(\frac{\pi t}{5}\right)\mathbf{i} - 5\cos\left(\frac{\pi t}{5}\right)\mathbf{j}$

$\mathbf{v} = \pi\cos\left(\frac{\pi t}{5}\right)\mathbf{i} + \pi\sin\left(\frac{\pi t}{5}\right)\mathbf{j}$

b) $\mathbf{r} = 5\sin\left(\frac{\pi t}{5}\right)\mathbf{i}$

$+ \left(5 - 5\cos\left(\frac{\pi t}{5}\right)\right)\mathbf{j}$

$\mathbf{v} = \pi\cos\left(\frac{\pi t}{5}\right)\mathbf{i} + \pi\sin\left(\frac{\pi t}{5}\right)\mathbf{j}$

8 997 m s^{-1}
9 3.083×10^3 m s^{-1}
10 25.3 m s^{-1}

Exercises **16.1 home** (p.330)

1 a) 1.26 rad s^{-1} **b)** 6.28 m s^{-1}
2 a) 2.51 m **b)** 0.503 s
c) 12.5 rad s^{-1}
3 a) 524 rad s^{-1}, 0.012 s
b) 3.46 rad s^{-1}, 1.82 s
c) 20.9 rad s^{-1}, 0.3 s
d) 1.05 rad s^{-1}, 6 s
4 a) $\mathbf{v} = -6\sin(2t)\,\mathbf{i} + 6\cos(2t)\mathbf{j}$
b) $\mathbf{v} = 6$ m s^{-1} **c)** π s
5 a) 133.3 rad s^{-1} **b)** 1273 rpm
6 a) 80 rad s^{-1} **b)** 12 m s^{-1}
7 a) $\mathbf{r}_L = 0.14\sin\left(\frac{\pi t}{1800}\right)\mathbf{i}$

$+ 0.14\cos\left(\frac{\pi t}{1800}\right)\mathbf{j}$

$\mathbf{r}_s = 0.08\sin\left(\frac{\pi t}{21600}\right)\mathbf{i}$

$+ 0.08\sin\left(\frac{\pi t}{21600}\right)\mathbf{j}$

b) $\mathbf{v}_L = \frac{0.14\pi}{1800}\cos\left(\frac{\pi t}{1800}\right)\mathbf{i}$

$- \frac{0.14\pi}{1800}\sin\left(\frac{\pi t}{1800}\right)\mathbf{j}$

$\mathbf{v}_s = \frac{0.08\pi}{21600}\cos\left(\frac{\pi t}{21600}\right)\mathbf{i}$

$- \frac{0.08\pi}{21600}\cos\left(\frac{\pi t}{21600}\right)\mathbf{j}$

8 a) $\mathbf{v} = -5\pi\sin\left(\frac{\pi t}{10}\right)\mathbf{i} +$

$5\pi\cos\left(\frac{\pi t}{10}\right)\mathbf{j}$ **b)** 117 202 J

9 a) $\mathbf{v} = -4\sin(20t)\,\mathbf{i} + 4\cos(20t)\mathbf{j}$
b) $1.22\,\mathbf{i} - 3.81\mathbf{j}$ **c)** $2.25\,\mathbf{i} - 7.68\mathbf{j}$, moves at constant velocity when the string breaks.
10 a) 7.85 m s^{-1} **b)** 0.55 s
c) 8.4 m s^{-1} at 20.9° to tangent.

Exercises **16.2 class** (p.335)

1 a) 1.8 m s^{-2} **b)** 2 m s^{-2}
c) 1.97 m s^{-2}
2 As close to outside as possible.
3 b) 10584 N **c)** 8.82 m s^{-2}
d) 21 m s^{-1} **e)** No
4 b) 8.58 m s^{-2} **c)** 0.0011 rad s^{-1}
d) 5603 s
5 b) 202914 N
c) 52518 N, 2.63 m s^{-2}
d) 36.2 m s^{-1} **e)** The same speed.
6 a) 7.27×10^{-5} rad s^{-1}
b) $5.29 \times 10^{-9}mr$
c) $\dfrac{GM_E m}{r^2}$ **d)** 4.23×10^7 m
7 a) Yes **b)** 10.8 m s^{-1}
8 a) 18.4 m s^{-1} **b)** 35.5 m s^{-1}
9 b) 3.37×10^{-2} m s^{-2}
c) $3.37 \times 10^{-2}m$ N **d)** Yes
10 b) 5971 m s^{-2} **c)** $5961M$ N
$5981M$ N
11 c) 6.26 m s^{-1}

Exercises **16.2 home** (p.337)

1 a) 140 m s^{-2} **b)** 80 m s^{-2}
c) 1.25 m s^{-2}
2 a) 1667 N **b)** 432 N **c)** 9995 N
3 a) 3290 m s^{-2} **b)** 3290 N
4 a) $\mathbf{a} = -24\pi^2\cos(2\pi t)\,\mathbf{i} - 24\pi^2\sin(2\pi t)\mathbf{j}$ **b)** $24\pi^2$
5 a) 411.6 N **b)** 2.05 rad s^{-1}
c) No **d)** Possible if children do not hold on.
6 a) 11 805 N **b)** 8.3 m s^{-1}
c) Could be greater as 8.3 m s^{-1} is about 19 mph.
7 38.34 m s^{-1}
8 5.6 s
9 a) 0.277 N, 2.21 m s^{-1}
b) Causes the ball to roll.
10 4.6 rad s^{-1}

Exercises **16.3 class** (p.341)

1 b) $T\cos\theta = mg$, $T\sin\theta = \dfrac{mv^2}{r}$
c) 76.2°
2 a) 520 N **b)** 1.32 rad s^{-1} 4.8 s
c) Inextensible and light.
d) Tension increased, time not changed.
3 a) 1.67 rad s^{-1} **b)** 18.79°
c) 1.04 N
4 1.68 m s^{-1}
5 b) 9.8 N **c)** $r = 0.54$ m, $l = 0.91$ m
6 a) 71 m s^{-2} **b)** 2.14 N, 13.4 N
7 c) 54.6° **d)** 9.63 rad s^{-1}
e) No tension in lower rod.

8 b) $T = m\sqrt{g^2 + \dfrac{v^4}{r^2}}$

Exercises 16.3 home (p.343)
1 a) 0.41 m **b)** 31.3 N
 c) 2.95 rad s^{-1}
2 a) 1967 N **b)** 0.67 m s^{-1}
3 3.45 m s^{-1}
4 a) 0.18 m s^{-1}, 4.93 N
 b) 0.925 m s^{-1}, 10.7 N
5 b) 0.566 N **c)** 5.66 m s^{-2}
 d) 0.577 **e)** Yes
6 a) $T = \dfrac{mv^2}{l\sin^2\alpha}$ **b)** $\tan\alpha = \dfrac{v^2}{rg}$
7 a) $\dfrac{Mg}{\sqrt{2}}$ **b)** $\omega = \sqrt{\dfrac{Mg}{2\sqrt{2}mr}}$
 c) $M = \dfrac{2\sqrt{2}}{\sqrt{3}}\,m$ **d)** 4.43 rad s^{-1}
8 121 N, 132 N

Exercises 16.4 class (p.346)
1 a) 4.43 m s^{-1} **b)** 196 N **c)** 101 N
2 a) 4.95 m s^{-1} **b) i)** 38.3 N
 ii) 90.6 N **iii)** 6.80 N
3 a) $v = \sqrt{2gl\cos\theta}$
 b) $T = 3mg\cos\theta$
4 6.82 m s^{-1}, 2940 N
5 b) Reaction becomes zero
 c) 48.2° **d)** Straighten out slide
 at 42°

Exercises 16.4 home (p.347)
1 a) no **b)** no **c)** yes
2 a) $v = \sqrt{2ga(1-\cos\theta)}$
 b) $R = 3mg\cos\theta - 2mg$
 c) 48.2°
3 3.70 m s^{-1}
5 a) 3.96 m s^{-1} **b)** 21.0°

Consolidation Exercises for Chapter 16 (p.348)
1 a) i) 7.5 m s^{-1} **ii)** 3.75 m s^{-2}
 b) 10.5 m s^{-1}
2 11.5°
3 a) 10000 N
 b) $L = m\sqrt{\dfrac{v^4}{r^2} + g^2}$
 c) α and L both increase
4 a) 1.01 N and 1.99 N
 b) 1.02 m s^{-1}

CHAPTER 17
Energy and work: Variable forces and scalar products

Exercises 17.1 class (p.354)
1 a) $163\frac{1}{3}$ N m^{-1} **b)** $32\frac{2}{3}$ N
 c) 6 cm
2 a) 174.2 N m^{-1} **b)** 6.75 cm
3 a) 3920 N m^{-1} **b)** 0.9 cm
4 a) 13.1 N m^{-1}

b) $0.131 \le T \le 0.653$
5 a) 2.45 N **b)** 3.2 cm **c)** 2.4 cm

Exercises 17.1 home (p.355)
1 a) 588 N m^{-1} **b)** 117.6 N
 c) 3.75 cm
2 a) 327 N m^{-1} **b)** $\frac{2}{3}$ kg
3 a) 327 N m^{-1} **b)** 2.4 cm
4 a) 19.6 N m^{-1}
 b) $0.392 \le T \le 1.568$
5 a) 7.84 N **b)** 2.5 cm **c)** 2 cm

Exercises 17.2 class (p.357)
1 a) 400000 J **b)** 28.3 m s^{-1}
2 b) 882 J
3 a) 4500000 J **b)** 17.3 m s^{-1}
4 a) $m = 50 - 4x$ **b)** 1960 J
5 a) 17.1 J **b)** 33.7 m s^{-1}
6 a) 4.21×10^9 J **b)** 4100 m s^{-1}
 c) 2.14×10^3 N

Exercises 17.2 home (p.358)
1 a) 9.875 J **b)** 0.628 m s^{-1}
2 16 537 500 J
3 a) 350 000 J **b)** 26.5 m s^{-1}
4 b) 1078 J
5 a) 625 000 J **b)** 4.44 N m^{-2}
6 a) 3.8×10^{13} J
 b) 6.18×10^5 m s^{-1}

Exercises 17.3 class (p.360)
1 a) 0.0882 J **b)** 0.0882 J
 c) 1764 N m^{-1}
2 a) 37.5 J **b)** 37.5 J **c)** 19 cm
 d) Brakes probably applied.
3 a) 0.075 J **b)** 1.73 m s^{-1}
 c) 0.495 m **d)** Some energy
 retained in the plunger.
4 a) 0.588 J **b)** 4.85 m s^{-1}, 1.2 m
5 a) 1000 N **b)** 0.1 m
6 a) 3.038 J **b)** 15 190 N m^{-1}

Exercises 17.3 home (p.361)
1 50 J
2 10 m s^{-1}
3 $x\sqrt{\dfrac{k}{m}}$ **a)** $x\sqrt{\dfrac{k}{2m}}$ **b)** $x\sqrt{\dfrac{k}{2m}}$
 c) $x\sqrt{\dfrac{k}{m}}$
4 0.894 m s^{-1}
5 a) 2.12 m s^{-1} **b)** 1.5 m
6 0.14 m

Exercises 17.4 class (p.364)
1 a) 14.4 m s^{-1} **b)** 6.60 m s^{-1}
2 $y = 64$
3 630 J
4 a) 17604 J **b)** 3 m s^{-1}
 c) 108 m s^{-1}
5 $v = 5$
6 $\alpha = \pm\sqrt{2}$

Exercises 17.4 home (p.364)
1 a) 10.2 m s^{-1} **b)** 7.45 m s^{-1}
2 a) $Y = 8.75 - \dfrac{X}{2}$
 b) −62.5 **c)** -7.75

3 a) 263 552 **b)** 3 m s^{-1}
 c) 256.7 m s^{-1}
4 10 W
5 47 540 J
6 a) $\alpha = 1$ **b)** 5 m s^{-1}

Consolidation Exercises for Chapter 17 (p.365)
1 a) 145 J **b)** $\lambda = 6$
2 a) 8820 N **b)** 9.39 m s^{-1}
3 a) 7 m s^{-1} **b) ii)** $x = 1.2$

CHAPTER 18
Differential equations in mechanics

Exercises 18.1 class (p.370)
1 a) $\dfrac{-v}{2}$ **b)** $10e^{-0.5t}$
 c) $20(1 - e^{-0.5t})$.
2 b) $60(1 - e^{-\frac{1}{60}gt})$ **c)** 4.24 s
3 a) 4 m s^{-1} **b)** $4 + 6e^{-\frac{1}{4}gt}$
 c) $4t + \dfrac{24}{g}(1 - e^{-\frac{1}{4}gt})$
 d) 4 m s^{-1}, 42.45 m
4 9.94 m
5 a) $\dfrac{1}{v} = kt + \dfrac{1}{20}$, $v = 20e^{-kx}$
 b) $\dfrac{3}{200}$, 92.4 m
10 Distance tends to gT.

Exercises 18.1 home (p.371)
1 a) $-16v$ **b)** 1000 m
2 a) Zero **b)** $-300v$
 d) $10(1 - e^{-\frac{t}{4}})$ **e)** 2.8 s
3 a) Surface area of hull, depth of
 hull etc.
4 a) 1.71 m
 b) Air resistance, friction,
 $v\dfrac{dv}{dx} = -200x - 10kv - \mu g$
5 a) $\dfrac{2 - kv^2}{v}, \dfrac{2 - 2e^{-2kt}}{k}$ **b)** $\dfrac{1}{72}$
6 86 m

Consolidation Exercises for Chapter 15 (p.372)
1 6.4 m

CHAPTER 19
Simple harmonic motion

Exercises 19.1 class (p.376)
1 a) $-375x$ **b)** $-50x$
2 a) 2 **b)** 10
3 a) 0.444 s **b)** 0.126 s
4 a) $-160x$ **b)** 0.497 s
 c) $0.03\cos(\sqrt{160}t)$
 d) $-0.03\cos(\sqrt{160}t)$
5 Parallel system has half the period.
6 a) 0.444 s
 b) $F = -10x$, $a = -200x$
 c) 0.444 s **d)** None
7 a) $\sqrt{200}$ **b)** $\dfrac{\pi}{2}$ **c)** $-\dfrac{2}{\sqrt{200}}$

Exercises 19.1 home (*p.377*)
1 a) $-40x$ b) $-10x$
2 a) $-80x$ b) $-400x$
3 a) 5 b) 9
4 a) 0.795 s b) 0.889 s
5 a) $-300x$ b) 0.363 s
  c) $x = 0.05\cos\left(\sqrt{300t}\right)$
  d) $x = -0.05\cos\left(\sqrt{300t}\right)$
6 $\frac{\lambda}{l} = 118$
7 a) Different amplitudes, same period. b) 0.314 s

Exercises 19.2 class (*p.380*)
1 a) 0.0625 J b) 1.12 m s^{-1}
  c) 0.25 J, 2.24 m s^{-1}
2 0.157 m s^{-1}
3 0.314 m s^{-1}
4 5.97 cm
5 a) 0.9 cm b) 0.047 m s^{-1}
  c) 0.052 m s^{-1}
6 2.05 cm, 0.0562 s

Exercises 19.2 home (*p.381*)
1 1.57 m s^{-1}
2 0.314 m s^{-1}
3 a) 15π b) 3.53 m s^{-1}
  c) 2.63 m s^{-1}
4 a) 3.2 m b) 3.87 m s^{-1}
  c) 3.23 m s^{-1}
5 6.15 cm, 0.084 s
6 a) 8.26 cm b) 0.260 s

Consolidation Exercises for Chapter 19 (*p.381*)
1 a) $\frac{\pi}{50}$ s b) 2.5 m s^{-1}
2 a) $e = \frac{a}{6}$ b) $2\pi\sqrt{\frac{a}{6g}}$
  c) $\frac{1}{3}\sqrt{6ga}$ d) $t = \frac{2\pi}{3}\sqrt{\frac{a}{6g}}$

CHAPTER 20
Discrete probability distribution

Exercises 20.1 class (*p.389*)
1 a) 1 b) 0.0965 c) 0.579
2 a) 0.6 b) 0.24 c) 0.096
  d) 0.0384 e) 0.0256
3 a) 0.25 b) 0.7344 c) 0.4219
4 a) 0.444 b) 0.556 c) 0.444
5 0.8062
6 30

Exercises 20.1 home (*p.389*)
1 a) 0.1667 b) 0.1157
  c) 0.5787 d) 1
2 a) i) 0.25 ii) 0.1875
  iii) 0.1406 iv) 0.4219
  b) 1 d) i) 0.4219
  ii) 0.0751
3 a) 0.4225 b) 0.0150
  c) 0.001 84 d) 0.000 03
4 a) 0.237 b) 0.763
  c) 0.316
5 0.969
6 14

Exercises 20.2 class (*p.395*)
1 a) 1 b) 1.429 c) 0.6122
3 1.111, 0.1235
4 1.8
5 0.5041

Exercises 20.2 home (*p.395*)
1 a) 0.128 b) 5 c) 20
3 4, 28
4 0.7806
5 2.5

Exercises 20.3 class (*p.399*)
1 a) 54 b) 0.0545
  c) 0.378 d) 1
2 a) 1 b) 8
  c) 56 d) 0.30
3 a) 0.049 b) 0.607 c) 0.344
4 a) 0.0387 b) 0.735
6 a) i) 0.004 12 ii) 0.008 23
  iii) 0.996 b) i) 1 ii) 0.031 25

Exercises 20.3 home (*p.400*)
1 a) 2 b) 1
2 a) modal
3 a) 0.079 b) 0.925 c) 0.422
4 8
5 a) 0.75 b) 0.25 c) loss of £1
6 a) 0.1 b) 0.0424 c) 0.01
  d) i) 0.740 ii) 0.049

Exercises 20.4 class (*p.404*)
1 a) 0.294 b) 0.496 c) 0.945
2 a) 0.192 b) 0.233 c) 0.745
3 a) 0.651 b) 0.851
  c) 0.954
4 a) 0.045 75 b) 0.3138
  c) 0.004 430

Exerciese 20.4 home (*p.405*)
1 a) 0.951 b) 0.0751; 2
3 a) 0.336 b) 0.294
  c) 0.797 d) 0.203
5 a) 0.784 b) 0.870
  c) 0.953 d) 6 e) 10

Exercises 20.5 class (*p.411*)
1 0.741
3 a) 0.2825 b) 0.018 c) 0.253
4 a) 0.523 b) 0.895 c) 0.174
5 a) 0.507 b) 0.253
  c) 0.158 d) 0.038

Exercises 20.5 home (*p.411*)
1 4
3 a) 0.986 b) 0.02
  c) 0.101 d) 0.665
4 a) 0.0040 b) 0.6171 c) 0.2023
5 a) 0.412 b) 0.994 c) 0.994

Exercises 20.6 class (*p.415*)
1 a) 0.1493 b) 0.2668 c) 0.1503
2 a) 4, 2 b) 6.4, 1.28
3 a) 0.180 b) 0.4044 c) 4.8
4 a) 4.5, 2.475 b) 2, 1.6
  c) 0.0949
5 a) $n = 12, p = 0.85\ q = 0.15$,
  b) 0.4435

Exercises 20.6 home (*p.415*)
1 a) 0.9983 b) 0.251 c) 0.8327
2 0.258
3 a) 0.4073 b) 0.0222
4 a) 4, 0.8; 0.4096
  b) 11.1, 2.886; 0.2101
5 a) B(3, 0.5), B(4, 0.5), B(7, 0.5)

Consolidation Exercises for Chapter 20 (*p.416*)
1 a) 0.5 b) 0.125
2 a) i) 0.167 ii) 0.139
  iii) 0.579 b) £28.94
3 a) 0.625 b) 0.375 c) 0.125
4 a) 0.25 b) 0.316 c) 0.0791
5 a) 5 b) 0.128 c) 0.410
6 a) i) 0.8929 ii) 0.179
  b) i) p different at weekends
  ii) n not constant
7 a) 0.0100 b) 0.4148 c) 25
8 a) 0.493 b) 0.0144
  c) 0.0886 d) 3
9 a) 0.512 b) 0.104 c) 0.669
  d) 0.056 e) 0.238 f) 0.299
10 a) 0.107 b) 0.302
  c) 0.678 d) 0.624
11 a) 0.9722, 10.5826
  b) 3.889, 42.3302
12 a) 5, 0.2 b) 10, 0.1
  c) 20, 0.05 d) 200, 0.005
13 a) 2 b) 5, 0.4
  c) 11.7, 38.9, 51.8, 34.6,
  11.5, 1.5
14 a) 1.34, 1.83 b) ii) 1.25, 0.968
  c) greater variability
15 a) 0.0353 b) 49.32, 6.906

CHAPTER 21
The Poisson distribution

Exercises 21.1 class (*p.428*)
1 a) 0.1641 b) 0.0050
  c) 0.9950 d) 0.1016
2 a) 0.2975 b) 0.7306
  c) 0.8347
3 a) 0.1494 b) 0.2240
4 a) 0.3679 b) 0.1839
5 a) 0.1353 b) 0.0.0677
  c) 0.2707 d) 0.2707
  e) 0.0803 f) 0.0064
6 a) 0.4036 b) 0.2033
  c) 0.9162 d) 0.3730
7 a) 0.2217 b) 0.8365
  c) 0.2302

Exercises 21.2 home (*p.429*)
1 a) 0.2700 b) 0.6204
  c) 0.8386 d) 0.2882
2 a) 0.2385 b) 0.3978
  c) 0.8407 d) 0.3474
3 a) 0.1933 b) 0.3772
  c) 0.9281 d) 0.6584
4 a) 0.3753 b) 0.9233
5 a) 0.0902 b) 0.5940 c) 0.9473
6 a) 0.0067 b) 0.9596 c) 0.2246
7 a) 0.2306 b) 0.4685 c) 0.2007

Exercises 21.2. class *(p.434)*
1 **a)** 0.4335 **b)** 0.5665 **c)** 0.1465
 d) 0.4558 **e)** 0.7405
2 **a)** 0.3528 **b)** 0.8153 **c)** 0.7674
3 **a)** 0.4405 **b)** 0.3840 **c)** 0.5595
4 4, 2
5 0.1563
6 **a)** 0.2792 **b)** 0.3424 **c)** 0.8506

Exercises 21.2 home *(p.435)*
1 **a)** 0.6792 **b)** 0.3208 **c)** 0.9347
2 **a)** 0.5608 **b)** 0.2717
 c) 0.6588 **d)** 0.2992
3 1.8, 1.8
4 8, 0.0916
5 0.1606
6 **a)** 0.8148 **b)** 0.7399
 c) 0.4103 **d)** 0.6771
7 **a)** 0.1967 **b)** 0.1189
 c) 0.7035 **d)** 0.641; 0.0614
 e) 10 **f)** 11 **g)** 13

Exercises 21.3 class *(p.437)*
1 **a)** 0.5488 **b)** 0.0231 **c)** 0.1606
 d) 0.9161 **e)** 0.8298
2 **a)** 0.6063 **b)** 0.2560
 c) 0.4142 **d)** 0.1378
 e) 0.6335 **f)** 0.7189
3 **a)** 0.1614 **b)** 0.0729
 c) 0.1944 **d)** 0.4631
4 **a)** 0.1912, 0.9814
 b) 0.0498, 0.1493, 0.2241
5 **a)** 0.1708 **b)** 0.1157
 c) 0.4495 **d)** 0.8843
6 **a)** 0.2231 **b)** 0.0111 **c)** 0.0500
 d) 0.1125 **e)** 0.0023

Exercises 21.3 home *(p.438)*
1 **a)** 0.3712 **b)** 0.1953
 c) 0.3134 **d)** 0.0382; 9
2 **a)** 0.4416 **b)** 0.5423 **c)** 0.6797
 d) 0.9450 **e)** 0.2187
3 **a)** 0.1054 **b)** 0.8858
 c) 0.9260 **d)** 0.0111
4 **a)** 0.6065 **b)** 0.3679
 c) 0.6065 **d)** 0.6065
5 **a)** 0.0261 **b)** 0.1559 **c)** 10
6 **a)** 0.1353 **b)** 0.0166
 c) 0.1954 **d)** 5

Consolidation exercises for Chapter 21 *(p.439)*
1 **a)** 0.0408 **b)** 0.3223 **c)** 0.2087
 d) 0.2226 **e)** 0.1443
2 **a)** 0.0656, 0.8088
 b) 0.2241, 0.654
3 **a)** 0.0608 **b)** 0.0079 **c)** 0.0001
4 **a)** 0.4232 **b)** 0.3528
 c) 0.1791 **d)** 0.1606
5 0.0613
6 **a)** 0.2240 **b)** 0.3347
 c) 0.5276 **d)** 0.0620
7 **a)** 0.0404 **b)** 0.6925
 c) 0.2650 **d)** 0.0067
8 **a)** 0.1801 **b)** 0.6204 **c)** 0.0470
9 **a)** 0.0067 **b)** 0.2138 **c)** 0.0472
11 **a)** 0.9989 **b)** 0.0010

12 **a)** −2, 7 **b)** 10, 10
13 **b)** at least 7.5% **c)** 0.1847
14 **i)** 0.835 **ii)** 2.94
15 **a)** 0.0016 **b)** 0.432 **c)** 4.8, 48

CHAPTER 22
Continuous random variables

Exercises 22.1 class *(p.450)*
1 **a)** 10%
 b) $f(x) = 4.58 \times 10^{-8} \times (425 - x) \times (x + 100)$
2 **a)** 2 **b)** $0; 2x - x^2; 1$
 c) 0.293 **d)** 0.4
3 **a)** 0.002
 c) $0; 0.002(x - 0.0005x^2); 1$
 i) 0.36 **ii)** 0.36 **iii)** 292.89
4 **a)** 12 **b)** 0.667
 c) $0; x^3(4 - 3x); 1$ **d)** 0.614
5 **b)** 0.025
 c) $0; 0.0125t^2; 0.2t - 0.8; 1$
 d) 6.32 **e)** 0.3875
6 **b)** 0.25 **c)** $0; 0.125x^2;$
 $0.125(8x - 8 - x^2); 1$ **d)** 0.75
7 **b)** 35% **c)** $0.003x^2$
 d) 0.316

Exercise 22.1 home *(p.452)*
1 **b)** 52% **c)** 0.05 **d)** 0.5
2 **b)** 25%
 c) $0.000\,732\,4(x - 16)^3$ **d)** 0.27
3 **b)** 0.167
 c) $0; 0.0833(t^2 + 2t - 3); 1$
 d) 0.583
4 **b)** 0.0333 **c)** 15
5 **a)** 0.004
 c) $0; 0.004(x - 0.001x^2); 1$
 d) i) 0.36 **ii)** 0.28 **e)** 146.45
6 **a)** 78.82 **b)** 0.25
 c) 61.6%; 77.8%
7 **a)** 4 **b)** $0; 2 - 4x^{-1}; 1$
 c) i) 0.143 **ii)** 0.4
 d) 2.67; 2.29, 3.2; 0.914
 e) 3.64

Exercises 22.2 class *(p.459)*
1 **a)** 24 **b)** 4, 0.636
 c) 3.328 **d)** 0.0215 **e)** 0.304
2 **a)** 7.5, 2.083 **b)** 0.16
3 **a)** 0 **b)** 0.822
 c) $0; 0.5 + 0.3183x; 1$
4 **a)** 0.0833 **b)** 1
 c) 1.125, 0.6094 **d)** 0.935
5 **a)** 0.5 **b)** 0, 0.333 **c)** triangular
 d) $0.25y + 0.5; 0.5 - 0.25y$
 e) 0.281 25
6 **a)** 0.1875 **c)** 0.2375 **d)** 61.4%

Exercises 22.2 home *(p.460)*
1 **a)** k **b)** $0.333k^2$
2 **a)** $1 \div (b - a)$
 b) $0; (x - a) \div (b - a); 1$
3 **a)** 0. 093 75 **b)** 2
 c) 0.8944 **d)** 0.156 25
4 **a)** $1 \div (3a^2)$ **b)** $2.5a^2$
 c) 0.417

5 **a)** 0.006 **b)** 15
 c) 2.236 **d)** 0.3778
6 **a)** 0.167 **c)** 2.78; 1.62
 d) 0.056 **e)** 0.0208

Consolidation Exercises for Chapter 22 *(p.465)*
1 **a)** $1 - e^{-x}$ **b) i)** 0.693
 ii) 0.132
2 **a)** 6.93 **b)** 0.239
 c) $0.1e^{-0.1x}$ **d)** 10; 100
3 **a)** 0.313 **b)** 0.249
4 **a)** 0.025 **b) i)** 0.487
 ii) 0.250 **iii)** 0.128
 c) 0.487
5 **a)** 100, 10 000 **b)** 0.607
6 **a)** $a^{-1}e^{-\frac{t}{a}}$ **c)** 0.135
7 **a)** 4 **b)** 1.33, 0.889
 d) 1.17; 0.536, 2
8 **a)** 0.75
 b) $0; 0.5 + 0.75t - 0.25t^3; 1$
 c) i) 0.156 **ii)** 0.688
 d) 0, 0.2
9 **a)** 7.5, 2.083 **b)** 15, 4.167
 c) 0.92
10 17.5, 52.083; 0.3456
11 **a)** 0.777 **b)** 0.204
12 **a)** $0.01e^{-0.01x}; 1 - e^{-0.01x}$
 b) 0.3935
13 **i)** 1–8 **ii)** 16/17 **iii)** less
14 c = 0.048 **a)** 0.352 **b)** 2.5, 1.25
15 **b)** 2.4 **c)** 3.167
16 **b)** 2.42 **e)** 0.65 **f)** 0.612

CHAPTER 23
Samples and populations

Exercises 23.1 class *(p.474)*
1 **a)** 276, 29, 86, 225, 72
 b) 3440, 355, 1065, 2812, 897
 c) 102, 11, 32, 83, 27
 d) 41 269, 4249, 12 779,
 33 738, 10 764
 e) 137 561, 14 161, 42 595,
 112 460, 35 880

Exercises 23.1 home *(p.475)*
5 **b)** 76%

Exercises 23.2 class *(p.478)*
6 9.5

Exercises 23.2 home *(p.479)*
5 **b)** 4.33

Consolidation Exercises for Chapter 23 *(p.484)*
3 **c)** 0.0420
4 **a)** 0.2×0.8^x, $x = 0, 1, 2, \dots$
8 **a)** 5, 3, 1, 7, 8
 b) 5, 2, 0, 7, 9 **c)** 1, 0, 0, 1, 1
9 9, 2, 1, 19, 29
14 **a)** quicker/cheaper, not the full picture
 b) register of pupils
 c) individual pupils
17 **a)** 2, 1.414

CHAPTER 24
Approximating distributions

Exercises 24.1 class *(p.492)*
1 a) i) 0.0527 **ii)** 0.9834
 b) i) 0.0183 **ii)** 0.1953
2 a) i) 0.180 **ii)** 0.143
 iii) 0.143 **b) i)** 0.027
 ii) 0.340
3 a) not at 5% level **b)** no
4 a) Poisson, 0.1205
 b) binomial, 0.6528
 c) Poisson, 0.632

Exercises 24.1 home *(p.492)*
1 a) i) 0.080 **ii)** 0.981
 b) i) 0.744 **ii)** 0.039
2 a) i) 0.176 **ii)** 0.384
 iii) 0.384 **b) i)** 0.019
 ii) 0.429
3 a) yes at 2% **b)** no

Exercises 24.2 class *(p.497)*
1 no
2 a) 0.0996 **b)** 0.0485
3 a) no **b)** no **c)** more difficult
4 a) 0.156 **b)** 0.139
 c) 0.115 **d)** 0.0664

Exercises 24.2 home *(p.497)*
1 no
2 a) 0.2650 **b)** 0.912
3 a) no **b)** not at 5% **c)** yes
4 a) 0.318 **b)** 0.067
 c) 0.125 **d)** 0.0630

Exercises 24.3 class *(p.501)*
1 a) 0.010 24 **b)** 0.247
 c) 0.136
2 yes at 2.5% level
3 a) 0.999 **b)** 0.989 **c)** 0.0266
4 a) reject claim **b)** accept claim

Exercises 24.3 home *(p.502)*
1 a) 0.077 76 **b)** 0.873
 c) 0.944
2 not at 5%
3 a) 0.068 **b)** 0.721
 c) 0.008 68 **d)** 0.345
4 a) denies the claim
 b) supports claim

Exercises 24.4 class *(p.504)*
1 a) N(420, 1440)
 b) 0.0569 **c)** 0.56
2 a) N(2400, 10 800) **b)** 0.805
3 a) 0.132 **b)** 0.000 21
4 a) 0.042 **b)** 50.5

Exercises 24.4 home *(p.504)*
1 a) N(230, 90) **b)** 0.146
 c) 0.837
2 a) N(1440, 768) **b)** 0.406
3 a) 0.710 **b)** 0.892
4 a) 0.222 **b)** 12.35

Consolidation Exercises for Chapter 24 *(p.505)*
1 a) 0.907 **b)** 0.283
2 a) 0.783 **b)** 1 **c)** no, more
3 a) 0.706 **b)** 0.923
4 a) 113 **b)** 0.3712
5 0.315
6 a) 0.0058 **b)** 0.4604 **c)** 0.1377
7 , Yn B(60, 0.07), 0.210, 0.003
8 a) 5, 4.75, 0.031
 b) 0.034
9 a) Poi(2.25) **b)** 0.105
 c) 0.391
 d) 0.clustering, not random
 e) 0.109
10 a) normal, 0.977
 b) i) Poisson, 0.1912
 ii) normal, 0.246
 c) i) binomial, 0.1702
 ii) 0.6477

CHAPTER 25
Continuous random variables

Exercise 25.1 class *(p.515)*
1 a) no **b)** yes **c)** no
2 a) yes **b)** no
3 a) yes **b)** no **c)** yes
4 b) 6% or more **c)** $x \geq 16$
 d) 0.608
5 c) 4% or more **d)** 0.405

Exercise 25.1 home *(p.516)*
1 a) no **b)** yes **c)** no
3 a) no **b)** yes
4 b) $x < 4$, 2% or more
 c) 0.4114
5 b) 13% **c)** 15 **d)** 89.8%

Exercise 25.2 class *(p.518)*
1 Yes
2 Yes
3 No difference
4 a) 0.908 **b)** 9
5 a) not at 5% levels **d)** no

Exercise 25.2 home *(p.519)*
1 No
2 No
3 Satisfactory
4 b) leass than 3%
5 a) No **c)** not at 5% **d)** Yes

Exercises 25.3 class *(p.525)*
1 a) 0.023 **b)** 0.0127
 c) 0.673 **d)** £30
2 a) 0.3085 **b)** 0.2146
 c) 0.3085 **d)** 0.4115
3 a) 20.5, 0.0833
 b) 0.0142 **c)** 0.0005
4 a) other **b)** top grade
 c) 196.3

Exercises 25.3 home *(p.526)*
1 a) 0.091 **b)** 0.228
 c) 0.294 **d)** 7.2 kg
2 a) 0.159 **b)** 0.023
 c) 0.124 **d)** 0.993
3 a) 0.061 **b)** 0.863
 c) 0.02 m
4 a) other **b)** other
 c) 147.6 g

Exercises 25.4 class *(p.530)*
1 0.7865 > 0.5494 yes
2 −0.2118, compared with −0, 5822, not linearly correlated
3 c) 0.3367 < 0.5822, no
 d) −0.2697, no
4 −0. 6602 compared with −0.6021, yes at 2.5%
5 b) 0.8335 compared with 0.6581, yes at 2%
6 0.6057 compared with 0.5823, yes at 1%

Exercises 25.4 home *(p.532)*
1 yes, 0.8355
2 a) 0.9762 **b)** 0.9762
4 a) yes, −0.8798 compared with −0.8114 at 2.5%
5 c) no, 0.2709 compared with 0.4973
6 a) 0 **c)** clearly correlated but not linearly

Exercises 25.5 class *(p.537)*
1 b) 0.5714 **c)** < 0.6429, not positively correlated
2 b) −0.3 **c)** no
3 a) 0.8333 **b)** yes at 1%
4 a) 0.66
 b) evidence of correlation
5 0.152, no evidence of correlation

Exercises 25.5 home *(p.539)*
1 0.7
2 b) 0.6611 **c)** yes at 10%
3 0.4198; seems a wise decision
4 a) i) 0.3810 **ii)** 0.3095
 iii) 0.0952
 b) no evidence of agreement
5 b) −0.0425 **c)** no evidence
 d) −0.8124, significant evidence at 1%

Exercise 25.6 class *(p.542)*
1 No
2 No
3 a) significant
 b) not significant
4 Yes

Exercise 25.6 home *(p.542)*
1 Yes
2 Yes
3 a) significant
 b) not significant
4 Yes

Consolidation Exercises for Chapter 25 *(p.543)*

1 a) No **b)** Yes
2 a) No **b)** Yes **c)** Yes
3 No
4 b) 0.350 **c)** 0.0106
5 b) No bias **c)** X = 0
6 Improved
7 0.0913 **a)** X ≥ 18
b) X ≥ 19 **c)** X = 20
8 a) Ho: p = 0.30
Hi: p < 0.30 not significant
b) Ho: p = 0.10 Hi X ≤ 4 and X ≥ 17
c) 0.056 or 5.6%
9 i) Ho: p = $\frac{1}{4}$ Hi: p< $\frac{1}{4}$
ii) not significant
10 Significant
11 b) 1.912 **c)** close
12 a) No **b)** Not at 5% **c)** Yes
13 a) Yes at 2% **b)** No
14 Yes at 5%
15 a) No
16 a) 20, 20 **b)** significant
c) not significant
17 a) reject Ho
b) i) same **ii)** dubious
18 a) significant at 5%
b) 0.05
19 i) 0.915 **ii)** 33.7; 0.821
20 i) 11.16, 3.87 **ii)** Significant
iii) a) Still valid **b)** Not valid
21 ii) 0.025 **iii)** 0.0938
22 a) 0.184 or 18.4%
b) < 1150.65
c) batch is substandard
23 a) 0.9281 **b)** linear
24 a) 0.7496, linear
b) non-linear
c) 0.8381, squared is better
25 b) Yes
26 b) 0.7608 **c)** agreement
27 b) 0.1687 **c)** not correlated
28 b) –0.3571, no evidence
29 0.6
30 a) 0.9516, significant
b) cause not established
31 Ho: p = 0.5, Hi: p ≠ 0.5, 0.3222, not biased
32 0.545, sufficient
33 a) Yes **b)** No
34 a) i) 0.36 **ii)** Yes
b) i) 0.14 **ii)** Not supported
35 Upheld

CHAPTER 26 Validating models – the chi-squared distribution

Exercises 26.1 class *(p.559)*

1 a) 48.0, 82.3, 52.9, 15.1, 1.7
c) 18.75 > 9.488
d) model does not fit
2 a) 150, 60, 6, **b)** 11.29 > 5.99, model does not fit
3 b) 5.1, 38.4, 115.2, 172.8, 129.6, 38.9 **c)** 10.09 > 9.236, model does not fit
d) 10.09 < 11.070, model fits
4 b) 15.4, 9.2, 9.1, 7.2, 9.1
c) 10.13 < 11.668 fits

Exercises 26.1 home *(p.560)*

1 b) 6.17 < 9.488, good fit
2 a) 5.1, 30.7, 69.1, 69.1, 26.0
b) 7.48 < 13.277, fits
3 a) B(2, 0.5) **b)** 12.5, 25, 12.5; 7.08 < 7.824, fits
c) i) does not fit **ii)** fits
d) yes at 5%, no at 2%
4 a) 33.5, 67.1, 58.7, 29.4, 11.3
b) 0.624 < 7.779, fits
c) very good
5 a) 7.3, 85.1, 396.9, 926.1, 1080.5, 504.1
b) 11.02 < 11.07, model fits (just)
d) 22.07 > 11.07, very poor fit

Exercises 26.2 class *(p.566)*

1 b) 2.01; 13.4, 26.9, 27.1, 18.1, 9.1, 5.4
c) 24.63 > 9.488, very poor fit
2 a) 33.3, 36.6, 20.1, 7.4, 2.6
b) 1.70 < 11.668
c) good fit
3 a) 250
b) 33.99 > 13.388, very poor fit
4 5.75 < 7.815, good fit
5 b) 184, 512, 104
c) 1.36 < 4.605, manuscript may have been written by the novelist

Exercises 26.2 home *(p.567)*

1 a) 106.36 > 15.507, unsuitable
b) 29.82, unsuitable
2 Poi (1.465), 9.454 < 9,488, just about fits
3 20.52 > 9.488, does not fit
4 9.62 > 7.815, distribution is different
5 a) 5.9, 14.8, 38.5, 20.8
b) 0.105 < 6.251, exceptionally good fit

Exercises 26.3 class *(p.574)*

1 a) 3410 **b)** 2040: 1370; 1287: 1243: 557: 323
c) 769.9, 743.6, 333.2
d) three **e)** strongly associated
2 4.68 < 9.488, independent
3 a) yes
b) Support staff decidedly against; few academic staff are against the designated smoking area
4 b) 17%; no
c) 12.14 > 10.645, associated
d) The 1200 spin are rarely of reject quality. There is a tendency for the 800 spin machines to need repairing and the 600 spin machines to be reject quality.
5 a) 1.462 **b)** 1.639, no evidence of association

Exercises 26.3 home *(p.575)*

1 a) i) 40 **ii)** 207.5
iii) 142.5 **b)** three
c) 82.56 > 12.838
d) equal to, males positively associated whereas females negatively associated
2 no association
3 yes, very strongly; first class passengers survived whereas third class did not
4 b) 20% **c)** 4.736 < 9.488
d) factors are independent
5 evidence of association; people living 'elsewhere' favour tunnel option, those who live in the town do not want any change

Consolidation Exercises for Chapter 26 *(p.577)*

1 a) 246.6, 345.2, 241.7, 112.8, 39.5, 14.2
b) 32.15 > 11.07, do not accept the Poi(1.4) model
2 b) 36.3, 96.8, 96.8, 43.0, 7.1
c) 18.98 > 9.49 poor fit
d) 9.45 < 9.49, fits
3 a) 7.3, 85.1, 396.9, 926.1, 1080.5, 504.1
b) 11.02 < 11.07, fits
c) 22.07 > 11.07, very poor fit
4 b) i) 8.8 > 6.251, inappropriate
ii) 8.8 > 7.815, inappropriate
iii) 8.8 > 9.837, appropriate
5 b) 168, 50.4, 15.1, 6.5
c) 23.71 > 11.345, poor fit
d) p = 0.609; 146.2, 57.1, 22.3, 8.7, 5.7; 4.22 < 11.345, fits
7 not independent; female fund to be self-funded.
8 b) 18, 12, 8, 5.3, 3.6, 7.1; model is a poor fit
9 11.102 > 5.991, evidence of association
10 language and gender are independent
11 a) 6.74 < 7.815, independent
b) independent
c) 14.56 > 7.815, not independent
12 27.8, 23.1, 19.3, 16.1, 13.4, 67 9.0 < 12.592, appropriate
13 a) Girls 15.6, 34.4
Boys 12.4, 27.6
14 521 > 9.21; highly significant
15 a) 72.8 > 7.815, related
b) Sufferers snore more **c)** No

Index